Environmental Science
A Need for Living Sustainably
Version 1.0

Joseph Shostell

978-1-4533-9137-2

Environmental Science: A Need for Living Sustainably
Version 1.0

Joseph Shostell

Published by:

FlatWorld
292 Newbury Street
Suite #282
Boston, MA 02115-2832

Gen: 202303131732

Brief Contents

Contents

About the Author

Joseph Shostell is Professor of Biology and Environmental Sciences at the University of Minnesota, Crookston. Joseph earned his PhD in environmental biology from the University of Louisville with a concentration in limnology/ecosystems ecology. He holds a master's degree in zoology, with a concentration in limnology/community ecology, from North Dakota State University and is a certified Hazwoper Trainer (to teach about hazardous chemicals), STEM Education Trainer from the Center for the Advancement of STEM Education, and Wind Senator for Kidwind. Joseph has received numerous awards including Penn State's 2008 and 2012 Scholarly Excellence Awards, and key grants from the Department of Environmental Protection and from the National Science Foundation. He has written or cowritten articles published in journals such as *Ecosystems*, *Journal of Freshwater Ecology*, *Freshwater Biology*, *Aquatic Ecology*, and *The Journal of Heredity*, and co-written or contributed to several academic books and monographs.

Acknowledgments

Many people have contributed to the creation of this book. Most certainly, the accuracy and readability of the text have significantly improved because of these contributor's generous and helpful suggestions. I am indebted to the thousands of environmental science students who have filled my classes over the years. Their positivity, enthusiasm, ideas, and discussions continue to be the sources of my motivation. Professional colleagues, governmental agencies, businesses, university libraries, and international organizations, have provided support in the form of data, images, and other information, which have improved the quality of the book. Special thanks to Dr. Joshua Marvit, my friend and former colleague at Penn State University, who spent many hours with me discussing environmental science topics. For example, the idea for writing "birds without boundaries" in chapter ten, came out of one of our conversations.

A heart-felt thanks goes to the team at FlatWorld. What a wonderful professional team of editors, artists, and managers. At no point in the process did I feel alone or unsupported. In particular, Vice President, Product and Editorial, Sean Wakely and Senior Digital Project Manager, Lindsey Kaetzel have been exceptional, kind, and dependable throughout the entire project. Special thanks to copy editor Lisa Starr who reviewed all eighteen chapters. Her comments were invaluable in improving the quality of the book. A sincere thanks to the proofreader for working tirelessly behind the scenes to check grammar and spelling. Credit also goes to FlatWorld's artists who graciously took my make-shift drawings and descriptions and used them as a basis to create accurate, useful, high-resolution illustrations and graphs. Special thanks to Eve Howard who strategized with me about chapter outlines before any text was written. The creation of these outlines streamlined the writing process. In addition, special thanks to chapter reviewers who reviewed earlier drafts of the chapters. Many of their recommendations are incorporated in the book.

The University of Minnesota Crookston provided continual support throughout the development of the textbook. Special thanks to Chancellor, Dr. Mary Holtz-Clause; former Vice Chancellor of Academic Affairs, Dr. John Hoffman; and Division Head, Dr. Anthony Kern, who approved my request for a one-semester faculty leave during the copyediting phase of the book.

For mega-projects such as this one, family support is critical. My wife, Joelle, and daughter, Sophia exuded endless patience and support as I worked long hours to write and revise each chapter. Joelle was a sounding board for my ideas and provided an endless supply of constructive feedback. During our daily one-hour walks, she would often say, "Have you considered this . . ." Climate change, acid rain, and biodiversity became part of our everyday conversation around the home. Sophia, an artist and software engineer, developed the prototype of several of the illustrations used in the book. She also reviewed many of the book's images and offered suggestions for their improvement. Thank you! And special thanks to my father, Tony Shostak, who always wanted updates of the book's progress and would cheer for me from afar.

In addition, special thanks to chapter reviewers who reviewed earlier drafts of the chapters. Many of their recommendations are incorporated in the book.

- Reginald Black, Trinity Washington University
- Christine Bozarth, Northern Virginia Community College
- James S. Godde, Monmouth College
- James Hauri, Assumption University
- Angela Hung, Prairie State College
- Joseph D. Husband, Florida State College at Jacksonville
- James M. Hutcheon, South Puget Sound Community College
- Sara E. Lahman, University of Mount Olive

- Tatyana Lobova, Old Dominion University
- Paul M. McLain, Polk State College
- Sean Moroney, Windward Community College
- Joe Poston, Catawba College
- Lis Regula, University of Akron
- Erin Stuart, Robert Morris University
- Mark Wilcox Hawkeye Community College
- Jeffery Wooters, Pensacola State College

Preface

As the world's population continues to climb by over 70 million people a year, it has become painfully clear that the resources we rely on are not infinite. In fact, there is mounting evidence about the far-reaching negative effects humanity's actions have on the environment. Climate change is real, the earth is getting warmer, and there is glaring evidence of pollution in our waters, land, and air. Species habitats have degraded, species extinction rates have accelerated, and biodiversity has declined. Why do we allow this to happen? Why aren't more people trying to prevent and solve environmental problems? What prompts people to care about the environment and act in sustainable ways?

I have asked such questions throughout my research and teaching career—and as part of my work with many community groups, private foundations, other scientists, and thousands of college students. I have concluded that it comes down to relevance. That is to say, if people don't see the connection between the environment and their own lives, they are often not motivated to do anything meaningful to protect and sustain the environment. What is the best way to build such connections? It will come as no surprise that as an educator, I believe education holds the keys to understanding the changing world around us and stimulating action. Consequently, I decided to write *Environmental Science: A Need for Living Sustainably* as a contemporary approach to the introductory environmental science course for non-science college majors and upper-level high school students.

What Makes This Book Stand Apart?

As an environmental scientist and professor, I have gained a valuable perspective about what inspires people to care about environmental issues. Students seem to respond best to an approach that combines engaging case studies, critical-thinking experiences, applied learning activities both in and out of the classroom, regular and rapid self-assessments, short discussions about research, and the presentation of clear pervading themes, such as sustainability. There are many high-quality environmental science textbooks on the market today, but I have yet to find one that truly meets the needs of my students.

Further, I am reminded every semester how expensive most college textbooks are when students tell me they cannot afford to buy the course text. That is why I am delighted to publish my book with FlatWorld. FlatWorld's affordable prices do not force students to choose between buying a textbook or purchasing necessities. The company's digital-first product model is also more environmentally sound than relying primarily on printed books, although print is available to students who learn best in that medium.

The accelerating pace of environmental change we are experiencing in an astonishingly compressed period of time makes the environmental science course a crucial component in every student's education. It is today's young people who will bear the brunt of environmental degradation and, at the same time, be tasked with finding solutions to reverse and adapt to ongoing changes. My mission is to offer a fresh, more modern perspective on environmental science and sustainability by applying the strategies that follow.

A Thematic Approach

This book takes a thematic approach. The first chapter presents seven themes applicable to environmental issues and are reflected in all subsequent chapters. In my experience, a thematic approach facilitates student learning, because themes serve as guideposts to help students navigate the massive amount of information they will encounter. Themes also make more apparent how individual chapters and subtopics connect. Without these themes, students are more prone to lose their way and get caught up on insignificant details of a specific topic. The seven integrating themes that structure this book are:

1. Life and society need a healthy environment (clean air, clean water, clean soil).
2. Science informs us about the environment.
3. Society, corporation, and consumer decisions affect the environment.
4. Environmental issues have a social and cultural context.
5. A global perspective is needed to deal with many environmental issues.
6. Society relies on many disciplines to solve environmental problems.
7. Sustainability in thought, word, and deed will allow future generations to enjoy a healthy environment.

Focus on Sustainability

Sustainability is the main tenet of environmental science. It encourages us to consider nature's resources as finite. Society's use of these resources should neither outpace nature's ability to replenish them nor compromise the quality of life for future generations. Therefore, to protect the environment and and safeguard the future, there is a vital need for us to live sustainably. This core strategy is reflected in the book's title and the cover image. One example of acting sustainably is by relying on solar as a source of energy, rather than on fossil fuels. In the cover image, thousands of solar panels are spread across sections of the lush Taihang Mountains in Hebei Province in northern China, demonstrating how scalable energy production can live in harmony with nature.

Full Chapter on Ethics

To my knowledge, this is the first environmental science textbook to devote a chapter entirely to ethics. Furthermore, introducing this topic early signals ethics as a priority and an integral part of all discussions of environmental issues that follow (see Chapter 2). Ethical considerations are fundamental to environmental science, as they deal with attitudes of influence and decisions about consumption and activities. For example, sustainable-minded individuals base their decisions about which products they consume on the effects those products potentially have on the environment and those around them. On a larger structural level, the same can be said for businesses. When small to multi-conglomerate companies fail to be responsible environmental stewards, large areas of the world can be negatively affected as pollutants and waste accumulates. Environmental science issues can be complex and may involve environmental injustice, education, poverty, health, and many other factors.

Full Chapter on Matter and Energy

Many of the environmental problems we face are the result of our decisions about how we use matter and energy. Therefore, it is helpful to have a foundational chapter on matter and energy early in the textbook. Our understanding of the structure of matter and how it cycles within the environment is an essential first step when planning sustainability efforts and solving environmental problems. For example, tracing carbon, sulfur, and mercury pollutants to the use of fossil fuels—sources of potential energy—helps us to address climate change, acid rain, and bioaccumulation of contaminants in food chains.

Relevant Case Studies

Each chapter begins with a meaningful, narrative case study. These case studies create important context and build an inviting, non-threatening pathway to understand complex environmental issues. Based on a large body of evidence, a case study approach in science education enhances student performance and creates a more enriching experience. Case studies engage students immediately and entice them to explore unfamiliar topics. They also sharpen critical thinking skills. Because case studies can be adapted to large classroom discussions, small-group work, or individual assignments, they are a flexible learning tool. I have chosen case study topics that resonate with students that also highlight key topics most faculty want to cover. "A Look to the Future" section at the end of every chapter revisits the chapter opening case study in light of what the student has just learned and hint at what future outcomes might be.

The first two chapter-opening case studies set the stage for the rest of the book in unusually compelling ways.

- In Chapter 1, a scenario based on the grasshopper effect takes students through the discovery of toxins in breast milk of Arctic peoples to the source of these toxins thousands of kilometers to the south. As with each subsequent chapter, the case study is revisited several times throughout the chapter when new topics are introduced. Thus, when the process of science is described later in the chapter, examples of how to form a hypothesis pertains to toxins in breast milk and Arctic food.

- The case study in Chapter 2 is based on the article "Tragedy of the Commons," by Garett Hardin published in the journal *Science* in 1968. The case study explores how the individual is pitted against the larger society, wherever a common area exists. An individual can personally benefit from maximizing their removal of a resource from the common area, even though on a larger scale, this action pushes a society toward overusing resources, which in the end, harms society.

"Critical Thinking Activity" Features

Environmental science is a stew of traditional disciplines, environmental issues, and arguments. As a result, learning about this topic can seem messy, complex, and therefore a challenge to comprehend, let alone attempt to resolve. Possession of a critical thinking mindset offers us a way to disentangle arguments and conflicting information so we may clearly navigate the issues. With this in mind, every chapter has at least one critical thinking exercise. These are clearly labelled, boxed, and support the main text. For example, for the first "Critical Thinking Activity" in Chapter 1, students evaluate the impact of well-known environmentalists' writings.

"Bringing It Closer to Home" Activities

Solving environmental problems by taking a pathway toward sustainability begins with the individual decisions each of us make many times a day. The path to action expands from there to encompass decisions and responses by groups of individuals ranging from neighborhoods to small towns, large cities, countries, and, eventually, shared international spaces. The key, therefore, is to first reach the individual in their own, local contexts. With this in mind, each chapter describes home-based activities to help the student (the individual), convert discussion and thinking to action in the local space. While the manuscript was being written, it was evaluated by a number of manuscript reviewers. Many of them were particularly excited about this learning feature.

For example, in the first "Bringing It Closer to Home" activity, we focus on the calculation of a carbon footprint, a measurement of activities and decisions and the impact they have on the environment. "Bringing It Closer to Home" activities also assist the student in further study of an important topic. There are many benefits to these activities including improvements in learning and memory, support of independent thinking and working, cultivation of responsibility, and development of problem-solving skills.

Embedded Links

Today's students prefer to learn through multiple media. This makes good sense, because there are many concepts that take on important new meaning or foster deeper engagement when students can see or hear them. Think for example of a close-up experience of swimming with manatees (see Chapter 7) or how ranching practices impact the Amazon rain forest (see Chapter 9). These short videos transport the learner to a near or faraway place to briefly experience the situation up close. Each chapter features three to six embedded web links students stream on their own devices using FlatWorld's online reader.

"Visual Overview" Summary Figures

Many students benefit from seeing information presented in a variety of formats. With this idea in mind, I have created one comprehensive figure per chapter called "Visual Overview." The text, illustrations, and photos in a "Visual Overview" align with preceding chapter's Learning Objectives. It pulls together the main points of the entire chapter to reinforce the information just learned in a visually engaging way. "Visual Overview" summary figures appear toward the end of every chapter in the "A Look to the Future" section.

Organization and Sequence

Environmental Science: A Need for Living Sustainably reflects an intentional chapter sequence and chapter structure layout. This structure is intended to assist the instructor in teaching the course and the student as they are learning. It is not just the inclusion of specific chapters, but the specific sequence of those chapters that optimizes student learning.

Chapter 1 describes the themes that are woven through the subsequent chapters.

Chapter 2 focuses on ethics, making that topic a priority, rather than covering it at the end of the book. Given the rapid advancements we have witnessed in biotechnology and other areas, it is necessary to place ethics at the forefront of any discussion. We need to ensure ethics becomes a core component of every student's foundational knowledge.

Building upon this base, in Chapter 3, students learn about matter and energy and their connection to life and the environment. The inclusion and placement of this topic is a distinguishing feature of this book. Some textbooks do not cover this material at all. However, I believe that matter and energy play a crucial role in understanding many of the topics that follow.

In Chapter 4 and Chapter 5, students explore the structure and function of natural environmental systems (populations, communities, biomes, ecosystem) without a heavy emphasis on environmental problems. This makes later coverage of complex environmental issues much easier since students will have already mastered the essentials of ecology.

Then in Chapter 6, the focus turns to human populations, which is at the heart of most environmental problems. This chapter highlights carrying capacity and factors (biological, cultural, and political) affecting population growth through in-depth discussions on China and India, the two most populous countries.

Chapter 7 covers biodiversity. Observations of student performance, my doctoral degree in environmental biology, and my research training encouraged me to place biodiversity in the first third of the book, close to coverage of human populations. Why? Although biodiversity is introduced in Chapter 4, the coverage of biodiversity is more comprehensive in Chapter 7, including coverage of species distribution patterns, how to calculate biodiversity, biodiversity decline, as well as a transition section into human impacts on biodiversity.

Once students complete the first seven chapters, they have the prerequisite background to begin any of the resource chapters (Chapters 8–14) covering agriculture, land, water, air and climate change, mining, renewable energies, and non-renewable energies. The resource chapters follow a sequence of 1) description of resource, 2) value of resource, 3) state of resource/misuse/overuse, 4) sustainable management, and 5) future outlook. The first section introduces the new topic, say for example, water resources in Chapter 10. This segues into an explanation of the value of the resource to life and society in the next section. Experience in the classroom has informed me that determining the value of a topic is very useful before forging forward with a discussion on degradation. For instance, in the water chapter, this section discusses the important uses of water for drinking, agriculture, etc. My students are much more attentive and engaged about degradation and misuse of water, air, or other resources after they see them as valuable to themselves and to society. During coverage of misuse and overuse of a resource, students usually inquire about what we can do to protect a resource and to manage it sustainably. Answers to these questions occur in the next section: sustainable management.

After Chapter 14, the focus shifts to toxins (see Chapter 15) and wastes (see Chapter 16) and then culminates with sustainable community development (see Chapter 17) and sustainable economics (see Chapter 18). I consider the last two chapters, especially Chapter 17 as capstone topics where students have the opportunity to apply their gained knowledge from earlier chapters to the next hierarchal level.

Chapter Structure

Including the distinctive in-chapter learning features described earlier in "What Makes This Book Stand Apart?" each chapter is structured with the following learning aids:

Chapter-Opening Case Studies As described above in more detail, each chapter is introduced by a contemporary and inherently fascinating example of a current environmental science issue or topic.

Learning Objectives Most textbooks present a long list of learning objectives at the beginning of a chapter. Many students find it hard to remember them after they progress through the chapter. For this reason, I have placed learning objectives at the beginning of each main head section instead. Learning objectives are based on Fink's taxonomy that identifies six areas of learning: foundational knowledge, application, integration, human dimension, caring, and learning how to learn.

"Critical Thinking Activity" Features As described above in more detail, at least one "Critical Thinking Activity" per chapter prompts students to analyze key topics in depth, such as genetically modified organisms (see Chapter 2 Section 3) or solid waste disposal (see Chapter 16 Section 2).

"Bringing It Closer to Home" Activities As described above in more detail, each chapter features one "Bringing It Closer to Home" activity. These activities invite students to go beyond the computer or classroom to investigate their personal environments. Examples include topics such as product designs (see Chapter 2 Section 3), estimating habitat loss (see Chapter 7 Section 3), and identifying risk of exposure to ozone (see Chapter 11 Section 4).

Key Terms Key terms are bold faced in the text. In the online reader version of this book, key terms pop up with a mouse rollover. In the printed version, key terms are defined and appear in the margins. All key terms are reflected in the glossary.

High-Quality Visual Learning Aids I made a special point to incorporate high-quality, pedagogically sound figures that will appeal to all students, especially visual learners. Illustrations and photographs are supported by relevant informative captions that provide context and new information, including alt text information to support full accessibility for every learner.

Key Takeaways These summary points appear at the end of every main head section and echo the section's corresponding Learning Objectives. They succinctly summarize the most important points while the information is fresh in the student's mind to increase retention.

Embedded Links As described above in more detail, each chapter features three to six embedded web links designed to help students further explore environmental topics and bring topics to life. Students can stream the videos using FlatWorld's online reader version of the book.

"Visual Overviews" Summary Figures and "A Look to the Future" Sections As described in more detail above, a "Visual Overview" appears toward the end of every chapter in the "A Look to the Future" section. The overviews provide an engaging summary of key concepts and "A Look to the Future" provides hints for how the chapter-opening scenario may unfold in coming years.

References Information is easily accessible in today's information age, but not all sources of information are reliable. For this reason, learning about how to determine trustworthy sites and how to appropriately cite an information source are important skills to develop. In addition, accurate referencing gives credit to the original author. To this end, all chapters include citations and there is a complete list of references at the end of each chapter.

Supplements

Environmental Science: A Need for Living Sustainably is accompanied by a robust supplements program that augments and enriches both the teaching and student learning experiences. I have personally prepared all of the supplements to ensure accuracy and full alignment with the book's narrative. Faculty should contact their FlatWorld sales representative or FlatWorld support at support@flatworld.com for more information or to obtain access to the supplements upon adoption.

Sample Syllabi

Sample syllabi based on either 16-week, 10-week, or 8-week terms provide useful templates that help new adopters transition from their current course textbook to *Environmental Science: A Need for Living Sustainably*. Faculty can download the syllabi from the FlatWorld website or they can be obtained by contacting your local FlatWorld representative or FlatWorld support (support@flatworld.com).

Instructor's Manual

The instructor's manual (IM) includes a chapter overview, chapter outline, and possible responses for the critical thinking and home activities. Teaching tips, online resources, and suggestions for active learning, such as additional home activities and critical thinking applications, class discussion questions, group activities, and video link discussion questions, are also included.

PowerPoint Slides

PowerPoint Slides organized by chapter include a concise and thorough outline, Learning Objectives, Key Takeaways, and figures and tables contained in the text. These slides work well for both face-to-face and online learning environments, enliven lectures, and stimulate class discussions. Adopters can use the slides as composed to support lectures or customize and build upon them to suit their particular teaching goals.

Test Item File

The Test Item File (TIF) includes more than fifty questions per chapter in multiple-choice, fill-in-the-blank, true/false. and essay-question formats. All answers are provided, including possible responses to the essay questions, and each question is assigned a difficulty level. The items have been written specifically to reinforce the major topics covered in each chapter and to align with FlatWorld Homework and in-text quiz items. The Test Item File questions are also available in pre-formatted form for easy export into popular learning management systems such as Canvas or Blackboard.

Test Generator—Powered by Cognero

FlatWorld is pleased to provide a computer-generated test program powered by the leading assessment provider Cognero to assist instructors with selecting, randomizing, formatting, loading online, or printing exams. Please contact your local FlatWorld representative or FlatWorld support (support@flatworld.com) for more information or to request the program.

FlatWorld Homework

FlatWorld Homework is provided in an easy-to-use interface. Multiple choice, fill-in-the-blank, matching, image labeling, and other question types are available for use and are all auto-gradable. Students who utilize the homework questions should see their performance improve on examinations that are given using the Test Item File questions that accompany this book.

Online Quizzes and Flashcards

Autograded Quiz questions and Flashcards for student self-evaluation are organized by chapter and section and embedded in the online version of the book. Students can use the Quizzes and Flashcards to test their comprehension by section as they read and learn, once they have completed a chapter, or for test review.

CHAPTER 1
Introduction to Environmental Science: Sustainability

Case Study: Grasshopper Effect

In 1987, Canadian scientist Dr. Eric Dewailly was researching the presence of environmental toxic substances in human breast milk within Quebec province. As part of his study, he requested breast milk samples from Nunavik, one of the most isolated areas in Quebec. High above the Arctic Circle, Nunavik was far from cities, factories, and industries and the pollution they generate. Surprisingly, the analysis indicated extremely high concentrations of toxins among the Nunavik samples. Worried there was a mistake or the samples had been contaminated, Dr. Dewailly ran the samples again. The second analysis confirmed the first: there were high concentrations of toxic substances in the breast milk of women living in the Arctic region. How could this be?

FIGURE 1.1
The vast, pristine-looking Arctic is a reservoir of environmental toxic substances that originated from lower, warmer latitudes. The highest concentrations of the substances are found in apex predators of the food chain—polar bears and people. A) A mother polar bear with her cub moving across ice floes; B) An Arctic settlement.

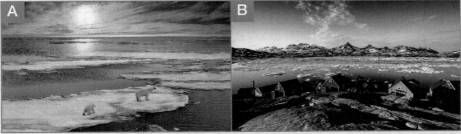

Source: © Shutterstock, Inc.

The sparsely populated and seemingly pristine Arctic has some of the highest concentrations of deadly environmental toxic substances on Earth. These substances, including the persistent organic pollutants dichlorodiphenyltrichloroethane (DDT), toxaphene, chlordane, polychlorinated biphenyls (PCBs), and the heavy metal mercury, do not originate in the Arctic; rather, they are carried by air currents from lower, warmer latitudes. Collectively, the toxic substances are called persistent organic pollutants (POPs) because unlike most organic compounds they do not readily degrade in the environment. POPs can move over long distances in a series of evaporation and condensation events (or "hops")—essentially riding parcels of air. As air warms near Earth's surface, it picks up evaporated toxins from the soil, then expands, becomes less dense, and consequently rises and moves toward a polar region. Within the northern hemisphere, air parcels move in the direction of the North Pole (Arctic), whereas in the southern hemisphere, the air parcels end up in the South Pole (Antarctica). Not all of these toxic substances evaporate from the soil; some are released from industrial and power plant chimneys directly into the atmosphere. For example, when we combust coal, we convert mercury from solid to gas form and consequently make it mobile. Once airborne, mercury hops like a grasshopper, and in the final jump, settles on Arctic land and waters alike. On land, mercury and other persistent organic pollutants contaminate lichens, shrubs, mosses, and grasses that serve as food for Arctic animals such as caribou. As the toxins move up the **food chain**, they become more concentrated (**biomagnification**). Therefore, tissues of caribou have a higher concentration of the toxins

food chain

A linear arrangement (a chain) of organisms showing feeding relationships. Food energy and matter are transferred up this linear chain from lower to higher trophic levels.

biomagnification

An increase in the concentration of a substance as it moves up the levels of a food chain.

bioaccumulation

An accumulation of a substance into a living thing.

than the tissues of the plants they eat; tissues of Inuits, the Indigenous population who hunt and eat caribou, have an even higher concentration. In the ocean, the toxic substances are taken up (**bioaccumulation**) by algae (small plant cells) and bacteria and then biomagnify as they move up the food chain to zooplankton, fish, seals, and polar bears (see Figure 1.1). Inuits are the apex predator of this system because they hunt seals and polar bears.

These environmental toxic substances are a serious concern to Inuits and all peoples exposed to them, because they negatively affect human health. Mercury, for example, damages the nervous, circulatory, and immune systems. Fat-soluble toxic substances such as mercury concentrate in fat tissue and are released in breast milk and transferred to newborns. Persistent organic pollutants are linked to hormonal disruptions, changes in the reproductive system, neurological and learning disabilities, and cancer (Bonefeld-Jørgensen et al. 2017).

As you can see, the Arctic has, more or less become a sink for environmental toxic substances produced in other parts of the world. Deciphering the issue was a complex endeavor, from first detecting toxic substances within people and the environment of the Arctic, to understanding associated health risks, to identifying their sources hundreds or thousands of kilometers away, to determining how they are transferred geographically and how they move through the food chain. Environmental scientists, in collaboration with Arctic peoples, health scientists, and climatologists, pieced together the complete story, and this information was put forward to the United Nations to find a solution. No matter the size of the environmental issue, history has chronicled how the actions of individuals and groups of people have led to positive environmental change. On May 22, 2001, in Stockholm, Sweden, representatives from 152 countries discussed the presented information and then signed an international treaty to eliminate or reduce the release of persistent organic pollutants with the intention of simultaneously protecting the environment and people. The treaty was entered into force on May 17, 2004, and the list of POPs identified in the treaty has expanded since that time.

1.1 Earth's Interconnected Systems Furnish Goods and Services

Learning Objective

1. Understand and appreciate the diversity and interconnectedness of Earth's ecosystems.

environmental science

An interdisciplinary approach to the study of environmental systems; this approach helps us to understand how our actions can support environmental health or diminish it.

Welcome to our world, an oasis in space teeming with an array of living things in a complex variety of different, yet connected habitats. In this opening chapter, we explore the connectivity of the world, from the extremely cold Arctic where Inuits and polar bears live, to the warm and wet tropical rain forests, to the deep and vibrant seas. After a brief tour of the global environment, we discuss the goods and services the environment continually provides or upholds for all living things and human society. We delve into the value of science and the usefulness of **environmental science** in helping us to understand how our actions can either support the environment's health or diminish it (see video link: "Why the World Needs Environmental Science").

To assist in this aim, we identify key environmental themes that pervade and, like pillars, tie together all environmental issues. The chapter wraps up with a look to the future—a discussion of **sustainability** and recommendations for solving environmental problems.

■ Why the World Needs Environmental Science

Listen to Sir David Attenborough explain how society has affected the world and the need to save Earth's ecosystems by working toward sustainability.

View in the online reader

sustainability

The main tenet of environmental science stating that nature's resources are finite and society's use of these resources should neither outpace nature's ability to replenish them nor compromise the quality of life for future generations.

The Environment Is an Interconnected Global System

Our opening case study of the grasshopper effect demonstrates the interconnected nature of the environment, where, for example, the burning of coal can indirectly lead to high concentrations of mercury in polar bears thousands of kilometers away. We use environmental science to understand the environment and the effects our activities—including the burning of coal—have on the environment's health. The Arctic is part of the global **environment**, a large system composed of smaller departments or spheres, which in turn consist of smaller components. These spheres are the **lithosphere** (rock/ground), **atmosphere** (air), **hydrosphere** (water), and **biosphere** (all living things). Matter, including toxic substances, moves among and within these spheres.

environment

The entire surroundings of organisms, including matter, energy, conditions, and factors both living and nonliving.

lithosphere

The solid portion of the Earth.

atmosphere

A layer of gases surrounding the Earth and overlaying its surface.

hydrosphere

All the water of the world, including ground water, lakes, rivers, and oceans.

biosphere

All of the world's living organisms.

carbon dioxide

CO₂, the most abundant of the greenhouse gases, which enhance climate change; released by burning of fossil fuels and by respiration.

greenhouse gas

A gas (i.e., carbon dioxide) that contributes to the greenhouse effect by absorbing infrared radiation and trapping heat in the atmosphere.

acid rain

Rainfall that is more acidic than normal; it has a pH value of five or less.

system

A set made of smaller components, each with its own purpose or function.

ecosystem

An environmental system that includes one or more communities and their non-living environments.

For instance, coal is mined from the lithosphere in West Virginia, Kentucky, and Wyoming, and then, after processing, is transported to power plants, where it is combusted to release stored energy. Coal is mostly carbon, but it also contains small percentages of impurities such as mercury and sulfur. When coal is incinerated to transform energy stored in carbon–carbon bonds to electricity, the reaction releases gaseous products into the atmosphere, including **carbon dioxide** (CO_2) and sulfur dioxide (SO_2). Carbon dioxide, a **greenhouse gas**, contributes to climate change, and sulfur dioxide is a precursor to **acid rain**, two glaring environmental issues. Mercury, a focus of the opening case study, becomes airborne too when coal is combusted and is carried by wind into new locations, where it settles on both water (hydrosphere) and land. The mercury enters the biosphere at the base of the aquatic and terrestrial food webs and then biomagnifies as it moves up the food chains. Similar to our skeletal system, the environment is a **system** or assemblage made of smaller components, each with its own purpose, yet they work together to perform a common function. In a skeletal system, each bone has structure and as long as the structure is maintained, the bone can continue to uphold its function. Its ability to complete its function also depends on the other bones of the body. The structure within this and any other system is hierarchical—meaning the structure of the system is more complex than that of its components. Furthermore, the system can accomplish things that its components individually cannot, and the components interact with each other. Systems can be various sizes, from as large as the entire global environment to as small as an island, pond, or even a puddle.

Environmental Systems Have Characteristics

Systems are characterized by their complexity, integration, and openness. Systems that are more complex have more components than do less complex systems. In the case of the grasshopper effect example, a high level of complexity led to an unexpected effect of high concentrations of mercury in the Arctic. Integration refers to the strength of the interactions between components. It was the strong connectedness between the lithosphere, atmosphere, hydrosphere, and biosphere that led to the ease of movement of toxins from one department to another. The degree of a system's openness reflects its isolation. Certainly, no natural system is fully isolated, but some systems are more isolated than others. For example, a natural lake is probably less connected (less open) to other environmental systems compared to a reservoir, which receives water from upriver. Within the global environmental system lies our society with all of its cities and all of our activities (see Figure 1.2). When we comprehend the reality of the environment as our home, we add the prefix *eco-*, which means house or environment, to the root word *system*. Therefore, **ecosystem** means environmental system.

FIGURE 1.2

Up until about eleven thousand years ago, humans lived in small, nomadic bands that subsisted by hunting wild animals and foraging for wild produce. As our ancestors learned about agriculture and domestication of animals, they began to turn away from a sparsely populated nomadic life and settled in specific environmental areas. In contrast, today we see concentrated human populations living in large cities. In both cases, either living as nomads or living in today's cities, we still are products of the environment and live within it. A) A nomad in Kashmir, India, often moves to find fresh pastures for her family's goats. B) New York City with Central Park.

Source: klublu/Shutterstock.com; © Shutterstock, Inc.

To understand environmental systems and how we interact with them, we rely on the multidisciplinary approach of environmental science. There is a little something for people of every interest in environmental science because it incorporates ecology, political science, economics, biology, engineering, psychology, chemistry, sociology, and other disciplines, and it uses this information to solve environmental issues. All environmental problems are the result of resource depletion and/or pollution, and we rely on environmental science to help us learn how to not overuse or misuse natural resources. In other words, it helps us to live sustainably—to use natural resources at a pace slow enough to allow the environment to replenish what is used. This strategy helps the environment to continue to uphold a quality habitat not only for us, but also for non-human organisms with whom we share this planet. Living sustainably also allows the environment to offer clean air and water, on which all living things depend.

A Tour of Our Shared Environment

From a vantage point on the moon or the international space station, the Earth looks like a small blue marble hovering in space (see Figure 1.3). What might seem like an ordinary planet, one of eight orbiting an average star in an average galaxy, is our home. What makes Earth's environment so unique? Besides its condensed matter, it has a developed atmosphere of nitrogen, oxygen, and trace amounts of other gases, and widespread soil often rich in organic carbon. Plus, there is water! The majority (about 72 percent) of Earth's surface is covered by water, a necessity for life as we know it. Life also needs energy, and almost all life on Earth is directly or indirectly dependent on our sun to meet energy demands. In addition, Earth's proximity to the sun allows it to receive just the right amount of solar energy to have reasonable, life-supporting temperatures. By comparison, the next closest planet to the sun, Venus, has an average surface temperature of 477°C (890°F), plenty hot enough to melt lead and be inhospitable to all forms of life on Earth.

The global environment has a great array of ecosystems, from, for example, the warm and wet tropical rain forest to the cold and dry Arctic (see Figure 1.4). These are vastly different in structure, species, and climate. Similarly, there are glaring contrasts between the hot Sahara desert and the Great Barrier Reef. All four of these ecosystems are beautiful to behold, and like all ecosystems across our seven continents and oceans, each supports an assortment of interacting individuals living in **populations**—individuals of the same species—and **communities**—individuals of different species.

The diversity of life, or **biodiversity**, is an important part of the environment (see Chapter 7). Altogether, Earth's ecosystems have an immense diversity of living things, yet individually the degree of diversity within an environmental area varies based on physical features, resources, climate, and stability, among other factors. Each species is uniquely adapted to its surroundings and has a special functional role that helps maintain the structure and function of the community and ecosystem.

Humans share the environment with an estimated 8.7 million eukaryotic species (Mora et al. 2011). These species and the physical environment they inhabit support a continuous series of processes and goods necessary for life and society. Next, we discuss these benefits.

FIGURE 1.3
Compared to the cold void of outer space, Earth is an inviting oasis.

Source: NASA/NOAA/GSFC/Suomi NPP/VIIRS/Norman Kuring

populations

Groups of individuals of the same species living in a particular geographical area.

communities

Groups of two or more species interacting together.

biodiversity

Biological diversity; variety of life at all organizational levels from genes through ecosystems.

FIGURE 1.4

Some ecosystems are relatively similar in appearance. Others, as shown here, are quite different. A) The vibrant green of a tropical rain forest, the ecosystem with the greatest number of different species; (B) The cold and dry Arctic; (C) Dunes of the Sahara; (D) Brilliantly colored and biodiverse tropical coral reef.

Source: © Shutterstock, Inc.

Humans Rely on Goods and Services the Environment Provides

bacteria

A large group of single-celled microorganisms lacking a nucleus and organelles. They can cause infections and diseases, but also have a number of important functions, such as nutrient cycling.

ecosystem goods

Tangible things from the environment we consume (vegetables, firewood, etc.).

pollination

The transfer of pollen (e.g., by animals and wind) from the male part of a flower (anther) to the female part of a flower (stigma), a requirement for fertilization and seed production.

As humans, we consume industrial products, foods, and pharmaceuticals wholly or partially derived from animals, plants, fungi, and **bacteria**. Society's consumption necessitates the existence of a wealth of different species, or biological diversity. The pharmaceutical industry alone is estimated to rely on thousands of medical compounds derived from a wide variety of plant species (Arraiza et al. 2017). Take, for instance, the rosy periwinkle (*Catharanthus roseus*) endemic to Madagascar (see Figure 1.5). This plant makes two anticancer compounds that we use to treat cancer and Hodgkin disease. There is also salicylic acid, used since 400 BC and the basis of aspirin, a very popular pharmaceutical used as a blood thinner, anti-inflammatory, and painkiller. Originally, salicylic acid was extracted from the bark of willow trees. The medicinal compounds from the periwinkle and willow tree are examples of goods produced by healthy ecosystems. Consider all of the other tangible goods you consume. Do you like seafood, eat carrots, use wood furniture, have copper pipes in your house, or rely on energy stored in coal? Of course, this is an incomplete list of **ecosystem goods**, but you probably get the sense that we depend on these goods daily. Healthy ecosystems also provide free services such as purification of water and **pollination** of plants.

There are three general types of **ecosystem services**: provisioning, regulating, and cultural. Provisioning services consistently supply food, fresh water, timber, coal, and other ecosystem goods. Another type of ecosystem service regulates climate, disease, and water, and is therefore titled regulating services. The third type, cultural, refers to the spiritual, religious, and inspirational value of an ecosystem. A fourth group of services, supporting services, supports the other three groups. Supporting services are fundamental ecosystem services like nutrient cycling, soil formation, the water cycle, and photosynthesis. Let's reconsider the Arctic ecosystem from the opening case study and identify some of its goods and services. The Arctic ecosystem continually supplies seals and caribou (examples of goods) as sources of food. Purifying water and other regulatory services in this environment are already taxed due to the influx of environmental toxic substances coming from southern latitudes (see "Critical Thinking Activity: Exploring Ecosystems and Their Services").

FIGURE 1.5

Society relies on the environment for many goods and services. For instance, the pharmaceutical industry uses tens of thousands of different plant species, including the rosy periwinkle endemic to Madagascar and shown here.

Source: © Shutterstock, Inc.

ecosystem services

Services (provisioning, regulating, or cultural) such as air purification and soil formation upheld by the environment.

Critical Thinking Activity: Exploring Ecosystems and Their Services

The objectives of this exercise are to understand ecosystem services and to identify services provided by particular ecosystems. We begin by reobserving the Arctic as an example of an ecosystem (see Figure 1.6). The services mentioned in the figure continue as long as the Arctic remains healthy. Unfortunately, humankind has dramatically altered many of Earth's ecosystems so that they are no longer able to perform their original functions. As an example, between 1860 and the early 1900s, many wetlands within the contiguous United States were drained to create croplands and homesteads. Therefore, places like Rake, in north central Iowa, are now agricultural rather than wetlands. For the second part of this exercise, access Google Earth and view the area surrounding the small town of Rake. Go to Google Earth here and click on Launch Earth. Doing so displays an image of Earth. Click on the search icon at the legend on the left and type in Rake, Iowa. View the agricultural lands and ask yourself which services are no longer provided. As one final step, choose another ecosystem from a geographical area of your choice and describe its ecosystem services.

FIGURE 1.6
A healthy ecosystem provides many services used by society. As an example, the Arctic ecosystem shown in the images offers food production, recycling of nutrients, biodiversity, regulation of climate, and cultural value.

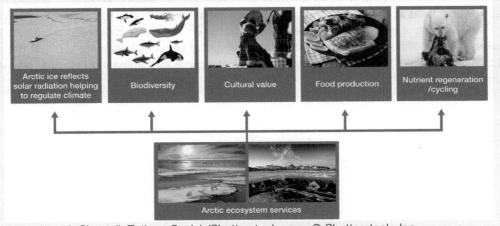

Source: Joseph Shostell; Tatiana Gasich/Shutterstock.com; © Shutterstock, Inc.

Key Takeaways

- The global environment consists of diverse interconnected systems.
- Society relies on services the environment provides.

1.2 The Need for Environmental Science

Learning Objectives

1. Explore how early environmentalists helped shape today's environmental movement.
2. Explain how environmental scientists use the scientific method and critical thinking skills to find solutions to climate change and other environmental problems.

Why is there a need for environmental protection? The existence of pollutants in the Arctic informs us about the far-reaching effects society's actions can have on the environment. When we do not live sustainably, the environment becomes overburdened and ecosystem goods and services begin to decline. One of these services is the maintenance of a phenomenal biodiversity, which we rely on to provide other services, such as nutrient cycling and various tangible goods. According to the International Union for Conservation of Nature (IUCN), the respected international entity that monitors the Earth's biodiversity, approximately 41 percent of all amphibians are currently threatened. If the threats to the environment continue, these species will become extinct and all of the goods and services they help provide will be imperiled. Furthermore, 26 percent of all mammals, 14 percent of all birds, and 39 percent of all known plants (Nic Lughada et al. 2020) are also at risk of extinction. We are losing species hundreds to thousands of times faster than what would occur naturally (Barnosky et al. 2011, Ceballos et al. 2015, Pimm et al. 2015). What is the cause of these losses? All of the anthropogenic (human-caused) threats to the environment radiate from humans living non-sustainably. Pollution, habitat destruction, and global climate change are some of the many culprits (see Figure 1.7). With this knowledge, we have come to understand just how fragile and finite Earth is.

FIGURE 1.7

When we are not careful and live unsustainably, our actions have negative effects on the environment. A) An Atlantic grey seal tangled in a discarded fishing net; B) Sewer pipes emptying into a stream; C) Air pollution in Beijing, China; D) Floating plastic garbage; E) A rain forest cut down to make room for agriculture.

Source: StrippedPixel.com/Shutterstock.com; © Shutterstock, Inc.

Origin of the Contemporary Environmental Movement

Our appreciation for the environment and its replenishing capacity evolved slowly as individuals noticed the early effects of environmental neglect and wrote about them in persuasive, carefully reasoned works.

Frontier Mentality and the Industrial Revolution

frontier mentality

An anthropocentric worldview held by European explorers and colonists who arrived in North America beginning in the sixteenth century and believed that natural resources were limitless and available for use.

The first European settlers of North America had a hardened **frontier mentality**. They deforested primary virgin forests to make way for croplands, homes, and towns without concern for the effects of their actions on the environment. Why would they think otherwise, when forests stretched for hundreds if not thousands of miles in all directions? While the United States expanded westward, the Industrial Revolution spread across Europe and then took hold in the United States. American cities grew dramatically as workers came to fill factory positions, and the United States evolved from relying on hand tools to using machines. Such a rapid change was historically unprecedented and dramatically changed how people lived—raising the standard of living for the common American. These great advances came with environmental consequences. Early environmentalists such as George Perkins Marsh, John Muir, and Aldo Leopold warned the public of the dangers of an endless frontier mindset and negative effects of the Industrial Revolution (see Figure 1.8). To explore their writings, see "Critical Thinking Activity: Quotes from Environmentalists".

FIGURE 1.8
Some of the most influential early environmentalists and naturalists who helped to pave the way for our environmental efforts today: (A) George Perkins Marsh, (B) Teddy Roosevelt, pictured next to John Muir, is considered to be the most environmentally friendly U.S. president, (C) Gifford Pinchot, and (D) Aldo Leopold.

Sources: Hon. George Perkins Marsh of Vermont. [Between 1855 and 1865] Photograph. https://www.loc.gov/item/2017895581/; Underwood & Underwood. ROOSEVELT, T. [1903] Photograph. http://loc.gov/pictures/resource/ppmsca.36413/; Harris & Ewing, photographer. PINCHOT, G. , None. [Between 1905 and 1945] Photograph. https://www.loc.gov/item/2016856530/; Aldo Leopold with quiver and bow seated on rimrock above the Rio Gavilan in northern Mexico while on a bow hunting trip in 1938. Courtesy of Wikipedia.

Critical Thinking Activity: Quotes from Environmentalists

The goal of this CTA is to recognize and evaluate the impact of well-known environmentalists' writings. Read the quotes in Table 1.1 and write either "yes" or "no" in the third column depending on whether the author's words positively moved you or not. Rank the quotes from strongest to weakest impact and then discuss your rankings with other students.

TABLE 1.1 Well-Known Environmentalist Writings

Environmentalist/Quote	Do You See Value in This Author's Words?	Ranking of Quotes from Most to Least Impactful (1–5)
George Perkins Marsh (1801–1882)". . . Man, who even now finds scarce breathing room on this vast globe, cannot retire from the Old World to some yet undiscovered continent, and wait for the slow action of such causes to replace, by a new creation, the Eden he has wasted" (Marsh 1864).		
Henry David Thoreau (1817–1862)"Each town should have a park, or rather a primitive forest, of five hundred or a thousand acres, where a stick should never be cut for fuel, a common possession forever, for instruction and recreation" (Thoreau 1859).		
Gifford Pinchot (1865–1946)". . . the common word for our forests was inexhaustible. To waste timber was a virtue and not a crime. There would always be plenty of timber and everything else in America for everybody, world without end. . . . The lumbermen . . . regarded forest devastation as normal . . . And as for sustained yield, no such idea had ever entered their heads. . . . What talk there was about forest protection was no more to the average American than the buzzing of a mosquito, and just about as irritating" (Pinchot 1947).		
Aldo Leopold (1887–1948)"A thing is right when it tends to preserve the integrity, stability, and beauty of the biotic community. It is wrong when it tends otherwise" (Leopold 1949).		
Rachel Carson (1907–1964)"Why should we tolerate a diet of weak poisons, a home in insipid surroundings, a circle of acquaintances who are not quite our enemies, the noise of motors with just enough relief to prevent insanity? Who would want to live in a world which is just not quite fatal?" (Carson 1962).		

Early environmentalists also described the threat our actions had on individual species (see Figure 1.9).

FIGURE 1.9
(A) A hill of bison skulls provides a snapshot of the effects of a frontier mentality in the nineteenth century; (B) The American bison would have become extinct if not for small private herds and those protected in Yellowstone National Park, as shown here.

Source: © Shutterstock, Inc.

Today's Environmental Movement Developed from Multiple Viewpoints on Conservation

The contemporary environmental movement and society's increased awareness of environmental issues developed from exposure to the writings of early conservationists and opposing views on conservation thinking.

deforestation

The action of removing (clearing) a forest.

    As time passed, early environmentalists began to note that the frontier attitude was not a path of sustainability. George Perkins Marsh (1801–1882), usually considered America's first environmentalist, wrote about the negative effects of **deforestation** in the book *Man and Nature* (1864) (see E in Figure 1.7). Overlapping this period, the Scottish-born naturalist John Muir (1838–1914) was a staunch supporter of a type of wilderness preservation called **preservationist conservation**. This viewpoint, also referred to as biocentric preservation, is based on nature having value for just being nature. In other words, the value of nature does not depend on its usefulness to humans. In his many travels, John Muir witnessed the devastation of mountain meadows and forests by domesticated animals. His writings and efforts led to the creation of Sequoia, Mount Rainier, and Yosemite National Parks, among others, and encouraged people to experience and protect nature. He also helped found the Sierra Club, one of the most powerful environmental organizations in the United States.

preservationist conservation

A viewpoint of conservation in which the environment is left unscathed by human intervention.

utilitarian conservation

The conservation viewpoint that the environment is to be used and sustainably managed by humans.

    Gifford Pinchot (1865–1946), the first chief of the U.S. Forest Service, supported **utilitarian conservation** and advocated for forests to be managed like an agricultural crop. This type of conservation was in direct opposition to preservationist conservation, which essentially called for forests to be left untouched. Both Pinchot and President Theodore Roosevelt valued forests because they furnished manufacturing supplies for homes and provided jobs for people. From this viewpoint, the goals of forest conservation would be to have a sustained yield of trees, and to only cut down what was needed and could be replaced through growth and planting. Early environmentalists like Pinchot noted the public's lack of environmental awareness as well as a mild distaste for sustainability because it was at odds with the frontier mentality. Under Pinchot's leadership, the number of national forests increased by over 365 percent, to 193 million acres. Which type of conservation do you support, preservationist or utilitarian?

The prolific writings of another naturalist observer, Aldo Leopold (1887–1948), a U.S. Forest Service employee, philosopher, and professor, helped stir interest in the science of ecology and the environmental movement. **Ecology** is the scientific study of the interactions that determine the distribution and abundance of organisms. In one of his most recognized works, *A Sand County Almanac*, Leopold describes the relationship between people and the environment, and in *A Land Ethic*, he stresses ethics and the interdependence of humans with all other animals and plants. Even now, seventy years after its first printing, *A Sand County Almanac* still sells tens of thousands of copies each year.

The environmental movement is a result of the collective thoughts and efforts of Aldo Leopold and many other naturalists. Perhaps the most widely influential of these early environmentalists was Rachel Carson, who informed the world in 1962 about the dangers of pesticides in her book *Silent Spring* (see Figure 1.10). Her writings alerted the larger public to the degradation of the environment by a society that still maintained the frontier mentality. Today, Rachel Carson's work, and especially *Silent Spring*, is considered the beginning of the grassroots environmental movement, which led to the establishment of the Environmental Protection Agency in 1970.

FIGURE 1.10

Rachel Carson's 1962 book, *Silent Spring*, was a wake-up call to the public about the dangers of using DDT in pesticides. After years of widespread controversy among scientists, government officials, and the general public, DDT was banned in the United States, except for emergency use, in 1972. In the photo, Carson works with Bob Hines on the Atlantic Coast in 1952.

Source: U.S. Fish and Wildlife Service, *Rachel Carson with Bob Hines Conducts Marine Biology Research*, 1952, https://digitalmedia.fws.gov/digital/collection/natdiglib/id/8515/rec/1/

ecology

The scientific study of the interactions that determine the distribution and abundance of organisms (Krebs 1972).

Issues of the Twentieth Century and Beyond

Beginning in the twentieth century, America began to focus more on wildlife habitat protection. An example was the establishment of the National Park Service in 1916 to protect national parks for the generations yet to come. A little bit earlier, in 1903, President Theodore Roosevelt had approved and signed off on America's first federally protected wildlife refuge, Pelican Island. Today, we have 566 similar wildlife refuge areas across the United States. Another important milestone occurred in 1940 with the establishment of the United States Fish and Wildlife Service (USFWS), whose mission is to conserve, protect, and enhance fish, wildlife, and their habitats.

Environmentalists came to realize the growing problem of fragmenting the environment with highways, cities, and other human structures. Urbanization, poor city planning, and sprawl became key concerns, and they continue to plague us today (see Chapter 17). Out of the need to address these threats, the Nature Conservancy was formed, and it soon became the world's leading conservation organization. Its mission is to protect habitats and it now oversees 1,500 preserves totaling some 9 million acres. Thirteen years later, in 1964, Congress passed the Federal Wilderness Act to protect wildlife habitats, from the nation's many roads. The Act established the National Wilderness Preservation System, which so far has set aside over 111 million acres for protection.

What Are the Main Issues Environmental Scientists Are Working on Today?

In the latter half of the twentieth century and into the twenty-first century, environmentalists turned their attention to a broad range of growing environmental issues, many of them interrelated and all of them consequences of nonsustainable living (see Figure 1.11). Some of the larger environmental issues we will explore in this book are overpopulation, climate change, pollution (land, water, and air), habitat degradation and fragmentation, and loss of biodiversity. Like those before us and those to follow, we rely on sound science to inform us about connections between human activities and the health of the environment (see video link: "Thoughts of a Conservation Scientist").

FIGURE 1.11

When we do not live sustainably, our actions negatively affect the environment. Look through the major environmental threats the world faces today.

Sources: Joseph Shostell; zaferkizilkaya/Shutterstock.com; IR Stone/Shutterstock.com; StrippedPixel.com/Shutterstock.com; © Shutterstock, Inc.

Overpopulation

Today we see strong evidence of human overpopulation. Our population has increased above **carrying capacity**, to a size beyond what the environment can sustain. Quite simply, there are insufficient natural resources for our population to grow exponentially forever. Human overpopulation is an outcome of multiple factors, including a decline in the mortality rate due to increased health care and advances in medicine, lack of family planning, overuse of natural resources, and scant education about sustainability. As long as the number of births exceeds the number of deaths, the human population will continue to increase. At the time of printing of this book, there were approximately 330 million people in the United States, and over 7.8 billion in the world. Each of these people has an ecological footprint and needs resources to maintain their way of life. A pathway of continued population growth despite limited resources leads to conflicts, poverty, stress on agricultural systems, and unemployment, in addition to climate change, pollution, habitat degradation, and loss of biodiversity.

Climate Change

Climate change is real, and Earth is getting warmer. Most of this warming has occurred within the last forty years and is the result of human-made greenhouse gas emissions. The burning of fossil fuels to power our cars and laptop computers and to heat our homes releases carbon dioxide, nitrous oxide, methane, and other greenhouse gases that accumulate in Earth's atmosphere. Very similar to the glass of a greenhouse, greenhouse gases trap solar heat in the atmosphere and raise surface air temperatures. In burning fossil fuels, we are releasing carbon that has been sequestered for millions of years within the ground. This storage of carbon is an example of a carbon reservoir. Other examples of carbon reservoirs include soils, plants, and oceans. We now understand that destruction of these carbon reservoirs by burning in the case of fossil fuels, or through deforestation or by climate change itself, enhances the rate of climate change (Crowther 2016, Eglinton et al. 2021, Freidlingstein 2015). Society's "business as usual" strategy and the continued destruction of carbon reservoirs will only further exacerbate some of our most daunting environmental issues, such as warming oceanic waters, shrinking ice sheets, melting glaciers, rising sea levels, and severe inclement weather events. To confront climate change, countries have established international agreements limiting greenhouse gas emissions, and individuals are encouraged to reduce their reliance on fossil fuels (see video link: "What Is Climate Change?").

Pollution (Land, Water, and Air)

A telltale sign of nonsustainable living is environmental pollution, and unfortunately there is glaring evidence of pollution in our water, land, and air. Pollution comes in different forms, some easily seen (like garbage), while others (including DDT and mercury) are invisible to the naked eye. As we learned from the opening case study, some solid pollutants (like mercury) can be converted to gases and transported great distances. Pollution originates from nonsustainable living, society's reliance on fossil fuels, inefficient energy transformations, and poorly designed cradle-to-grave products that we purchase. One of the objectives of this book is to identify pollution, its origins, and methods of remediation, which can be very expensive. Who should cover the cost of this remediation? Also, looking to the future, how do we encourage sustainable living? Future pricing of products we purchase may very well reflect their sustainability, meaning wholly sustainable items will be cheaper. Can you think of other ways to cover remediation costs?

Thoughts of a Conservation Scientist
Listen to Dr. Helen Taylor talk about her life as a conservation scientist and her recommendations for creating a sustainable planet.

View in the online reader

carrying capacity

The maximum population size that can be indefinitely sustained by the environment.

climate change

Long-term weather patterns across Earth are changing due to increased greenhouse gases in the atmosphere. For example, the average air surface temperature is steadily rising (global warming).

What Is Climate Change?
Listen to Bill Nye's explanation of climate change.

View in the online reader

Habitat Degradation, Destruction, and Fragmentation

A **habitat** is the living space of an organism and includes everything the organism needs for survival. Just like a human, all wildlife depends on physical space, food, clean air, and clean water. Therefore, loss of habitat reduces an organism's likelihood of success, and on a larger scale, diminishes biodiversity. The National Wildlife Federation recognizes habitat degradation as the primary threat to the survival of wildlife because a degraded habitat leads to reduced survival and lower reproductive success. What are the causes of habitat destruction? The principle ones are the conversion of natural habitat to agricultural fields, housing development, pollution, and climate change. We would be remiss to neglect mentioning the network of roads dividing the natural environment into smaller sections, dams on rivers, water diversions, and invasive species. Looking to the future, smart city growth will be a necessity to curtail sprawl and meet the needs of the growing human population while protecting natural habitats (see Chapter 17).

Loss of Biodiversity

Climate change, pollution, and habitat degradation negatively affect biodiversity. We are in the midst of a significant extinction event. The late Harvard professor E. O. Wilson started the Hundred Heartbeat Club to recognize species on the verge of extinction. The title of the club symbolizes species that have fewer than 100 hearts still beating on Earth. We are witnessing extinctions with our own eyes (see video link: "Extinction of the Chinese River Dolphin").

Extinction of the Chinese River Dolphin
Hear English scientist Dr. Samuel Turvey discussing the extinction story of the Chinese river dolphin.

Goodbye to the **baiji**, the **Yangtze River dolphin**

View in the online reader

Bringing It Closer to Home: Calculating Your Contribution to the Carbon Cycle

We depend on environmental science to understand how our actions and decisions affect the environment and to comprehend how our own health is intertwined with the health of the environment. Through good science we identify the origins of environmental problems, and with ingenuity, an eye on sustainability, and technology we find solutions to those issues. Pollution in the Arctic, climate change, and acid rain are examples of daunting large-scale problems that ecosystems face today. Solving these problems by taking a pathway toward sustainability begins with the individual, and from there it expands to small towns, large cities, countries, and shared international spaces. The key, therefore, is the individual. In this exercise, we focus on the calculation of your carbon footprint, a measurement of your activities and decisions and the impact they have on the environment. A carbon footprint is usually expressed in total equivalents of carbon dioxide released. Equivalent, in this case, refers to the conversion of other carbon compounds to a common unit, carbon dioxide.

A carbon footprint varies from person to person and is dependent on personal decisions, habits, and geographical location. For example, a person's carbon footprint includes fuel burned when driving a car, coal incinerated to heat a residence, and buying of various goods. The connection of purchased goods to a carbon footprint may be less obvious, but greenhouse gases are released during the production and transportation of goods. Your journey in environmental science really begins here because you will see how your life and standard of living impacts the world. Click on the following links to calculate your carbon footprint: World Wide Fund, Nature Conservancy, and Environmental Protection Agency.

FIGURE 1.12
A carbon footprint is a measurement of your activities and decisions and the impact they have on the environment. (A) Your actions affect the global carbon cycle.

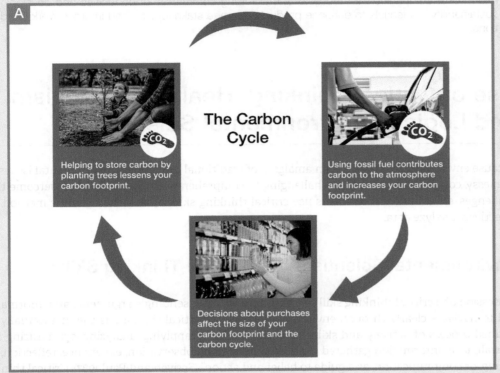

Source: Joseph Shostell; © Shutterstock, Inc.

(B) Average carbon footprint per person (metric tons per year) in select countries or regions.

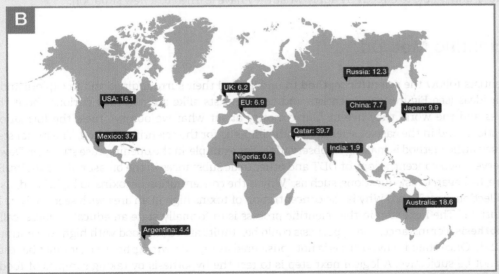

Source: Joseph Shostell; © Shutterstock, Inc; data from the European Commission and Netherlands Environmental Assessment Agency.

Be prepared to spend a few minutes per site. They will ask questions such as how many rooms you have in your house, what type of car you drive, or your involvement in carbon offsetting projects like recycling and planting trees. Once you obtain your carbon footprint, analyze it and determine how it compares to the average carbon footprint per household in the United States and in other countries, and how it compares to what the environment can replenish. Are you equal to, above, or below the U.S. average? How does it compare with India, Thailand,

Argentina, Ghana, Germany, and other countries? Calculating carbon footprints is now a common practice in the business world, and companies earn money by assisting other companies with not only calculating carbon footprints, but also helping to decrease them. Take, for example, Carbon Footprint Ltd. Their niche is the calculation of the carbon footprints of blue-chip and mid-market companies with the goal of maximizing commercial opportunities and developing sustainability credentials to enhance products, engage stakeholders, and improve work conditions.

Use of Critical Thinking, Healthy Skepticism, and Logic in Environmental Science

Because environmental science is an amalgam of traditional disciplines, environmental issues can be messy, complex, and therefore challenging to comprehend, let alone solve. To overcome these challenges, environmental scientists use critical thinking skills, follow the scientific method, and objectively analyze data.

Environmental Scientists Use Critical Thinking Skills

Possession of a critical thinking skill set offers us a way to disentangle arguments and information, and to navigate clearly through environmental issues. "Critical thinking is the intellectually disciplined process of actively and skillfully conceptualizing, applying, analyzing, synthesizing and/or evaluating information gathered from, or generated by, observation, experience, reflection, reasoning, or communication, as a guide to belief and action" (Scriven and Paul 1987). Critical thinking transcends all disciplines because it holds firm to clarity, consistency, relevance, precision, evidence, and fairness. A critical thinker detects biases, reflects on previous information, values quantitative literacy, and is able to effectively apply what they have learned to a new situation.

Scientific Method

scientific method

A rigorous method in science to gather and interpret information; consists of observation, hypothesis, experimentation, analysis, conclusion, and repetition of process.

hypothesis

An educated guess.

Scientists follow the **scientific method** to understand their surroundings and to explore and test their ideas (see Figure 1.13). Scientists and nonscientists alike are naturally curious about themselves and the world they live in. Our curiosity about what we observe fuels the formation of questions, and in the case of scientists, is the impetus for the scientific method. The initial step of the scientific method is making an observation. For example, in the opening case study, Dr. Dewailly observed high concentrations of DDT and other toxic substances in the breast milk of Inuits. From there, he began to ask questions, such as, "Why is the concentration of toxins so high?" and, "Is this a collection error?" and "Why is the concentration of toxins high in an area with seemingly so little pollution?" The next step in the scientific process is to formally state an educated guess, called a **hypothesis**. For instance, one hypothesis could be, "Inuits are eating food with high concentrations of DDT." Once stated, a hypothesis is not considered as right or wrong; however, it must be testable and not be subjective. A logical next step is to test the hypothesis by taking samples of food the Inuits eat (e.g., fish, seals, and polar bears) and then analyzing the food for DDT. Scientists often rely on advancements in technology to detect and quantify the toxic substances. For instance, to detect mercury in tissue collected from a seal or a polar bear, an atomic absorption spectrometer (AAS) is used. The AAS provides numerical data that the scientist studies, graphs, and statistically analyzes. After analysis of the food and determination of high concentrations of DDT in the seals and polar bears, Dr. Dewailly concluded that the hypothesis was supported. Repeatability is extremely important in science to minimize the chance that the finding was a fluke. Therefore, the experiment is repeated, and if the results are similar, the information is then communicated to the larger scientific community and to the public through oral presentations and/or through publications. However, before science findings are published, they go through a rigorous review process by other scientists. A hypothesis that is well tested by many research groups is ultimately considered a theory.

In addition to hypothesis-driven science, scientists also use exploratory science to understand their environment and to clarify poorly defined problems. A person conducting exploratory science will immerse themselves in the subject matter and let their curiosity lead the way, without setting up a hypothesis and conducting an experiment. Exploratory science helps in the discovery of new information and the formulation of questions to pursue.

FIGURE 1.13
Environmental scientists use the scientific method to test hypotheses and to understand their environment. Observations, hypotheses, experiments, analyses, graphing, writing, explaining, and repeating are all parts of the scientific process.

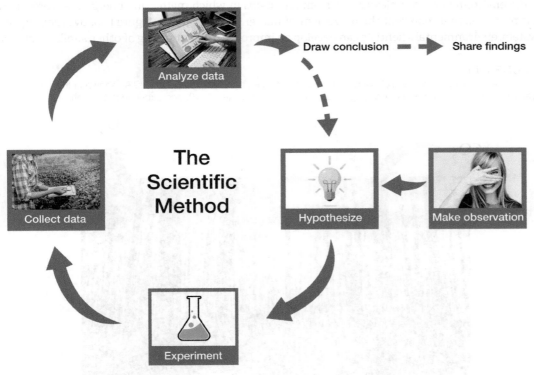

Source: Joseph Shostell; © Shutterstock, Inc.

Statistics, Precision, and Accuracy

Scientists use **statistics** to objectively analyze the data they collect. Statistics, for example, informs us of the likelihood (the probability) of an event from zero or no chance to 100 percent chance. For example, there is a zero percent chance of rolling a seven with a six-sided die, and there is a 100 percent chance of landing heads on a double-headed coin. Returning to the case study, measurements showed the concentration of DDT to be higher in polar bears compared to fish; a statistical analysis of this data revealed that the difference in DDT concentrations between fish and polar bears was the result of more than chance alone.

Scientists need to be precise and accurate in their work. Precision describes how close individual measurements of the same item are to each other, and accuracy refers to how close a measurement is to the actual value. For instance, maybe a scientist is interested in determining the weight of male polar bears, and they take three measurements of each bear. Ideally, the individual measurement values are almost the same, and in such a case, they would be a good example of high

statistics

A mathematical way to objectively analyze data.

precision. However, should the scientist be sloppy, they could have three very different weight values of the same bear. This would be an example of low precision. Accuracy in this example would refer to how close the measured values are to the bear's true weight. The closer they are to the actual weight, the greater the accuracy.

Environmental Scientists Consider the Characteristics of Systems When Studying Environmental Issues

Environmental scientists use a systems approach when studying the environment to better understand environmental complexity. A system has states in which matter and energy are stored, and has processes that represent the movement of matter and energy (see Figure 1.14). By studying one system, environmental scientists can develop an improved understanding of other, similar systems.

FIGURE 1.14
Environmental systems come in all sizes and are characterized by having components. As shown in this forest system example, they receive inputs (e.g., CO_2), produce outputs (e.g., O_2), and experience throughputs.

O_2

CO_2

H_2O

Organic Matter

Source: Joseph Shostell; © Shutterstock, Inc.

Inputs, Outputs, and Throughputs

Common terms in reference to systems are inputs, throughputs, and outputs. A system may receive matter and energy, referred to as **inputs**, from outside itself. The movement of matter and energy in, through, and out of a system is referred to as **throughput**. The **outputs** are the matter and energy that leave the system, going to another juxtaposed system. In the opening story, you read about the Arctic, which can be considered a system. Besides nonliving components (e.g., water) the Arctic contains living components (e.g., caribou and polar bears), and it receives inputs of mercury and DDT carried from southern latitude systems as well as energy from the sun. Examples of outputs from this system include oxygen released through photosynthesis by algae, and organic matter lost as a result of tourists who might fish off the northern coast of Alaska and then return home with their catch. Remember, energy and matter are stored within the tissues of the caribou, fish, algae, and bears.

inputs

Matter and/or energy moving into a system.

throughput

The movement of matter and/or energy in, through, and out of a system.

outputs

Matter and/or energy moving out of a system.

Closed and Open Systems

Systems can be either closed or open. **Closed systems** only exchange energy and do not exchange matter, while **open systems** can exchange both matter and energy with other systems. As we learned from the opening case study, no natural ecosystem is truly isolated, although some might come close. The Arctic receives matter inputs from the atmosphere, so it qualifies as an open system.

closed systems

Isolated environmental systems that do not exchange matter or energy with other systems.

open systems

Environmental systems that exchange matter or energy with other systems.

Positive and Negative Feedback in Systems

Systems are controlled by positive and negative feedback processes. In **positive feedback**, the output of a system becomes an input of the same system and encourages continuation of or enhances the process, whereas in **negative feedback**, the output becomes an input and inhibits the process. These feedback loops are useful in environmental systems to maintain **homeostasis**—to continue normal conditions and functions—but they also apply to degraded environmental systems and can magnify environmental problems (see Figure 1.15).

positive feedback

The output of a process becomes an input and signals the process to continue.

negative feedback

The output of a process becomes an input and signals the process to stop.

homeostasis

The dynamic process systems and organisms use to maintain normal (steady state) conditions and functions.

FIGURE 1.15
Positive and negative feedback control systems. A) In an example of positive feedback, the rise in average air temperatures is thawing tundra, which in turn encourages microbial activity that releases more CO_2; B) As an example of negative feedback, reproductive success in a population of Arctic barnacle geese that is near the maximum size the environment can support leads to increased competition and lower reproductive success.

Source: Joseph Shostell; © Shutterstock, Inc.

Key Takeaways

- Early environmentalists helped shape today's environmental movement.
- The main issues environmental scientists are working on today include overpopulation, climate change, pollution, habitat degradation and fragmentation, and loss of biodiversity.
- Environmental scientists use the scientific method and critical thinking skills to find solutions to environmental problems.
- Environmental scientists consider the characteristics of systems when studying environmental issues.

1.3 Environmental Themes

Learning Objective

1. Identify, understand, and discuss the key environmental science themes.

Environmental science has several pervading themes, and you will find these themes throughout the chapters of this book. No matter the environmental issue, these themes will hold relevance, and by keeping them in your focus, the subject matter will be clearer and easier to remember and master. Interestingly, the themes are not mutually exclusive, meaning that they all connect to each other in some degree. These broad environmental themes cover 1) the coupling of society and life to a healthy environment, 2) science, 3) decision making, 4) the social and cultural context of environmental issues, 5) global perspectives, 6) the interdisciplinary nature of environmental science, and 7) sustainability. Read the explanations of the themes that follow and then reexamine the opening case study.

Life and Society Need a Healthy Environment

Healthy ecosystems provide goods and services necessary for life and society. For example, provisioning ecosystem services consistently supply food, fresh water, timber, and coal, among other goods. Healthy ecosystems also uphold regulating services that control, for instance, climate, disease, and water.

Science Informs Us about the Environment

Science is more than just the collection of mere facts. Scientists use critical thinking to analyze these facts and then to determine what they have learned. Educated guesses (hypotheses), for example, about a newly engineered product are tested with experiments, and then the findings are discussed with other scientists and then shared with nonscientists. Individuals, companies, and the larger society weigh the new information against previously gained knowledge and then apply the information to continue or adapt their future actions. Science provides us with the tool set to be in tune with the environment and to adjust our actions to support societal productivity and a healthy environment simultaneously.

Society, Corporation, and Consumer Decisions Affect the Environment

Human activities underlie nearly all environmental problems by altering natural systems and diminishing ecosystem goods and services. Currently, the human population is not living sustainably, and therefore a continued high human population growth rate exacerbates all of the world's environmental problems. Naturally, every environmental issue includes a piece about population growth. People have the capacity to live sustainably, but they need the education to interpret the scientific information and the will to make a behavioral change (see Figure 1.16).

FIGURE 1.16
At a car dealership, a young couple considers an electric car. Because our decisions affect the environment, environmentally minded consumers will opt for environmentally safe products. In the case of cars, a consumer would look for an energy-efficient hybrid or completely electric car.

Source: © Shutterstock, Inc.

A pathway toward sustainability also means understanding all of the effects of your daily activities, but sometimes we cannot see the effects with our naked eyes. Remember the grasshopper effect in the opening case study? It was through experimentation and following pollution to its source that we now understand how toxins produced in one area of the world can affect populations thousands of miles away. We have come to realize the absence of pollution close to us does not necessarily imply we live sustainably. In the end, success in sustainability comes down to every decision and action made by society, corporations, and consumers. A person supports sustainability by choosing to purchase a product that is not harmful to the environment. A sustainable business elects to invest in and rely on renewable wind, solar, and other energies rather than on nonrenewable energies.

Environmental Issues Have a Social and a Cultural Context

environmental injustice

All groups and communities in a population do not have the same degree of protection from environmental and health hazards and/or do not have equal access to the decision-making process of environmental issues.

environmental justice

All groups and communities in a population have the same degree of protection from environmental and health hazards and equal access to the decision-making process of environmental issues.

Each environmental issue involves a system of values and social justice. Often, environmental degradation influences a population unequally (**environmental injustice**). For example, one segment of a population may be exposed to the majority of the pollution generated by the whole and, as a consequence, experiences a disproportionately higher rate of cancer. To combat environmental injustice and to promote **environmental justice**, the United States Environmental Protection Agency strives for all Americans, regardless of race, color, national origin, or income, "to enjoy the same degree of protection from environmental health hazards, and equal access to the decision-making process to have a healthy environment in which to live, learn, and work." Even with these protections, environmental injustice happens today. Insufficient water treatment and exposure of Flint, Michigan, residents to lead in drinking water is a current example of environmental injustice. Speaking on behalf of her community, Flint's mayor, Karen Weaver, said, "It's a minority community. It's a poor community. And our voices were not heard." At the international level, the United Nations takes on a similar role to that of the EPA to support environmental justice. Have you witnessed environmental injustice in your life?

A Global Perspective Is Needed to Deal With Many Environmental Issues

We can think about this from a scientific perspective and point out the movement of toxins among the lithosphere, hydrosphere, atmosphere, and biosphere to show the interconnectivity of these spheres. Added to this is the interdependent nature of ecosystems, with no ecosystem completely isolated from all others. Such interconnectivity and interdependence among the world's systems means acid rain, DDT, and other toxic substances can move across national borders. Global warming is a fine example of a global environmental issue. No single country can solve the problem on its own, because the origin of the problem, greenhouse gas emissions, comes from many countries. The United Nations and international accords such as the Kyoto Protocol and Paris Agreement help band countries together to address global environmental issues. However, just as a single country can't resolve a global problem on its own, a global network of countries is only as strong as the commitment of each of the countries. On a smaller scale, the commitment of a country is dependent on the willpower and actions of individual citizens. Thus the common environmental motto: Local changes have global effects.

Society Relies on Many Disciplines to Solve Environmental Problems

Environmental science helps us to understand environmental systems and the interactions between human society and the natural world. Consequently, environmental science includes disciplines such as ecology, political science, economics, biology, engineering, psychology, chemistry, and sociology, among many others. Environmental science also draws on ideas, expertise, and research from these disciplines to find appropriate solutions to environmental problems, which can be complex and large in scale.

Sustainability in Thought, Word, and Deed Will Allow Future Generations to Enjoy a Healthy Environment

The health of both humans and the environment relies on collective society conducting all of its activities sustainably (see Figure 1.17). Sustainable living implies that society's use of resources is not greater than the environmental rate of replenishment. If society followed a sustainable pathway, all new growth and development would support a healthy environment, so future generations would have the opportunity to experience the same environment. Wouldn't it be great if you could write a letter to your great-great-great granddaughter about your experience visiting a national forest (or even the quality of the air you breathe outside your house) knowing that she can have the same experience one hundred years later, and in some way, share the experience with you?

FIGURE 1.17
Sustainability in thought, word, and deed allows future generations to enjoy a healthy environment. Wind turbines like the ones shown here harness wind energy to generate electricity and reduce society's reliance on fossil fuels. They do this without releasing greenhouse gases or other pollutants.

Source: © Shutterstock, Inc.

Key Takeaways

- Environmental science has several pervading themes.
- Life and society need a healthy environment.
- Science informs us about the environment.
- Societal, corporate, and consumer decisions affect the environment.
- Environmental issues have a social and a cultural context.

- Global collaboration is needed to deal with many environmental issues.
- Society relies on many disciplines to solve environmental problems.
- Sustainability in thought, word, and deed allows future generations to enjoy a healthy environment.

1.4 A Look to the Future: New Approaches and the Arctic

Learning Objective

1. Looking forward, identify and explain different strategies society can use to solve environmental problems.

Advances in science and technology, along with having information only a click away, make it an exciting time to study environmental science. Access to knowledge about how the environment is an interconnected series of systems, past and contemporary environmental issues, and pervading themes across environmental science provides a strong informational foundation for understanding how human activities affect the environment. This information plus critical thinking and the process of science form the toolkit needed to work through environmental issues and plan for a sustainable future. In this last section, we turn our attention to the future and developing sustainable solutions to environmental problems.

Sustainability and Stewardship

environmental stewards

People who practice responsible use and management of natural resources.

Everyone wants to enjoy ecosystem goods and services, and to have the chance to live a long and healthy life. To reach this goal, individuals must choose to act as **environmental stewards**—to look after the environment by supporting sustainability in thought, word, and deed. An environmental steward also acts as a role model for others and promotes logical and science-based ideas to inform and encourage sustainable actions among friends, peers, and communities. As Drs. Hossain and Ali of the University of Chittagong of Bangladesh point out (2014), society does not exist independently of the individual; rather, it is influenced by actions of the individual. The power of the individual voice should not be underestimated in the change it can make (see video link: "The Power of Individual Action").

The Millennium Assessment

Assessments play a vital role in the development and continuous improvement of environmental management plans. An environmental management plan is a plan that considers all potential environmental impacts of proposed activities and helps to ensure that a project is implemented in a sustainable manner to reduce environmental impacts. There are two general parts to assessment in environmental management. To create an effective management plan, the environment itself needs to be assessed, just as a person might be evaluated by a medical doctor when they feel ill. Only after the person is assessed does the doctor decide on a course of action. Environmental managers collect and then analyze data to assess the health of an environmental area, and then develop a management plan tailored for that environment. In a second assessment step, the management plan itself is assessed after it is implemented to determine if management objectives and goals were achieved.

On World Environment Day, June 5, 2001, United Nations Secretary General Kofi Annan officially launched the first assessment of the world's ecosystems, the **Millennium Assessment**. Over a period of four years, more than a thousand social and natural scientists assessed Earth's ecosystems and their services, and the options to restore, conserve, or enhance their sustainable use. This impressive show of international cooperation and work produced several reports that are freely available here. What did they find? Based on the assessment, human demands for food, water, energy, timber, and fiber have extensively altered ecosystems and diminished biodiversity. If this course of action remains unchanged, future generations will not have the same access to ecosystem goods and services as today's generation. Environmental management plans at the national and international levels need to reverse environmental degradation and simultaneously meet the needs of a growing population. The reports also reaffirm the value of continuing to address climate change and habitat loss, two key environmental issues mentioned earlier. Remember, assessments also help us to determine how management plans might need to be changed to meet new challenges. With this in mind, we mention two additional findings. Although for some time now we have been aware of the negative impacts of nutrient discharges into water resources (see Chapter 10), the Millennium Assessment formally recognized the seriousness of this issue and the need to address it. In addition, of all of the world's ecosystems, drylands are the most seriously threatened and need sustainable management. Drylands are of special concern because they have low biological productivity, have limited soil moisture, and are inhabited by over two billion people, many of whom live in poor socioeconomic conditions in developing countries. Therefore, future management plans must include a stronger focus on nutrient loading and dryland areas.

The Millennium Assessment was an important milestone in the development of **sustainable development goals** for the planet. On September 25, 2015, the United Nations set these goals to end poverty, protect the planet, and ensure prosperity of all world citizens (see Figure 1.18). Will we reach these goals by 2030? We have a much better chance to do so if every person becomes involved. Follow this link to learn what you can do at your home and at work to support these sustainability goals.

The Power of Individual Action
Hear Google Sustainability Officer Kate Brandt stressing the importance of individual actions in improving the health of the planet.

View in the online reader

Millennium Assessment

The first assessment of the world's ecosystems.

sustainable development goals

Global goals adopted by the United Nations in 2015 to end poverty, protect the planet, and ensure prosperity of all people by 2030.

FIGURE 1.18

The United Nations has set seventeen sustainable development goals to end poverty, protect the planet, and ensure prosperity for all. These are goals for the world and therefore need the involvement of all countries, cities, and individuals. Look through the goals listed and see what role you might play to help transform the world.

Source: United Nations

Rethinking Our Use of Energy

Our knowledge of fossil fuels as a source of greenhouse gases and the root of several environmental issues encourages us to rethink our use of energy. In a nation long dependent on fossil fuels, such thoughts and particularly change can prove to be a challenge. Currently, the United States receives 88 percent of its energy from a combination of petroleum (35%), natural gas (34%), coal (10%), and nuclear (9%). Still, the United States is slowly weaning off fossil fuels, with renewable energies projected to make up larger shares of the market each year. The shift to renewable energy sources is occurring at a much greater rate internationally, and there are clear leaders in this area. Costa Rica is at the top with 99 percent of its energy needs coming from hydroelectric, geothermal, and other renewable sources. Sweden and Denmark, building and planning for the future, announced they will be fossil fuel–free by 2040 and 2050, respectively.

We Can Use Economic Tools to Deal With Environmental Problems

One recommended strategy to achieve a more sustainable world is to have the price of each product reflect direct costs plus the impact the product has on the environment (see Chapter 18). **Full-cost pricing** also takes into account the costs of remediation. Professor Nancy Olewiler of Simon Frazer University argues that society has failed to take into account the full measure of the consequences of production and consumption on the environment (Olewiler 2012). Her comments were in reference to the Canadian government, but they could be directed toward any public or private sector of any country. What do you think? Should indirect or hidden costs be a part of the price of goods we purchase? For example, what would this mean for purchasing a new laptop? The current retail value of a laptop might be $600, but its true cost would be higher, potentially much higher. The extra amount would cover the full environmental impact of the product, from inception, mining, assembly, transport, and use, to end recycling and disposal. The exact amount is difficult to estimate because economists often don't place specific dollar values on streams and biodiversity lost due to, for example, mining of metals used in computers. Twenty dollars might be acceptable to a consumer, but what if it were $300 or even $600? Full-cost pricing, combined with a reward system that recognizes sustainability practices, and taxes on pollution and wastes, would incentivize businesses to develop more environmentally friendly products. On the negative side, low-income groups could be penalized if the increased cost means they could no longer afford the products. Small businesses could also suffer since they may not have sufficient capital for research and development of more environmentally friendly products and therefore may no longer be competitive in the market. Full-cost pricing can also be applied to agricultural products. In this case, the increased costs would cover any negative effects that farming might have on the environment and even on human health. They would cover financial costs stemming from pesticide pollution, soil degradation, and loss of biodiversity; that is, if we assign dollar amounts to nature and fully understand the connection between farming and human health.

Another economic tool is eco-labeling, which informs shoppers of a product's environmental impacts and helps consumers be environmentally informed before they make a purchase. There are also certification programs such as Green Seal, whose mission is "to transform the economy for a healthier, greener world." Green Seal develops Environmental Leadership Standards and then certifies products and services that meet these regulations. A hotel marked with a green seal, for instance, is energy efficient and generates minimal waste.

> **full-cost pricing**
>
> The price of a product that reflects direct costs, the impact the product has on the environment, and any remediation costs.

Slowing Down Climate Change

The rate of climate change and global warming will continue unabated if we don't reduce greenhouse gas emissions, control population growth, and implement strategies to remove carbon dioxide from the atmosphere. Because greenhouse gas emissions and population growth have already been discussed, we turn our attention to carbon capture and storage, which is the removal of carbon from the atmosphere followed by its storage elsewhere. One low-tech method to remove carbon dioxide from the atmosphere is to plant trees, because through photosynthesis, they take in carbon dioxide and store carbon in their tissues.

In 2018, China began an ambitious tree-planting campaign to reduce air pollution. With the help of the People's Liberation Army, China forested 7.7 million hectares (32,500 mi^2) in the first year. This is part of China's larger goal to increase their total forested area from 21.7 percent to 26 percent by 2035. Other countries are also engaged in forestation. Kenya is in the middle of planting 235 million seedlings as part of the "Save Our Trees" campaign. At the time of the printing of this book, Kenya will have increased their forest cover from 6 percent to 10 percent.

Interconnectedness of Sustainability, Health, and Poverty

A pathway of living sustainably includes actions to reduce poverty, eradicate hunger, and improve human health. Today's 700 million people living in extreme poverty care less about the larger picture of sustainability because they are trying to survive day to day (see Figure 1.19). Their time is spent on finding enough food and water for themselves and their families. They also require a source of energy to keep warm and to cook their food. In these situations, people often do not have access to treated water, electricity, and many other services tied to the standard of living expected in developed countries. Their inadequate living conditions afford little protection from the pollution they release or from the environmental degradation caused by others. They are often stuck within a vicious cycle of poverty, poor health, and exposure to environmental pollution unless assistance is offered. Both the assisted and those who assist will certainly benefit from a cleaner and healthier environment. And once a person's physiological needs (food, shelter, etc.) are met, they can be an environmental steward too.

FIGURE 1.19
Those living in extreme poverty are exposed to environmental degradation more directly than are other groups of people. Unfortunately, they usually do not have the means to improve their conditions without assistance. Examples of living conditions of those living in extreme poverty in Cambodia (A) and Indonesia (B).

Source: © Shutterstock, Inc.

As we look to the future, what is the solution to improve living conditions, education, and sustainability in the impoverished areas around the world? To answer this question, we will turn to sustainability efforts in Guatemala, the world's leading grower and exporter of the spice cardamom, often referred to as the green gold of Guatemala (see Figure 1.20). Despite the name (gold), cardamom farmers in Alta Verapaz, Guatemala, live in extreme poverty and barely carve out a living. Many of the farmers have little knowledge of sustainable methods of agriculture, and their crops increasingly suffer from infestations of thrips. To help meet the United Nations' sustainability goals, Heifer International taught beekeeping skills to over one thousand cardamom crop farmers. Now, the farmers sell honey in addition to their spices and have increased their revenues. In partnership with Texas A & M University, Heifer International is also trying to develop sustainable ways to control the thrips. New international partnerships can similarly help other groups of people living in extreme poverty.

FIGURE 1.20
Cardamom, popular in Middle Eastern countries, is a spice grown in Guatemala and India and used to season a variety of foods. Green cardamom pods still on the plant (A) and in the hand (B).

Source: © Shutterstock, Inc.

Win–Win Solutions

Solutions to environmental problems can simultaneously support progress and sustainability. To reach these win–win solutions, we need to change our terminology and mindset about forward progress and sustainability. In American culture, we commonly refer to the term "balance" when we juggle responsibilities of work with dedication to family, friends, and relaxation. Taleb Rifai, secretary general of the World Tourism Organization, recommends dispensing with the term "balance" because the word implies while one thing goes up, a second thing goes down. Why does there have to be one or the other, and not both? For example, Biodiversity International (BI) proposed and tested an innovative solution to offer food security and protect biodiversity in Kenya, Africa. Western Kenya has a history of malnutrition and loss of biodiversity, and with global warming these environmental issues are projected to worsen. BI worked with local farmers to grow indigenous and nutritionally healthy vegetables and then to improve food access by building networks linking farms to local schools. This agricultural and economic model protects local plant diversity and eliminates malnutrition.

Companies also look for win–win solutions to address growth and waste problems, and to satisfy the environmentally minded consumer. Today's companies are pressed more than ever to be environmentally responsible while staying competitive. Take, for example, Marriott International and their initiative *Serve 360: Doing Good in Every Direction*. Part of this initiative aims to reduce the company's plastic waste, so every hotel managed by Marriott no longer uses disposable plastic bottles of soap, shampoo, and conditioner. These products are now offered in shower dispensers. Win–win strategies abound in business. Maybe you will be one of the consumers or employees to suggest a new win–win strategy.

The Arctic's Future

As this chapter closes, we return our attention to the fragility of the Arctic system, the threats it faces, and the prosperity of Indigenous people living there. The future condition of the Arctic hinges on a continued heightened awareness of environmental threats it faces, and international collaboration efforts to support sustainability. If relatively recent decisions reached about the Arctic are any indication, it may not have such a bleak future after all. Strong evidence of the Arctic's positive future came about with the recent decision of nine countries (United States, Canada, Russia, China, European Union, and others) to ban fishing in the now ice-free central Arctic Ocean until at least 2033. Doing so will give the international community opportunity to monitor the Arctic system to better understand it before a new pressure (fishing) is added. If not carefully managed, overfishing can occur as it has in many oceanic areas, which would jeopardize the Inuit's food supply and culture.

Key Takeaways

- We engage in environmental stewardship to protect the environment and human health.
- Assessments are necessary in environmental science.
- Because greenhouse gases are at the root of several environmental issues, many nations are trying to reduce their dependence on fossil fuels.
- We can use economic tools to help solve environmental problems.
- Poverty and hunger are connected to environmental issues.

FIGURE 1.21 Visual Overview: Introduction to Environmental Science

Summarizing figure: (1.1) The global environment consists of diverse interconnected systems that furnish goods and services necessary for life. (1.2) There is a need for environmental science. (1.3) Environmental scientists use a thematic approach to study environmental issues. (1.4) We have multiple strategies to help deal with future environmental problems.

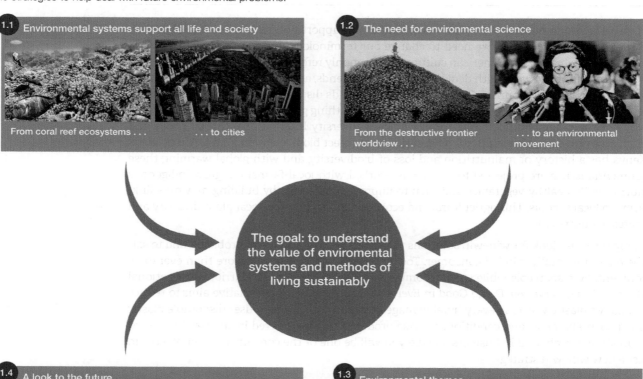

Sources: Joseph Shostell; See previous citations for image credits. (Rachel Carson) Everett Collection Inc / Alamy Stock Photo.

1.5 References

- Carson, R. 1962. *Silent Spring*. New York: Houghton Mifflin Company.
- Hossain, F. M. A., and M. Korgan Ali. 2014. "Relation between Individual and Society." *Open Journal of Social Sciences* 2, no. 8: 130–37.
- Leopold, A. 1949. *A Sand County Almanac: And Sketches Here and There*. Oxford, UK: Oxford University Press.
- Marsh, G. P. 1864. *Man and Nature: Physical Geography as Modified by Human Action*. London: Sampson Low, Son and Marston.
- Olewiler, N. 2012. "Smart Environmental Policy with Full-Cost Pricing." SPP Research Paper No. 12-6. https://doi.org/10.2139/ssrn.2028120.
- Pinchot, G. 1947. *Breaking New Ground*. Washington, DC: IslandPress.
- Ruiz-Garcia, M., and J. M. Shostell. 2010. *Biology, Evolution, and Conservation of River Dolphins within South America and Asia: Unknown Dolphins in Danger*. Hauppauge, NY: Nova Science Publishers, Inc.
- Scriven M., and R. Paul. 1987. 8th Annual International Conference on Critical Thinking and Education Reform.
- Thoreau, H. D. 1859. *The Journal of Henry David Thoreau Volume XIII*. Gibbs Smith. Layton, Utah.

CHAPTER 2
Environmental Ethics, Law, and Policy

Case Study: The Tragedy of the Commons

In Eastern Europe, Giorgi stares across the wide open prairie in search of a small group of cows being led by his eldest son, Nikoluz (see Figure 2.1). The luscious green grass has been plentiful ever since the rainstorms passed through two weeks ago. At first it proves a little difficult to find them from his vantage point, standing on a mid-sized boulder and looking across an expansive area of land. He continues to scout the area with his hand held above his eyes to shield out the glaring sun. There, in the far distance, past other similarly sized herds belonging to his neighbors, he spies his lanky teenage son and the herd. "Good." Just as instructed, Nikoluz gently shepherds the animals to the thicker grass areas a little farther northward, allowing the cattle to graze on the finer vegetation.

FIGURE 2.1
The needs of individuals and the community are at odds with each other in commonly used areas (the commons) such as pasturelands. To avoid overuse by livestock owned by any one shepherd, the shared space is carefully managed. In the photo, cows graze in the commons.

Source: © Shutterstock, Inc.

Giorgi considers himself lucky today because after six months of hard work he is finally going to add another cow to his herd and therefore increase the family's income. As Giorgi continues to look on, he observes some of the other herds being steered in the same direction, following his son's lead. A momentary thought of discontent crosses Giorgi's mind at this sight. However, it is fleeting, for he sees there is plenty for all—in the commonly owned pasture. "Doesn't every villager have the right to use the common area for pastureland?"

In Giorgi's culture, cows provide a value of currency. Simply put, the more cows you own, the better off you are. Each cow provides a cache of milk to be sold at the local daily market, and each additional cow makes it easier for Giorgi to feed and grow his own family. With a bit more luck and hard work, Giorgi will be able to continually add cows, probably in the order of two per year. In other words, Giorgi considers it lucrative to keep adding cows. After all, his cows are feeding on common land that he is not solely responsible for, rather it's an area used by all and not owned by any one person. Thus, Giorgi understands the relationship: more cows equals greater wealth. This would appear to be a sound strategy if it were not for all of the other cattle owners in the village. They, like Giorgi, desire to gain personal wealth and maximize their numbers of cows. When they follow these desires, the common area will be eventually overgrazed, all of the grass will die, and the area will no longer be beneficial to any herder. Therefore it would seem, in the long term, that the whole community will suffer if each person in the village tries to maximize his or her personal gains.

In this story, based on the article "The Tragedy of the Commons" by Garrett Hardin (*Science*, 1968), the individual is pitted against the larger society, wherever a common area exists. An individual can personally benefit from maximizing their removal of a resource from the common area. On a larger scale, this action pushes a society toward overusing resources, which in the end harms society. Herein lies the dilemma for conservation managers trying to prevent overuse of Earth's common areas: water bodies, air, and public land areas.

The concept of "The Tragedy of the Commons" applies not only to removal (overuse), but also to addition (pollution). A common area can probably easily absorb pollution from one or a few polluters, and remain healthy, but pollution from the masses will quickly overwhelm it. A polluter may not even think the pollutant is a problem unless they have to pay for amelioration, which can be quite expensive. After a cost analysis, an individual or a company may determine that it's cheaper to release pollutants into the atmosphere than to individually incur the full expense of taking care of the problem. The polluter may point out that society (the city, state, or nation) has the resources to effectively deal with remediation. Spreading out the cost to every citizen makes it economically beneficial for an individual person or even an individual company to pollute.

This chapter explores environmental ethics and considers how people make their decisions. For example, why do some choose to pollute and others do not? Clearly, different people must have different points of view regarding the environment.

2.1 Environmental Views and Attitudes of Influence

Learning Objectives

1. Identify five different worldviews and consider whether each of them does or does not support environmentally sustainable methods.
2. Provide examples of environmental stewardship at the individual, group, and federal levels.

The "Tragedy of the Commons" helps us understand why people may not act in a way that benefits the larger community. Within the example, only two points of view are presented: that of the cattle owner and that of the collective society. It's very likely that not all community members where Giorgi lives agree with his decision to use the common field as pastureland. Maybe some prefer to use the open field for recreational sports, like soccer. Perhaps other villagers consider it inhumane to own and keep cows for the sake of milking them. Most of us live in even more complex and pluralistic societies that foster many cultural worldviews regarding the environment. These differing worldviews add a layer of complexity to environmental issues.

Our perception of the world, or our **worldview**, and the decisions we make about the environ-ment and other things reflect the **culture** we grew up in. In other words, our culture affects the belief system, behavior, and social learning that we have experienced throughout our lives. How we view something as either good or bad depends upon our moral principles, which also developed in the culture we grew up in. For example, you may have been taught to follow the "golden rule"—that is, to treat others as you would want to be treated. Society commonly uses the terms **moral** and morality to refer to our concern with being able to distinguish between what is good and what is bad. Morality may involve human actions or human characters, and it isn't only associated with religion. Individuals who consider themselves agnostic or atheist also have moral principles, con-sidered "common sense," that help to maintain goodwill in society. Common-sense principles and those based in religion encourage us to find value in doing charity work, being honest, promoting freedom, loving others, and numerous other activities that tend to stabilize society.

The branch of philosophy that deals with standards of right and wrong is referred to as **ethics**. Your personal ethics might have you refrain from stealing a can of soda and instead choose to pay for it. Application of ethics to environmental issues is **environmental ethics**. Such an application would lead you to recycle your used soda can rather than throw it in the garbage to be carted away to a landfill. When ethics is applied to environmental science, we become interested in understand-ing the best way to treat the environment.

worldview

The overall perspective from which one sees and interprets the world.

culture

The behaviors, knowledge, and beliefs of a particular group of people.

moral

Being concerned with the rules of good (right) conduct.

ethics

Branch of philosophy that deals with standards of right and wrong.

environmental ethics

The application of ethics to environmental issues.

Views and Attitudes of Influence: Anthropocentrism, Biocentrism, and Ecocentrism

As the "Tragedy of the Commons" shows, the environment is accessible by a community with more than one worldview. People can have different worldviews such as self, anthropocentrism, biocen-trism, and ecocentrism (see Figure 2.2).

FIGURE 2.2
People can have different worldviews, such as self, anthropocentrism, biocentrism, and ecocentrism. As you move to the right in the figure, there is a greater willingness of the individual to see value of things beyond self.

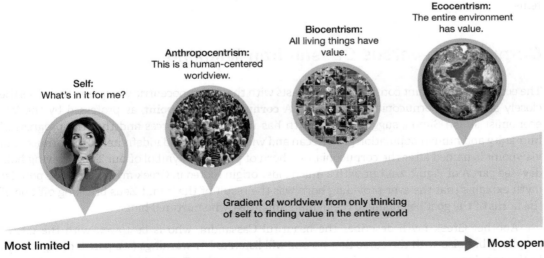

Source: Joseph Shostell; jan kranendonk/Shutterstock.com; © Shutterstock, Inc.

Anthropocentrism

anthropocentrism

A worldview that considers human beings as the most important part of the universe.

A human-centered view of the world, or **anthropocentrism**, values humans above all other living things and the rest of the environment. Anthropocentrism considers human beings the most important part of the global environment, which provides a basis for how environmental questions are answered. Aristotle, an early supporter of this thinking, wrote, "Nature has made all things specifically for the sake of man" (Morton 2007). For example, this view would consider that the harvesting of tuna from the oceans for human food would override any issues of dolphin mortality—still an issue in Mexico—associated with the fishing nets. Anthropocentrism is at the heart of **development ethics**, an egocentric philosophy that suggests humans should use Earth's resources in whatever way necessary to support the continued socioeconomic development of our civilization.

development ethics

An egocentric philosophy that suggests humans use Earth's resources in whatever way necessary to support the continued development of our civilization. In this view point, humans are seen as the masters of the environment.

Biocentrism

biocentrism

A worldview that values all living things, human and otherwise.

In contrast to anthropocentrism, **biocentrism** recognizes value in all living things, not just in humans. The foundation of biocentrism is usually traced back to Paul Taylor's 1986 book, *Respect for Nature: A Theory of Environmental Ethics*. People following this worldview see all living things as a part of an interdependent system. Let's reconsider our example of fishing for tuna. A biocentric person would not agree with harming dolphins to capture tuna nor promote the killing of tuna because in both cases they are living things.

Ecocentrism

ecocentrism

A worldview that values the entire environment, both living things and nonliving things.

Different from both anthropocentrism and biocentrism, **ecocentrism** includes the whole environment—human beings, all other living things besides humans, and the landscape. This **ecosystem** worldview accounts for living and nonliving components. Returning to our fishing example, an ecocentric person would consider the ethical treatment of dolphins, fish, and the nonliving components of the ocean such as the water. They would be mindful of changing the ocean's structure or negatively affecting its health. Leaking fuel tanks, physical damage of an anchor to the seabed, and general pollution would be kept at a minimum to prevent damage to oceanic ecosystems.

ecosystem

An environmental unit (like a forest) that includes living and nonliving components.

Cornucopian versus Cassandran Thinking

cornucopian viewpoint

The world has unlimited resources and with technological advances the human population can continue to grow indefinitely.

The ecocentric viewpoint conflicts and contrasts with the anthropocentric viewpoint, as well as the closely associated cornucopian perspective. A **cornucopian viewpoint**, as professed by the late economist Julian Simon, suggests that Earth has unlimited resources and that the progress of humanity and human population growth can and will be maintained indefinitely. The cornucopian viewpoint is named after the cornucopia, or a horn of plenty—a symbol of our Thanksgiving holiday (see part A of Figure 2.3), but with a much older origin rooted in Greek mythology. One popular myth explains that the ever-providing horn was the result of the infant Zeus breaking off one of the horns of the goat belonging to the nymph Amalthea, who nurtured him.

Cassandra viewpoint

A viewpoint of the world where your warnings about impending disasters and problems are constantly being ignored.

Another Greek myth describes the beautiful Cassandra, who is bestowed with the gift of prophecy, but also with the curse that no one will listen to her warnings (see part B of Figure 2.3). In the opening case study about the commons, a person with a **Cassandra viewpoint** would warn Giorgi and the other villagers, trying to explain that their grazing methods would lead to overexploitation. In contrast, a nearby villager, a cornucopian, would not be concerned with potential overgrazing, but would assume that the village will always find a way for its population to be fed and sustain growth.

FIGURE 2.3
A cornucopia is a symbol of plenty and has roots in ancient Greek mythology. (A) A cornucopian viewpoint would suggest that the world has an endless surplus of resources (like the cornucopia in this picture with bountiful food) that will provide for never-ending population growth. (B) In the Greek myth of Cassandra, the god Apollo gives Cassandra the ability to see into the future. After her refusal to love him, Apollo curses her so that no one will believe her prophesies. Evelyn Morgan's rendition of Cassandra was painted around 1898.

Sources: © Shutterstock, Inc.; De Morgan, Evelyn, Cassandra, Oil on canvas, 1898, De Morgan Collection, https://www.demorgan.org.uk/collection/cassandra/.

Conservation versus Preservation Ethics

It's important to recognize the difference between conservation and preservation because they are commonly misused and have been lumped together as interchangeable terms. **Conservation ethics** describes a viewpoint in which people interact with the environment and actively manage it so that others may enjoy it far into the future. Such a viewpoint strives for a balance between development and preservation. **Preservation ethics** supports the viewpoint that the environment itself is worth protecting in its unaltered condition. A distinct difference here is that preservation ethics allows for no artificial manipulation of the environment by humans. Instead, preserved areas are areas set aside and free from human influence and management.

In regards to our dolphin and tuna example, a conservationist would push for continued fishing, but with strict regulations to prevent overfishing and unnecessary harm to dolphins that get caught in fishing nets. A preservationist would set aside a large body of water that would be off-limits from any human activity. This would no doubt be difficult in international water. In a second example, a conservationist would support the idea of intentionally setting controlled fires to maintain a prairie, and preventing the growth of shrubs and small trees that would convert the area into a forest over time. A preservationist would not try to manage the prairie, but would allow the environment to undergo the natural process of succession and become a forest.

conservation ethics

Supports a viewpoint in which environmental resources can be used and that the environment is managed such that resources will be available to future generations.

preservation ethics

Supports a viewpoint that protects environmental areas that are free from any human activities.

Stewardship and Ethics

Environmental **stewardship** (to serve as a steward) has grown into existence because of our observations of environmental degradation caused by an anthropocentric frontier mentality. Clear-cutting of huge tracts of land, as described by early environmentalists such as Aldo Leopold and Gifford Pinchot, or over-hunting of animal species, such as the passenger pigeon, can have negative consequences that may be irreversible. To offset any overuse or any misuse of public land (recall the "Tragedy of the Commons"), individuals, groups, and in some cases corporations and nations have embraced and promoted stewardship. In the most basic sense, a steward is a position of responsibility that looks after and takes care of something else. For instance, you could be the steward of an estate—taking care of the particulars of the estate such as supervising of servants and collection of rents. Another steward might be responsible for managing a particular resource, such as fish in the oceans.

Responsible stewardship of Earth's commons has been set as a high-priority objective by individuals, groups, and the U.S. federal government. In this context, the power of the individual cannot be overstated. Groups like the Ocean River Institute (ORI) are dedicated to supporting environmental stewardship initiatives for individuals and small grassroots groups in areas where people live (see video link: "Ocean River Institute"). The ORI also provides updated news to the general public about stewardship issues, such as overfishing in our oceans.

Ocean River Institute
Listen to Dr. Rob Moir, executive director of Ocean River Institute (ORI), discuss the work of the ORI.

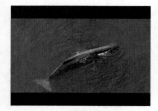

View in the online reader

In 2005, the Environmental Protection Agency (EPA) formally recognized the significance of environmental stewardship by putting forth a draft of an environmental stewardship strategy for the United States (EPA 2005, EPA 2006a). The EPA's vision of sustainability states, ". . . all parts of society actively take responsibility to improve environmental quality and achieve sustainable results." At an even higher federal level, the executive branch of the government can support environmental stewardship too, but this support can be weakened or revoked by a succeeding presidential administration. In Executive Order 13547, Stewardship of the Ocean, Our Coasts, and the Great Lakes, President Barack Obama wrote, ". . . this order establishes a national **policy** to ensure the protection, maintenance, and restoration of the health of ocean, coastal, and Great Lakes ecosystems and resources, enhance the sustainability of ocean and coastal economies. . ." (Federal Register 2010). The key words here are "stewardship" and "sustainability"—taking care of the environment and engaging in activities that are sustainable; that is, they don't overuse or abuse Earth's resources. President Donald Trump revoked this executive order in 2018, and then in 2021, the Biden–Harris administration put forth a new initiative to conserve and restore lands and waters across the United States. Based on these changes, it is clear that our individual votes make a difference in environmental policy.

Key Takeaways

- The "Tragedy of the Commons" helps us understand why people may not act in a way that benefits the larger community.
- The environment is accessible by a community with more than one worldview.
- People can have different worldviews such as self, anthropocentrism, biocentrism, and eco-centrism.
- Responsible stewardship of Earth's commons has become a high priority for many individuals, groups, and governments.

2.2 Ethics of Consumption

Learning Objectives

1. Identify and explain five examples of individual ethical consumption.
2. Discuss possible conflicts regarding consumption between people having different world-views and formulate potential resolutions.

As individuals, we rely on and consume many resources and products to maintain our particular lifestyle. On a weekly or biweekly basis, you may purchase food, toiletries, clothes, and other necessities to replace those that you previously used up and perhaps even discarded as they lost value to you. Ethical consumption implies that the consumer is aware and cares about the larger consequences of a purchase. Ethical consumers take into account the design, processing, and packaging of a product. They weigh the overall effects of their purchases and may choose to buy a product that uses recycled paper for its packaging material, and doesn't support sweatshops overseas or cruelty to animals. Remember, not everyone has similar worldviews, so different individuals make different purchasing choices.

Individual Ethical Consumption

The choice to engage in an ethical decision-making process is up to the individual. Determining what to purchase in the store calls for ethical consumers to see the "big picture"; they must see the interconnections between what they buy and the world community, in a time when corporations may have their operations on different continents. Take, for example, a product such as chocolate, which is sold at just about every convenience store, gas station, restaurant, and grocery store in the United States. Before it became a chocolate bar or other tasty treat, chocolate began as part of a cacao plant, most likely somewhere in western Africa (see Figure 2.4). The Ivory Coast is the world's largest producer and exporter of cocoa beans, producing between 1.5 million and 2.0 million metric tons per year, of which approximately 20 percent goes to the United States (CRS 2005, ICCO 2017). Chocolate consumers may not realize that more than 1.5 million children work in the cocoa plantations of western Africa (NORC 2020) (see video link: "Chocolate and Child Labor"). In this case, an ethical consumer would only choose to purchase chocolate from companies not relying on child or slave labor. However, this can be challenging for the consumer when the labeling on most chocolate bars does not identify labor practices.

FIGURE 2.4
There are many reports of children being exploited to work the cocoa plantations in western Africa. Scenes from the chocolate industry: (A) cacao plant; (B) chocolate dessert; and (C) a child laborer.

Sources: © Shutterstock, Inc.; Charles William Adofo/Shutterstock.com

Societal Ethical Consumption

Societal ethics can conflict with individual ethics; what's good for society may not necessarily be good for the individual. In our opening story, Giorgi benefited from having additional cows, but if each villager took the same action, the group would suffer. In other examples, the worldviews of individuals are the same as that of a group or society.

When the ethical conduct of people living within a society complements the ethical code of the society, there is less reason for disagreements between individuals and the larger populace. The healthy functioning of the society (towns, cities, etc.), which includes maintaining sustainability, really relies on the ethical actions of individuals regarding all activities related to the environment. Consider solid waste management, for example. Many urban communities depend on everyone disposing of garbage in curbside containers, from which it is picked up and hauled away to a transfer station, an incineration center, or a landfill. If you lived in this type of community and chose not to participate in this process, the rest of the community would not tolerate your decision. In this situation, an individual's ethical conduct would be unsupportive of the community's ethical code. Soon you would have a group of neighbors protesting the infestation of rodents and nasty odors emanating from your residence. As members of a community, it becomes our responsibility to maintain community ethical practices. Individually, you may have an ethical issue with the city's garbage truck dumping your garbage in a landfill, but you would still need to comply with the concept of not hoarding trash. Ethical consumption at the community level would support recycling, composting, and other activities that would reduce the use of landfills. This brings up a larger ethical question: Is it ethical to transport and dispose of garbage elsewhere—for example, to another state? Is it ethical for the city of New York to export garbage out of the city limits and outside the state every day?

As we will discuss later in this chapter, society can pressure individuals to perform ethically when one person's actions disrupt the ethical practices of the larger group. Sometimes societal consumption ethics fail; for example, when a particular group of people as defined by class or economic status have to deal with a disproportionate amount of environmental contaminants. It would be unfair for a select few to bear the environmental problems of the many. When this happens, people protest to initiate positive change.

The actions of vocal protestors encouraged President William Clinton to create Executive Order 12898 in 1994, which states ". . . each Federal agency shall develop an agency-wide environmental justice strategy that addresses disproportionately high and adverse human health or environmental effects of its programs, policies, and activities on minority populations and low-income populations" (Federal Register 1994). In the end, protestor actions resulted in an executive order, the establishment of the Office of Environmental Justice within the Environmental Protection Agency, and a change in societal ethics of consumption in the United States.

2.3 Corporate Ethics

Learning Objectives

1. Distinguish between different types of human exploitation and suggest methods companies can use to inhibit exploitative practices.
2. Compare and contrast "cradle-to-grave" and "cradle-to-cradle" designs.
3. Evaluate a company in regards to local and global environmental stewardship.

Today's challenge for corporations is to be able to conduct their business operations from product idea to post-consumer in a closed-loop cycle that creates zero waste and supports environmental sustainability. This can be difficult for small family-run businesses, as well as for mega-corporations such as Nike, which has tens of thousands of workers in over forty countries. Companies following ethical codes of conduct are serious about compliance and have measures set in place to inhibit corruption and environmental crimes, and to never support child labor or discrimination of any kind. They also stress transparency and accountability; for example, by setting up a whistle-blowing protocol for employees to report violations of policy. Today, following a growth strategy that includes environmental sustainability is smart business. The benefits of environmental stewardship at the corporate level include improving a company's image, lowering costs, and creating a safer workplace.

Exploitation of Humans

To stay viable, a business has to be competitive and make money. One unethical way to reduce costs is to exploit the rights of factory workers, having them work long hours for little pay—or no pay, in the case of slave labor—in unsafe conditions. The cruelest form of human exploitation is slavery. Enslaved people, like those in several unregulated cocoa plantations in western Africa, never get to leave, and when they try, they may be beaten. Conditions like these, which promote a low standard of living and poverty, promote environmental degradation. Why? People first must have their basic needs (i.e., access to food, clean water) met before they can focus on environmental protection.

FIGURE 2.5

Sweatshops are businesses that exploit employees (the injustice is the exploitation) where employees are forced to work long hours with little pay, many times in unsafe environments. At a textile sweatshop in Burma, young female migrant workers sew together shoes.

Source: catastrophe_OL/Shutterstock.com

sweatshop

A place where people work long hours for very low wages.

In another form of exploitation, workers are not considered enslaved people because they can leave, but they receive extremely low pay and may have to work overtime for no extra pay. Workers in these sorts of conditions are said to work in **sweatshops** (see Figure 2.5). Nike, an international company that specializes in making tennis shoes and other sports apparel, was accused of relying on sweatshops in the 1970s through the 1990s. As a consequence, Nike's sales and stock value decreased. Nike has since improved its image by changing some of its practices and hiring a large (almost one-hundred-person) inspection team that randomly checks Nike's international factories. In 2018, Nike began to work with Worker Rights Consortium, an independent group, to inspect its overseas facilities. This agreement came about because of protests at college campuses by students and faculty about the poor work conditions of garment workers overseas. It has also improved the safety of its factories by reducing the amount of toxic chemicals used in shoes. The level of toxicity within tennis shoes (or any other product), the amount of waste it generates, and its overall sustainability in the environment are reflected in the product design. These changes in Nike's business practices prompted consumers to change their opinion of Nike, allowing the company to bounce back from its economic slump.

Cradle-to-Grave Product Design

"Cradle-to-grave" is one type of design plan that companies might follow for their products. The phrase is commonly used in the ecodesign field and encompasses the life of a product from inception to disposal. It is basically a life-cycle analysis to measure environmental impacts of a product. This analysis begins with the gathering of raw materials from the Earth to create the product and ends at the point when all materials are returned to the Earth (EPA 2006b). Possible end-points of a product's components are a recycling line, a composting facility, or as waste stored in a landfill. Continuous waste generation is a key environmental concern linked to water, soil, and air pollution. In 2018 alone, Americans created 292 million tons of trash, of which they recycled and composted 94 million tons (EPA 2020) (see Figure 2.6). Even accounting for these efforts as well as energy recovery, over 50 percent of the accumulated trash ended up in landfills. On top of this, an uncalculated amount of society's waste never makes into the waste management stream and is instead discarded into the environment.

FIGURE 2.6
Cradle-to-grave products fail to meet environmental sustainability standards because they eventually end up as waste. Most of this waste ends up in landfills like this one.

Source: © Shutterstock, Inc.

Cradle-to-Cradle Product Design

Critics of the cradle-to-grave model point out that it isn't ecologically sustainable because it helps to generate waste. A more ambitious and ecologically sustainable model for companies to follow is cradle-to-cradle design, which calls for all "wastes" of a product to be recycled back into production or to be completely biodegradable (McDonough & Braungart 2002, Spierling 2018). How do companies shed their antiquated cradle-to-grave production processes? The nonprofit Cradle-to-Cradle Products Innovation Institute based out of San Francisco, California, works with companies to develop cradle-to-cradle products. It also assesses and certifies products as cradle-to-cradle if they meet the requirements in five categories, including the release of clean water.

Even if they desire to, companies can't reduce their waste generation to zero overnight. This doesn't mean other eco-friendly production strategies shouldn't be pursued and encouraged if cradle-to-cradle design isn't immediately attainable. Eco-Products, Climatex, and gDiapers are examples of companies producing eco-friendly products.

- In a world that focuses on Styrofoam and plastics, Eco-Products has specialized in providing biodegradable food serviceware (see part A of Figure 2.7). Their innovative, holistic strategy has created a lucrative business that produces cups, bowls, plates, and utensils made of sugarcane and corn. Their efforts have debunked the idea that there is no alternative to serving cafeteria food, or even picnic food, on paper or polystyrene (foam) plates. Polystyrene is functional, but not biodegradable, and usually isn't recycled. That means polystyrene products are one-use-only items and do not qualify as part of a cradle-to-cradle model. Imagine the effect if major fast food companies such as Burger King and McDonald's adopted the use of a strategy similar to that of Eco-Products. On a good note, in 1991 McDonald's switched from polystyrene "clamshell" containers for their sandwiches to paper-based wrappings made from recycled material, resulting in an estimated 70–90 percent volume reduction in their packing waste from sandwiches. It's important to mention that Burger King never used foam plates, but it, along with McDonald's, still uses polystyrene plastic utensils.

biodegradable

Can be broken down by living things.

- The Swiss company Climatex manufactures upholstery in a manner that indicates their support of environmental stewardship. They've created plant-based, pesticide-free, nontoxic upholstery products (see part B of Figure 2.7). Their product, based on a cradle-to-cradle design, stresses a life cycle approach that ends with returning the raw materials of the upholstery to the environment with no negative effects.

- In our third example, gDiapers has created and sells a flushable, compostable diaper lining (see part C of Figure 2.7). It's composed of 100 percent natural, **biodegradable** fibers that can be broken down by living things. Nature uses biodegradation, or decomposition, as a way of recycling matter in dead organisms for use in new soil and new growth. Unlike natural materials, artificial materials such as polystyrene and other conventional plastics (polyethylene terephthalate) do not break down very well in the environment. Precious few living things have enzymes that break down conventional plastics because evolution occurred in the absence of these materials. Other natural processes (such as UV) can break them down, but it takes a really long time.

FIGURE 2.7
Cradle-to-cradle designed products are becoming more common. (A) Biodegradable, plant-based containers for fast food and cafeterias. (B) Organic, pesticide free, nontoxic upholstery. (C) Eco-friendlier diapers with compostable/flushable liners.

Sources: © Shutterstock, Inc.; gDiapers hybrid diapers with washable cotton pants and absorbent compostable inserts, courtesy of gDiapers.

gDiapers has created a lucrative product in a very large market. Disposable diapers make up about 1.4 percent of all the municipal waste Americans create. This translates into roughly 4,100,000 tons of disposable diapers dumped into our landfills every year. gDiapers' sustainability efforts are making a difference, but they are a relatively small company in a global market valued at $55 billion per year.

Global Responsibility

The concept of the "commons" applies to companies, too. Go back to our opening story and replace all of the villagers with companies. Large areas of the world can be negatively affected by pollutants released by small to multi-conglomerate companies that fail to be responsible environmental stewards. Companies have a moral responsibility to act ethically with respect to the environment. They have the infrastructure and finances—more so than consumers—to appropriately create, recycle, and manage products. What else can a company do to promote environmental sustainability? We discussed this to some degree in the cradle-to-cradle section, but here we review one specific example in depth, and also discuss more broadly the limits of what a company can accomplish in regards to environmental sustainability.

NatureWorks, owned by PTT Global Chemical and Cargill, is the world's leading developer of plant-based polymers (see part A of Figure 2.7), which are replacing conventional plastics derived from petroleum. The development of a biodegradable substance to replace non-biodegradable conventional plastics demonstrates NatureWorks' commitment to environmental sustainability. It also takes 65 percent less energy to synthesize plant-based polymers (polylactic acid) relative to oil-based plastics. This is a home run, so to speak, creating a biodegradable substance that can replace conventional plastic and is cheaper to produce (see video link: "From Corn to Plastic"). However, without the adoption of these materials by other members of the business community, or by individual consumers, waste will continue to accumulate at the same rate as before.

Benefiting the environment, NatureWorks formed a partnership in 2005 with the world's largest corporation, Walmart. As a result of this partnership, Walmart now uses corn-based plastics in its produce area, cards, and lids (windows) of doughnut and cake containers. The adoption by Walmart—10,130 stores in twenty-seven countries—of corn-based plastics to replace oil-based plastics translated into saving 3.03 million liters (800,000 gallons) of gasoline per year and reducing greenhouse gas emissions by 5 million kilograms (11 million pounds). That's good news environmentally, but corn-based plastics are most effectively biodegraded in commercial composting facilities (CCF) where accepted materials are ground, piles of compost are regularly turned, and temperatures are maintained at 60°C (140°F). Unfortunately, there are too few CCFs available throughout the United States to service existing curbside compost recycling programs. In addition, small, homemade compost piles don't typically reach the high temperatures needed to degrade corn-based plastics efficiently. Thus, at least for now, corn-based plastics are less sustainable than they may seem. Cities do have infrastructure to deal with petroleum-based recyclables and solid waste, but this is not meant for corn-based plastics.

Global responsibility rests not only on corporations, but also on individuals and countries. In this case, citizens could put pressure on local, state, and federal governments to build additional CCFs that would be able to degrade corn-based plastics. In the end, not just companies, but also individuals and governments can play active roles in implementing environmentally sustainable and ethical methods. To protect the environment and their citizens, the French government announced a ban of all sales of noncompostable disposable dishware and utensils in 2020. This was a logical next step after the country's ban of plastic bags in 2016.

From Corn to Plastic
Hear about the benefits of corn-based plastic.

View in the online reader

Critical Thinking Activity: Ethics, Technology, and Genetically Modified Organisms

Genetically modified plants (GMO-P), a category of genetically modified organisms (GMO), were introduced into the agricultural industry in the late 1990s and now make up a significant part of the crops in many countries. These GMOs are created by changing the genetic content of an organism, such as removing or inserting specific genes that code for desired traits. To illustrate the potential of bioengineering work, geneticists produced a glowing tobacco plant that contained the phosphorescent genes of a firefly (see Figure 2.8) (Ow et al. 1986). As you can see, the benefits of GMOs are really only limited by our imagination and identification of individual genes and their functions.

FIGURE 2.8
The possibilities of bioengineering seem endless when the insertion of firefly genes into a tobacco plant's DNA results in glowing (photo courtesy of Dr. Stephen Howell).

Source: National Science Foundation; https://www.nsf.gov/news/mmg/mmg_disp.jsp?med_id=51552.

Monsanto and other seed companies understand the power of bioengineering technology and have used it to create herbicide-resistant seeds. Monsanto is also the world's leading producer of the herbicide Roundup. By inserting a gene from a bacterium resistant to glyphosate, the active ingredient in Roundup, into soybeans, corn, canola, sugar beets, wheat, and other crops, Monsanto has monopolized a large portion of the agricultural industry. Monsanto has had great economic benefits from patenting their herbicide-resistant seeds and also selling herbicide that the seeds are resistant to. Is the company, and others like it, engaging in environmental steward-ship and supporting environmental justice? To help answer this question, let's consider patents, monocultures, toxicity, super-weeds, and small farmers.

A patent protects an inventor, letting them not worry about someone else taking their idea and using it for profit. Inventors can mass produce the new product, and if they are lucky they will financially benefit from their invention. In the age of technology, new computer designs, cell phones, and other electronic gadgets are patented all the time, but these are nonliving things.

Think again about the "commons." What happens if a bioengineering company sells GM annual ryegrass seeds to the shepherds, who, in turn, plant the seeds throughout the majority of the vil-lage's pastoral area (see opening story)? This is a hypothetical question on two accounts. Unlike in the United States, in Turkey—where the shepherds live—it is illegal to plant GM crops. Sec-ondly, as of 2021, none of the twenty-eight countries that grow GM crops has approved the commercial use of GM ryegrass. Where once the grazing was free, now the shepherds must purchase patented GM seeds each year. Would this be ethical? How does your answer reflect your worldview?

Now imagine that the genetically modified grass contains a gene making it resistant to an her-bicide the bioengineering company also sells. Company representatives gather the villagers and tell them that their entire field and the larger prairie can grow more grass if they kill all the non-edible plants. All they have to do is spray their new chemical formula (containing glyphosate). "What about the grass seeds I just planted, will your chemical kill the grass too?" asks Giorgi. The company representative replies, "No, that's the best part about this. The new grass is resis-tant to the herbicide. Therefore, you don't have to worry about where you spread it because it can't hurt the grass." The dairy farmers—all but those with only one cow, who can't afford the price—then pay for the herbicide in addition to the genetically modified seeds. Is this envi-ronmental injustice? In 1998, Indian farmers burned their fields planted with GM seeds because they were concerned about a seed monopoly controlled by Monsanto. Farmers in Brazil and Thailand have also protested the use of GM plants.

Concerns over the use of GM crops include the further spread of monocultures that do not have the diversity of plant species needed to adapt to potential environmental change (see Chapter 4 and Chapter 8). The diversity of the plants in natural environments is the direct result of evolutionary forces that have been at work for millions of years. Does the creation of large monocultures—where only one species might be found in a huge area—support environmental sustainability? With the use of monocultures, are we setting ourselves up for a problem when a new virus or bacterial agent might wipe out a significant amount of our crops?

FIGURE 2.9
Pigweed is labeled as a superweed because it has built up resistance to herbicide treatment.

Source: © Shutterstock, Inc.

Continual application of herbicides can create superweeds resistant to herbicide treatments. Evolution shows us that surviving organisms pass on their genes to their offspring. With each generation of pigweed treated with Roundup, a larger proportion of plants will be resistant to the herbicide. Roundup use selects for herbicide-resistant weeds.

A perfect example of an herbicide-resistant weed is the pigweed (see Figure 2.9). It is becoming more abundant in the southern United States, disrupting millions of acres of cotton and soybean fields. The plant's resistance, fast growth, and small pollen granules, which allow for their easy spread by wind, present a real problem to farmers. What's the solution? Should the genetic-engineering industry design another genetically altered species, or come up with a new herbicide?

Herbicides are designed to kill plants and therefore contain ingredients harmful to living things. Should consumers of Roundup be concerned about the active ingredient glyphosate? The Environmental Protection Agency has set acceptable concentration levels for glyphosate in drinking water, but does not list glyphosate as a carcinogen, although the International Agency for Research on Cancer concluded that it is probably carcinogenic. Whom do we believe? Clearly, our knowledge is deficient on the effects of widespread use of glyphosate on ecosystems.

Bringing It Closer to Home: Product Designs

Are you an ethical consumer? Do you consider the impact of each of your purchases on the environment, as well as whether the companies you purchased them from are following ethical codes of conduct that do not include injustice or environmental degradation? There are many products available to the consumer in today's stores. What percentage of these products provide good examples of cradle-to-cradle designs, or at least attempt to support environmental sustainability? Visit your local supermarket or other vendor, randomly select two products on the shelf, and determine whether they are examples of cradle-to-cradle designs. If they're not, consider how the companies who manufactured the products could improve their design. Next, randomly select five items you purchased in the last six months and brought to your residence. Begin by looking at the structure of the product and the ingredients within it, which sometimes are listed on the container if, for example, it's a food item or cleaning solution. Search online to see if you can find the larger impact of your product. For example, does the product support slavery, or does its manufacturing process introduce toxins into the environment? Finally, try to estimate the true cost of the five products to reflect recycling, detoxifying, storing, or other process that takes care of all the parts of the product, including packaging, after it is no longer useful to the purchaser.

Key Takeaways

- A closed-loop cycle creates zero waste and supports environmental sustainability.
- A corporate growth strategy that includes environmental sustainability is smart business.
- Poverty impacts the environment.
- "Cradle-to-grave" products fail to meet environmental sustainability standards because their production and disposal generate waste that accumulates waste.
- "Cradle-to-cradle" design strategies support sustainability.
- Individuals, companies, and governments can take active roles in implementing environmentally sustainable and ethical methods.

2.4 Policies and Laws

Environmental laws, regulations, and policies are needed whenever individuals, companies, cities, or states do not follow environmental ethics, and when their actions negatively affect others and/or the environment. These laws also help to prevent activities, even those by the federal government, that might significantly affect environmental quality. In our opening story, villagers use the "commons" area as pastureland for their cows. Let's change the story slightly and have all the villagers get together and mutually agree that no one can have more than five cows, thus ensuring that the commons will not be over-grazed. Weeks go by, and everyone has abided by this "law" except for Davit, Giorgi's brother. Davit has secretly been grazing an extra four cows each night, in addition to his five cows during the day. A whistleblower, his own daughter, brings this to the attention of the village council. The council is furious—rightly so—and as a penalty makes Davit sell all but one of his cows, and the profits of his sale are divided among the other herders.

To help protect and preserve the health of people and the environment, Congress writes environmental laws that are then sent to the president for approval or veto (see Figure 2.10). If the law is approved, the Environmental Protection Agency (EPA), an arm of the federal government, is directed to write regulations that support the law; they are also directed to enforce it. The EPA also helps with compliance. A company not compliant with the regulations may be fined and may also receive an injunction, which requires the company to perform or not perform a specific activity.

FIGURE 2.10
Changes in presidential administration can have a direct effect on approval of environmental protection bills. In contrast to President Donald Trump's (A) strategy to roll back many environmental protective measures and significantly weaken the EPA, President Joseph Biden (B) strongly supports legislation and international agreements to enhance environmental protection.

Sources: Evan El-Amin/Shutterstock.com; Andrew Cline/Shutterstock.com

As an example of environmental enforcement, we'll draw upon America's worst oil spill, a tragedy highlighted in movie theaters in 2016. On April 20, 2010, an explosion aboard the oil-drilling rig *Deepwater Horizon* in the Gulf of Mexico killed eleven people. The rig began to leak oil, eventually amounting to over 200 million gallons (see Figure 13.1 and Figure 13.2). Later, on December 15 of that same year, the United States filed a complaint in a U.S. District Court stating that the company MOEX Offshore, which was a 10 percent owner of the lease for the drilling well, violated part of the Clean Water Act. In response, on February 17, 2012, MOEX Offshore agreed to pay $90 million, with sizeable monies going toward environmental projects and acquisition of lands to be marked for preservation and protection.

Paying True Costs versus Market Costs Helps Sustainability

The **market price** of a product refers to the dollar amount that the consumer actually pays, whereas the **true cost** includes this cost plus environmental cleanup and any other activities related to dealing with all of the wastes associated with the manufacturing, packaging, and use of a product. True costs rather than market prices account for hidden expenses related to the negative effects of a product on the environment and on human health. Accordingly, when these hidden costs are included, the price of a product increases. Therefore, true costs are higher than market costs.

> **market price**
>
> The price of a product that a consumer pays.
>
> **true cost**
>
> The price a consumer pays for a product plus any expenses related to the environmental cleanup and negative effects of wastes associated with the manufacturing, packaging, and use of a product.

Consider, for example, the price of gasoline. The price we pay at the pump is market cost, which does not include mitigating the damage caused by the release of carbon dioxide into the atmosphere by your car as it burns the gas, and the resulting rise in global temperature; that is, global warming. How does this type of thinking about costs affect our decisions about using other sources of energy, such as coal and natural gas? The United States generates approximately 30 percent of its electricity from burning coal and 34 percent from burning natural gas. Hidden costs of using coal to generate electricity include (for example) medical expenses for associated major health issues such as black lung disease among miners, and mitigating the impact of associated pollution. Accounting for hidden expenses, the price of electricity generated from coal-fired power plants almost triples. There is a wealth of natural gas in Pennsylvania, Texas, and other key states, but extracting, processing, and burning natural gas takes its toll on the environment (see fracking, discussed in Chapter 10 and Chapter 13). Similar to coal, the costs of environmental cleanup are not included in the market price.

Major U.S. Environmental Laws

Environmental laws help to protect people and the environment by preventing and regulating pollution in its various forms. Here, we briefly list three major federal laws: the Clean Water Act, the Clean Air Act, and the Toxic Substance Control Act. See Table 2.1 for descriptions of some other significant federal environmental laws.

- The Clean Water Act (CWA) (see Chapter 10) was enacted in 1972 to maintain healthy waterways. It regulates discharges of pollutants and states that it is unlawful to discharge pollutants into navigable water.

- The Clean Air Act (1970) (see Chapter 11) regulates air emissions and authorizes the EPA to set air standards. One group of chemicals monitored by the EPA under the Clean Air Act is chlorofluorocarbons, which can leak from older refrigerator systems, enter the atmosphere, and destroy Earth's protective ozone layer (which shields against harmful ultraviolet rays).

- A third major environmental law, the Toxic Substance Control Act of 1976 (see Chapter 15 and Chapter 16) deals with restrictions on the use of chemicals such as asbestos, polychlorinated biphenyls, and lead found in paint. Each of these chemicals has deleterious effects on humans.

TABLE 2.1 Examples of Significant Federal Environmental Laws

Federal Law	Description
National Environmental Policy Act (NEPA) (1969)	This act created the Council on Environmental Quality and requires the federal government to provide an environmental impact statement (EIS), which is an explanation detailing the potential impacts of a proposed project on the environment.
Endangered Species Act (1973)	The ESA protects imperiled species and their habitats.
Marine Protection, Research and Sanctuaries Act (1972)	The MPRSA prohibits the dumping of materials into oceans.
Resource Conservation and Recovery Act (1976)	The RCRA gives the Environmental Protection Agency the authority to control hazardous waste.
Nuclear Waste Act (1982)	The aim of the NWA is to properly dispose of nuclear waste.

International Policies and Laws

globalization

Increased relationships across the world and the global integration of economics, politics, and cultures.

Our discussion of the "commons" applies at the international level too, because we can replace Giorgi and the other villagers with countries. Now, the "commons" refers to international areas, such as oceanic waters, or places like Antarctica, that are not owned by any single country. It can be challenging for corporations and nations involved in international commerce to follow sound ethical environmental practices, because each country may have a different cultural worldview and the vast numbers of people involved in its interactions are hard to monitor. In this time of rapid globalization and the challenge of monitoring all parts of a complex trade organization, it's easy to commit environmental exploitation, environmental degradation, and environmental injustice. **Globalization** refers to the increased interactions of people, companies, and governments across the world, and the integration of economics, politics, and cultures due to improved methods of communications, faster shipping of goods, and corporations' having facilities in multiple countries.

Countries have widely varying responses to international environmental issues. Some countries have formed tight collaborations for the betterment of a particular part of the environment, while others have bitterly opposed such collaboration, not willing to compromise or discuss substantive issues. Here we discuss some of these interactions by focusing our attention on two ecosystems—the Great Lakes and North Atlantic—and then on particular pollutants.

The United States and Canada Work Together to Protect the Great Lakes Ecosystem

Some ecosystems lie along the border of adjacent countries. In these cases, countries can choose to work together to protect the environment. The Great Lakes in North America is one such area and lies along the border between the United States and Canada (see part A of Figure 2.11). Four of the lakes (Superior, Huron, Erie, and Ontario) are partly within each country; the fifth (Michigan) is entirely within the United States. This is a vital region of the continent because it holds over 20 percent of the world's freshwater and offers an important commercial transportation route through its connection to the Saint Lawrence Seaway and the Atlantic Ocean. In response to the growing **sea lamprey** population in some of the Great Lakes, which parasitized lake trout, and to facilitate fishery cooperation, the **Great Lakes Fishery Commission** (GLFC) developed as a binational partnership between the United States and Canada (see Figure 2.11) (see video link: "GLFC"). The GLFC, with half of its eight members appointed by each government, conducts research and makes management recommendations to both countries. Also, to support the sustainability of the Great Lakes at the international level, the Great Lakes Water Quality Agreement between the United States and Canada was signed. The goal of this international agreement is to "restore and maintain the chemical, physical, and biological integrity of the Great Lakes Basin Ecosystem" (EPA 1978). For further information about international agreements, see Table 2.2.

sea lamprey

A large parasite of fish that attaches to the outside of the fish's body.

Great Lakes Fishery Commission

An eight-member team appointed by the United States and Canada that works on ecological and environmental issues related to the Great Lakes fisheries.

FIGURE 2.11
The United States and Canada collaboratively manage and protect the Great Lakes (A) located between their countries. (B) They formed the Great Lakes Fishery Commission to prevent lake trout from being parasitized by sea lampreys, as seen here.

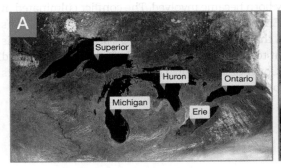

Sources: Joseph Shostell; Provided by the SeaWiFS Project, NASA/Goddard Space Flight Center, and ORBIMAGE; M. Gaden, GLFC

GLFC
Listen to Paul Sullivan from the Sea Lamprey Control Centre talk about the significance of the Great Lakes Fishery Commission (GLFC) in controlling the sea lamprey population.

View in the online reader

TABLE 2.2 Examples of Key International Environmental Bodies and Agreements

International Agreement/Body	Description
United Nations (1945)	An international organization of many countries that addresses international issues and also supports environmental sustainability.
Great Lakes Fishery Commission (1954)	A partnership between the United States and Canada to protect the fisheries of the Great Lakes.
Convention on Wetlands or Ramsar Convention (signed 1971/effective 1975)	An international treaty among 168 countries for the conservation and sustainable use of wetlands.
Convention on International Trade in Endangered Species of Wild Fauna and Flora (CITES) (1975)	An agreement among 183 countries to restrict international trade of endangered species.
United Nations Environmental Program (UNEP) (1972)	An entity within the United Nations that addresses environmental issues such as the killing of elephants.

International Agreement/Body	Description
Great Lakes Water Quality Agreement (1972)	Agreement between the United States and Canada to restore and maintain the chemical, physical, and biological integrity of the Great Lakes Basin ecosystem.
Kyoto Protocol (adopted 1997/ effective 2005)	An agreement among many countries to reduce greenhouse gas emissions by 5 percent relative to Earth's 1990 values.
Stockholm Convention on Persistent Organic Pollutants (signed 2001/ effective 2004)	An international treaty among 190 nations to restrict and eliminate production and use of persistent organic pollutants such as DDT.
Paris Climate Accord (adopted in 2015/effective in 2020)	An agreement signed by 195 countries to curtail greenhouse gas emissions.

Cod Wars between England and Iceland

FIGURE 2.12

The cod wars between England and Iceland indicated that peaceful solutions for sharing resources can be difficult to achieve. At times, Iceland's and England's vessels were dangerously close together, as can be seen here with an Icelandic patrol boat fast approaching an English trawler.

Source: Icelandic Coast Guard; https://arcticportal.org/ap-library/news/529-the-cod-wars-iceland-vs-britain.

cod wars

Disagreements between England and Iceland about the right to fish for cod in North Atlantic waters.

endangered species

A species in danger of becoming extinct.

The **cod wars** between England and Iceland, beginning in 1958, provide an example of a dispute over a resource within the North Atlantic (see Figure 2.12). Similar to the Great Lakes region of North America, the North Atlantic is considered a valuable resource by more than one country. In contrast to the interactions between the United States and Canada, which gave rise to a tight partnership, England and Iceland had trouble from the beginning. Iceland's fishing fleet widened its fishing region and labeled the region as a zone in which only they had a right to fish. English fishermen became acutely aware of this when they found their fishing nets severed. From this small beginning, the Icelandic Coast Guard and English Navy both became involved. The conflict culminated in a standoff in 1976. In the end, England relinquished any claim to fish in Iceland's new fish zone because Iceland threatened to close a NATO base. Because of this turbulent history over the right to use cod fishing grounds, Iceland and England plan to use the International Court of Justice in The Hague if fishing incidents between the two countries happen in the future.

International Efforts to Protect Global Biodiversity

Many nations work together as environmental stewards to protect global biodiversity. International cooperation that brings together many nations can be critical for efforts to solve global environmental problems, such as transporting threatened and endangered species, or rising greenhouse gas emissions. Out of concern for threatened and endangered species, the U.S. Congress passed the Endangered Species Act, which was sent to President Richard Nixon and signed into law in 1973. **Endangered species** are species that are in danger of becoming extinct. A slightly less severe category is "threatened," which means that a species is likely to become endangered. The preservation of species listed in these categories is important, so as to maintain the diversity of animal and plant communities and to help stabilize ecosystems and biomes (see Chapter 5).

The enactment of the Endangered Species Act led to the signing by eighty countries of (now grown to 183) the **Convention on International Trade in Endangered Species of Wild Fauna and Flora (CITES)** in Washington, DC. CITES restricts international trade of endangered species. The agreement is one of respect, and countries can elect to participate as they choose. Individual countries are encouraged to use their national laws to support CITES. It should be noted that CITES is also strongly affiliated with the United Nations Environment Program (UNEP), which has been called "the voice for the environment within the United Nations system" (UNEP 2012). Recently, for example, UNEP has expressed its concern about the killing of elephants in Cameroon (see Figure 2.13). The United Nations as a whole is also devoted to environmental sustainability. Consider United Nations Secretary General Ban Ki-moon's words in Qatar in 2011: "We have only this Earth and it is up to us to preserve it." These words echo with strength when we remember that the secretary general is the spokesperson for 193 countries.

> **Convention on International Trade in Endangered Species of Wild Fauna and Flora (CITES)**
>
> An international organization that monitors and restricts the transport of endangered species.

FIGURE 2.13

Elephants in Cameroon and other areas of Africa are being targeted by poachers for their ivory tusks. (A) A herd of elephants in Amboseli National Park, Kenya. (B) One of an estimated two hundred elephants slaughtered by poachers in 2012 in Bouba Ndjida National Park, Cameroon. (C) A collection of ivory tusks collected from captured poachers in Libreville, Gabon.

Source: © Shutterstock, Inc.

Greenhouse Gases and International Agreements

Countries have also elected to work together to solve global environmental problems. The **Kyoto Protocol** and **Paris Agreement** are two examples of international agreements to reduce the emissions of greenhouse gases. Scientists have documented that **greenhouse gases** such as carbon dioxide, methane, nitrous oxide, and sulfur hexafluoride act analogously to a greenhouse and impede the loss of heat from the atmosphere. Although adopted in 1997 in Kyoto, Japan, the Kyoto Protocol did not become active until 2005. Its goal was to reduce overall greenhouse gas emissions by 5 percent relative to Earth's 1990 values. Each country can meet its goals however it can, even if it means creating sinks to offset their sources. If a country has difficulty reducing its emissions, it can compensate for this by planting forests of trees (examples of sinks) that can absorb emitted carbon dioxide. Even though the United States is one of the largest emitters of greenhouse gases, it never ratified the Kyoto Protocol. Then, in 2015, at the climate conference in Paris, a more comprehensive international agreement (the Paris Agreement) was reached to curtail greenhouse gas emissions beginning in 2020. This time, the United States and China pledged commitment. Although the Trump administration announced in 2017 that the United States would withdraw from the Paris Agreement, President Biden reversed this decision in 2021.

> **Kyoto Protocol**
>
> An accord signed by countries in 1997 that intended to reduce greenhouse gas emissions.
>
> **Paris Agreement**
>
> An international agreement reached in Paris in 2015 to curb emissions of greenhouse gases and mitigate global warming beginning in 2020.
>
> **greenhouse gas**
>
> Gases that absorb infrared radiation, trap heat in the atmosphere, and contribute to the greenhouse effect.

Birds Know No Boundaries: Collaboration among Political Adversaries

Human interaction with the environment can also be of value in establishing improved relations between countries. In the late 1990s, a program called "Migrating Birds Know No Boundaries" was initiated to increase the positive interactions among three regions—Israel, Jordan, and Palestine—located in a politically turbulent area of the world. Schools from all three countries became involved with monitoring banded white storks, showing that the countries could have a mutual interest when it comes to the environment. The program was a success for fifteen years and demonstrates the value of wildlife and the natural environment to people. International groups can form to protect wildlife, and complementary to this, as shown in the "Birds Know No Boundaries" program, wildlife can help nations interact positively together.

Key Takeaways

- True costs rather than market prices account for hidden expenses related to the negative effects of a product's manufacturing, packaging, and use on the environment and on human health.
- Federal environmental laws (e.g. Clean Water Act, Clean Air Act) help to protect people and the environment by preventing and regulating pollution in its various forms.
- Countries have widely varying responses to international environmental issues.
- The United States and Canada work together to protect the Great Lakes ecosystem.
- The cod wars between Iceland and England provide an example of a dispute over a resource.
- Through international efforts we can protect global biodiversity.
- The Kyoto Protocol and Paris Agreement are international agreements to reduce the emissions of greenhouse gases.
- Human interaction with the environment can also be of value in establishing improved relations between countries.

2.5 Obstacles and Solutions for Creating a Sustainable Society

Learning Objectives

1. Explain why population growth, suburban sprawl, and nuclear energy present unique ethical questions for society.
2. Identify infrastructural and behavioral obstacles to following environmentally sustainable methods.

The environmental movement came about because Aldo Leopold, Rachel Carson, and many others observed and wrote about the potential harm a frontier mentality can cause to Earth's intrinsically valuable resources. They pointed out environmental degradation due to the Industrial Revolution, as well as the extinction of formerly abundant species like the passenger pigeon. The question for all of us, in every state and country—indeed, for all of Earth—is, will we learn from our past mistakes and continue to move forward with the environmental movement to achieve a state of sustainability?

Learning from Past Mistakes

The education of future generations regarding historical environmental issues is key to guiding the environmental movement forward in a positive direction, while simultaneously reducing the chance that people will repeat past mistakes. Society's continued degradation of the environment may indicate that we are not adequately learning from the large number of studies published each year linking environmental degradation to human activities. What can historical incidents of, for example, population growth and nuclear power teach us about environmental ethics?

Population Growth

Historical and archeological records of villagers on small, isolated Easter Island in the Pacific Ocean (see Chapter 6) provide important insights about events that can lead to overexploitation of resources and overpopulation. The idea that living things can outstrip the resources of their environment is not new; population biologists have long understood that nonhuman animal populations will decrease when they run out of food. Yet, people have a tendency to consider human population trends to be different.

FIGURE 2.14
The human population is growing exponentially. Many areas of the world are becoming very densely populated, such as Hong Kong, China (A) and Varanasi, India (B).

Sources: oneinchpunch/Shutterstock.com; arindambanerjee/Shutterstock.com

Earth's two most populous countries, China and India (see Figure 2.14), have tried to curtail their population growth with some controversial measures. Some have worked, while others have not (see Chapter 6). An analysis of how countries try to control their growth by limiting the number of children a family can have raises another ethical dilemma. What worldview supports limiting human reproduction? Here, it seems that in order to protect the larger ecosystem, a single species—namely, humans—must be held in check.

Fukushima, Chernobyl, Three Mile Island

The world's nations rely on several energy sources, including nuclear energy, to meet the needs of their growing populations. Every energy source has its pros and cons, and nuclear is no different in that regard. What is unusual about nuclear energy is its potential for contaminating land, water, and air environments with harmful, even deadly, radiation. A meltdown at the Fukushima power plant in Japan in 2011 and earlier incidents at Chernobyl, Ukraine, in 1986 and at Three Mile Island, Pennsylvania, in 1979 remind us of the potential damage nuclear radiation can cause to the environment. Scientists and governments have to weigh the value of using nuclear energy as an energy source that does not emit greenhouse gases against its risk of radiation leaks. Here lies another ethical dilemma.

Creating a Sustainable Society

Creating a sustainable society begins with the individual and begins now (see Figure 2.15). Individuals are the functional units within all group sizes. They can incite action such as what occurred in Kingsnorth, England, where protests encouraged the German energy company E•ON to halt a plan to build a new coal-fired power plant. A rising swirl of protests across the world are pushing for better protection of the environment.

potential energy

Stored energy.

Individuals induce change by practicing environmental stewardship. For instance, ethical consumerism at the level of the individual supports ethical conduct in corporations. Certainly, individual citizens don't have the resources to completely recover matter and **potential energy** in waste from poorly designed products, but they can assist. Offsetting waste accumulation through recycling efforts and improving upon these efforts are helpful in creating a sustainable society. Maybe future companies will only have products with cradle-to-cradle designs that also incorporate the waste of earlier, failed products. The term "failed" refers to products that were not environmentally sustainable.

FIGURE 2.15
In 2020, sixteen-year-old Greta Thunberg speaks to thousands of protestors in Lausanne, Switzerland, and calls for action to prevent rapid climate change.

Source: dominika zara/Shutterstock

We Need to Improve Dialogue Between Scientists and Laypeople

In addition to teaching the current generation about past examples of nonsustainability, establishing a sustainable society also depends on improving discourse between scientists and laypeople. The average citizen, the layperson, doesn't have the science background to adequately discuss cutting-edge technology with the scientists who are creating and studying it. Furthermore, scientists are mostly at work in their laboratories and offices, out of sight of the general public.

To speed up communication with one another, scientists have developed their own technical language they use when presenting their findings orally at conferences or in written form as papers published in scientific journals. The jargon is hard to understand to the nonscientist. Even if laypeople attended a science conference or obtained a scientific paper, the same scientific shorthand that allows succinct peer-to-peer communication would be incomprehensible for most of the public. Ideally, we need more intermediaries to help translate complicated scientific research findings to understandable language for the benefit of the public. The reality of living in a sustainable society is partly dependent on breaking down the communication barriers between scientists and laypeople.

Overcoming Infrastructural and Behavioral Obstacles

To reach our sustainability goals we must address infrastructural and behavioral obstacles.

Communities Need Updated Infrastructure

Environmental policy is based on environmental government laws and the EPA's written regulations that support those laws. Thus, laws and regulations are used as guidelines, or rules, for making environmental decisions. But do environmental protection laws such as the Clean Air and Clean Water Acts lead to changes in the nation's infrastructure so that we don't violate written regulations of those same laws?

Infrastructure is the basic structure—physical or operational—that our society needs to function. The answer is "yes" from the standpoint that changes in infrastructure are supposed to happen, but the reality is that physical and operational changes can be expensive. For example, a new wastewater treatment plant or a wind farm might both support environmental policy, but funds must be available to build them.

infrastructure

The basic structure, physical or operational, that a society needs to function.

Corn-based plastics seem to be an environmentally sound alternative to conventional, oil-based plastics, but the United States lacks the complete infrastructure to provide for properly composting them. Remember, corn-based plastics do not efficiently break down in most homemade compost sites, and even if they did, the majority of consumers do not have a designated compost site at home. Problems like this challenge us because we see that we have the technology to move toward greater environmental sustainability, but we lack the physical structures to make the whole-scale change overnight. In these situations, it's important to recognize that society is moving toward sustainability and needs adequate time to adapt.

Behavioral Obstacles: NIMBY, Free Riders, and Lack of Engaged Citizenry

FIGURE 2.16

After sixteen years (2001–2017) of protests from local residents against the development of a commercial wind farm off the coast of Cape Cod, Massachusetts, the project was canceled. A new site, off the coast of Rhode Island, was located for America's first wind farm. Shown here, the Block Island Wind Farm, developed and constructed by Deepwater Wind, became operational December 12, 2016. Wind power harnessed by the new wind farm and transformed into electricity enabled nearby Rock Island to close its diesel-powered electric plant, thereby eliminating the combustion of 3.8 million liters (one million gallons) of diesel oil annually.

Source: Courtesy of Ørsted.

not in my backyard (NIMBY)

A phenomenon where people oppose development or change near their homes although they support the same development or change elsewhere.

"Not in my backyard" (NIMBY) is a statement expressed by people who agree with a change in infrastructure as long as the new building, bridge, windmill, etc. isn't near their home. This attitude is common and can lead to delays in moving toward environmental sustainability. Is the NIMBY mentality a sign that an individual really doesn't agree with the larger (community) change, and if so, why? Wouldn't a structural change in support of government environmental laws be a benefit, not a detriment?

Some people oppose the construction of wind farms because they are not aesthetically pleasing (NIMBY syndrome), even though they would reduce a region's reliance on fossil fuels. Against nine years of bitter protests, U.S. Secretary Ken Salazar approved the nation's first wind farm off the coast of Cape Cod, Massachusetts (see Figure 2.16). Even with financial backing from the federal government, developers could not overcome strong local protests. In 2017, after sixteen years, plans for America's first wind farm were scrapped. This is an example of how the NIMBY syndrome can impede actions of prudent environmental stewardship (see video link: "NIMBY"). However, as hope faded for the Cape Cod project, a new site three miles off the coast of Rhode Island was selected, and in December of 2016, America's first offshore commercial wind farm became operational.

Individuals who use the "commons" but don't take care of it can be considered free riders, also known as freeloaders. They use a resource—fish, for example—and don't ever do anything that might be considered environmentally beneficial for the community in which they fish. If everyone had this mindset, Earth would be on a direct path toward environmental destruction. The trick for environmentalists is to get freeloaders involved in the environmental stewardship process; in essence, converting the freeloader into an engaged citizen. This can happen with education that links the personal situation of the environmental freeloader to the larger environmental issues. Most people, when they understand the link between their own health and the health of the world around them, become spurred to action.

 NIMBY

Listen to John Stossel's interview about Not In My Backyard Syndrome disrupting the development of offshore wind farms.

View in the online reader

Ethical Advertising and Falsification of Research Data

Unethical behaviors of individuals, corporations, and nations make challenging obstacles for those following ethical standards. By definition, unethical is the direct opposite of ethical. It would be impossible to discuss all possible unethical environmental practices, but it's a good idea to mention a couple of the main ones—false advertising and falsifying scientific results. These are obstacles for consumers who are trying to make ethical decisions about their purchases and activities.

We use our written words and voices to communicate our thoughts and ideas to others. Those people around us believe in what we communicate, and why wouldn't they? We tend to trust things that are familiar to us, even companies that tell us about the products they manufacture. Perhaps it is our faith in others or naiveté that makes us not question what is told to us, so we continue to habitually consume a company's product. A company's false advertising about a product's impact on the environment, or a scientist's falsifying data collected from experiments, can cause us to commit an unethical act, or worse, put ourselves, other people, and the environment in harm's way. Claims are now mounting that Monsanto has not been transparent about the potential effects of using the pesticide glyphosate. The story is still unfolding, but researchers are pushing for additional research, following studies about how glyphosate may cause birth defects in frog and chicken embryos. The lack of transparency is an obstacle to sustainable-minded farmers, because they do not want to use chemicals that harm the environment.

Key Takeaways

- Education about historical environmental issues helps to prevent a repeat of past mistakes and helps to guide today's environmental movement.
- Every energy source has its pros and cons, and nuclear is no different in that regard.
- Creating a sustainable society begins with the individual.
- We need to improve dialogue between scientists and laypeople.
- Communities need updated infrastructure to support sustainability goals.
- NIMBY, free riders, and lack of engaged citizenry are all behavioral obstacles to creating a sustainable world.
- False advertising and falsifying data create obstacles for ethical people who are trying to make decisions about their purchases and activities.

2.6 A Look to the Future: Revisiting the Commons

Learning Objective

1. Identify general ethical practices that help to create a sustainable future.

At the chapter's close, we return to the opening story of Giorgi and Nikoluz. Commonly owned pastureland is often a source of farmer conflicts, some verbal and some physical, in Africa, Central Asia, and the Caucasus. Disputes in these areas arise from livestock keepers, having different interests in resource management and because overuse of pastureland causes erosion and general pasture degradation (Neudert et al. 2018). Conflicts in these areas arise, from length of time on common pastureland to whether village pastures should be rested or not. However, conflict is usually avoided by moving personal livestock to distant pastures and only using community land for veterinary checks and selling of livestock. A balanced, mutually agreed upon system works as long as it protects the long-term health of community-owned pastureland as well as the rights of the various stakeholders.

In this chapter on ethics, we have discussed viewpoints, consumption, corporate ethics, national and international policies, as well as obstacles and solutions for creating a sustainable future. How do we as a society address the anthropocentric and frontier mentality viewpoints mentioned in the beginning of the chapter? Do we let our society crash like the Easter Islanders did with theirs (see Chapter 6)? Part of the answer to this question is recognizing that every living thing is connected, and that we all inhabit a world with limited resources and fragile environments. The wastes associated with the products we use do affect the local and global communities. The world, on one hand, seems immensely large relative to our size as individuals, yet on the other hand it is one tiny oasis floating in space within one small solar system within one galaxy among billions within the universe. Our environment and resources therein are indeed limited. It would seem, perhaps obviously, that if someone or some company repeatedly failed to treat the "commons" with respect as a shared resource, the Environmental Protection Agency would use its power to slap on fines and incarcerate offenders of the law. Maybe we move forward into the future with governments offering strong incentives to companies to pursue environmental stewardship policies. This is probably easier to address with local companies whose employees are part of the local community, but what about multinational companies where ownership is elsewhere? Part of the answer here might be greater involvement and oversight by the federal and state governments to create a nationwide infrastructure to support sustainability methods. Is it too much to imagine electrical charging stations replacing gas stations, or systems set up to handle compostables that are no further than a stone's throw from every house? Moving forward with transparency and with a willingness to acknowledge mistakes and work toward improvement is certainly a large part of a winning environmental strategy for every company, nation, and individual. What's your green strategy?

Key Takeaways

- We inhabit a world of limited resources and fragile environments.
- Ethical practices help to create a sustainable future.

FIGURE 2.17 Visual Overview: Environmental Ethics, Law, and Policy
Summarizing figure: Society's path toward sustainability depends on: (2.1) environmental views and attitudes of influence; (2.2) ethics of consumption; (2.3) corporate ethics; (2.4) creating and upholding environmental laws; and (2.5) overcoming current and (2.6) future obstacles.

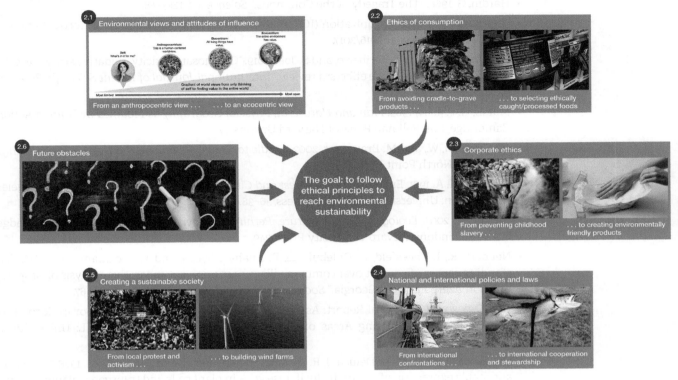

Sources: Joseph Shostell; © Shutterstock, Inc.; See previous citations for image credits.

2.7 References

- Cradle-to-Cradle Products Innovation Institute: http://c2ccertified.org.

- CRS Report for Congress. 2005. "Child labor in West African cocoa production: issues and U. S. policy." United States Congress: Washington, DC.

- EPA. 1978. "The Great Lakes Water Quality Agreement." Environmental Protection Agency: Washington, DC.

- EPA. 2005. "Everyday Choices: Opportunities for Environmental Stewardship." Environmental Protection Agency Innovation Action Council. Environmental Protection Agency: Washington, DC, 1–19.

- EPA. 2006a. "Everyday Choices: Opportunities for Environmental Stewardship Implementation Plan-Project List Introduction and Summary." Environmental Protection Agency Innovation Action Council: Washington, DC, 1–55.

- EPA. 2006b. "Life Cycle Assessment: Principles and Practice." EPA/600/R-06/090.

- EPA. 2011. "Solid Waste and Energy Report EPA-530-F-11-005." Environmental Protection Agency: Washington, DC.

- EPA. 2016. "Advancing Sustainable Materials Management: 2014 Fact Sheet. Assessing Trends in Material Generation, Recycling, Composting, Combustion with Energy Recovery and Landfilling in the United States." Environmental Protection Agency: Washington, DC.

- Federal Register. 1994. "Executive Order 12898—Federal actions to address environmental justice in minority populations and low-income populations." *Presidential Documents*, 59, no. 32.

- Federal Register. 2010. "Executive Order 13547—Stewardship of the ocean, our coasts, and the Great Lakes." *Presidential Documents*, 75, no. 14.
- Hardin, G. 1968. "The Tragedy of the Commons." *Science* 162: 1243–48.
- International Cocoa Organization (ICCO). 2017. "ICCO Quarterly Bulletin of Cocoa Statistics," XLIII, no. 3, Cocoa year 2016/2017.
- Jazmin, S., T. Dheni, T. Heriberto, and S. Joel. 2019. "Glyphosate toxicity, oxidative stress, carcinogenicity and reproductive effects: a review." *International Journal of Recent Scientific Research* 10, no. 6: 32865–69.
- Marsh, G. P. [1864] 1965. *Man and Nature; or, Physical Geography as Modified by Human Action*. Cambridge, MA: Belknap Press of Harvard University.
- Mcdonough, W., and M. Braungart. 2002. *Cradle to Cradle: Remaking the Way We Make Things*. New York: North Point Press.
- McKean, M. A. 1981. *Environmental Protest and Citizen Politics in Japan*. Berkeley, Los Angeles, and London: University of California Press, 36–38.
- Morton, T. 2007. *Ecology: Without Nature. Rethinking Environmental Aesthetics*. Cambridge, MA, and London: Harvard University Press, 249.
- Neudert, R., I. Theesfeld, A. Didebulidze, B. Allahverdiyeva, and V. Beckmann. 2020. "Understanding causes of conflict over common village pastures—a comparative analysis of property rights in Azerbaijan and Georgia." *Society and Natural Resources* 33, no. 3: 347–67.
- NORC. 2020. "NORC Final Report: Assessing Progress in Reducing Child Labor in Cocoa Production in Cocoa Growing Areas of Côte d'Ivoire and Ghana." Chicago, IL: University of Chicago.
- Ow, D. W., K. V. Wood, M. Deluca, J. R. DeWet, D. R. Helinkski, and S. H. Howell. 1986. "Transient and stable expression of the firefly luciferase gene in plant cells and transgenic plants." *Science* 234: 856–59.
- Schorger, A. 1955. *The Passenger Pigeon*. Madison: University of Wisconsin Press.
- Sethi, S. P. 2003. *Setting Global Standards: Guidelines for Creating Codes of Conduct in Multinational Corporations*. Hoboken, NJ: John Wiley & Sons, Inc.
- Spierling, S., C. Rottger, V. Venkatachalam, M. Mudersbach, C. Herrmann, and H. Endres. 2018. *Procedia CIRP* 69: 573–78.
- Taylor, P. 1986. *Respect for Nature: A Theory of Environmental Ethics*. Princeton, NJ: Princeton University Press.
- UNEP. 2012. www.unep.org.

CHAPTER 3

Matter, Energy, and the Environment

Case Study: San Diego Bay's Green Sea Turtles

In many ways, endangered green sea turtles (Chelonia mydas) are emblematic flagships for the oceans. They are truly unique, for their habitat stretches from hundreds to thousands of kilometers across multiple terrestrial and aquatic ecosystems. They are also one of the largest reptile species, weighing up to 395 kg (871 lbs) and having shell lengths of up to 152.4 cm (60 in). These enigmatic creatures begin their long lives on land. After hatching, baby turtles make a hazardous scramble away from avian and terrestrial predators to the "safety" of the open ocean, until they return years later.

A small population of green sea turtles inhabits San Diego Bay, in California, but for how long remains unclear (see Figure 3.1). As one hypothesis hints, their origin dates back to the 1850s, when it was legal to catch and harvest sea turtles from Mexican waters. The numbers of sea turtles transported by the commercial turtling vessels during the mid- to late 1880s are impressive. For instance, an estimated one thousand turtles were sent to San Diego per month by a weekly schooner from Scammon's Lagoon in Baja California, Mexico (Townsend 1889).

FIGURE 3.1
San Diego Bay likely has the only year-round population of green sea turtles in the world. For fifty years, this population enjoyed the discharge waters from the Chula Vista power plant. A) A sailboat in San Diego Bay, with San Diego skyline in the background. B) An adult green sea turtle.

Source: © Shutterstock, Inc.

Into the first part of the twentieth century, turtle fishing was increasingly seen as a profitable business because turtles were numerous and easy to catch, and turtle products were considered valuable and eagerly purchased in major cities. Commercial fishers would haul their catch to San Diego Bay, among other ports, and then move the turtles from ships to holding ponds, where they resided until slaughter. In the first hypothesis, turtles routinely escaped into San Diego Bay. At that time, the National City Commercial Company based in San Diego was the largest producer of canned turtle foods, including a variety of soups, white meat, green meat, and oil derived from turtle fat. At peak yield in 1920, the California Fish and Game Commission reported almost 34,900 kg (77,000 lbs) of turtles brought into San Diego from Baja California (Radcliffe 1922). Just one year later, there were clear signs that sea turtle populations were no longer able to recover from large-scale harvesting, and in four years no turtles were delivered to San Diego.

Today, the green sea turtle is an endangered species, with a 48–67 percent decline in the number of nesting females in the last three generations. Therefore, information relating to the quality of green sea turtle habitat is of great interest to environmental scientists.

In a second hypothesis of their origin, turtles migrated to San Diego Bay. Either way, by escape from holding ponds or by migration, this population is different from all others on the West Coast because they are year-round residents. To our knowledge, all other green sea turtles regularly migrate long distances to nesting and foraging sites. What encourages these turtles to remain in one habitat, even during the winter, for such a prolonged period?

In 1958, to meet the electricity needs of a growing San Diego population, San Diego Gas and Electric Company began construction of an oil-fueled power plant on the south end of the bay in Chula Vista. The plant went online in 1960 and had the potential of generating up to 700 megawatts of electricity. This and other fossil fuel power plants, as well as nuclear power plants and industrial facilities, needed to cool machinery to prevent overheating. A common method in that era, and still used in some areas today, is to tap into a cool, natural aquatic resource. Hence, power plants and other facilities in need of a coolant are traditionally found alongside a river, lake, or coastline. They have water intake pipes to bring in cool water, and outlet pipes to return warm discharge back to the natural environmental system. The temperature of water discharged from the Chula Vista power plant reached up to 26.1°C (79°F), far higher than the bay's ambient temperature of 11.1°C (52°F), and the same temperature as warm Mediterranean Sea waters. Of course, the warm discharge dissipates when it mixes with the bay's water, but the result is a warmer, temperature-stable environment year round. Green sea turtles are drawn to the warm discharged waters, and they feed on the extensive beds of eelgrass in the bay.

From the perspective of a green sea turtle, a safe refuge against cold temperatures, where it can forage, would be valuable. Why expend valuable energy on unnecessary migration? All organisms depend on energy to maintain life, and adapting and evolving strategies to improve their energy efficiency can be beneficial. Sea turtles obtain their energy from the eelgrass and other foods they consume, but only a small fraction of the energy stored in the food is used for production by the turtle. Approximately 90% of the energy is lost as heat, and therefore, conserving energy by not migrating can be a good life strategy. Under year-round warm conditions, sea turtles have higher metabolisms and grow faster and larger than those in colder waters.

Based on the evidence provided so far, thermal energy from the Chula Vista power plant and similar facilities benefits sea turtles. However, there is more to this story. Natural sources of thermal energy in a pristine environmental system would be a positive for sea life, but this is not the case in San Diego Bay. This particular bay has an extensive history of pollutants, including persistent organic pollutants (POPs) polychlorinated biphenyls (PCBs), and heavy metals (Komoroske et al. 2011). According to the National Oceanic and Atmospheric Administration, San Diego Bay is the sixth most polluted bay in the entire United States. Up until 1979, PCBs were used in hundreds of products, such as caulks, paints, sealants, motor start capacitors, dental castings, printing inks, stucco, and insecticides. PCBs volatize out of products, do not readily break down in the environment, and are carried by storm water into the bay. Mercury, principally originating from power plants, also pollutes the bay. Environmental scientists are concerned about the green sea turtles in San Diego Bay because they are in a highly contaminated food web, and they have increased consumption rates compared to turtles living in cooler waters.

Widening our scope to include all green sea turtles, not just the small population in San Diego Bay, we then consider all power plants and other sources of greenhouse gases and begin to comprehend larger environmental issues. For example, greenhouse gas emissions and the resulting increase of global air temperatures have also affected water temperatures (see Chapter 11). Oceanic temperatures have increased, and even though the change has been small, it affects the sex ratio of green sea turtles (Jensen et al. 2018). Temperature is the key environment factor that determines the sex of developing turtles. A small increase in temperature easily sways the ratio to almost 100 percent females. Thus, global warming is causing feminization of green sea turtles at the global level. Having more females initially raises the number of clutches for the population, which can be beneficial. However, higher incubation temperatures also cause a high mortality of developing clutches (Hays et al. 2017). Furthermore, continued warming of waters can lead to extremely female-biased populations, which may create a problem for turtles in successfully finding mates. Sea turtles are facing other threats too, such as habitat destruction, illegal harvesting, by catch in commercial fisheries, and ocean acidification. The San Diego Bay population faces these threats in addition to the pollutants already mentioned.

As you can see, the plight of the green sea turtle is a result of society's non-sustainable activities, including the use of fossil fuels that release thermal pollution and physical pollution into the environment. This chapter builds on this story and focuses on energy and matter as basal parts of environmental issues.

3.1 Atoms and Molecules

Learning Objectives

1. Describe what matter is, and provide living and nonliving examples.
2. Explain the chemical structure of matter.
3. Identify some common atoms and molecules in living things.
4. List five molecules that are pollutants.

Sea turtles, the Chula Vista power plant, petroleum, and everything else that takes up space and has mass in the environment are examples of **matter**. All matter, whether a power plant or a person, consists of smaller building units, just as a house is made of bricks and boards. The larger structures eventually break down, returning their building blocks to the environment, where they are recycled into something new. For environmental scientists, understanding the structure of matter and how it cycles within the environment is an essential first step when planning sustainability efforts and solving environmental problems. For example, tracing carbon, sulfur, and mercury pollutants to coal combustion and other sources helps us to address climate change, acid rain, and bioaccumulation of contaminants in food chains.

Matter is conserved in chemical and physical transformations—in other words, matter cannot be created or destroyed. Instead, it cycles between living and nonliving structures and among the land, air, and water. This phenomenon is called the **Law of Conservation of Mass** (see video link: "Conservation of Mass").

matter
Anything that takes up space and has mass.

Law of Conservation of Mass
A physical law stating that matter cannot be created or destroyed in a chemical reaction. The atoms of matter are instead rearranged.

📹 **Conservation of Mass**

Learn more about the Law of Conservation of Mass.

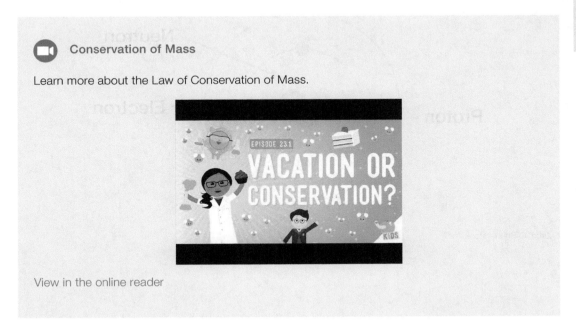

View in the online reader

The Atomic Theory of Matter

The idea that all matter consists of tiny structures called atoms dates back to the ancient Greeks. Other theories about what constitutes matter were proposed, but in 1803, the British chemist John

Dalton (1766–1844) published a very convincing atomic theory, including estimated masses of atoms known at that time (Dalton 1803). Our understanding of matter today is quite advanced from Dalton's ideas, but they all trace back to his pioneering work.

Atoms Are the Building Blocks of All Matter

Atoms are the smallest parts of **elements** still having their chemical properties, such as reactivity and flammability. Yet an atom contains even smaller structures called subatomic particles—electrons, protons, and neutrons. The number of subatomic particles in an atom is what gives its properties. **Electrons** (negatively charged) orbit around fixed **protons** (positive) and **neutrons** (neutral) at the nucleus in the center of the atom (see Figure 3.2). Scientists know of ninety-four naturally occurring elements and twenty-four more that have been synthesized artificially in huge atom-smashing machines, all listed for convenience in the periodic table (see Figure 3.3). Each element's name is abbreviated with one or two letters, based on its name in English or other language. Iron, for example, used in making steel, is abbreviated as Fe, from the Latin name *ferrum*. Carbon (symbol C) and hydrogen (symbol H) are examples of common elements found in green sea turtles and in other living things as well as in fossil fuels. The periodic table arranges elements by the number of protons within their atoms, with those in the same column having similar chemical properties. For example, carbon, with an **atomic number** of 6, has six protons, and is chemically similar to silicon directly below it.

FIGURE 3.2

Each atom—like this lithium atom—contains subatomic particles (protons, neutrons, and electrons). Protons and neutrons are located in the nucleus (center of the atom) and electrons orbit in shells (shown as lines) around the nucleus.

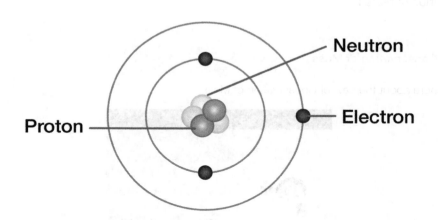

Source: © Shutterstock, Inc.

---

atoms

Small building blocks of matter. They are the smallest parts of an element that still have the element's chemical properties.

elements

Substances that cannot be broken down by ordinary chemical means into simpler substances.

electrons

Negative subatomic particles that moves around the nucleus of an atom.

protons

Positive subatomic particles located in the nucleus of an atom.

neutrons

A neutral subatomic particle found within the nucleus of an atom.

atomic number

The number of protons within an atom. Each element listed in the periodic table has a different atomic number.

FIGURE 3.3
The periodic table, partially shown here, lists all known elements in order of increasing atomic number. Every element has a name and a symbol. Arrows point out examples of common elements.

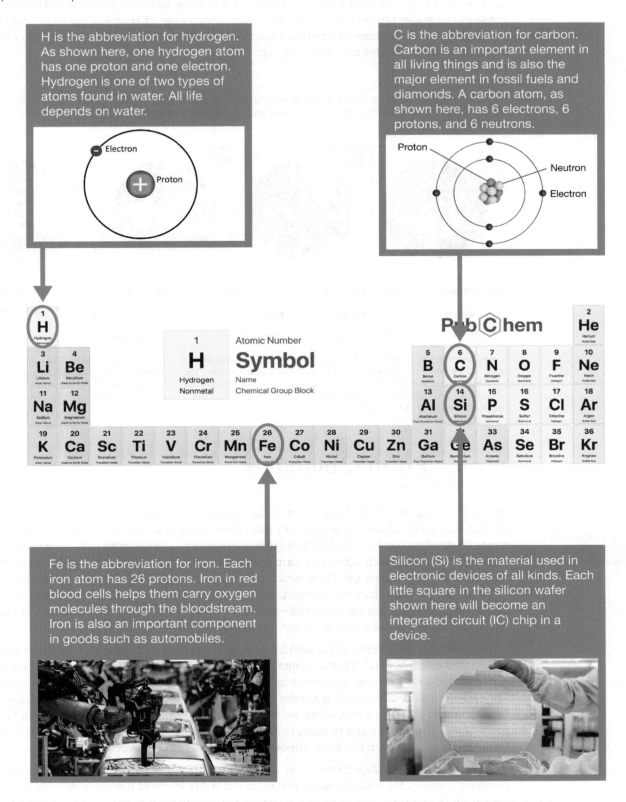

H is the abbreviation for hydrogen. As shown here, one hydrogen atom has one proton and one electron. Hydrogen is one of two types of atoms found in water. All life depends on water.

C is the abbreviation for carbon. Carbon is an important element in all living things and is also the major element in fossil fuels and diamonds. A carbon atom, as shown here, has 6 electrons, 6 protons, and 6 neutrons.

Fe is the abbreviation for iron. Each iron atom has 26 protons. Iron in red blood cells helps them carry oxygen molecules through the bloodstream. Iron is also an important component in goods such as automobiles.

Silicon (Si) is the material used in electronic devices of all kinds. Each little square in the silicon wafer shown here will become an integrated circuit (IC) chip in a device.

Sources: Joseph Shostell; National Library of Medicine: Periodic_Table_of_Elements_w_Chemical_Group_Block_PubChem.pdf; © Shutterstock, Inc.

Some elements are more common than others. By weight, oxygen is the most common element in Earth's crust, in the oceans, and in living things (see Figure 3.4). Within the atmosphere, oxygen is the second most common element (21 percent), following nitrogen (78 percent). However, if we consider the entire universe, hydrogen—the main component of stars—is the most common (75 percent). All of these elements constitute matter, but they are different from one another in number of subatomic particles, and therefore in properties.

FIGURE 3.4
Percentage of main elements (by weight) in (A) Earth's crust, (B) oceans, (C) atmosphere, and (D) animals. Oxygen is the most abundant element in the crust, oceans, and animals, and nitrogen is the most abundant element in the atmosphere.

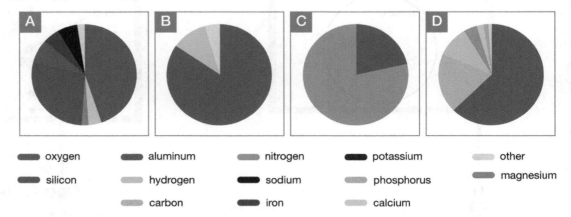

oxygen   aluminum   nitrogen   potassium   other

silicon   hydrogen   sodium   phosphorus   magnesium

carbon   iron   calcium

Source: Joseph Shostell; data from Michael Fleischer, "Recent Estimates of the Abundances of the Elements in the Earth's Crust," USGS, (1953), https://pubs.usgs.gov/circ/1953/0285/report.pdf; Alan Buis, "The Atmosphere: Getting a Handle on Carbon Dioxide," NASA News, October 9, 2019, https://climate.nasa.gov/news/2915/the-atmosphere-getting-a-handle-on-carbon-dioxide/#:~:text=By volume, the dry air,methane, nitrous oxide and ozone; JOHNSTONE, J. Chemical Composition of the Animal Body. Nature 130, 890 (1932). https://doi.org/10.1038/130890b0.

Atoms Form Molecules

ions

Atoms or small molecules that carry a positive or a negative charge.

Atoms bond together to make larger structures called molecules, such as sulfur dioxide, carbon dioxide, and water. When atoms join, they form chemical bonds. Two common types of bonds are ionic and covalent bonds. In ionic bonds, such as in sodium chloride (table salt), oppositely charged **ions** are attracted to each other and form strong electrical connections. Covalent bonds occur in molecules such as oxygen gas, O_2, in which two oxygen atoms share some electrons. Often, molecules consist of more than one element, so they are classified as compounds. The air pollutant sulfur dioxide (SO_2) is one such example—this one coming from industrial chimneys and tail pipes of cars. It consists of one sulfur atom and two oxygen atoms.

The effect of a molecule on the environment, or on another molecule, depends on its structure, including the number and types of atoms it has. A difference of one oxygen atom can turn oxygen gas, with two oxygen atoms (molecular formula O_2), to ozone, which has three oxygen atoms (O_3). The two-atom oxygen molecule is needed by most living things to burn fuel molecules (i.e., sugar) for energy and growth. Ozone, which we will discuss more completely in Chapter 11, can be found in the upper atmosphere and protects living things by absorbing harmful ultraviolet light coming from the sun. However, in the lower atmosphere it is a pollutant within smog.

Living things also depend on water (H_2O), which always makes up a high percentage of an organism's weight. For instance, water makes up about 60 percent of human body weight, and up to 95 percent of plants such as tomatoes. Why is water so important to life? Scientists describe water as a polar molecule, for it has a small amount of positive charge at the hydrogen ends and a small amount of negative charge at the oxygen end. Because of these "partial" charges, water molecules are strongly attracted to ionic materials such as salt and help dissolve them rapidly. Because so many different kinds of molecules can dissolve in water, it is an excellent medium for transporting food and other molecules throughout an organism, whether it's a sea turtle, a tree, or a human.

Organic Molecules Are Building Blocks of Life

All organisms are composed of abundant water as well as complex carbon-based compounds called organic molecules (see Table 3.1). The four main types of organic molecules in living things—**carbohydrates**, **proteins**, **nucleic acids**, and **lipids**—make up 80–90 percent of a cell's dry weight. The first three are polymers consisting of smaller repeating molecules called monomers. The type and arrangement of monomers help to determine a polymer's function.

Carbohydrates serve as raw materials for a cell's structure, and also as a source of energy. Glucose ($C_6H_{12}O_6$) is an example of a simple sugar and an example of a monomer (a monosaccharide) found in larger carbohydrates. Common examples of large complex carbohydrates (polysaccharides) are cellulose in plant cell walls, starch in plant cells, and glycogen in animal cells. Cellulose and starch are used to produce biofuels. Proteins are polymers of amino acids linked into chains, and serve a number of functions, from disease protection, to elasticity of skin, to upholding cell structure, to muscle contraction. The blueprints of these proteins are encoded in deoxyribonucleic acid (DNA), a nucleic acid polymer found in the nuclei of cells. Zoologists, ecologists, and environmental scientists take tissue samples of turtles and other organisms in the environment and then analyze their DNA to confirm species identification and to determine the diversity and genetic health of a population. The fourth group of complex organic molecules—lipids—contains fats, oils, waxes, phospholipids, and steroids. These molecules consist mostly of long chains of carbon atoms, with hydrogen atoms attached to the carbons, or in the case of steroids, ring structures. Steroid hormones coming from human and animal **excretions** and pharmaceutical waste enter the environment and disrupt aquatic organisms (Pratush et al. 2020). For example, metabolites of trenbolone used to increase the growth rate of cattle leach from urine and manure into nearby aquatic areas, where they lower the fecundity of fish and skew the sex ratios of fish populations (Stokstad 2013).

carbohydrates

Organic compounds usually with the formula $C_n(H_2O)_n$. Examples are sugars, starch, and cellulose.

proteins

Organic macromolecules composed of one or more chains of amino acids that are linked together by peptide bonds. Examples include enzymes, hemoglobin, hormones, and antibodies.

nucleic acids

Organic macromolecules that are polymers composed of nucleotide monomers. The two classes are DNA and RNAs. DNA contains the blueprint of proteins. RNA assists with protein synthesis.

lipids

Organic molecules that are composed of mostly carbons and hydrogens and do not dissolve in water. Examples are phospholipids, fats, and steroids.

excretions

Releasing of waste products by organisms.

TABLE 3.1

Living things have four main groups of complex organic molecules: carbohydrates, proteins, nucleic acids, and lipids. Each type of macromolecule consists of a particular subunit or group of subunits.

Main Groups of Complex Organic Molecules in Living Things	Monomer/Subunit	Example of Complex Organic Molecule
Carbohydrates	Glucose	Starch in potatoes (potential energy)
Proteins	Leucine	Hemoglobin, the iron-containing protein in red blood cells
Nucleic Acids	Nucleotide	Deoxyribonucleic acid (carries hereditary information)
Lipids	Fatty acid chain	Steroids (e.g., cholesterol, testosterone), fats, phospholipids (in cell membranes)

Some Compounds Threaten the Environment

The overabundance of particular molecular compounds due to society's activities threatens our environment and relates to global environmental issues. Sulfur dioxide and carbon dioxide, for example, originate from the combustion of fossil fuels and contribute to acid rain and climate change, respectively (see Chapter 11). Familiarize yourself with these and other molecules within Table 3.2 to better understand the sources and solutions of key global environmental issues.

TABLE 3.2
Atoms are structural building blocks of all matter. In certain combinations, atoms form molecules that can be very destructive to the environment.

Examples of Molecules That Are the Basis of Key Environmental Issues	The Compound Is Linked to This Environmental Issue
Carbon dioxide (CO_2)	Climate change
Methane (CH_4)	Climate change
Ozone (O_3)	Smog (ozone close to ground), loss of protective ozone (ozone higher in atmosphere)
Sulfur dioxide (SO_2)	Acid rain
Methyl mercury (CH_3Hg)	Mercury contamination/poisoning
DDT ($C_{14}H_9C_{15}$)	Reproductive success of birds, cancer
Nitrogen oxides (NO_x)	Acid rain
Phosphate (PO_4^{-3})	Cultural eutrophication

FIGURE 3.5
As you saw in Table 3.2, smog is an environmental issue. A) Los Angeles is covered by a thick blanket of smog from vehicular traffic. B) In Beijing, China, a young woman wears a mask during a smog day.

Source: © Shutterstock, Inc.

Isotopes Are Relevant in Nuclear Energy Applications

Isotopes are variants of elements that have the same number of protons, but a different number of neutrons. The most common isotopes of elements tend to be stable, but many elements have isotopes that are radioactive, which means they change into other elements by emitting energy, subatomic particles, or both. Common isotopes in nuclear power plants are uranium-235 (^{235}U), plutonium-239 (^{239}P), and uranium-233 (^{233}U). Note how the two different uranium atoms differ in their atomic mass, which is the number written next to the atomic symbol. The atomic mass is equal to the number of protons plus neutrons, so it is unlike the atomic number because it includes the number of neutrons, which can vary within an element.

isotopes

Variant forms of an element that have different numbers of neutrons.

Besides their usefulness in nuclear reactors, isotopes are also valuable in elucidating the diets of organisms. For example, ecologists used stable isotopes to show contrasting diets of small and large green sea turtles in Bermuda (Burgett et al. 2018). Large turtles almost exclusively feed on sea grasses, whereas smaller turtles have a mixed diet of plants and animals. We also use isotopes to find the age of fossils. Perhaps you have heard of carbon dating?

Ions, Acids, and Bases Are in Living Things and the Environment: Changes in Their Concentrations Have Consequences

Healthy organisms depend on the right concentrations of ions, acids, and bases. Simple ions are atoms that have lost or gained one or more electrons and thereby have acquired an electric charge. Polyatomic ions consist of several atoms bonded together and have a net electric charge as a group.

Plants and animals, including humans, require just the right concentration of ions to maintain good health. For example, deficiency of iron ions in animals (Tympa-Psirropoulou et al. 2008) or plants (Tindall et al. 2012) can have deadly consequences. Plants need iron to synthesize the chlorophyll molecules essential for absorbing sunlight during photosynthesis. Insufficient iron quickly leads to an easily observable pale or yellow color. In animals, iron ions are essential components of the hemoglobin used by red blood cells to transport oxygen. Insufficient iron levels—a form of anemia—result in a feeling of tiredness, and, if severe, could lead to death (Tympa-Psirropoulou et al. 2008).

acid

A substance that releases hydrogen ions (H$^+$) in a solution.

base

A substance that accepts hydrogen ions (H$^+$) in a solution.

An important factor in the health of an organism is the amount of hydrogen ions (H$^+$) and hydroxide ions (OH$^-$) in its biological fluids. Any substance that releases hydrogen ions in a solution is called an **acid**. Similarly, any substance that accepts hydroxide ions in a solution is a **base**. The two terms are complementary, meaning that a very acidic substance is a very poor base, and a very basic substance is a very weak acid. For proper health and body function, blood and other biological fluids must not be too acidic or too basic. This sensitivity to change in hydrogen ions makes living things susceptible to acid rain, which is one outcome of burning fossil fuels.

The pH Scale and Acid Rain

acidophiles

A group of species that thrive in highly acidic conditions.

We use the pH scale to report the concentration of hydrogen ions. The scale ranges from 0 to 14 and is counterintuitive because higher concentrations of hydrogen ions are equated to lower pH values. Take, for instance, orange juice. It is an acidic solution with a pH of around 3, whereas distilled water has a neutral pH value of 7 (see Figure 3.6). In contrast, bleach and similar cleaning solutions have much higher pH values, closer to 13. Environmental systems with very low pH conditions are stressful to most organisms except **acidophiles**, evidenced by little or no growth, inability to reproduce, and even death. For instance, pH values of 4.0 are lethal to many fish (Ikuta et al. 1992). Because excess hydrogen atoms, or acidification, is harmful to trees and aquatic organisms, environmental scientists are trying to identify sources of hydrogen atoms and, where possible, reduce or eliminate these sources.

One major source of hydrogen ions entering the environment is through burning of fossil fuels. Emissions of sulfur dioxide and nitrogen oxides from power plants combine with water in the atmosphere to form strong acids, and eventually acid rain. Not all sources of these atmospheric pollutants are equal. For instance, in considering our opening case study, automobiles in San Diego give off more nitrogen oxides in one day than the Chula Vista power plant did in one year. Keep these sorts of relative comparisons in your thoughts as you tackle environmental issues. Acid rain doesn't just harm plants and animals—over time, it can also destroy human-made objects such as buildings and monuments (see Figure 3.6) by corroding metals and weakening building materials. Limestone structures literally dissolve in the presence of acid rain. A pH value less than 7 does not necessarily mean there is an environmental concern, because normal nonpolluted rain and snow have a pH of around 5.6. However, acid rain with pH values less than 5.6 are a concern.

FIGURE 3.6

pH is a measure of the number of hydrogen ions in a solution. A) pH scale with some examples. The number of hydrogen ions increases as pH declines; solutions with pH values lower than 7 are acidic, and those higher than 7 are basic. A one-unit difference in pH—say, from 5 to 6—is equal to a ten-fold increase in the number of hydrogen ions. Therefore, a small change in pH can have drastic consequences for organisms dependent on a stable concentration of hydrogen ions. B) In Germany, a forest of Norway spruce trees that died as a result of acid rain. C) Years of exposure to acid rain have erased much of the detail from this sandstone sculpture in Cambodia.

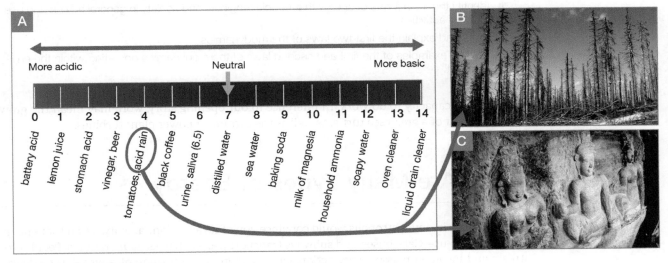

Sources: Joseph Shostell; © Shutterstock, Inc.

Key Takeaways

- Anything (turtles, humans, water, etc.) that takes up space and has mass in the environment is an example of matter.
- Atoms are the building blocks of matter.
- Atoms join to form molecules.
- Organic molecules (carbohydrates, proteins, nucleic acids, and lipids) are building blocks of life.
- Some compounds threaten the environment.
- Isotopes are relevant in nuclear energy applications.
- Ions, acids, and bases are in living things and the environment. Changes in their concentrations have consequences.

3.2 All Forms of Energy Follow Natural Laws

1. Identify the main forms of energy that people, engines, and society in general rely on and use for daily activities.
2. State and explain the first two laws of thermodynamics.
3. Provide examples of the first and second laws of thermodynamics operating within the environment.

Energy is the capacity to do work. In reference to our opening story, work may mean the growth and movement of a green sea turtle, as well as the turning of power plant turbines.

There Are Many Types of Energy

A quick glance in any metropolis would convince you of its abundant activity, a sign that energy is present and in use. Cars, buses, and subways transport people. Trucks haul products. People crowd streets and move en masse. Every action, either a step or the turning of a wheel, is evidence of energy being used, much of it originating from the sun. What are the different types of energy and how do they relate to issues in environmental science?

Kinetic Energy and Potential Energy

kinetic energy

Energy of motion.

potential energy

Stored energy.

Kinetic energy is energy of motion. Cars driving on the road, people walking on the street, and electromagnetic radiation from the sun (see Figure 3.7) are examples of kinetic energy. Stored energy is **potential energy**. For example, gasoline has potential energy; that is, energy that can be used at a later time. Upon combustion, its potential energy is transformed into kinetic energy. Combustion also produces heat, which is lost to the surroundings.

The main sources of energy that society relies upon include petroleum, natural gas, coal, nuclear, hydroelectric, wind, solar, and geothermal. The first three sources—petroleum, natural gas, and coal—are called fossil fuels because they formed from vegetation buried in the ground and subjected to heat and pressure over millions of years. Fossil fuels are nonrenewable energy sources, which means we can't make more of them. The latter four, however, are renewable. Hydroelectric refers to the generation of electricity from flowing water. Similarly, we use wind energy and solar energy to produce electricity. The last renewable energy, geothermal, refers to Earth's internal heat. It too can be transformed into electricity. Each of these sources, whether nonrenewable or renewable, has positive and negative attributes (see Chapter 13 and Chapter 14).

FIGURE 3.7

All energy falls into two types, potential or kinetic. An example of potential energy, also known as stored energy, is the chemical energy within gasoline in a car's tank (A). Examples of energy in motion (kinetic energy) are (B) a speeding car and (C) the range of electromagnetic radiation (ER) types within the electromagnetic spectrum. ER types differ in size of wavelength (distance between crests of successive waves).

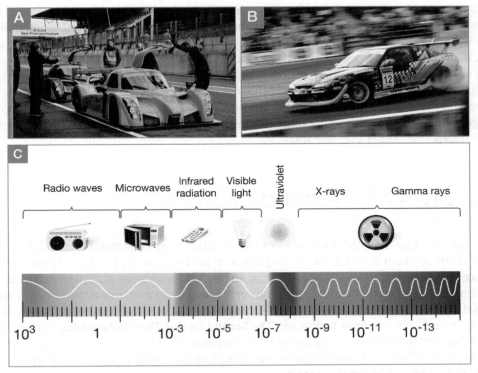

Sources: defotoberg/Shutterstock.com; Jordan Tan/Shutterstock.com; © Shutterstock, Inc.

Nuclear energy comes from uranium used in nuclear power plants. Petroleum, natural gas, and coal are examples of **chemical energy**, a type of potential energy within the bonds between atoms that can be transformed into another form of energy—thermal energy (heat), and then electrical energy. We rely on electrical energy to power lamps, appliances, computers, cell phones, and televisions in our homes. Overall, nuclear energy provides approximately 20 percent of the electricity in the United States. We still rely on nuclear energy, even considering environmental problems due to nuclear waste generation, because one gram of uranium has far more potential energy than one gram of coal. In fact, it only takes 8.5 grams (0.3 oz) of uranium to produce the same amount of energy as one ton of coal!

Our food contains energy too (see Figure 3.8). Energy is stored in the chemical bonds of the food's organic molecules when they form, and this energy is released when the bonds are broken. Hikers and mountain climbers often carry small hard candies packed with sugar to help "fuel" themselves in their activities. In these cases, potential energy stored within food molecules is transformed into human actions of hiking or climbing, both examples of kinetic energy. This energy transformation is also not perfect—body heat is lost through the skin and lungs to the external environment.

FIGURE 3.8

Food is a source of fuel for us. A runner in the Krispy Kreme Challenge in Raleigh, North Carolina, eats a donut to have sufficient energy to complete the race.

Source: EPG_EuroPhotoGraphics/Shutterstock.com

chemical energy

Energy stored within bonds of molecules.

Heat

heat

Energy transferred from an object of higher temperature to an object of lower temperature.

convection

The transfer of heat through air or water.

thermal radiation

Transfer of heat by electromagnetic radiation between two objects not in direct contact with each other.

conduction

The transfer of heat through solid matter.

conservation of energy law

Also called the First Law of Thermodynamics; energy can't be created or destroyed.

Second Law of Thermodynamics

Every energy conversion results in a lower quality and less usable energy for performing work.

omnivore

An animal that consumes animals and plants.

entropy

A measure of disorder or randomness of a system.

Up to this point we have considered heat as simply unusable energy that has been "lost" during energy transformations. However, **heat** is itself a form of energy—energy being transferred from one object to another. Some homeowners use **convection**—the transfer of heat through the movement of molecules in air or water—to warm up their houses. People also rely on **thermal radiation**, which is a direct transfer of heat by electromagnetic radiation (e.g., light, infrared, etc.) from a body with a high temperature to a body with a low temperature. On a small scale, space heaters and fireplaces are good examples of this. In contrast, large amounts of heat are transferred from the sun by radiation every day. You feel the effect of this, for example, as the heat warming your face when you stand outside on a sunny day. Heat is also transferred via **conduction**—the transfer of heat through solid matter—such as in stovetop coils heating up a frying pan. In all of these cases, heat always travels from hotter to cooler areas.

The Laws of Thermodynamics

When engineers first designed the Chula Vista power plant, they understood it would abide by the laws of thermodynamics, just as everything else does in the universe. The first, the **conservation of energy law**, states that the total amount of energy in the universe always remains the same. Therefore, energy is neither created nor destroyed. Energy, however, can move between systems within the universe, such as between Chula Vista's power plant and San Diego Bay. Energy can also be transformed from one form to another. The **Second Law of Thermodynamics** states that with each energy transformation, energy becomes less usable to perform work. The energy is still there, but it is more diffuse, and due to limitations in technologies we are unable to recover this less usable energy before it leaves the system.

Based on these laws and available technology, the engineers at the Chula Vista power plant knew the new facility would not be very efficient. In the end, they constructed a power plant system capable of converting a little over 31 percent of the energy stored in oil into electricity; the remainder, some 69 percent, was lost from the power plant as heat to the surrounding environment. This lost heat is considered an example of thermal pollution. The Chula Vista power plant increased its efficiency when it switched from oil to natural gas, but the power plant still fell short of transforming all of the potential energy within a primary energy source (i.e., oil and natural gas) into electricity. Very similarly, only a small percentage of energy stored in eelgrass is passed onto the **omnivore**, in this case, the green sea turtle.

The engineers also understood that every energy transformation increases the randomness or disorder of the matter within a system. We use the term **entropy** as a measure of this disorder. Therefore, as the system becomes more disordered, entropy increases. Now, let's consider specific physical systems. Arbitrarily, we may define a lump of coal or a liter of petroleum as a system. The entropy in these systems increases when the physical structures of the systems degrade to ash and smoke. In these cases, the end physical products are wastes. Therefore, the planning of a new power plant must consider waste removal. What about living things? Green sea turtles mentioned in the opening story replenish their energy by eating eelgrass. Organisms require a constant supply of energy to run the ongoing chemical reactions needed to maintain their structure and essential bodily functions. Like the power plant, they also lose energy to the surrounding environment with every energy transformation.

Key Takeaways

- Energy is neither created nor destroyed, but it can be transformed.

- With each energy transformation, the overall amount of energy useful for doing work declines.
- There are two general forms of energy: kinetic and potential.
- The main sources of energy that society relies upon include petroleum (NR), natural gas (NR), coal (NR), nuclear (NR), hydroelectric (R), wind (R), solar (R), and geothermal (R). NR=nonrenewable, R=renewable.

3.3 Environmental Structure and Energy Flow

Learning Objectives

1. Identify the characteristics of life.
2. Explain the structural organization of an organism.
3. Outline the interactions of species within terrestrial and aquatic food chains, focusing on energy transformations.

All living things are made of matter and depend on energy. In this regard, they are similar to the Chula Vista power plant in the opening story. Nevertheless, living things stand apart because they have specific traits we refer to as the characteristics of life. Can you come up with some of them before reading further? Perhaps the ones most applicable to our discussion about structure and energy flow are that living things have cells and use energy.

Structural Organization and Abilities of Organisms

A cell consists of several structural levels, from subatomic particles to macromolecules, but what about the structural levels in more complex, multicellular creatures? In highly complex multicellular organisms, cells work harmoniously together in tissues, and tissues in turn work collectively within organs, which are components of organ systems (see Figure 3.9). Every structural level above the cell provides additional abilities, also known as emergent properties. Consider for a moment the structure and abilities of a single brain cell (a neuron) versus a brain, which is an organ. If you are given a choice between taking a test using a single brain cell or doing so using your entire brain, you might be quick to say "brain." Individual neurons can communicate with each other and answer very challenging questions when working together as part of the brain. However, thinking is an ability that a single neuron does not have.

Some advanced organisms have all of these structural levels, but there are also self-sufficient organisms existing at each level. For instance, an amoeba lives at the single-cell level, and a sponge lives at the multicellular level and has no tissues. The abilities of each organism are limited by the level of its structure.

FIGURE 3.9

Levels of organization in living things. Atoms, molecules, cells, tissues, organs, and organ systems are the hierarchal levels in complex animals such as human beings. It's important to note that many organisms consist of single cells, so they do not have higher levels of complexity.

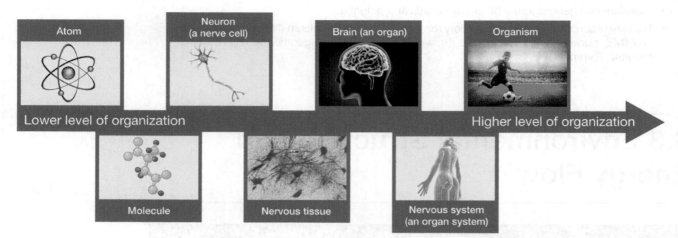

Source: Joseph Shostell; © Shutterstock, Inc.

Chemical Reactions in Living Things

metabolism

The ongoing reactions in a living thing.

anabolic

Promoting anabolism (metabolic process of building molecules).

catabolic

Promoting catabolism (metabolic process of breaking down complex molecules).

autotrophs

Organisms that can make their own food, such as through the process of photosynthesis.

adenosine triphosphate

The main energy currency molecule in living things. Potential energy is stored in the bonds between its phosphate groups.

All living things have a **metabolism**, whereby molecules are built up in **anabolic** processes and molecules are broken down through **catabolic** processes (see Figure 3.10). Two examples of metabolic processes in living things are photosynthesis, used to synthesize sugar; and cellular respiration, used to break down sugar. The following equation is a summary of the reactions of photosynthesis:

$$\text{carbon dioxide}(6CO_2) + \text{water}(6H_2O) + \text{solar energy} \rightarrow \text{glucose }(C_6H_{12}O_{6)} + \text{oxygen }(6O_2)$$

In photosynthesis, plants depend on chloroplasts to absorb solar energy and drive the synthesis of sugars and other carbohydrates. Animal cells do not have these structures, and as a result they must rely on plants and other **autotrophs** for their energy demands (see Figure 3.10). As seen here, the summary reaction for cellular respiration is the opposite of that for photosynthesis:

$$\text{glucose }(C_6H_{12}O_2) + \text{oxygen }(6O_2) \rightarrow \text{ carbon dioxide }(6CO_2) + \text{water }(6H_2O) + \text{energy}$$

Sea turtles, for instance, feed on and digest plants and other animals, breaking organismal parts into small molecules that move from the digestive tract into the bloodstream, and from there to individual cells. There, at the cellular level, the simple molecules are used for ongoing repairs, growth, and fuel. Take for instance, glucose. Cells in most animals and in some plants can link monomers of glucose together to form the polysaccharide glycogen. Cells can also break the chemical bonds of glucose and transform some of its stored energy into newly formed chemical bonds within **adenosine triphosphate** (ATP) molecules. The remaining energy is lost from the cell as heat. Each of the many reactions involved in breaking down and building molecules is reliant on enzymes, which are a type of protein. Since the blueprint of every protein synthesized in the body is encoded in DNA, we have a vested interest in protecting our DNA from harmful pollutants that might damage it.

FIGURE 3.10
Activities that disassemble and assemble molecules (catabolic and anabolic metabolism, respectively) inside a cell can be likened to the (A) demolition and (B) construction of buildings. C) In photosynthetic organisms such as this sunflower, sunlight drives a series of cellular reactions that break apart molecules of carbon dioxide and water (catabolism) to drive the synthesis of sugar molecules (anabolism).

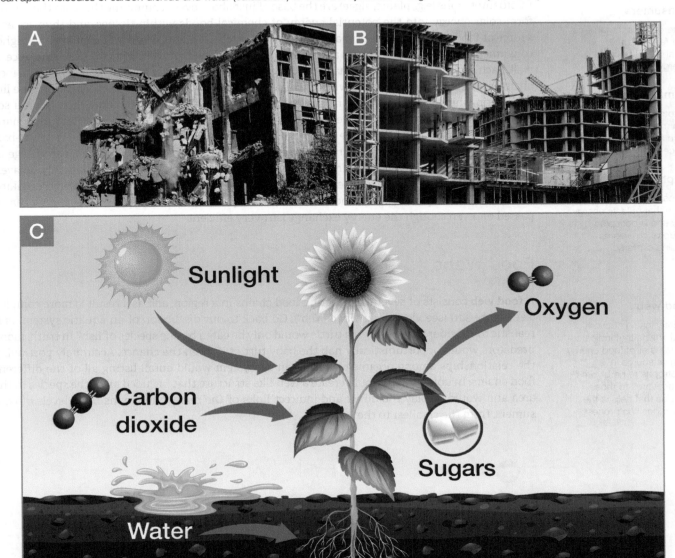

Source: © Shutterstock, Inc.

Species Make Up Communities

No animal or plant is completely isolated from all others. Similarly, no species—or group of individuals within one species—is completely isolated from all other species. What we observe in the environment is a complex network of organisms that interact with one another in a community.

Food Chains and Energy Transfers

consumers

Heterotrophs; organisms that feed on other organisms to obtain energy and nutrients.

primary producer

Autotroph; organism that can make its own food, such as through the process of photosynthesis.

trophic level

A position in the food chain that reflects energy flow and is occupied by a group of organisms feeding similarly.

Photoautotrophs (e.g., plants, algae) are the base of just about every community because they transform solar energy into the potential energy of chemical bonds within tissues, and thus act as a source of food and energy for primary **consumers**, which eat plants directly. Secondary and higher consumers eat primary consumers and therefore indirectly depend on plants for their existence as well. Each separate level, from **primary producer** at the base to higher levels of consumers in a food chain, is called a **trophic level**, in which "trophic" refers to nutrition. Putting this together, the linear relationships within food chains depict food pathways and indicate energy flow. Do you see why environmental scientists strive to protect trees, shrubs, and algae? San Diego Bay offers many examples of food chains (see "Case Study: San Diego Bay's Green Sea Turtles"). One is a four-part chain of predatory fish, baby sea turtle, invertebrate, and eelgrass. A much larger percentage of energy is lost than is passed on during energy transfers between organisms. Remarkably, an average of 90 percent is lost as unusable energy, which means that only 10 percent is passed on, making this another example of the Second Law of Thermodynamics. Life depends on the energy that is passed on, even though the energy exchange isn't very efficient.

Food Webs

food web

An interlinking network of food chains that indicate the transfer of food energy from its source in autotrophs to herbivores to carnivores to those species that help in the decomposition process.

A **food web** consists of several interacting food chains in a region, and as a result is more complex (see Figure 3.11) (see video link: "Food Web"). Go back to our discussion of an aquatic system. Is it realistic to consider that a baby sea turtle would only be eaten by one species of fish? In truth, many predators would opportunistically nab the baby turtles if given the chance. Accurately portraying the relationships among organisms within an ecosystem would entail listing all of the different food chains. In doing so, we would create a web-like structure that included all of the species in the area and would display the direct and indirect links of the many autotrophs to all levels of consumers, from the smallest to the largest.

 Food Web

Enter a kelp forest and explore a coastal food web.

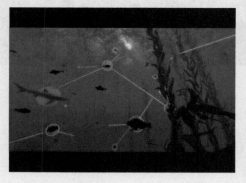

View in the online reader

FIGURE 3.11
Food webs consist of food chains. (A) A food web in a deciduous forest of North America. Notice the many arrows showing how all of the organisms are connected to one another, either directly or indirectly. (B) Look for the individual food chains that make up the larger food web.

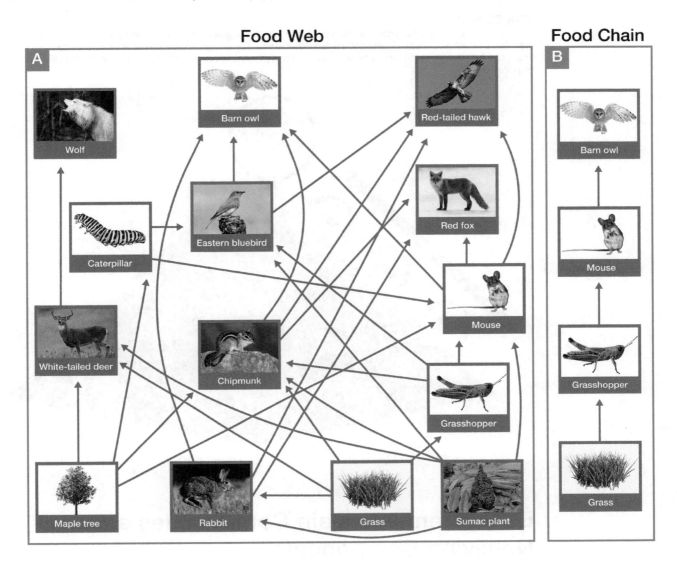

Source: Joseph Shostell; © Shutterstock, Inc.

Energy Pyramid

The concept of a pyramid is used to show the funneling of energy from autotrophs to apex predators (see Figure 3.12). Each rung position of the pyramid, whether that of a consumer or a producer (the autotroph), is considered a trophic level. With this in mind, a simplistic food web of only three organisms—say, grass, grasshopper, and mouse—would have three trophic levels. Our knowledge of inefficient energy transfer between trophic levels allows us to make predictions as to how many top predators can exist within an environment.

The structure of the energy pyramid suggests that as you move up in trophic level, less energy is available for the next level to use. Consequently, the mass of those organisms at a higher trophic level must be less than that of any below it. Is this true? Mostly yes, except we should also consider that not all organisms grow at the same rate. Also, the current mass of the primary producers that are transforming sunlight into tissues might not be that much different from that of those that eat them. A primary consumer such as a cow does need to meet its energy demands, but on the whole, it grows much more slowly than the grass it eats. What would you conclude about the number of possible trophic levels within an environment?

FIGURE 3.12
Energy pyramid, in which energy is transferred from one trophic level to the next. Energy is lost during each transfer, so each successive level contains a smaller amount of energy. By the time energy passes to the top level, most of it has already been lost as heat. Thus, only a relatively few number of upper-level predators can be supported.

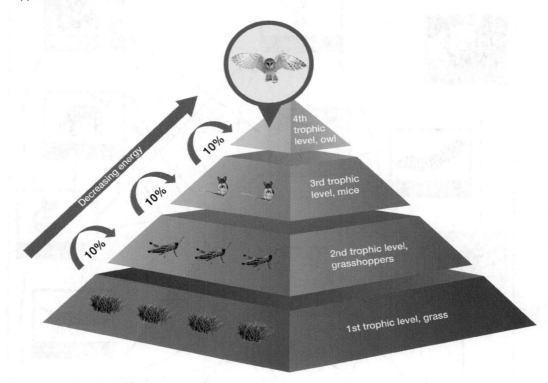

Source: Joseph Shostell; © Shutterstock, Inc.

Ecosystems Contain Communities and Nonliving Components

Ecosystems (see Chapter 1) are one of the hierarchal levels of the environment, one step up from a community. They are a combination of the living and the nonliving components of the environment and their interactions. The world consists of many different ecosystems, and each one contains matter and energy. One example is a deciduous forest ecosystem whose trees lose their leaves in the fall. Besides living trees, this ecosystem has animals, bacteria, and fungi, as well as nonliving soil particles, rocks, and any present surface waters. Matter cycles between and within the living and nonliving compartments. Energy from living things is also lost as heat to the larger environment. Pulling from our case study, another example of an ecosystem is San Diego Bay with its contaminated sediments, eelgrass, and green sea turtles.

Physical Laws and the Environment

Solving environmental pollution problems is a priority for environmental scientists. A study of the Conservation of Mass Law and the first two laws of thermodynamics can help us solve these problems. The Conservation of Mass Law states matter cannot be destroyed during chemical or physical transformation. Atoms can be rearranged into different molecules, but they don't disappear. This knowledge makes us reconsider how we deal with accumulated pollutants, and how we prevent them from being generated in the first place. Transforming a toxic pollutant from a solid to a gas, for example, may make it invisible to the naked eye, but the toxin is still present in the environment, so it can still negatively affect living things.

In our study of the Second Law of Thermodynamics, we learn that entropy (disorder) increases with energy transformations, and, indirectly, by using energy we generate waste. For instance, when we burn wood—a highly ordered (has low entropy) substance—we disperse heat, release smoke, and generate ash. Lessons learned here and applied to society's wider use of different types of energy helps us to prioritize our choices of fuels based on type and quantity of wastes and the effects these wastes have on the environment. One of our priorities is to avoid sources of energy that when used release greenhouse gases and nitric oxides, because these pollutants become highly dispersed (high entropy) and extremely difficult and expensive to recapture.

Remember, waste energy typically stays in its less useable state, whereas matter is used again in endless cycles of building and breaking. Think about the uncaptured heat "lost" to San Diego Bay in the opening story. However, unusable energy by human standards can still have an influence in nature. The low-quality energy (heat) stemming indirectly from society's burning of fossil fuels, for example, is absorbed by oceans and has a profound effect upon global weather patterns. Although a good portion of this low-quality energy will remain unusable to us, new developments in technology enable us to harness and utilize some of this lower-quality energy to perform work. As an example, windmills today are more sensitive than in the past and can now use slower winds to generate electricity.

Key Takeaways

- Living things are made of matter and depend on energy.
- An organism's structure and ability are linked.
- Species are part of food chains and food webs in communities.
- Ecosystems include communities and nonliving components.
- Knowledge of the first two laws of thermodynamics and the Conservation of Mass Law helps us to understand and solve pollution problems.

3.4 Biogeochemical Cycles

Learning Objectives

1. Explain how the cycling of matter connects the living and nonliving components of ecosystems.
2. Describe four examples of biogeochemical cycles in the environment.

lithosphere

The compartment in the environment that consists of rocks.

biosphere

A compartment in the environment that consists of living things only.

As we learned earlier this chapter from studying the Law of Conservation of Mass, physical matter can neither be created nor destroyed. When we apply this knowledge to elements, we understand that elements cycle among Earth's compartments: the atmosphere, **lithosphere** (rock), hydrosphere, and **biosphere** (living things). Therefore, individual atoms can be billions of years old. A carbon atom in your body may have already spent hundreds of years as part of carbon dioxide in the atmosphere and hundreds of millions of years as coal in the ground. This same atom may have been part of carbon dioxide dissolved in the oceans before it was taken up by algae to build carbohydrates and, in turn, by larger aquatic organisms that eat the algae. The movement of an element's atoms among Earth's departments is called a biogeochemical cycle (see video: " Biogeochemical Cycles "). Some of the more important biogeochemical cycles to living things are those for carbon, nitrogen, phosphorus, and sulfur. Besides elements, water also cycles among these compartments and has its own biogeochemical cycle.

 Biogeochemical Cycles

Listen to Paul Anderson give an overview of biogeochemical cycles.

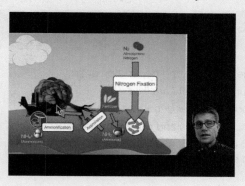

View in the online reader

The Hydrologic Cycle

Of all the biogeochemical cycles, water's biogeochemical cycle (**water cycle**) is most familiar to us (see Figure 3.13). Water covers about 71 percent of Earth's surface. We drink it, cook with it, swim in it, and a good portion of our bodies is composed of water. Water is a small molecule consisting of two hydrogens and one oxygen atom, and as in other biogeochemical cycles, it moves amongst Earth's enivornmental compartments. In addition, it can exist as a liquid, gas, or solid.

water cycle

Also called the hydrologic cycle; the repeated movement (a cycle) of water on, above, and below Earth's surface involving the atmosphere, oceans, aquifers, soils, glaciers, lakes, rivers, and living things. The continuous process includes evaporation, condensation, precipitation, surface runoff, transpiration, and storage.

FIGURE 3.13
The water cycle. All water on Earth is connected through the water cycle (shown here). Arrows depict the movement of water between departments.

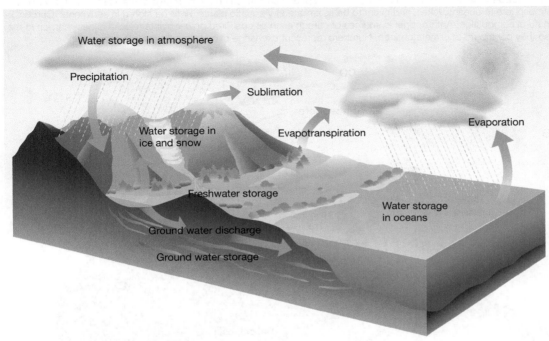

Source: Joseph Shostell; © Shutterstock, Inc.

Surface waters evaporate to gas form and become part of the atmosphere. Air near the ground warms up, expands, and moves upward, carrying the water vapor with it. As the parcels of air move further from the ground, they cool, and water within condenses. Eventually, precipitation forms and comes down on terrestrial and aquatic areas alike. Depending on the temperature, it can be rain, snow, or hail. In warm areas, liquid water infiltrates the soil and becomes part of ground water, and when it comes in contact with impervious material, it will collect and form an **aquifer**. Water moves into the biosphere when, for example, plant roots uptake it from the soil or when animals drink it. Another route of moving liquid water into water vapor is through **transpiration**. In this process, water moves through roots to leaves and then out pores to the atmosphere. In cold climates, for example in polar areas, snow and ice form and can tie up water molecules for hundreds to thousands of years. Yet, as part of a planet-wide cycle, it is entirely possible for you to drink the same water molecules that, in the past, were stored in the ground, part of a glacier, within the atmosphere, or within another living thing.

aquifer

When water infiltrating the ground comes in contact with impervious material and collects.

transpiration

Water is transported from roots to leaves of plants and then moves through pores into the atmosphere.

The Carbon Cycle

carbon cycle

The movement (cycling) of carbon among Earth's departments (biosphere, hydrosphere, lithosphere, atmosphere).

Many sources of carbon appear in the **carbon cycle**, including anthropogenic ones such as emissions from automobiles (see Figure 3.14). Natural concentrations of carbon dioxide in the atmosphere are expected, but elevated levels due to anthropogenic factors are linked to rapid climate change.

FIGURE 3.14

The carbon cycle. Carbon cycles among the biosphere, atmosphere, lithosphere, and hydrosphere compartments. Photosynthesis moves carbon from the atmosphere into the biosphere. When animals and plants respire, they release carbon to the atmosphere; when they die, carbon in their tissues is recycled by decomposers. Carbon is naturally stored in the ground (lithosphere) until taken up by microorganisms. Carbon in the form of carbon dioxide moves from the atmosphere to oceans, lakes, and rivers to be assimilated by aquatic plants, or to be stored in sediments. Carbon also comes from volcanoes and natural combustion. Anthropogenic sources of carbon such as coal-fired power plants release excess carbon in the form of CO_2 to the atmosphere, so they contribute to climate change. Numbers represent exchange of carbon per year in gigatons (Gt).

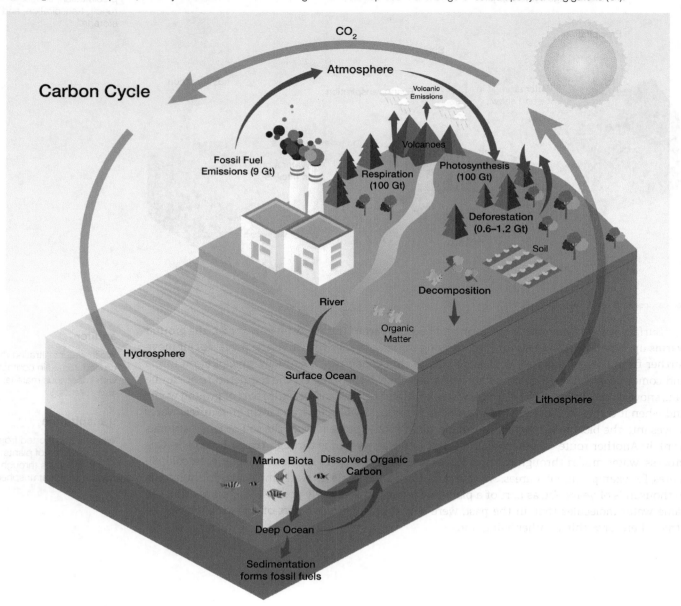

Carbon in the form of carbon dioxide is a product of respiration and is released to the atmosphere by many living things. In turn, it is taken back up by plants during photosynthesis and then stored within plant tissues. The stored carbon atoms, now in molecules within plants, become part of the food chain and are consumed and incorporated into higher and higher trophic levels. Eventually, the organisms holding on to these carbons die. Then bacteria and fungi colonize the remains, helping to cycle the carbon atoms back into the biosphere. Overall, just a small fraction of Earth's carbon is found within the biosphere at any given time; most—some 99 percent—of carbon is stored, long-term, in the lithosphere. About 5 trillion tons of this amount is within fossil fuels, which is significantly greater than the total in the atmosphere (750 billion tons), but less than that found in oceans (40 trillion tons).

Note the connecting arrows in Figure 3.14, for they show the direction of movement and links among compartments. Even carbon stored in gasoline, created through a process extending over millions of years, becomes released as carbon dioxide when combusted. Although less than half of a percent of the atmosphere is carbon dioxide, small changes in this concentration can have large effects on global temperatures.

The Nitrogen Cycle

A large percentage of our atmosphere (78 percent) consists of **nitrogen gas**, which is a molecule of two nitrogen atoms covalently bonded together (N_2) (see Figure 3.15). The stable nitrogen atoms in this molecule are unusable to most organisms. Nitrogen gas, therefore, presents a dilemma for these organisms because nitrogen is a critical component of nucleic acids, proteins, and vitamins. A critical step in the **nitrogen cycle** is the conversion of nitrogen gas (N_2) to ammonia (NH_3) and **ammonium** (NH_4^+) by a few species of bacteria and **archaea** (see Figure 3.17). This step is called **nitrogen fixation**, and the organisms involved in the process are called nitrogen fixers. Some nitrogen fixers such as blue-green algae (cyanobacteria) inhabit lakes and other aquatic ecosystems. Nitrogen-fixing bacteria also live in nodules on the roots of pea plants and other legumes. Farmers strategically use legumes with their symbiotic nitrogen-fixing bacteria to increase the nitrogen content in soil and then yearly alternate between planting legumes and planting non-legume crops (e.g., corn).

nitrogen gas

N_2; the form of nitrogen in the atmosphere.

nitrogen cycle

The movement (cycling) of nitrogen among Earth's departments (biosphere, lithosphere, hydrosphere, atmosphere). Key parts of the nitrogen cycle include nitrogen fixation, nitrification, ammonification, and denitrification.

ammonium

NH_4^+; a form of nitrogen that is created through nitrogen fixation.

archaea

Unicellular microorganisms that do not have nuclei or membrane-bound organelles and are of the domain Archaea.

nitrogen fixation

The conversion of the inert nitrogen gas in the atmosphere to nitrogen compounds that can be used by living things.

FIGURE 3.15
Composition of air.

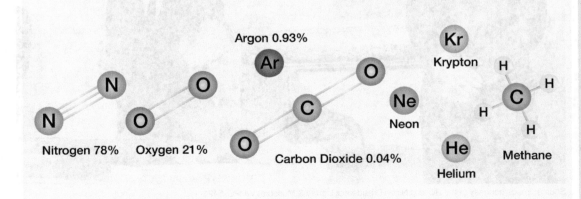

Nitrogen 78%   Oxygen 21%   Argon 0.93%   Carbon Dioxide 0.04%   Krypton   Neon   Helium   Methane

Source: © Shutterstock, Inc.

nitrite

NO$_2^-$; a form of nitrogen that can be used by most living things.

nitrate

NO$_3^-$; a form of nitrogen that can be used by most living things.

herbivores

Organisms that eat only plants.

denitrification

Conversation of nitrates and other nitrogen-containing compounds to nitrogen gas.

eutrophication

Enrichment of nutrients and increase of phytoplankton in bodies of water.

In the second step of the nitrogen cycle, nitrification, ammonia and ammonium are chemically converted by bacteria to **nitrite** (NO$_2^-$) and to **nitrate** (NO$_3^-$). Plants use their roots to take in ammonia, ammonium, and nitrate, and then the plants incorporate nitrogen into organic molecules they build. **Herbivores** and omnivores eat the plants and use the nitrogen-containing organic molecules to meet their own metabolic needs and build their own organic molecules. Upon death, nitrogen locked up in the organic molecules of plants and animals and other life forms is recycled by fungi and bacteria that colonize remains. The organic nitrogen in the remains is chemically converted to NH$_3$ and NH$_4^+$ in a process called ammonification.

In the reverse of nitrogen fixation, another group of bacteria (denitrifiers) chemically convert nitrate to nitrogen gas. This process—**denitrification**—occurs in low-oxygen areas such as in bogs.

Humans have unbalanced the nitrogen cycle by adding nitrogen-containing synthetic fertilizers to croplands and by adding to the atmosphere copious amounts of nitrous oxides (NO$_x$), which are produced by fossil fuel combustion. The excess nitrogen in the soil is taken up by rain runoff and makes its way into rivers, lakes, and the oceans, where it disrupts normal conditions and enhances **eutrophication** (eu = true, troph = nutrition) (see Chapter 10).

In the atmosphere, the nitrous oxides from fossil fuel combustion react with other gases to form nitric acid, which cause acid rain. Acid rain is to blame for the acidification of Earth's oceans, a principle threat to corals, sea urchins, shellfish, and some types of plankton. Nitrogen within the same acid enhances eutrophication of our aquatic ecosystems. To help protect air quality, the United States passed the Clean Air Act, which gives power to the Environmental Protection Agency to regulate and monitor the concentration of nitrous oxides and other potentially harmful compounds in the atmosphere (see Figure 3.16).

FIGURE 3.16
President Richard Nixon signs the Clean Air Act.

Source: Image courtesy of the Richard Nixon Presidential Library & Museum, WHPO-5421-11.

FIGURE 3.17

The nitrogen cycle. In the nitrogen cycle, nitrogen atoms move among environmental compartments and become components of different molecules (N_2, NH_3, NH_4, NO_2, and NO_3). The five main parts of the nitrogen cycle are nitrogen fixation, nitrification, ammonification, denitrification, and assimilation. Anthropogenic activities, including the combustion of fossil fuels and application of nitrogen-containing fertilizers to croplands, have disrupted the natural nitrogen cycle. Because this is a cycle, a nitrogen atom in a cow (for example) would, over time, move among the compartments as shown by the arrows. Numbers represent the amount of nitrogen in teragrams (1 Tg = one trillion grams).

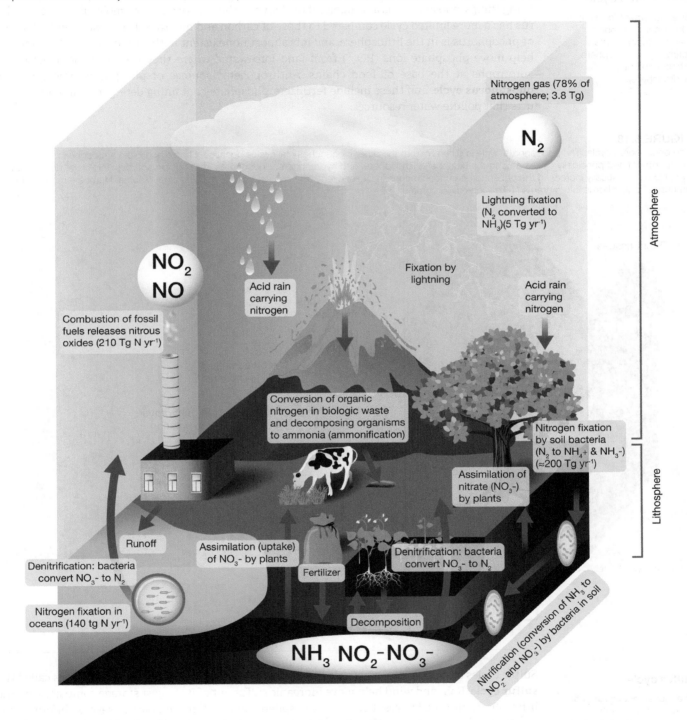

The Phosphorus Cycle

phosphorus cycle

The movement (cycling) of phosphorus among Earth's departments (primarily the biosphere, lithosphere, and hydrosphere).

Phosphorus cycles among environmental departments (see Figure 3.18). Among its many uses in living things, phosphorus is a component of DNA and the energy currency molecule ATP. Phosphorus has a more limited cycle compared to those of carbon and nitrogen. The most abundant source of phosphorus is in the lithosphere, and it is almost nonexistent in the atmosphere. Wind and rain help move phosphate ions (PO_4^{3-}) from land into water, where they then become accessible to autotrophs at the base of food chains. Anthropogenic sources of phosphorus imbalance the **phosphorus cycle**, and these include fertilizers, phosphate-containing detergents, and other products that pollute water resources.

FIGURE 3.18

The phosphorus cycle. The phosphorus cycle is different from the other biogeochemical cycles because it has a negligible atmospheric compartment and principally cycles among the biosphere, lithosphere, and hydrosphere. Phosphorus from human sources (fertilizers, detergents, etc.) have dramatically increased the phosphorus concentrations in lakes, rivers, and coastal waters, causing algal blooms. Numbers represent the amount of phosphorus in teragrams (1 Tg = one trillion grams).

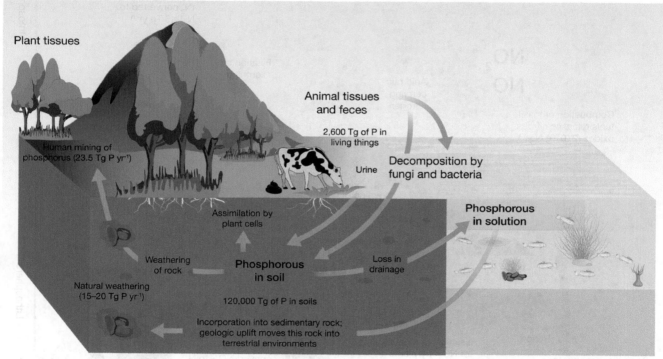

Plant tissues

Animal tissues and feces

2,600 Tg of P in living things

Urine

Human mining of phosphorus (23.5 Tg P yr⁻¹)

Decomposition by fungi and bacteria

Phosphorous in solution

Assimilation by plant cells

Weathering of rock

Phosphorous in soil

Loss in drainage

Natural weathering (15–20 Tg P yr⁻¹)

120,000 Tg of P in soils

Incorporation into sedimentary rock; geologic uplift moves this rock into terrestrial environments

Source: Joseph Shostell; © Shutterstock, Inc.

The Sulfur Cycle

sulfur cycle

The movement (cycling) of sulfur among Earth's departments (biosphere, atmosphere, hydrosphere, lithosphere).

Sulfur cycles among Earth's environmental compartments (see Figure 3.19). This cycle is called the **sulfur cycle**. Rain and wind help move inorganic sulfur out of its largest storage compartment, the lithosphere, into the hydrosphere and atmosphere. Sulfur atoms are part of several different ions and molecules, including sulfate (SO_4^{2-}), hydrogen sulfide (H_2S), sulfur dioxide (SO_2), and sulfuric acid (H_2SO_4). From a biological standpoint, sulfur is important because it is a component of proteins.

FIGURE 3.19

The sulfur cycle. Sulfur cycles among the lithosphere, hydrosphere, atmosphere, and biosphere compartments. Sulfur dioxide (SO_2) emitted from fossil fuel combustion combines with water to form sulfuric acid (H_2SO_4), a major contributor to acid rain. Sulfur enters food webs in the form of sulfate (SO_4^{2-}). Volcanoes also are a source of sulfur because they release hydrogen disulfide (H_2S_2), sulfur dioxide, and sulfate.

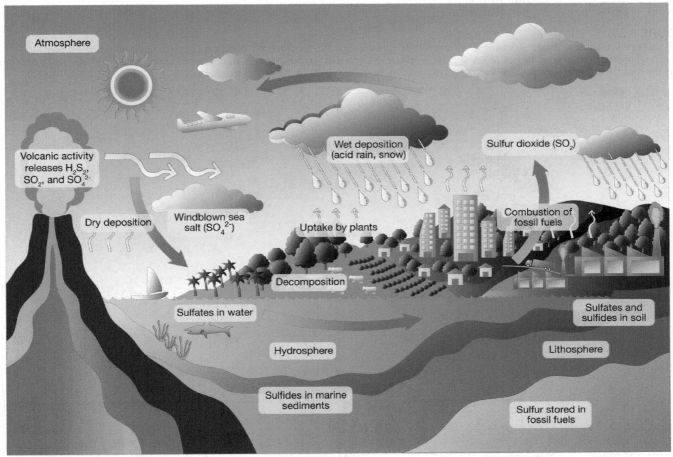

Source: Joseph Shostell; © Shutterstock, Inc.

Plants rely on sulfur in its sulfate form, taking it up from the ground through their roots. Sulfur is then available to the animal community because each animal either eats plants or eats animals that graze on plants. Sulfate ions are also present in trace amounts in the atmosphere, originating from sea water and soil particles being blown by wind. Volcanoes also provide a route for transferring sulfur stored in the lithosphere to the atmosphere. They release sulfur dioxide, which eventually becomes converted into sulfates. Sulfur dioxide can also combine with water to form sulfuric acid, a major contributor to acid rain.

Burning of fossil fuels adds to the atmosphere significant quantities of sulfur dioxide that would otherwise stay locked and unavailable within the lithosphere. However, not all fossil fuels are equally damaging to the environment. For example, burning natural gas releases only minuscule amounts of sulfur dioxide compared to oil or coal. In 2005, President George W. Bush announced a Clear Skies Initiative in his State of Union address, with the goal of reducing emissions of nitrous oxides and sulfur dioxide in order to protect human health. However, this initiative never made it past the Senate Environment and Public Works Committee, and therefore never became law.

Roughly 65 percent of sulfur dioxide emissions in the United States come from electrical utilities, and the majority of this is from coal-fired power plants. China, in its leaps of economic growth, has surpassed the sulfur dioxide emissions of the United States and released a record 36.6 million tons back in 2007 (Li et al. 2017). High emissions of sulfur dioxide and other pollutants have led to the poor air quality we observe in many Chinese cities today. There is some good news, however: China implemented an ambitious reduction plan and has steadily decreased its SO_2 emissions by

8.4 million tons per year. By 2016, annual emissions of sulfur dioxide had already dropped by more than 75 percent (see Figure 3.20). India, on the other hand, has sharply increased its sulfur dioxide emissions by 50 percent, and if it continues on this track, it will surpass China's in the not-so-distant future.

FIGURE 3.20

NASA's Aura satellite detects sulfur dioxide (SO_2) and monitors its concentrations across the world's surface. The two images show SO_2 concentrations at different time periods (2005 & 2016) in India and China and surrounding countries. Highest concentrations of SO_2 are in dark red. Note the reduction of SO_2 emissions in China and simultaneous increase in India between these periods.

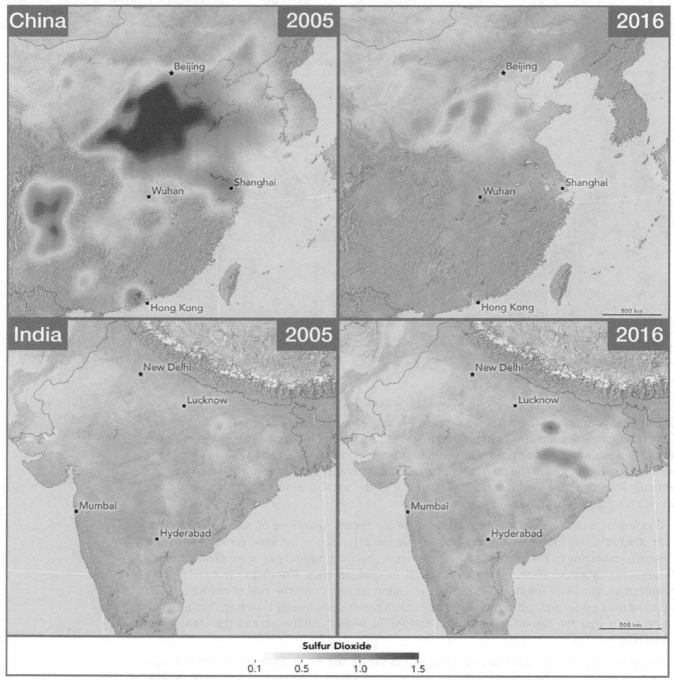

Source: NASA's Earth Observatory / Jesse Allen

3.5 Obstacles and Solutions For Society in Using Energy and Matter

Learning Objectives

1. Identify three ways to reduce energy use in the household.
2. Explain how and why new technologies and governmental initiatives intend to lower energy costs and make renewable energies like solar more cost-competitive.

In this chapter we have discussed how energy, chemical matter, and physical matter are conserved and cannot be created or destroyed. All living things and machines require energy to function. In our opening story, the Chula Vista power plant would not have been able to provide electricity for residential communities without having oil or natural gas as an initial source of energy (see Chapter 13). Similarly, sea turtles in San Diego Bay cannot swim without first acquiring energy from eelgrass.

Our lives can be active as long as we have energy sources available to meet our needs. How can we prepare for a future in which we might need new sources of energy? In other words, how can we change the way we use fuels to become more efficient and generate less unusable energy? How we proceed in the future with our energy use and the manufacturing of our products could be a direct reflection of our knowledge of thermodynamics and conservation of mass.

Choose Our Sources of Energy Wisely

Wouldn't it be prudent to at least partially select an energy source based on the efficiency of technology and the number of energy transfers involved; any pollution formed by using that particular source of energy; and any costs associated with that source? Remember, every additional energy transformation results in more energy that is unusable with current technology. Let's compare, for example, the use of chemical potential energy stored in coal and a coal-fired power plant to the use of solar energy and solar panels. Both energy sources, coal and solar energy, can be used to generate electricity in your house.

With coal as a source of energy, the coal must first be burned to convert the potential energy stored within it to heat. This is the first of four energy transformations. Heat from the combustion converts liquid water to steam. The rising steam pushes on turbine blades, turning a shaft and generating electricity. Inefficiencies in coal-fired power plants combined with energy transformations to generate electricity cause a loss of 66 percent to 68 percent of the original potential energy within coal. Even with these conversions and concomitant energy losses, the United States mostly relies on fossil fuels (65 percent) rather than other sources.

Solar panels are the technology society most commonly uses to harness solar energy. Sunlight strikes the photovoltaic cells of a solar panel and transforms the sunlight into electricity (see Figure 3.21). This is a single transformation from solar energy into electricity. Our most efficient solar panel designs convert about 45 percent of the sunlight that strikes them into electricity. Unfortunately, most solar panels fall woefully short of this top efficiency. Engineers are trying to figure out how to reduce this loss with more advanced technologies. Cost is another factor we use to determine which energy source to use. Generating electricity from solar energy is more economical than generating electricity from coal (see Figure 14.2). Cheaper and more efficient solar photovoltaic cells have been driving down the cost of electricity generated from solar energy (see Chapter 14). The cost of electricity from solar power has decreased by over 78 percent since 2010 and is projected to further decline by half by 2030 (see Figure 3.21). One way that the U.S. DOE is increasing the efficiency of using solar energy is by concentrating solar power using mirrors (DOE 2001). We'll likely see more of these thermal stations in the future.

FIGURE 3.21
We use photovoltaic cells to transform solar energy to electricity. (A) Photovoltaic cells, also referred to as solar cells, are made of semiconductor material. (B) The total cost of using solar energy as an energy source has decreased significantly. By 2017 the United States had already met the Department of Energy's 2020 cost reduction goal. As the image shows, photovoltaic cells are becoming more common on rooftops.

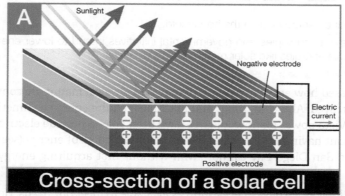

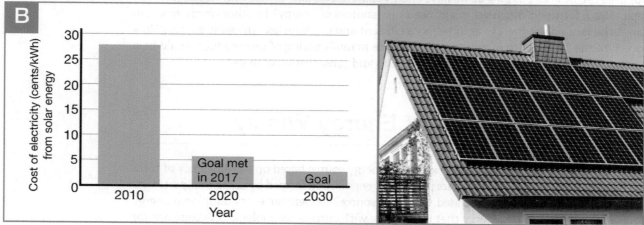

Source: © Shutterstock, Inc.; Joseph Shostell; data from the U.S. Department of Energy, SunShot Initative.

We would be remiss to not mention that use of different energy sources generates varying amounts of waste. Use of solar energy has negligible generation of emissions, whereas burning coal leaves a large carbon footprint because it emits sulfur dioxide, carbon dioxide, and nitrous oxides. Manufacturing photovoltaic equipment generates wastes, but their quantity and effects on the environment pale in comparison to those of mining and processing coal (see Chapter 13). As discussed in Chapter 2, it can be difficult to determine the true cost of a product, or in this case, the true cost of using an energy source, because true costs must reflect clean-up efforts when pollutants are released into the environment.

As individuals, we have some rather serious questions about energy use to consider, as well as about how we use matter—being cognizant of generated waste. Using less energy from the beginning and reducing the number of energy transfers is a good place to start. One way to reduce energy consumption is to evaluate how much energy we currently use, then aim to lessen it (see "Bringing It Closer to Home: Vampire Loads").

We should also use caution as to how we apply our knowledge of physical laws to our daily energy use. For example, it would be easy to conclude that, because energy transfers release unusable energy, eating uncooked foods would reduce energy loss. In general, cooked foods are more easily digested, so they take less energy from your body to process. What can be broadly stated is that not only from a household standpoint, but also from a business perspective, it makes economic sense to reduce energy use when possible, as well as to reduce waste generation.

Sometimes, Solving One Problem Leads to Another

Energy is crucial to society. People have come to depend on energy to power a wide variety of electronic products, to move vehicles, and to heat and cool homes. However, we have noted that pollution is generated when matter is incinerated to release potential energy. How can we deal with this waste? First, let us be clear that changing pollutants to a different form does not necessarily mean that the pollutants are eliminated. Putting pollution out of sight does not mean it is not still harming the environment (see Figure 3.22).

FIGURE 3.22
As the amount of trash piles up, some countries and cities are resorting to incineration. This changes the state of the matter, but does not eliminate the waste. In the image, a waste truck dumps materials and a crane moves waste to the incineration area.

Source: © Shutterstock, Inc.

For example, in 2021, the United States used coal-fired power plants to generate about 30 percent of its electricity. As we know, this process involves a series of energy transformations, from potential energy stored in the organic molecules of coal to heat and electricity. During these transformations, inefficiencies occur, and sulfur dioxide released into the atmosphere contributes to the formation of smog, acid rain, and haze. These emissions can be significantly reduced by installing flue scrubbers. Exhaust from the burning of coal is directed to the scrubber, where a limestone (or other reagent) spray reacts with the sulfur dioxide and removes the majority of the sulfur. An estimated 70 percent of America's coal-burning power plants currently use scrubber technology. But does this really take care of the pollutants? We have to be careful here that we are not just trading one pollutant for another. Let's look at the facts of adding scrubbers. Yes, sulfur dioxide emissions are drastically reduced, lowering atmospheric emissions. However, at the same time, the process amasses pollutants in solid form. Flue scrubbers capture an estimated 95 percent of sulfur dioxide. Approximately 30 percent of what is captured is recycled and used to manufacture wallboard and other products. This means that the remaining amount of captured sulfur is deposited in landfills. The overall amount of sulfur going into landfills is rather impressive, considering that more than one million tons of sulfur dioxide are released from coal-burning power plants annually in the United States. Most of the flue waste is calcium sulfate, an odorless, generally low-reactive compound. The issue isn't the chemical structure of calcium sulfate, but the toxic elements (i.e., Hg, Pb) that can also be present in the waste (Koralegedara et al 2019), and the volume of waste. Flue waste takes up valuable landfill space, and flue scrubbers are expensive to build, operate, and maintain. A sustainability strategy that relies on the laws of thermodynamics and conservation of mass should also attempt to reduce, and hopefully eliminate, the scrubber collections going into landfills.

Bringing It Closer to Home: Vampire Loads

Have you ever considered reducing your own energy use? This may not necessarily mean eliminating the use of electronic devices and machines you enjoy and rely on to make your life easier. What it may require, however, is a change in behavior regarding how you use energy.

For example, all of us can reduce a fair amount of the energy we waste by just not leaving electrical items plugged into wall sockets when we are not home or when we are not using them. Electronic devices that are plugged in—using energy, although not used by us—are referred to as vampire loads. Much like movie vampires, which prey on living things, vampire loads in your household suck out energy, effectively wasting it.

What is the current vampire load in your house? Estimate the number of electronic appliances, such as microwaves, alarm clocks, etc., currently plugged in but not being used. Then survey each of your rooms for plugged-in electronics. During the survey, record your findings for later analysis. The results may surprise you, as most people have more electronic gadgetry than they might expect. If you have a watt meter available, use it to test for vampire loads. Even without the watt meter, you can gain a sense of the economic value of your energy waste reduction by monitoring how much your electrical bill is each month. It is almost a certainty that your electric bill will drop after you change your behavior and unplug unused appliances.

Key Takeaways

- How we proceed with our energy use reflects our knowledge of thermodynamics, conservation of mass, and a desire to live sustainably.
- We should select our choice of energy source based on number of energy transformations and pollution generation.
- Converting a pollutant to a different form is not necessarily the same as eliminating the pollutant.

3.6 A Look to the Future: Society's Efforts to Live Sustainably May Save San Diego's Sea Turtles

Learning Objectives

1. Predict how future use of matter and energy may be as different as our present use is from our past use.
2. Compare and contrast how the laws of thermodynamics and law of conservation apply to sea turtles versus other entities, living or nonliving.
3. Hypothesize about the future of San Diego's population of green sea turtles.

After reading this chapter on matter and energy, you might imagine how our society will waste less matter and energy in the future. To help us glimpse the future, we can look to the not-so-distant past and the Industrial Revolution, a time of great pollution and little understanding of biogeochemical cycles and energy efficiency—at least, not compared to today's standards. One hundred years in the future may be as different from today as today is from one hundred years ago. Will we see charging stations supplied by solar energy, rather than gas stations? Will houses be strategically built around large windmills, and will coal-fired power plants be a thing of the past? This is an exciting time for all of us with the creation and adoption of new energy technologies. Have you seen the new dual-sided solar panels? These new panels absorb sunlight similar to how single-sided solar panels do, with the added advantage of taking in light reflected off of the ground. Efficiency increases by an estimated 30 percent without using a larger land footprint. Engineers and scientists design and experiment with new and greener energy technologies, but it is their adoption by governments and people that will help pave the way for a more sustainable future.

The Future Outlook of the Green Sea Turtle

As we wrap up this chapter about energy and matter, let us revisit the case of the green sea turtle, now listed as an endangered species. Today, it is illegal to hunt or hurt this species in Mexico and in the United States, as well as in most countries around the world. In the United States, sea turtles are protected by the Endangered Species Act. International agreements such as the Marine Turtle Memorandum of Understanding and the Inter-American Convention for the Protection and Conservation of Sea Turtles aim to protect, conserve, and recover sea turtles. Bycatch, destruction of habitat, entanglement in nets, vessel strikes, and climate change continue to threaten this species, but as the global community becomes aware of these and other environmental issues, needed changes occur, albeit slowly. For example, to confront the issue of bycatch, scientists from the National Oceanic and Atmospheric Administration (NOAA) Fisheries worked with the commercial shrimp industry to develop turtle excluder devices, now installed in trawl nets. These devices are escape doorways (see "Video: Escaping Sea Turtle").

Video: Escaping Sea Turtle

Watch this video to see a sea turtle exit through a turtle excluder device.

Environmental scientists have learned much from their monitoring of the small population of green sea turtles in San Diego Bay (see video link: " Tracking Endangered Sea Turtles "). We now know the City of San Diego can continue to meet its energy demands while diminishing environmental degradation. When the Chula Vista power plant was first constructed, it met a clear energy need for the San Diego community, and it was not considered as a negative to the landscape. Conversion to natural gas, and then demolition, along with the building of a newly designed combined-system power plant provide evidence of San Diego moving in the direction of sustainability. This new design improves overall efficiency by 50 percent to 60 percent, and releases about half of the nitrogen oxides! In addition, instead of drawing water directly from San Diego Bay, the new plant (now in Palomar) takes in recycled water from Escondido's wastewater treatment plant. South San Diego Bay is now listed as a National Wildlife Refuge thanks to a proposal from the United States Fish and Wildlife Service (USFWS).

Tracking Endangered Sea Turtles

Listen to Drs. Jeff Seminoff and Tomo Eguchi of the National Marine Fisheries Service discuss long-term monitoring of San Diego's green sea turtles.

View in the online reader

Critical Thinking Activity: Demolition of the Chula Vista Power Plant

After five decades of use, the Chula Vista power plant shut down in 2010. Witness the implosion demolition yourself (see video link: " Demolition "). Why was its demolition in 2013 part of a larger trend across the United States that continues today?

 Demolition

Watch the demolition of the Chula Vista power plant.

View in the online reader

Key Takeaways

- Our future use of matter and energy may be as different as our present use is from our past use.
- A hunting ban, the Endangered Species Act, and international agreements offer the green sea turtle a fighting chance to survive.

FIGURE 3.23 Visual Overview: Matter, Energy, and the Environment
Summarizing figure: Green sea turtles (3.1) contain atoms and molecules, (3.2) depend on and transform energy, (3.3) are components of the environment, (3.4) are part of biogeochemical cycles, (3.5) have a fate dependent on society overcoming obstacles related to energy and matter, and (3.6) will have a brighter future if we live sustainably.

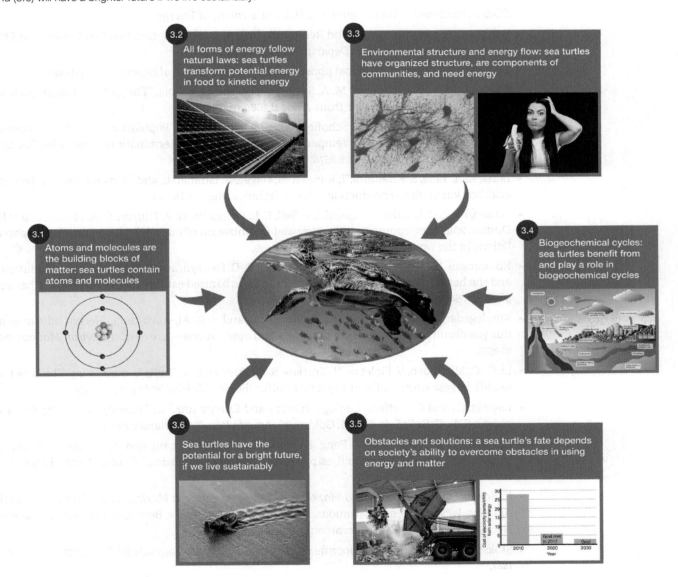

3.2 All forms of energy follow natural laws: sea turtles transform potential energy in food to kinetic energy

3.3 Environmental structure and energy flow: sea turtles have organized structure, are components of communities, and need energy

3.1 Atoms and molecules are the building blocks of matter: sea turtles contain atoms and molecules

3.4 Biogeochemical cycles: sea turtles benefit from and play a role in biogeochemical cycles

3.6 Sea turtles have the potential for a bright future, if we live sustainably

3.5 Obstacles and solutions: a sea turtle's fate depends on society's ability to overcome obstacles in using energy and matter

Sources: Joseph Shostell; See previous citations for image credits.

3.7 References

- Burgett, C. M., D. A. Burkholder, K. A. Coates, V. L. Fourqurean, W. J. Kenworthy, S. A. Manuel, M. E. Outerbridge, and J. W. Fourqurean. 2018. "Ontogenetic diet shifts of green sea turtles (Chelonia mydas) in a mid-ocean developmental habitat." *Marine Biology* 154: 33.

- Dalton, J. 1808. *A New System of Chemical Philosophy Part 1*. London: William Dawson and Sons LTD.

- Department of Energy (DOE). 2011. "Energy Efficiency and Renewable Energy-Concentrating Solar Power: Energy from Mirrors."

  SOE/GO-102001-1157. Washington, DC: U.S. Department of Energy.

- DOE. 2011. "Energy Efficiency and Renewable Energy Basics-Photovoltaic Cell Conversion Efficiency." Washington, DC: U.S. Department of Energy.

- Filippelli, G. M. 2002. "The global phosphorus cycle." *Rev. Mineral Geochem* 48: 391–425.

- Fowler, D., M. Coyle, U. Skiba, M. A. Sutton, J. N. Cape, et al. 2013. "The global nitrogen cycle in the twenty-first century." *Phil Trans R Soc B* 368: 20130164.

- Hays, G. C., A. D. Mazaris, G. Schofield, and J. O. Laloë. 2017. "Population viability at extreme sex-ratio skews produced by temperature-dependent sex determination." *Proc. Biol. Sci.* 284: https://doi.org/10.1098/rspb.2016.2576.

- Ikuta, K., T. Yada, S. Kitamura, T. Kaneko, M. Nagae, A. Ishimatsu, and M. Iwata. 1992. " Effects of acidification on fish reproduction." UJNR Technical Report No. 28.

- Jensen, M. P., C. D. Allen, T. Eguchi, I. P. Bell, E. L. LaCasella, W. A. Hiltron, C. A. M. Hof, and P. H. Dutton. 2018. "Environmental warming and feminization of one of the largest sea turtle populations in the world." *Current Biology* 28: 154–59.

- Komoroske, L. M., R. L. Lewison, J. A. Seminoff, D. D. Deheyn, and P. H. Dutton. 2011. "Pollutants and the health of green sea turtles resident to an urbanized estuary in San Diego CA." *Chemosphere* 84: 544–552.

- Koralegedara, N. H., P. X. Pinto, D. D. Xionysiou, and S. R. AL-Abed. 2019. "Recent advances in flue gas desulfurization gypsum processes and applications—a review." *J Environ Manage* 251: 109572.

- Li, C., C. McLinden, V. Fioletov, N. Krotkov, S. Carn, et al. 2017. "India is overtaking China as the world's largest emitter of anthropogenic sulfur dioxide." *Scientific Reports* 7: 14304.

- Ludwig, C., and C. Steffen. "Geologic History and Energy 2018." In *Encyclopedia of the Anthropocene* (Eds. E. DellaSala and M. Goldstein). Amsterdam, Netherlands: Elsevier.

- Pratush, A., X. Ye, Q. Yang, T. Peng, H. Wang, T. Huang, G. Xiong, and Z. Hu. 2020. "Biotransformation strategies for steroid estrogen and androgen pollution." *Applied Microbiology and Biotechnology* 104: 2385–409.

- Radcliffe, L. 1922. *Fisheries and Market for Fishery Products in Mexico, Central America, South America, West Indies, and Bermudas*. Department of Commerce, Bureau of Fisheries Document No. 931. Washington, DC: Government Printing Office, 9.

- Stokstad, E. 2013. "Zombie endocrine disruptors may threaten aquatic life." *Science* 341, no. 6153: 1441.

- Tindall, T. A., M. W. Colt, D. J. Barney, and E. Fallahi. 2012. *Controlling iron deficiency in Idaho Plants*. University of Idaho College of Agriculture Cooperative Extension System Agricultural Experiment Station CIS 104. Moscow, ID: University of Idaho.

- Townsend, R. H. 1889. *Report Upon the Pearl Fishery of the Golf of California.* "United States Fish and Wildlife Service, Fishery Bulletin, 9: 93.
- Tympa-Psirropoulou, E., C. Vagenas, A. Matala, and F. Skopouli. 2008. "Environmental risk factors for iron deficiency anemia in children 12–24 months old in the Thessalia in Greece." *Hippokratia,* 12, no. 4: 240–50.

CHAPTER 4
Evolution, Populations, and Communities

Case Study: Opossum Shrimp in Flathead Lake, Montana

Back in 1916, biologists began to stock Flathead Lake, in Montana, with non-native kokanee salmon in order to develop a sports fishery. Their efforts paid off for the kokanee salmon population, which grew in size, as did the number caught per year. By 1985, anglers reported a record catch of approximately 100,000 salmon. The surge in numbers came at the expense of native cutthroat trout, which declined as rapidly as the kokanee surged.

FIGURE 4.1

Example of an exotic species. (A) An opossum shrimp, about 2.5 cm (1 in) in length. (B) This species was introduced into the Flathead Lake ecosystem in Montana, where its presence led to the crash of the kokanee salmon population.

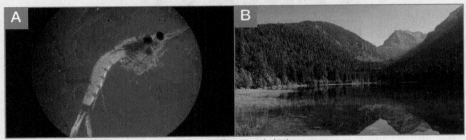

Source: NOAA Great Lakes Environmental Research Lab

At around four years of age, kokanee become mature and begin to spawn. They do this as a one-time reproductive event, similar to genetically related oceanic salmon. They swim up small tributaries connected to the main lake, lay their eggs, have them fertilized, and then die. Huge numbers of kokanee travel each year to the same upstream locations. In the case of Flathead Lake, McDonald Creek is one such area. Such a large movement of fish and their accumulated carcasses provide a food source that is utilized by a broad number of different species, thus supporting higher biodiversity. Some organisms—such as grizzly bears, American bald eagles, coyotes, mink, river otters, herring gulls, and common mergansers—increased in number with greater numbers of salmon (Spencer et al. 1991). Consequently, sightings of grizzly bears and bald eagles spiked at McDonald Creek. Bald eagles, initially quite low in number at thirty-seven in 1939, increased to 639 in 1981, the same year that kokanee peaked. The increased numbers of eagles and bears feasting on the plentiful kokanee brought many tourists to the area, boosting the local economy.

To further improve the sports fishery, lake managers introduced another exotic species, opossum shrimp, in the late 1960s to the mid-1970s (see Figure 4.1). Although intended as a food source for kokanee salmon, by 1981 the population of opossum shrimp had begun to have serious effects on the lake's food web and a negative effect on kokanee salmon, which normally concentrated in surface waters and fed during the day. Instead of providing a source of food for fish as they had in other lakes, the opossum shrimp in Flathead Lake migrated to deeper, cooler waters and would only visit the surface waters during the night. Then, the opossum shrimp would prey on the same type of zooplankton that the kokanee had historically eaten, thus becoming a competitor of kokanee rather than prey. The community structure within the lake changed. By 1989, the kokanee salmon population had completely collapsed. On the terrestrial side, mammal and bird species that relied on the dead and dying kokanee for food began to visit less, lowering local diversity levels. These ecological changes led to a reduction in the number of tourists. After the collapse of the kokanee population and peak in opossum shrimp, lake trout—a different species from native cutthroat—became the dominant predatory fish, mainly because its younger stages feed on the opossum shrimp in the deeper areas of the lake (Ellis et al. 2011).

The kokanee–opossum shrimp story provides an example of how an individual species population can fare well or poorly within a broader community and changing environment. Depending on a species' own unique set of characteristics, it can either be evolutionarily selected for, as in the case of opossum shrimp introduced to Flathead Lake, or selected against, such as what occurred with the kokanee (see "Searching for Mysis Shrimp").

 Searching for Mysis Shrimp

Tag along on a field trip to find Mysis shrimp in Flathead Lake.

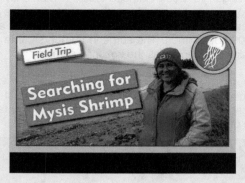

View in the online reader

4.1 Evolution Is the Source of Biodiversity

Learning Objectives

1. Explain how variations of individuals within a population provide a basis for evolutionary processes.
2. Articulate an explanation of evolution that mentions biological diversity, natural selection, genetic variability, selective factors, Darwin, and Wallace.
3. Describe how species can develop with or without geographical barriers.
4. Define and give examples of coevolution.
5. Recognize and comprehend the causes and effects of mass extinction events.

Earth's environment has continuously changed over the approximately 4.6 billion years since it first formed. Initially, Earth was too hot for life, but after the crust cooled and the synthesis of organic molecules took place, the first single-celled creatures appeared. Opossum shrimp and other life forms have radiated from this humble beginning 3.8 billion years ago.

This chapter explores populations and communities, along with the evolutionary processes that helped create the diversity of life observed today. We begin by examining biological evolution itself. **Biological evolution** is change in the genetic makeup of a population over time and is often described as descent with modification. An accumulation of genetic changes over a long length of time across successive generations can dramatically alter the shape and size of a species and can lead to the development of new species and even groups of new species. While this is an accurate statement for many animals and other groups of organisms, some forms of genetic change such as **polyploidy** do not depend on long bouts of time and can immediately cause reproduction isolation, which can lead to the development of a new species. Polyploidy is a condition in which an organism has extra chromosome sets. Each chromosome is an organized package of DNA, and each species has a particular number of chromosomes. Humans, for instance, have forty-six chromosomes and opossum shrimp (see "Case Study: Opossum Shrimp in Flathead Lake, Montana ") have fifty-two chromosomes (Salemaa and Heino 1990). A large percentage of flowering plants and ferns use polyploidy as a means to form new species. However, polyploidy often leads to sterility. Farmers have exploited this condition to develop seedless fruits we enjoy. A common example is the seedless commercial banana; without seeds there is no next generation. Wild bananas with normal sets of chromosomes have seeds.

The blueprint of an organism's characteristics is found within its DNA. Segments of DNA called **genes** code for specific traits, such as color in pea plants, the presence of a tail in cats, or the type of ear lobe in humans. All members of a species have the same genes, which is why they share the same set of traits that define the species. Each gene has one or more variants called **alleles**, which code for the same trait. However, the outcome (how a particular trait is expressed) is different depending on the allele. In pea plants, for example, the expression of two alleles for flower color (a trait) could result in purple-colored flowers or white-colored flowers. Therefore, variations in shared traits among individuals of the same species are due to the presence of different alleles. All of the alleles in a population—a group of individuals of the same species—are referred to as the population's gene pool. The greater the variety of alleles in a population's gene pool, the better chance it has of having the traits most helpful for surviving in a changing environment.

biological evolution

Change in genetic makeup of a population over time. This change is heritable and passed on to successive generations.

polyploidy

A condition in which an organism possesses more than two sets of chromosomes.

genes

A sequence of nucleotides in DNA that is considered a unit of heredity and that contains information needed to specify traits.

alleles

Variant forms of a gene.

Natural Selection, Genetic Variability, and Adaptation

The basis of "descent with modification" is the uniqueness of each individual of a population, to such an extent that even individuals within a litter of a sexually reproducing species are somewhat dissimilar. For example, the pups of a wolf litter are recognizable as wolves because they share the same set of genes. The wolf pups are also slightly different in size, weight, and coat pattern because the DNA in those genes varies just a bit. Whereas one may be the most muscular and most dominant of the litter, another is clearly the runt (see Figure 4.2). Organisms in the wild, including wolves, are subjected to a host of environmental factors, such as temperature and water abundance. Populations are larger at the optimal levels of these environmental factors, specific to their needs. If the environment is too hot or too cold, for example, the organisms are so stressed physiologically they cannot survive.

FIGURE 4.2

Each wolf pup in a litter is slightly different from the others. Natural selection acts on these differences; pups with the most helpful characteristics are most likely to survive and pass their genes to the next generation.

Source: © Shutterstock, Inc.

mutation

Any heritable change in a cell's genetic material.

evolution

See *biological evolution*.

natural selection

A process in nature in which those organisms more adapted to environmental conditions are more likely to survive and pass on their heritable traits to offspring.

Changes in DNA occur by **mutation**, which is a more or less random process. Artificial selection and natural selection drive **evolution** by operating on the effects (variations in shared traits) of genetic changes. Well before humans knew of the existence of genes, they understood that traits were hereditable. By selectively breeding plants and animals that had desirable traits, humans found that they could create ideal domesticated animals and crops. Because humans are doing the selecting (with the effect of changing the frequency of alleles) it is artificial selection. Early farmers, for example, used artificial selection to modify the structure of wild cabbage (*Brassica oleracea*) to produce broccoli, cauliflower, and brussels sprouts. They are all the same species. Similarly, we have selectively bred dogs over many generations, so that the original structure changed from that of a wolf to that of, say, a miniature Doberman.

Natural selection is a major driving force behind evolutionary changes in natural populations. Organisms with favorable traits have a greater chance of surviving and passing on their heritable traits to the next generation. Consider the peppered moth, *Biston betularia*. Prior to the Industrial Revolution, the charcoal form of the peppered moth was extremely rare in England. Where it did exist, birds easily detected it against the lighter-colored bark of trees. At the same time, a mottled-grey form of the peppered moth was very common and camouflaged on the light-colored bark. Over the course of the Industrial Revolution, soot from coal-burning factories blackened the skies around London and covered the bark of trees. Now the charcoal-colored moths were camouflaged and the mottled-grey moths were easily detected by natural bird predators. As a consequence, the allele for the mottled-grey color became less common in the peppered moth population. Once the Industrial Revolution ended and the skies around London cleared of soot, peppered moths with the mottled-grey color became more common again.

FIGURE 4.3
Geneticists such as Dr. Manuel Ruiz-Garcia, shown here with a pink dolphin, collect DNA from a variety of animals to better understand the genetic diversity of populations. A population's genetic diversity is one indicator of its resilience to environmental change.

Source: Manuel Ruiz-Garcia at Laboratorio de Genética de Poblaciones Molecular-Biología Evolutiva, Departamento de Biología, Facultad de Ciencias, Pontificia Universidad Javeriana.

Evolution also occurs by nonselective factors such as **genetic drift**, also known as random genetic drift. Genetic drift represents the random fluctuation of alleles each generation. Genetic drift is more likely to cause a change in allele frequencies in smaller populations. An analogy of this is flipping a coin three times. If each result of a flip (heads or tails) represents one of two possible alleles in an individual, we would not be surprised if we got three heads in a row. We would be astounded if we flipped the coin ten thousand times and only got heads. We would have expected an almost equal number of heads and tails. Therefore, in a small population, some alleles are more likely to be lost entirely and rare alleles may increase in frequency. An extreme example would be during a natural disaster (e.g. hurricane, flooding), when a significant part of the population dies. A sharp decline in a population and later expansion is a population bottleneck. In such situations, genetic drift can a have a profound effect on which alleles remain in the population. Many alleles could be eliminated from a population, lowering the diversity of a population's gene pool.

Founder effect also typically results in a great reduction in genetic diversity. **Founder effect** is what happens when a small group that is not genetically representative of the larger population founds a new population somewhere else, so the allele frequency of the new population is very different than that of the original population. Because populations with low genetic diversity are at a higher risk of extinction, environmental scientists collect and analyze DNA samples from individuals of populations with the objective of determining whether the population has low genetic diversity. If it does, the population is targeted for conservation measures (see Figure 4.3).

genetic drift

The random fluctuation of alleles each generation.

founder effect

When a small number of individuals from a population settle into a new area and establish a new population that, due to genetic drift, is not genetically representative of the original population.

Darwin and Wallace

Charles Darwin and Alfred Russel Wallace independently came up with explanations of how populations become modified over time (see Figure 4.4). Today, we give more credit to Darwin because he had a more substantial data record, mostly gained from his famous almost five-year expedition on the *HMS Beagle* to South America and other areas. Not all of his time was spent on ship; rather, for over three years Darwin was on land exploring and collecting specimens. After meticulous work, Darwin eventually published *On the Origin of Species by Natural Selection*, a book still popular today (Darwin 1859).

Selection Factors

The frequency of traits (e.g. size, color) within a population often follows one of three modes of selection: directional, stabilizing, and disruptive. In all three modes, individuals are selected based on specific traits. For example, in our opening story we learned that opossum shrimp are voracious predators of animals called zooplankton. What wasn't mentioned is that opossum shrimp prefer larger, slower-moving zooplankton, causing precipitous declines in zooplankton species with these traits (Spencer et al. 1999). Thus, disproportionate survival of smaller-sized zooplankton and their successful reproduction shifts the zooplankton community to smaller forms. This is an example of directional selection. In stabilizing selection, individuals with the largest and smallest values of a particular trait are selected against. Disruptive selection is the exact opposite of stabilizing selection. In this case, both extremes of a trait are selected for, and the middle form is selected against. One example is the shared trait of feather color in lazuli buntings. Males of this North American bird can have dull, intermediate, or bright feathers. Studies have indicated that males with dull feathers and males with bright feathers are more successful in gaining **habitat** space, attracting mates, and consequently having offspring (Green et al. 2000). If disruptive selection were operating on the trait of size, then smaller and larger individuals would have a better chance of surviving and passing their genes on to offspring than midsized individuals.

FIGURE 4.4
In his book, *On the Origin of Species by Means of Natural Selection*, Charles Darwin explains his theory of natural selection driving evolution. George Richmond's portrait of Charles Darwin as a young man in 1840.

Source: Portrait of Charles Darwin, Watercolor, Darwin Museum, 1840.

habitat

Where a species lives in the environment.

Speciation Leads to Species Diversity and New Types of Organisms

speciation

The development of new species.

allopatric speciation

The development of a new species after a geographical barrier arises and separates individuals of a population.

subpopulation

A subset of a larger population.

gene flow

The transfer of alleles between populations.

Over time, natural selection can modify a population so much that it becomes a new species. The development of new species, referred to as **speciation**, can occur with or without geographical barriers.

Allopatric speciation is the development of species because of geographical barriers. For example, a population may become divided into smaller **subpopulations** by a geographic feature such as a river or a mountain range. Eventually—in some cases after millions of years of being isolated—the two subpopulations become distinct species as each subpopulation evolves separately (see Figure 4.5). How could we determine if the subpopulations had evolved into different species? The test would be to bring representatives of each subpopulation together and see if they can interbreed. If they cannot interbreed and have viable offspring, they have become different species. If they can, then they are of the same species. Allopatric speciation can be prevented with sufficient **gene flow** by migrants moving between subpopulations. A migrant brings in alleles from one subpopulation to another, which reduces the difference in allele frequencies between the subpopulations.

FIGURE 4.5

An ancestral population of antelope squirrels is thought to have experienced allopatric speciation after the Colorado River divided its population. Today, two separate populations of antelope squirrels exist in the Grand Canyon: the Harris's antelope squirrel on the south side of the river, and the white-tailed antelope squirrel population on the north side.

Harris' antelope squirrel population

Colorado River and Grand Canyon

White-tailed antelope squirrel population

Source: Joseph Shostell; © Shutterstock, Inc.

sympatric speciation

The development of a new species in the absence of a geographical barrier that separates populations.

morphology

Form and structure of an organism.

Sympatric speciation, or the formation of new species without geographical barriers, seems to be less common in the evolution of animal species than it is in plant species. Polyploidy (defined earlier), sexual selection, and adaptation all can promote sympatric speciation. Sexual selection is a form of natural selection in which, for example, one sex prefers a certain morphological trait in the other sex. A continued preference for the trait over generations may lead to a runaway process creating elaborate morphological traits. Sexual selection is thought to have played an important role in the radiation of cichlid (SICK-lid) fish in African lakes, because females of many cichlid species choose mates based on color (Selz et al. 2016). Sympatric speciation in cichlids is also due to specialization in feeding **morphology** and feeding behavior (Takahashi et al. 2007). These specializations—feeding on sediments, fish, snails, and scales—partition a resource and reduce competition.

Natural Selection and Life History Traits

Some traits strongly affect the ability of an organism to pass genes on to the next generation. These life history traits include number of offspring, how often reproduction occurs, and degree of parental care. Elephants, for example, and other **k-selected species**, take a long time to reach sexual maturity, have few offspring, have a long delay between having offspring, and invest heavily in parent care. K-selected species tend toward repeatedly having reproduction events (iteroparity). In contrast, female Pacific salmon release thousands of eggs in a one-time reproductive effort (semelparity), and offspring receive no parental care. Salmon, insects, and bacteria are all examples of **r-selected species**, but there are exceptions to this generality, including the seventeen-year cicada. Based on selection theory, unstable, unpredictable environments would favor r-selection, as would new environments such as those created by volcanic eruptions. Most environments support somewhere between the opposite ends of the selection continuum (Taylor and Condra 1980). How we lend assistance to protect a particular species does depend on its life history traits.

k-selected species

Species such as elephants and humans that have few young and take a long time to reach sexual maturity. Such species have long gestation periods and low reproductive rates.

r-selected species

Species that mature rapidly and have a high reproductive rate. They also have relatively short life spans, and their offspring require little, if any, parental care.

Coevolution

Interacting species may experience coevolution, in which both species evolve together in such a way that one exerts a consistent selective pressure on the other. In the evolutionary arms race of predator–prey relationships, predators (e.g. large felines) attempt to capture, kill, and eat prey. When a predator is successful, they have removed an individual from the prey population, preventing it from passing on its alleles to any future offspring. Africa's savannah hosts the fastest and most maneuverable terrestrial mammals in the world. Here, for example, cheetahs attempt to catch slower, weaker impalas (see Figure 4.6). Comparatively, cheetahs have more muscle fiber power, greater acceleration, and greater deceleration capacity than impalas (Wilson et al. 2018). Yet, impalas successfully escape roughly 66 percent of the time. Those that survive have the ability to move unpredictably—slowing down and turning at the last moment. These successful impalas pass on their heritable traits to their offspring. So too do the cheetahs that successfully catch impala, pass their genes to offspring. Having a form of a trait that offers an advantage doesn't necessarily mean all of the individuals with other forms of the trait will not survive. In cases such as the impalla–cheetah relationship, advantages can be quite subtle. Coevolution in this relationship will likely take place over long periods of time, with gradual shifts in the populations' gene pools.

FIGURE 4.6
Cheetah chasing a young gazelle. The predator and prey are in a constant evolutionary arms race: the predator tries to catch the prey and the prey tries to evade capture. Genetic changes that offer even a slight advantage in this arms race tend to become more common in predator and prey populations over time.

Source: © Shutterstock, Inc.

Extinction and Mass Extinction

Evolution is a powerful process because it accounts for the great diversity of species we witness today. Biologists have already described approximately 1.8 million species. Yet, the majority of species once alive on Earth, including the famed *Tyrannosaurus rex*, are now extinct. Why? Species perform well when their physiologies and body structures are adapted to their environment, and if the environment changes more rapidly than a species can adapt, the species becomes extinct. In the opening story, opossum shrimp were superior competitors for the salmon's food source, and in the end, salmon were lost from the Flathead Lake ecosystem. At times in Earth's history, there have been large-scale environment changes resulting in mass extinction events (see Figure 4.7).

FIGURE 4.7

The progress toward Earth's biological diversity today has not always been steady or positive. The fossil record holds evidence of several mass extinction events caused by a combination of atmospheric, continental, and sea-level changes as well as meteor strikes. In each mass extinction event, an estimated 65–96 percent of all living species perished. Afterward, diversity rebounded until it crashed with the next major environmental change. Based on the accelerated rate of species extinction today due to anthropogenic activities, we are living within a new mass extinction event.

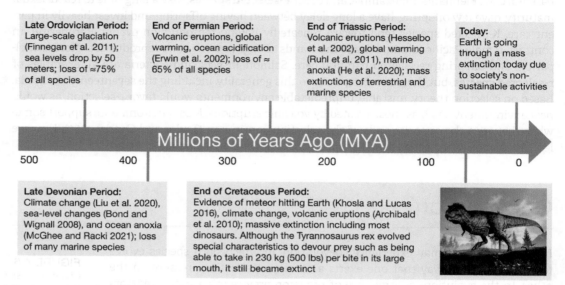

Late Ordovician Period:
Large-scale glaciation (Finnegan et al. 2011); sea levels drop by 50 meters; loss of ≈75% of all species

End of Permian Period:
Volcanic eruptions, global warming, ocean acidification (Erwin et al. 2002); loss of ≈ 65% of all species

End of Triassic Period:
Volcanic eruptions (Hesselbo et al. 2002), global warming (Ruhl et al. 2011), marine anoxia (He et al. 2020); mass extinctions of terrestrial and marine species

Today:
Earth is going through a mass extinction today due to society's non-sustainable activities

Millions of Years Ago (MYA)

500   400   300   200   100   0

Late Devonian Period:
Climate change (Liu et al. 2020), sea-level changes (Bond and Wignall 2008), and ocean anoxia (McGhee and Racki 2021); loss of many marine species

End of Cretaceous Period:
Evidence of meteor hitting Earth (Khosla and Lucas 2016), climate change, volcanic eruptions (Archibald et al. 2010); massive extinction including most dinosaurs. Although the Tyrannosaurus rex evolved special characteristics to devour prey such as being able to take in 230 kg (500 lbs) per bite in its large mouth, it still became extinct

Source: Joseph Shostell; © Shutterstock, Inc.

---

niche

The position or job of a species in an ecosystem.

Critical Thinking Activity: Is Evolution Always Positive for Life?

Up to this point we have more or less assumed that, because natural selection forces can drive changes in populations that lead to speciation, then the evolutionary process must have a positive outcome overall for living things. Is this true? Clearly, the development of new species and an abundant diversity are positive outcomes, but are there any negative outcomes with the evolutionary process—dead ends, so to speak?

Most species that have arisen are now extinct. If evolutionary processes were completely beneficial to the well-being of a species, wouldn't the total number of species and diversity increase as time goes on? It turns out that evolutionary dead ends do occur, and they occur with great frequency. With the help of natural selection, populations can adapt to their environment; however, there is no guarantee that they will also be adapted to a future environment, which could be drastically different from the past.

In the opening story, opossum shrimp vertically migrate up and down in Flathead Lake, preying on zooplankton in the surface waters at night and then returning to deeper, darker waters during daylight hours. Their **niche** or function is to migrate twice a day, eat zooplankton, and release waste. They continue to function like that because it allows them to survive through generations either within their natural distribution range or, often times, where they are introduced outside their native range. Individuals that have the behavioral trait of migration and survive because of this trait pass their genes on to offspring, who then do the same thing as their ancestors: vertically migrate. Filling a niche is a winning strategy until there is a change in the environment—for example, a surge in the population growth of lake trout that can feed in the colder, deeper part of Flathead Lake.

The fossil record has many examples of evolutionary dead ends that have already led to the extinction of species, or are leading to their extinction now. Specialists like the monarch butterfly fit this description well. They have evolved a strategy of relying on a single type of milkweed plant. What would happen to monarch butterflies if an overabundance of aphids killed all the milkweed? Being adaptable is a necessity for life, but in the game of survival, having the right traits adapted for your location and time are essential.

Key Takeaways

- Variations of individuals within a population provide a basis for evolutionary processes.
- Biological evolution is the change in the genetic makeup of a population over time.
- Natural selection is a major driving force behind changes in populations over time.
- Genetic change can lead to new species (speciation).
- Environmental change that happens too quickly for adaptation causes extinctions.
- In coevolution, interacting species reciprocally affect each other's evolution.
- Earth has endured mass extinction events, and we are in one today.

4.2 Interactions of Individuals Within Populations

Learning Objectives

1. Identify three distribution patterns of populations in the environment.
2. Describe how intraspecific competition and predation affect population structure.

Each species has at least one population of interacting individuals, and those individuals may be distributed in a particular pattern. The kokanee population from our opening story, for example, are not randomly distributed (nor are they evenly distributed) throughout an entire lake, for they tend to avoid deeper areas. Thus, if you were to try to capture kokanee, you would focus on the top half of the lake rather than on the bottom.

Species Have One of Three Types of Distribution Patterns

Populations usually follow one of three main distribution patterns: clumped, random, or uniform (see "Distribution Patterns"). These patterns may reflect interactions between individuals or the distribution within the environment of resources needed by the species. Clumped is the most common type of distribution pattern (see A in Figure 4.8). A population may be unevenly distributed in this way because its members are attracted to each other or to a common, unevenly distributed and needed resource. The formation of a group could be the result of offspring's wanting to stay with their parents. Individuals can also be attracted to each other for mating purposes, or for defense.

clumped distribution

A population distribution pattern in which individuals are grouped together in some areas, and other areas have no individuals at all.

random distributions

A distribution pattern in a population in which individuals are randomly spaced.

uniform distribution

A population distribution pattern in which individuals are equally spaced from one another.

intraspecific competition

Competition between members of the same species.

allelopathy

The use of chemicals to discourage other organisms.

Distribution Patterns
Explore the different distribution patterns of populations.

View in the online reader

One example of a **clumped distribution** occurs in deep oceanic areas, which are devoid of light, harshly cold, and at high pressure. Scientists hypothesized that these areas would be barren of life. This hypothesis was tested in 1977 by scientists aboard the submersible research vessel *Alvin*, who dove to the ocean's bottom for the first time and observed a hydrothermal vent supporting large clams and tube worms in the Galapagos Rift (Fiorenza et al. 2002). These and other organisms congregate around hydrothermal vents in order to use the hydrogen sulfide and heat emanating from the vent as resources for their survival. Therefore, deep benthic areas of the ocean exhibit clumped communities of invertebrates. **Random distributions** are least common in populations (see B in Figure 4.8). The existence of this pattern indicates that individuals of the species do not interact much with one another, nor are they noticeably influenced by the environment. When individuals avoid each other, a **uniform distribution** pattern becomes evident (see C in Figure 4.8). This pattern could be a result of intraspecific competition. "Intraspecific" refers to being within a single species, and therefore **intraspecific competition** implies competition between individuals of the same species. In animals, the maintenance of strong territorial boundaries could result in a uniform distribution. Exclusive space is the relevant resource for these territorial species. Plants may also exhibit this distribution type as they compete for water and nutrients. Some plant species use **allelopathy**—the use of chemicals such as terpenes—to discourage individuals from growing too close to each other.

FIGURE 4.8
Population distributions can be (A) clumped; (B) random; or (C) uniform. Each dot represents one organism, and each rectangle represents the habitat of a population.

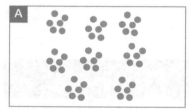  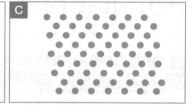

Source: Joseph Shostell

Interactions Between Individuals of the Same Species

Interactions between individuals can be helpful or negative. Helpful interactions might include caring for young until they can fend for themselves, or banding together as a safety mechanism (see A in Figure 4.9). Wildebeests in Tanzania apply the latter strategy when approximately 2–3 million of them migrate together in search of green grass. Banding together offers individual wildebeests some protection from the various predators that pursue the herds during this migration. Wildebeests also rely on the "safety in numbers" strategy when their population births all of its young for the year in a relatively short time period (about three weeks). A temporarily high population density of newborns can also cause predator satiation. When this happens, there are more potential prey than the predator populations can consume. Because the prey are not a reliable source of food all year long, the predator population does not increase in size.

Competition

Interactions such as competition and predation also occur within species. Although they seem more negative, they have their function as well.

Organisms compete for limited resources worth the investment of energy expended to access them. Individuals of the same species may compete for food, habitat space (where a species lives in the environment), and mates. Intraspecific competition in plants could be two young white oak trees that are close together—both needing and competing for the same patch of sunlight and the same sources of water and nutrients.

Competition can be direct, in which case it is called interference competition. In interference competition, two individuals arrive at the resource at the same time and then fight over use of it. For example, male whitetail deer intensely compete for access to mates (Newbolt et al. 2017). Competition can also be indirect, or exploitative, such as when a grey squirrel arrives to an acorn (a food resource) and then buries it, leaving nothing for another grey squirrel who arrives later (see B in Figure 4.9).

FIGURE 4.9
Interactions between members of the same species can benefit or harm individuals. A) Prairie dogs give alarm calls when they observe predators—informing others to return to the safety of the burrow hole. B) A grey squirrel exerts exploitative competition by collecting and burying an acorn before another competing grey squirrel arrives. C) Competition within a sand tiger shark population begins in the uterus with the eating of unborn siblings (intrauterine cannibalism).

Source: © Shutterstock, Inc.

Predation

Intraspecific predation, or cannibalism, is widespread in animal populations (Polis 1981). In Polis's review of over 900 papers, he noted intraspecific predation in around 1,300 species. One discernible pattern in his review is that larger individuals usually prey on younger, smaller individuals. This can have a pronounced effect on populations such as crows, where adults may destroy up to 90 percent of eggs. Cannibalism usually increases when food is in short supply and the density of individuals in the population increases. **Density** refers to the number of individuals per unit area. In this manner, cannibalism acts as a factor helping to keep a population within carrying capacity limits. In other words, the population remains below any size that cannot be sustained. Cannibalism has other perceived benefits as well, such as when parents may feed on dying offspring, thus preventing the spread of disease. For some species, cannibalism starts at the embryo stage. For example, in the sand tiger shark, sibling embryos feed on each other until only one survives (see C in Figure 4.9).

> **density**
> The number of individuals per given unit area (e.g., the number per square meter).

Key Takeaways

- Species have three types of distribution patterns: clumped, random, or uniform.
- Individuals of the same species interact with each other. Examples are intraspecific competition and predation (cannibalism).

4.3 Growth of Populations

natality

Birth rate.

mortality rate

Death rate.

The growth of every population depends on birth rate, known as **natality**, and death rate, or **mortality rate**. Reduced to the simplest equation, population growth equals the number of births minus the number of deaths. We can therefore predict a population increase when the birth rate surpasses the death rate. In contrast, if the number of deaths exceeds the number of births, than the population is decreasing in size. Finally, when the number of births equals the number of deaths, the population is stable, implying there is neither upward nor downward growth.

Exponential Growth

exponential population growth

Rapid growth of a population in a relatively short period of time; the pattern of growth indicates a geometric increase (i.e., 2, 4, 8 . . .) and is depicted as a J-shaped curve.

When unchecked, a population could theoretically increase forever. Take any species and imagine its population growing indefinitely. Grey wolves, for example, have pups each year and add new members to their population yearly. Shouldn't they be found in all areas of the world? In fact, they would if internal and external factors were not influencing their overall population growth. Unchecked growth (**exponential population growth**) can be described as a J-shaped curve that represents a population rapidly growing over time (see "Population Growth"). This is a common occurrence when organisms colonize newly formed habitats. For example, a ripe orange might be colonized exponentially by tiny microbes, or a new volcanic island might be a site of exponential growth for lichens. Remember the opossum shrimp? They increased exponentially from a very small number to billions throughout a very large connection of rivers and lakes.

Logistic Growth and Carrying Capacity

logistic growth curve

A population growth curve that shows an end to rapid population growth as the population nears its carrying capacity. The population size levels off at the carrying capacity.

In reality, no population can grow indefinitely. Multiple factors, including limited resources, predation, and competition, limit population growth. A **logistic growth curve** takes into account these limiting factors (see "Population Growth"). Note how it starts with a rapidly increasing rate and then levels off. As the population begins to reach a level that can be sustained—based on a habitat's resources, competition, and predation—it approaches carrying capacity (K). Think of K as the population size that can be sustained, so that if a population exceeds this value, mortality rate increases and the population decreases in size. Should a population greatly surpass K, then a population crash will follow.

FIGURE 4.10

Populations will increase in size until they reach carrying capacity levels. Simon et al (1999) conducted a census survey for forty years of the wildebeests in the Serengeti Plains of northern Tanzania and southern Kenya. Prior to the 1960s, a virus had limited the wildebeest population in this region to around 200,000 individuals. A vaccine eradicated the virus around 1963. Then, the population increased steadily until it stabilized in 1977. Note the carrying capacity line and the oscillations of the wildebeest population both above and below it.

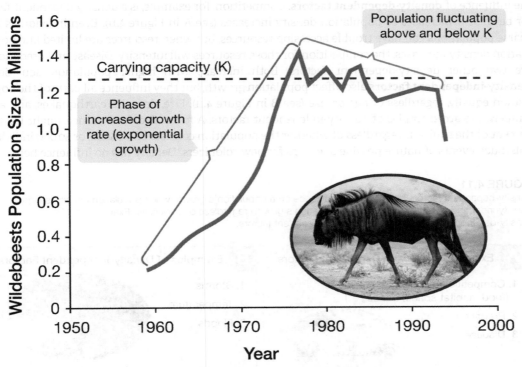

Source: Joseph Shostell; data from Simon, A. Mduma, R., Sinclair, A. R. E. and Hilborn, R. 1999. Food regulates the Serengeti wildebeests: a 40-year record. *Journal of Animal Ecology*, 68: 1101–1122; © Shutterstock, Inc.

Population Growth

Explore types of population growth with teacher Mary Neimeyer.

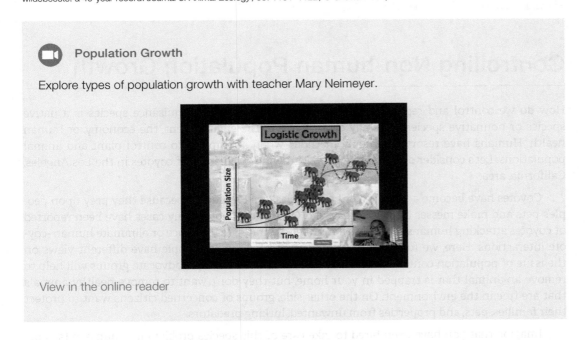

View in the online reader

Density-Dependent and Density-Independent Growth Factors

density-dependent factors

Factors that increase in influence as population density increases; examples are competition and predation.

density-independent factors

Factors that do not increase in influence as population density increases; examples are floods, fires, and hurricanes.

As the density of a population increases, the interactions of its individuals do so as well, along with the influence of **density-dependent factors**. Competition, for example, is a density-dependent factor because it increases as population density increases (see A in Figure 4.11). Even individuals in sparse populations can have trouble accessing resources, but when resources are limited and population density increases, the competition for those resources will intensify. Disease and predation are two other density-dependent factors. Both increase with higher population densities. **Density-independent factors** also affect population growth, but they influence all parts of the population equally, regardless of age or size (see B in Figure 4.11). Fire, drought, earthquakes, and air temperature are examples of density-independent factors. A forest fire, for instance, might kill 95 percent of the squirrels regardless of whether the population consists of 50, 5000, or 50,000 individuals. Such events of nature provide openings for new colonizers. Density has no influence here.

FIGURE 4.11

Density-dependent factors have a greater influence on a population's growth when population density is high. Density-independent factors influence a population's growth regardless of its density. Examples of (A) density-dependent factors and (B) density-independent factors.

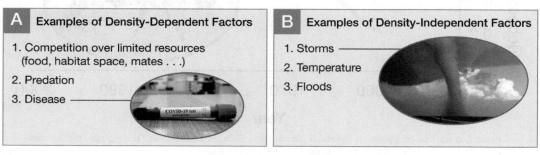

A	Examples of Density-Dependent Factors
	1. Competition over limited resources (food, habitat space, mates . . .)
	2. Predation
	3. Disease

B	Examples of Density-Independent Factors
	1. Storms
	2. Temperature
	3. Floods

Source: Joseph Shostell; © Shutterstock, Inc.

Controlling Non-human Population Growth

How do we control and regulate nuisance species populations? A nuisance species is a native species or nonnative species that may cause harm to the environment, the economy, or human health. Humans have resorted to many methods when attempting to control plant and animal populations. Let's consider one example here: a growing population of coyotes in the Los Angeles, California, area.

Coyotes have become a nuisance in Los Angeles (see Figure 4.12) because they prey upon people's pets and make messes of people's garbage. On a scarier note, many cases have been reported of coyotes attacking humans. There are a number of strategies to reduce or eliminate human–coyote interactions. Here, we focus on population control. As usual, people have different views on the issue of population control of wild animals. For example, animal advocate groups will help to remove an animal that is trapped in your home, but they don't want to remove healthy animals that are free in the environment. On the other side, groups of concerned citizens want to protect their families, pets, and properties from unwanted, lurking predators.

Imagine that you have been hired to take care of this species problem in a humane fashion. Specifically, you have been asked to reduce the coyote population number to an acceptable value. The plan is to relocate a particular number of the coyotes hundreds of miles to the east, to an area where few coyotes presently exist. Keeping your job relies on effectively dealing with the nuisance species. To what number ought you reduce the population so that there will be no incidences of coyotes bothering humans for many years? If the population size is at 10,000 and the carrying capacity is 10,000, would you reduce it to, say, 7,500, or perhaps to 5,000? This may seem like a large reduction, but in fact you would have placed the coyote population back into its exponential growth phase. You would be better off to reduce the coyote population to maybe 500, before the exponential part of the graph.

FIGURE 4.12
Sightings of coyotes in and near urban areas can be quite common in some parts of the United States. (A) In Plainfield, Illinois, a sign warns the public about coyotes. (B) A coyote on a road in downtown Tiburon, California.

Source: Kimberly Boyles/Shutterstock.com; © Shutterstock, Inc.

Key Takeaways

- Populations cannot sustain indefinite exponential growth.
- Different from exponential growth, logistic growth accounts for limiting resources, predation, and competition, resulting in a leveling off of growth as population approaches K.
- Density-dependent factors such as competition and predation have greater influence on population growth as density increases.
- Density-independent factors (fires, floods, etc.) affect members of a population equally, regardless of population density.
- We take into account growth curves and carrying capacity when controlling population size of nuisance species.

4.4 Species Interactions Drive Community Structure

Learning Objectives

1. Describe community structure.
2. Identify and explain the three main types of species interactions.
3. Summarize the functional roles of five different species.

Our chapter opener about Flathead Lake described a large community of different species interacting together. The term "community" can be rather specific—say, just involving fish (a fish community)—or the community may be more general and include all the organisms in the lake. For the second definition, we would state "the lake community." In both cases, a community's structure reflects environmental pressures and the evolutionary history of its species constituents. On an evolutionary scale, a species can change over time, and furthermore, multiple forms or species can develop from a single ancestral species. Each of these newer species exists because they have adapted to a specific niche. As we will discuss shortly, no two species can occupy the same niche.

Community Structure

The structure of a community varies based on the number and type of species it has and the relative abundance of each species (see video link: "Biodiversity").

species richness

The number of species in a community.

- The simplest characteristic of a community is called **species richness**, also known as the number of species. Generally, species richness is greater in healthier environments where there is little or no impact from humans.

evenness

A community measurement that represents the relative number of individuals of each species.

- Not all species have the same effect and role in the environment, and therefore some are more significant than others in defining community structure. In fact, the removal of some predators and competitors from a community can lead to drastic changes in community structure.

- The relative abundance of a species refers to its **evenness**. For instance, two different communities could each have ten different species, seemingly very similar to each other. However, the number of individuals per species category might differ greatly. One community might have nine species with one individual each, and one species that has 991. In this case, evenness would be very low—certainly much less then community two, which also has ten species, but has one hundred individuals in each species category. Together, species richness and evenness make up diversity.

habitat degradation

The quality of a habitat is lowered.

We typically think of healthy environments as having diverse communities. That statement is accurate, but it can also be deceiving because not all healthy environments can support the same community diversity. We could easily make the mistake of comparing two healthy communities, not influenced by **habitat degradation**, and conclude the less diverse community is less healthy. To avoid this trap, it is useful to remember that not all of Earth's environments are the same, and living things evolve and adapt to their environment. By the very fact of having different quantities and types of resources, different environments ought to support a range of community structures with various diversities. Habitats with more resources, including nutrients, should theoretically provide for larger populations and greater diversity.

Biodiversity

Learn about species richness and evenness and the significance of biodiversity.

View in the online reader

Interspecific Interactions

Any interaction between individuals of different species is referred to as **symbiosis** (biosis = life, sym = together). This broad definition takes into account associations that can have negative, beneficial, or no effect on the associating species. Table 4.1 lists predominant types of symbiotic interactions—or interactions between different species.

symbiosis

Life together; any interaction between two organisms.

TABLE 4.1
Types of interactions between species, and their effects.

Type of Interaction	Effects on Species 1	Effects on Species 2
Predation	+	−
Competition	−	−
Parasitism	+	−
Mutualism	+	+

Type of Interaction	Effects on Species 1	Effects on Species 2
Commensalism	+	0
"+" = positive effect, "-" = negative effect, "0" = no effect		

Interspecific Predation

Interspecific predation is similar to intraspecific predation, except that it involves predation between different species instead of within the same species (see A in Figure 4.13). Predation can have profound effects on community structure.

Robert Paine's work in the 1960s and 1970s in intertidal communities off the California coast showed how the presence of predatory starfish (*Pisaster ochraceus*) helps to increase community diversity (Paine 1966). Pisasters preferentially prey on *Mytilus californianus*, a mussel that colonizes and often monopolizes rocks in these communities. In their world, habitat space on the rocks of the intertidal zone—the coastal area that is above water at low tide and becomes submerged at high tide—is a valuable resource. Once a place is secure, the mussels feed on the small organisms like algae that are brought to them by constant wave action. Paine removed pisasters from some intertidal areas and noted that the number of species decreased from fifteen to eight as the mussels increased in number. Also along the West Coast, but a bit farther out from land, we can find two well-known interspecific predators: an apex predator, the killer whale (*Orca*), and a lower trophic-level predator, the sea otter.

FIGURE 4.13
Communities can have multiple types of interactions between species. A) A killer whale attacks a gentoo penguin. B) A parasitoid wasp digs a hole to bury a paralyzed caterpillar for her young to feed on. C) A mutualistic interaction between a bumblebee and a flowering plant. D) In an example of commensalism, a cattle egret feeds on insects disturbed by an elephant.

Source: © Shutterstock, Inc.

Interspecific Competition

Competition between two organisms occurs over a limited resource worth fighting over. We discussed this situation earlier between two members of the same species, or intraspecific competition. Now, we consider interspecific competition, which occurs between two different species. There are many examples of competition between individuals of different species, and often these competing species normally coexist, meaning neither species "wins" over the other. Based on Georgy Gause's experiments, there is a limit to this coexistence (Gause 1934). Garrett Harden stated it well when he wrote, "Complete competitors cannot coexist" (Hardin 1960).

This is referred to as the competitive exclusion principle. In 1934 and 1935, the Russian scientist Gause grew three paramecia—microscopic organisms that live in a water environment—in different tubes, each containing an oatmeal solution that provided a food source for bacteria and yeast, which in turn were preyed upon by the paramecia. When the paramecia species were grown separately, they experienced logistic growth, leveling off at some carrying capacity. However, when Gause combined one species (*Paramecium caudatum*) with a second species (*Paramecium aurelia*), *P. aurelia* reached the carrying capacity whereas *P. caudatum* went extinct (see Figure 4.14). In these experiments, *P. aurelia* was the stronger competitor, able to take in resources more efficiently and outgrow the less efficient *P. caudatum*.

An analogy in the human world would be two cashiers at the same cash register in a grocery store. The cashiers would end up fighting for access to the register. If this did happen, the manager might review their abilities and select the most efficient person to keep the job. The idea of efficiency would be related to how fast they could ring up customers while at the same time making few or no financial mistakes. The nonchosen cashier might be asked to go elsewhere or to change jobs; maybe they could become a courtesy worker instead, meaning the worker would have to exhibit new behavior, such as cleaning up spills in the aisles. Or, the cashiers could agree to occupy different "niches": niche one: using register during daytime; niche two: using register at night.

FIGURE 4.14
Russian ecologist Georgii Frantsevich Gause demonstrated the competitive exclusion principle, with *Paramecium aurelia* out-competing *P. caudatum*, another paramecium with the same niche. Note how *P. caudatum* peaks early and then steadily declines.

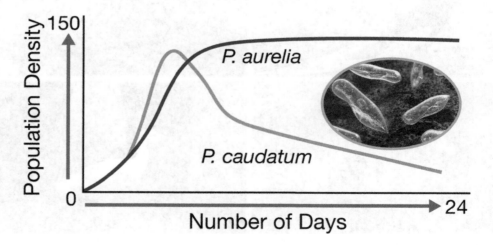

Sources: Joseph Shostell; data from Gause, G. F. 1934. *The Struggle for Existence*. Williams & Wilkins. Baltimore; © Shutterstock, Inc.

Parasitism

A **parasite** is an organism that lives in or on another organism (the **host**), causing the other organism harm. The strategy of a parasite works exceedingly well, so much so that more organisms exhibit **parasitism** than follow the typical lifestyle of a predator hunting and killing its prey (De Meeûs and Renaud 2002). Parasites provide a fine example in which one organism (the parasite) has coevolved with another organism in such a way that the host is disadvantaged, and the parasite benefits. A parasite gains nutrition from the host and may indeed kill a host, but the death is not immediate, and, depending on the parasite, sometimes death due to the parasite does not happen at all. On the other end of the range of parasite lethality, we find parasitoids—a type of insect that parasitizes and kills other insects. A parasitoid lays its eggs in or on a host, and in a short time the eggs hatch and larvae develop through immature stages that eat the host until it dies (see B in Figure 4.13). The parasitoid emerges from the dead host and enters the next phase of its life cycle, an adult ready to mate, reproduce, and parasitize another host.

Scientists have an increasing interest in parasites because they are linked to disease, they contaminate the foods we eat, and they are often considered a nuisance. The value of parasites to community structure cannot be overstated because their presence diminishes the health of some organisms (the coevolved host) and also provides a source of food for others. For example, **community ecologists** studying fringe areas between marine and terrestrial environments found spiders, scorpions, ants, and lizards more abundant on islands that had seabirds than on islands without seabirds. The increased numbers of these other organisms were a result of bird parasites that provided a rich source of food (Polis and Hurd 1996).

Mutualism

Mutualism is an interaction that has positive effects for both species (see C in Figure 4.13). It is both common and important. Without mutualism, the world would be quite a different place. Herbivores such as cows, for example, are only able to digest the grass they eat because of the existence of particular microorganisms in their stomachs. These microorganisms possess enzymes such as cellulase, which is needed to break down the organic molecule cellulose found in plants. In fact, many herbivorous mammals, including zebras, bison, moose, cows, horses, and giraffes, depend on a mutualistic relationship with microorganisms to extract the energy they need from plants. In turn, the microbes gain from having access to food in a moist, warm, and protected environment. Do you wonder how scientists figured out the existence of this relationship between ungulates and microorganisms? They formed and tested their hypothesis about microorganisms in cow stomachs by placing cellulose—the structural carbohydrate in plants—into two containers, each containing fluid extracted from a cow's stomach. To one of the containers they added an antiseptic solution that kills bacteria. The solution that didn't receive the antiseptic had its cellulose broken down (Hungate 1966).

Commensalism is an interaction between two species in which one species benefits while the second is neither benefited nor harmed (see D in Figure 4.13). It is difficult to find true examples of commensalism because in most cases, when the relationship is studied sufficiently, collected data typically point to mutualism, in which both organisms are positively affected. One common example of commensalism is algae growing on the back of a turtle, which has been suggested as a benefit to algae that neither harms nor benefits the turtle. The algae get transported to new locations and are exposed to nutrients in the water that they can absorb. Even this example might not qualify as true commensalism because the presence of attached algae might help to camouflage the turtle's shell from both prey and predators.

parasite

An organism that lives in or on another organism (the host), causing the other organism harm.

host

The organism negatively affected in a parasitic interaction.

parasitism

A symbiotic relationship between two species in which one species (the parasite) lives on or in another species (the host), causing harm and sometimes death to the host species.

community ecologists

Ecologists who study community structure and the factors that affect it.

mutualism

An interaction between two species that benefits both organisms.

commensalism

An interaction between two species in which one benefits while the second is neither benefited nor harmed.

Species Have Different Functional Roles

Through evolutionary processes, communities develop with unique species having their own physical attributes and behaviors. Some species have a greater effect on the overall community structure than do others. For instance, decomposers and keystone species have extremely valuable roles in communities.

Much of the plant matter in a community is never eaten by herbivores, so the energy it contains would be lost from the ecosystem if it were not for decomposers—mostly fungi and bacteria—that feed on organic matter and help recycle it (see A in Figure 4.15). The predation on these decomposers by higher consumers further utilizes the recycled organic matter. Because of their ability to recycle organic matter, decomposers play critical roles in both terrestrial and aquatic systems. Besides microscopic decomposers, terrestrial and aquatic systems have a variety of macro (large) decomposers. In terrestrial ecosystems, snails, flies, and worms have active roles in breaking down and recycling decaying matter. In marine systems, sea urchins, sea cucumbers, and crabs are some of the examples of macro decomposers. Macro decomposers (e.g. crabs) capable of ingesting greater quantities of decaying matter are called **detritivores**. One of the most common detritivores in freshwater ecosystems of the United States are gizzard shad. They are the most abundant fish in most reservoirs of the central and southern United States, and they have the ability to feed directly on sediments to extract needed nutrients. They then excrete nutrients wherever they swim in the water, making the nutrients available to other organisms (Schaus & Vanni 2000; Shostell & Buckaveckas 2004).

FIGURE 4.15
Decomposers and keystone species are important for maintaining normal structure and function of communities. A) A decaying log colonized by fungal decomposers. B) A sea otter is an example of a keystone species.

Source: © Shutterstock, Inc.

Keystone Species

Some species such as predatory starfish are labeled as keystone because despite their relatively low abundance or biomass, their removal can lead to large-scale changes in community structure (Paine 1966). Sea otters, which have a voluminous appetite for sea urchins, are considered **keystone species**. Without sea otters, sea urchin populations explode and decimate kelp forests (see Figure 4.15). James Estes and David Duggins (1995) documented the striking absence of kelp forests where sea otter populations have dwindled in coastal ecosystems. Globally we are still witnessing a recovery of sea otter populations from extensive hunting for their fur into the early part of the twentieth century. More recently, some scientists have suggested that overfishing by humans along the west coast of North America has resulted in killer whales, (*Orca*) targeting sea otters (Williams et al. 2004). If true, humans, once again, are indirectly damaging kelp communities.

What about our opener story? Does the opossum shrimp qualify as a keystone species? No, it does not. Opossum shrimp did cause the elimination of salmon and indirectly the loss of grizzly bears and other animals, but opossum shrimp are an abundant species. When it comes to keystone species, a relatively small population has a disproportionately large effect on community structure.

Key Takeaways

- Species richness and species evenness are two key characteristics of every community.
- Competition, predation, parasitism, mutualism, and commensalism are examples of inter-specific interactions.
- Different species have different functional roles in a community.
- Keystone species strongly influence community structure.

4.5 Community Properties

Learning Objectives

1. Identify the properties of communities and summarize their relevance.
2. Explain how communities are dynamic.
3. Describe the relationship between community succession and stability.

A community—a collection of populations—is more than the sum of its parts, much like a pie is greater than the sum of its individual ingredients. Communities have several distinct properties that populations and other lower hierarchical levels of life do not. The number of species and the relative abundance of each—that is, the diversity of the community (mentioned in Section 4)—may seem like the most obvious property. Here we build on this and discuss structure and the dynamic properties of succession, resilience, and productivity.

We begin with the general structure of the community. It can vary vertically and horizontally. Take a forest, for example, which has different plants in greater abundance at each vertical level. Small fern types might be close to the forest floor and canopies of large trees tower above. We also expect to find specific types of animals at each of these vertical levels, from soil microorganisms at the base to a range of bird species in the canopy. Where species occur vertically depends on environmental conditions such as light intensity. Communities can also exhibit horizontal variation in species type, evenness, and richness when distributed across a region with a gradient of resources. Water, pH, nutrients, and other environmental variables can vary over a landscape. For example, the relative composition of species within a community of trees can be substantially different between areas where the ground is saturated with water close to a river channel, compared to drier areas far from a water source.

Communities Are Dynamic

succession

Gradual, serial change in community structure.

primary succession

Ecological succession of a new environment that lacks organisms and soil.

secondary succession

Ecological succession of an environment that was previously colonized, but disturbed.

Communities are dynamic, for they can recover from disturbances, grow, and adapt to changing environmental conditions. Their serial change, or **succession**, is a gradual process of development that results in stable climax communities (see " Succession "). The two main types of succession are primary and secondary. **Primary succession** refers to the first colonization of a newly created region, such as a new volcanic island or sand dune, and the changes in the community structure that follow (see Figure 4.16). For example, the great weight of retreating glaciers scours away nutrient-laden soil and any evidence of earlier communities, leaving behind a barren landscape. The earliest successful colonizers of this new space are nitrogen fixers, which convert atmospheric nitrogen (N_2) to nitrogen-containing organic molecules in tissues. These pioneer colonizers facilitate the survival of future colonizers by increasing nitrogen concentrations in soil. As they die, their bodies provide other essential elements needed for life and help create a framework of soil. Soil conditions change as pioneer colonizers are replaced by new species. The community changes from mosses and herbaceous species to willows, alders, and eventually Sitka spruce and hemlock trees. In **secondary succession**, soil and fragments of the former community remain, including seeds. All existing communities experience secondary succession, making it more common than primary succession. An example is the regrowth of forests in abandoned agricultural fields. Similar to primary succession, an orderly sequence of community change takes place.

 Succession

Explore primary and secondary community succession.

View in the online reader

FIGURE 4.16

Succession is an example of how communities are dynamic. In primary succession—shown here—pioneering species arrive to a new, barren site and begin to form soil, making the site hospitable to additional species. With time, the pioneering community is replaced by an intermediate community, and finally a climax community.

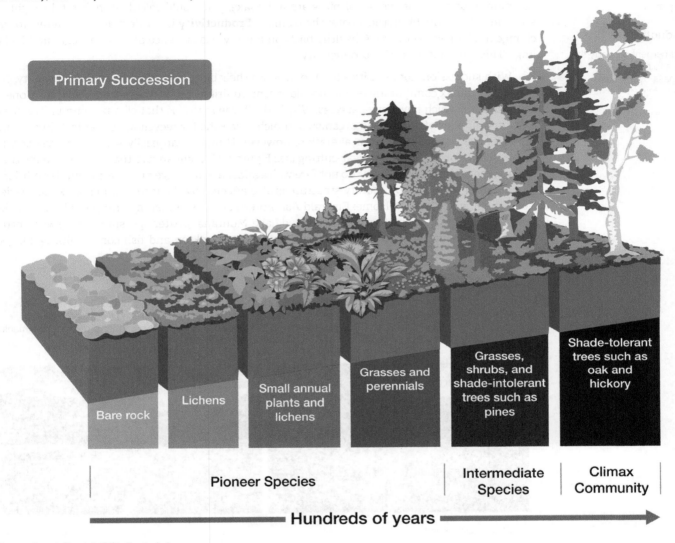

Source: Jospeh Shostell; © Shutterstock, Inc.

Resilience/Stability

The emergent properties of resilience and stability, along with diversity, set communities apart and at a higher structural hierarchy than the populations they contain. **Resilience** represents a community's ability to rebound from changes that result from natural and human-caused factors, whereas **stability** refers to the strength of a community in maintaining its structure. More stable communities do not change as much as less stable communities when presented with an external stressor.

resilience

A community's ability to return to its structure after being changed by a natural or human-caused disturbance.

stability

An emergent property in communities that represents its ability to resist being changed by external factors.

biomass

Weight of all living biological material in a given area.

productivity

An emergent property that refers to change in biomass over time.

How do stability and the other emergent properties of communities relate to succession? We can begin to answer this question by defining biomass and productivity. **Biomass** is the weight of all living biological material in a given area. For example, if you wish to determine the biomass of a community of different species of birds around a lake, you would calculate their total weight in kilograms. The more birds, the greater the biomass. **Productivity** is a little different; it refers to the change in biomass over time. A healthy bird community has evidence of growth—eggs and fledglings. This indicates a positive productivity.

With succession, communities tend to increase their biomass and increase their diversity. On the whole, climax communities—mature, older communities—tend to be more stable than pioneer communities, which have fewer species. Why is this? One reason is that climax communities have a greater number of specialized organisms in niches specific for recycling nutrients. Climax communities are not immune from alteration, however. Humans can easily set back succession to pioneer communities through clear-cutting (see Figure 4.17). Compared to the natural systems they replace, these simplified systems do not fare well against a wide range of environmental conditions (floods, droughts, etc.). Community structure is also affected by the introduction of exotic species (see "Bringing It Closer to Home: Emerald Ash Borer") such as opossum shrimp in Flathead Lake (see "Case Study: Opossum Shrimp in Flathead Lake, Montana "). After opossum shrimp were introduced into the Flathead River–Lake ecosystem, the zooplankton and fish communities changed significantly.

FIGURE 4.17
Mature tropical forest communities support great biodiversity. The clearing of forests to create agricultural areas greatly reduces biodiversity. (A) A view from a foot bridge in a tropical rain forest depicting the complexity and diversity of life far off the ground. (B) A tea plantation in San Jose, Costa Rica, shows a low bio-diversity community of plants growing very close to the ground. The tea plantation has replaced the rain forest.

Source: © Shutterstock, Inc.

Bringing It Closer to Home: Emerald Ash Borer

Just as the exotic opossum shrimp created havoc in the Flathead Lake ecosystem, so are the exotic Asian longhorned beetle and emerald ash borer disrupting our native hardwood communities. The insects were introduced accidentally, as opposed to opossum shrimp. Besides the threat to nature, the U.S. and Canadian economies are affected too, because the maple syrup, hardwood lumber, and tourism industries all depend on these communities. Of the two insect pests, the emerald ash borer is more host-specific—preying on ash trees—and has already killed more than 20 million trees across Michigan, Ohio, Indiana, and Ontario. Foresters are concerned that the parasite will continue to spread to healthy forests in Minnesota, North Dakota, and Wisconsin. How many trees are potentially affected, and how can you help to prevent the spread of these parasites? If single-state numbers offer any suggestion, Wisconsin alone has an estimated 700 million ash trees! In an attempt to inhibit their spread, the U.S. Army Corps of Engineers and U.S. Forest Service request that people not transport firewood beyond where it was collected. Then, get involved by assessing your local hardwoods—observing for signs of these exotic species (see "Signs of Emerald Ash Borer" here). Should you find evidence, take a photo and contact the U.S. Forest Service or your local university.

Key Takeaways

- Communities have distinct properties (diversity, resilience, and stability) that set them apart from the populations they contain.
- Communities can exhibit vertical and horizontal variation in structure.
- Communities are dynamic.
- A community's productivity refers to its change in biomass over time.
- Succession is a gradual process of change in community structure.
- Communities become more stable as they mature (climax).

4.6 Obstacles and Solutions to Protecting Populations and Communities

Learning Objectives

1. Explain why a genetically isolated population can be at risk of going extinct.
2. Describe the benefits of using metacommunity theory when trying to manage communities.
3. Discuss the conservation value of corridors in helping to maintain and even improve diversity.

When sections of the physical environment change significantly (e.g., new road, agricultural field, city), away from what populations and communities have adapted to, populations and communities can become discontinuous or fragmented. Instead of a continuous population or community over a large geographical area, there may be no individuals in some areas and then pockets of isolated populations and communities in other areas. Habitat disruption and fragmentation are problems. Unfortunately, habitat disruption and fragmentation of populations and communities are often associated with human activities. To put the problem of habitat loss and fragmentation in perspective, consider that approximately 40 percent of Earth's terrestrial areas have already been converted for agricultural use (Hedges and Olkin 1985; Prugh et al. 2008). All of these areas formerly supported natural populations and communities.

Anthropogenic habitat disruption can be broken down into three main categories: complete destruction of a habitat, degradation of a habitat, and disturbing a habitat (see Figure 4.18). It is reasonable to conclude that complete habitat destruction is harmful to populations and communities because organisms need habitat space to live. Deforestation is the leading example of large-scale habitat destruction. Habitat degradation—a lowering of the useful quality of a habitat to its resident organisms—can be severe, but is a step down from whole-scale habitat destruction. Habitat degradation can take a variety of forms, including a new road and pollution. We define **habitat disturbance** very specifically to include only the presence of people visiting a habitat, such as hiking through a forest or swimming in a lake. Visits by people to nature can eventually lead to habitat degradation and even large-scale habitat destruction. It's important to keep in mind that many people, ecologists included, lump habitat destruction and habitat degradation into the single category of habitat disturbance. Habitat disturbance, as we define it here, is less of a threat for communities than habitat degradation, but it too can have negative consequences to communities. Visits by curious people to natural habitats can disrupt nesting sites for birds or other animals. Cave

habitat disturbance

People visiting a habitat, such as when hiking through a forest; such visits can lead to habitat degradation.

communities, for example, are easily disturbed by visitors. People who visit caves contaminated with fungus spores can accidentally spread a disease known as white nose syndrome, which has killed an estimated 6 million bats since its discovery in 2006. Bats provide an important presence in the environment by being able pollinators and predators of insects.

FIGURE 4.18
Community diversity is lowered by complete habitat destruction, habitat degradation, and habitat disturbance, all results of human activities. (A) Deforestation in Sumatra (complete habitat destruction). (B) A pipe empties industrial waste into a stream (habitat degradation). (C) A hiker jumps across a stream and continues with her hike (habitat disturbance).

Source: © Shutterstock, Inc.

Fragmenting Populations and Genetic Isolation

Most populations of a species have at least some reproductive contact with other populations. The resulting exchange of genetic material keeps their gene pools similar. Loss of a population's connectivity and its increased isolation can cause low gene flow between populations and lead to genetic differentiation—that is, genetic change from other populations of the same species. In these situations, gene flow between populations can be insufficient to counteract genetic drift, which is a major driver of genetic divergence. Smaller isolated populations with low genetic diversity are at greater risk of extinction from unpredictable fluctuation in environmental conditions. This is a concern. One way conservation managers help isolated populations conserve their genetic diversity and even improve it is by increasing the connectedness among populations (Segelbacher et al. 2003). For example, by creating habitat corridors in which individuals can migrate between populations, diversity is maintained.

Metacommunities and Preservation Lands

metacommunity theory

A theory that describes processes that occur at the metacommunity scale.

A metacommunity is a group of local communities connected by thin habitat corridors. You can think of a metacommunity as a larger discontinuous community consisting of smaller semi-isolated communities. Similarly, a metapopulation is a collection of smaller isolated populations. Conservation managers have focused on **metacommunity theory** as a way to help maintain and improve biodiversity in a world where environmental destruction, degradation, and disturbance are ever increasing (see Figure 4.19).

FIGURE 4.19

Habitat destruction and degradation can cause populations and communities to be fragmented. Conservation biologists rely on metacommunity and metapopulation theories, which focus on trying to link fragmented communities (or populations) together by creating dispersal corridors. A) In British Columbia, Canada, deforestation has isolated populations and communities. What once was a continuous forest ecosystem has now been partly destroyed and cut into two parts. The green arrows represent the distance individuals must travel through a destroyed habitat to reach another forested area. B) In the Kaluga region of Russia, a habitat corridor connects two forested areas divided by a highway.

Source: © Shutterstock, Inc.

One solution to the loss of habitat and consequently diversity is to set aside tracts of wilderness areas that are protected from human influence. Although this is a solution, is it better to set aside one large section of land—say, millions of acres—or is it preferable to preserve a series of smaller acreages that are connected by habitat corridors? Both potential solutions provide an equal amount of land area, but structurally, they are arranged differently.

The second possibility is based on metacommunity theory and the interactions among individual communities. One large benefit to having multiple smaller communities connected by wildlife corridors is that should an environmental catastrophe occur in one geographical location, resulting in the local extinction of one community, the larger metacommunity still survives. Narrow land areas linking the destroyed community to healthy communities or to source communities of immigrants can be dispersal routes for the recolonization of a habitat. We are making some assumptions here, such as the environment's not being altered to the point it can no longer support life. A network of connected communities can also help the survival of organisms with good dispersal ability that might be poor competitors, or help prey avoid predators. Charles Huffaker (1958) demonstrated this on a small-scale ecosystem with oranges and the predatory and prey mites that colonize them. In his experiments, Huffaker placed oranges on trays and observed the migration and colonizing pattern of predatory mites and their prey from orange to orange. In later experiments, Huffaker replaced some of the oranges with rubber balls, hoping to create a patchy environment in which predator and prey populations could coexist. His work demonstrated that spatial heterogeneity, dispersal ability of organisms, and habitat corridors (wooden sticks in his experiments) can lead to a stability between predators and their prey.

Creating corridors between healthy communities and between healthy populations may be the only viable option for some communities, where large tracts of land are not available as preserves. In these situations, conservation managers direct their attention to wildlife corridors even if they include only privately owned land. The continued survival of some species depends on the dispersal ability of its individuals.

Key Takeaways

- Human activities can destroy valuable habitat space for populations and cause populations to become fragmented.
- Isolated populations diverge genetically and may eventually evolve into separate species.

- Metacommunity theory is based on the model of a community broken up into smaller, somewhat isolated communities connected through habitat corridors.
- Conservation managers have focused on metacommunity theory as a way to help maintain and improve biodiversity.

4.7 A Look to the Future: Predictions for the Flathead Lake Community

Learning Objectives

1. Recount the story of Flathead Lake to explain how introductions of non-native species can disrupt communities.
2. Hypothesize as to the future of the Flathead Lake ecosystem.

Returning to our opening story, what does the future have in store for species within Flathead Lake? Introductions of non-native opossum shrimp, kokanee salmon, and lake trout have overwhelmed evolutionarily evolved native species, including cutthroat trout and bull trout. For example, lake trout continue to devastate the bull trout population by preying on young and competing with adults for food. Looking to the future, it seems the Flathead Lake ecosystem will not support a strong return of native species populations until non-native species are removed. Because complete removal of every opossum shrimp and lake trout is impossible, we will have to wait and see how natural selection acts on these species over time. Tribal communities have been successful in lessening the effects of the invasive fish species by sponsoring events called "mack days." During the 2021 mack-day event, $200,000 in prizes attracted anglers to Flathead Lake to catch and kill lake trout. These efforts reduce the invasive lake trout population by 75 percent, which gives the dwindling native trout population a chance to survive. The Flathead Lake ecosystem's future may well depend on new fishing regulations, which, up to this point, have prohibited the removal of large lake trout, or, maybe a new species introduction will upend the entire system once again. Other serious threats to the survival of native trout are the presence of Hungary Horse Dam, because it blocks spawning routes, and warmer water temperatures in Flathead Lake due to the effects of climate change. If these threats are mitigated, we may observe a resurgence of native trout species in Flathead Lake.

Key Takeaways

- Native trout species face several threats in Flathead Lake.
- Eradication of problematic non-native species from Flathead Lake is impossible, but these species can be kept at low densities if fishing regulations change, and if concerted efforts targeting problem species are used.

FIGURE 4.20 Visual Overview: Evolution, Interactions, and Communities

Summarizing figure: Populations (4.1) are shaped by evolutionary forces, (4.2) contain interacting individuals, and (4.3) display growth based on environmental conditions. Communities (4.4) consist of interacting species and (4.5) have distinct properties. There are (4.6) obstacles to and solutions for protecting populations and communities. (4.7) Evolutionary processes may be too slow for native species in Flathead Lake to adapt to the current rate of change caused by anthropogenic activities. Their future depends on mitigation measures to lessen the effects of exotic species, climate change, and dam construction.

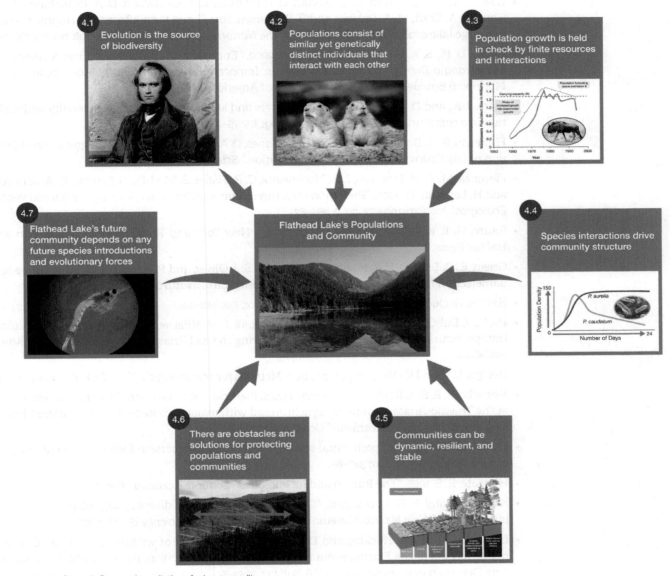

Sources: Joseph Shostell; See previous citations for image credits.

4.8 References

- Archibald, J. D., W. A. Clemens, K. Padian, T. Row, N. Macleod, et al. 2010. "Cretaceous extinctions: multiple causes." *Science* 328: 973.

- Bond, D. P. G., and P. B. Wignall. 2008. "The role of sea-level change and marine anoxia in the Frasnian–Famennian (Late Devonian) mass extinction." *Palaeogeogr Palaeoclimatol Palaeoecol* 263: 107–18.

- Darwin, C. R. 1859. *On the origin of species by means of natural selection, or the preservation of favoured races in the struggle for life.* London, England: John Murray.
- De Meeûs, T., and F. Renaud. 2002. "Parasites within the new phylogeny of eukaryotes." *Trends in Parasitology* 18: 247–51.
- Ellis, B. K., J. A. Stanford, D. Goodman, C. P. Stafford, D. L. Gustafson, D. A. Beauchamp, D. W. Chess, J. A. Craft, M. A. Deleray, and B. S. Hansen. 2011. "Long-term effects of a trophic cascade in a large lake ecosystem." *Proceedings of the National Academy of Sciences* 108, no. 3: 1070–75.
- Eriwn, D. H., S. A. Bowring, and J. Yugan. 2002. "End-Permian mass extinctions: A review." In *Catastrophic Events and Mass Extinctions: Impacts and Beyond* (Eds. C. Koeberl, and K. G. Mackleod) Boulder, CO: Geological Society of America.
- Estes, J. A., and D. O. Duggins. 1995. "Sea otters and kelp forests in Alaska: generality and variation in a community paradigm." *Ecol Monogr* 65: 75–100.
- Finnegan, S., K. Bergmann, J. M. Eiler, D. S. Jones, D. A. Fike, et al. 2011. "The magnitude and duration of late Ordovician-early Silurian glaciation." *Science* 331, no. 18: 903–6.
- Fiorenza, M., C. H. Peterson, L. S. Mullineaux, C. R. Fisher, S. W. Mills, G. Sancho, G. A. Johnson, and H. Lenihan, H. 2002. "Predation structures communities at deep-sea hydrothermal vents." *Ecological Monographs* 72, no. 3, 365–82.
- Gause, G. F. 1934. *The Struggle for Existence.* New York and Royal Oak, MI: Macmillan and Hafner Press.
- Green, E., B. E. Lyon, V. R. Muehter, L. Ratcliffe, S. J. Oliver, and P. T. Boag. 2000. "Disruptive sexual selection for plumage coloration in a passerine bird." *Nature* 407: 1000–3.
- Hardin, G. 1960. "Competitive exclusion." *Science.* 132: 348–49.
- He, T., J. Dal Corso, R. J. Newton, P. B. Wignall, B. J. W. Mills, et al. 2020. "An enormous sulfur isotope excursion indicates marine anoxia during the end-Triassic mass extinction." *Sci Adv* 6: eabb6704.
- Hedges, L. V., and V. Olkin. 1985. *Statistical Methods for Metaanalysis.* New York: Academic Press.
- Hesselbo, S. P., S. A. Robinson, F. Surlyk, and S. Piasecki. 2002. "Terrestrial and marine extinction at the Triassic-Jurassic boundary synchronized with major carbon-cycle perturbation: a link to initiation of massive volcanism?" *Geology* 30: 251–54.
- Huffaker, C. B. 1958. "Experimental studies on predation: dispersion factors and predator-prey oscillations." *Hilgardia* 27: 343–83.
- Hungate, R. E. 1966. "The Rumen and its Microbes." London: Academic Press.
- Khosla, A., and S. G. Lucas. 2016. "Cretaceous period: biotic diversity and biogeography—an introduction." *New Mexico Museum of Natural History and Science Bulletin* 71: 1–4.
- Liu, Z., D. Selby, P. C. Hackley, and D. J. Over. 2020. "Evidence of wildfires and elevated atmospheric oxygen at the Frasnian–Famennian Boundary in New York (USA): Implications for the Late Devonian mass extinction." *GSA Bull* 132: 2043–54.
- McGhee, G. R., and G. Racki. 2021. "Extinction: Late Devonian mass extinction." *Paleontology* 2: 1–8.
- Newbolt, C. H., P. K. Acker, T. J. Neuman, S. I. Hoffman, S. S. Ditchkoff, and T. D. Steury. 2017. "Factors influencing reproductive success in male white-tailed deer." *The Journal of Wildlife Management* 81, no. 2: 206–217.
- Nicholson, A. J., and V. A. Bailey. 1935. "The balance of animal populations, Part I." *Proceedings of the Zoological Society* 125: 551–98.
- Paine, R. T. 1966. "Food web complexity and species diversity." *American Naturalist* 100: 65–75.
- Polis, G. A. 1981. "The evolution and dynamics of intraspecific predation." *Annual Review of Ecology Systematics* 12: 225–51.

- Polis, G. A., and S. D. Hurd. 1996. "Linking marine and terrestrial food webs: allochthonous input from the ocean supports high secondary productivity on small islands and coastal land communities." *The American Naturalist* 147, no. 3: 396–423.

- Prugh, L. R., K. E. Hodges, A. R. E. Sinclair, and J. S. Brashares. 2008. "Effect of habitat area and isolation on fragmented populations." *Proceedings of the National Academy of Sciences-USA* 05, no. 52: 20770–775.

- Ruhl, M., N. R. Bonis, G. J. Reichart, J. S. S. Damsté, and W. M. Kürschner. 2011. "Atmospheric carbon injection linked to end-Triassic mass extinction." *Science* 333: 430–34.

- Schaus, M., and M. J. Vanni. 2000. "Effects of gizzard shad on phytoplankton and nutrient dynamics: role of sediment feeding and filter size." *Ecology* 81, no. 6: 1701–19.

- Segelbacher, G., J. Höglund, and I. Storch. 2003. "From connectivity to isolation: genetic consequences of population fragmentation in capercaillie across Europe." *Molecular Ecology* 12: 1773–80.

- Simon, A., R. Mduma, A. R. E. Sinclair, and R. Hilborn. 2001. "Food regulates the Serengeti wildebeests: a 40-year record." *Journal of Animal Ecology* 68: 1101–22.

- Spencer, C. N., B. R. McClelland, and J. A. Stanford. 1991. "Shrimp stocking, salmon collapse, and eagle displacement." *BioScience* 41: 14–21.

- Spencer, C. N., D. S. Potter, R. T. Bukantis, and J. A. Stanford. 1999. "Impact of predation by Mysis relicta on zooplankton in Flathead Lake, Montana, USA." *J Plankton Res* 21: 51–64.

- Shostell, J. M., and P. A. Bukaveckas. 2004. "Seasonal and interannual variation in nutrient fluxesfrom tributary inputs, consumer recycling and algal growth in a eutrophic river impoundment." *Aquatic Ecology* 38, no 3: 359–73.

- Takahashi, R., K. Watanabe, M. Nishida, and M. Hori. 2007. "Evolution of feeding specialization in Tanganyikan scale-eating cichlids: a molecular phylogenetic approach." *BMC Evolutionary Biology* 7: 195.

- Taylor, C. E., and C. Condra. 1980. "R- and K-selection in Drosophila psudoobscura." *Evolution* 34, no. 6: 1183–93.

- Williams, T. M., J. A. Estes, D. F. Doak, and A. M. Springer. 2004. "Killer appetites: assessing the role of predators in ecological communities." *Ecology* 85, no. 12: 3373–84.

- Wilson, A., T. Y. Hubel, S. D. Wilshin, J. C. Lowe, M. Lorenc, et al. 2018. "Biomechanics of predator-prey arms race in lion, zebra, cheetah and impala." *Nature* 554: 183–8.

CHAPTER 5
Ecosystems and Biomes

Case Study: A Tale of Early North America

Since its formation over 4.6 billion years ago, Earth has continually undergone change. An atmosphere and continents formed, and life developed. Because humans have an average lifespan of only seventy-eight years—only an instant in comparison to the age of Earth—it can be challenging to comprehend these changes. For example, without the help of sophisticated equipment, we cannot detect the continents moving at rates of 2–15 centimeters a year (Atwater, T. 1970; Riddihough 1984). Yet, they do move. An accumulation of small movements over the course of hundreds of millions of years has resulted in North America and the other continents, changing from being connected as one supercontinent to their present positions. Even the development of landscapes on existing continents might take, at a minimum, tens of thousands of years to develop. Some complex communities and their physical habitats—collectively referred to as ecosystems—such as forests, lakes, and rivers, can also take thousands of years or even longer to form. Here, in this opening story, we focus on a relatively small change—the rise and fall of ecosystems—in one section of the east coast of North America.

Approximately 20,000 to 25,000 years before the first European explorers arrived in North America by ship, a massive ice sheet covered most of what would become Canada and the northern United States, including New England. Named the Laurentide ice sheet, it was over two miles thick, and at its maximum extent covered over thirteen million square kilometers (5 MM km^2), including New Plymouth, which was the region settled by the Pilgrims thousands of years later (Sugden 1977; Carroll et al. 2002). As the leading section of the ice sheet advanced southward, it ground down everything in its path (see Figure 5.1). In response to the advancing ice, plant and animal distributions shifted southward as well.

FIGURE 5.1
Natural and artificial disturbances affect forest ecosystems. Glaciation events are examples of disturbances to ecosystems. In the image, a group of tourists view Perito Moreno Glacier in Los Glaciares National Park, Argentina.

Source: © Shutterstock, Inc.

With uptake of water into the growing ice sheets, sea levels were 120 m (394 ft) lower than what they are today. Populations of trees such as those in the temperate deciduous forests found in the current Northeast shifted south of the encroaching ice sheet, to at least present-day Atlanta and on to the exposed continental shelf, which is usually submerged in relatively shallow water, and the dry Gulf of Mexico (Delcourt and Delcourt 1984). Tree populations had a dramatic response to the changing climatic conditions during the Earth's transition into this last ice age. Forests that grew during the glaciation would probably have been less dense and most likely have grown in clumps in more protected and less abundant wet areas.

The low sea levels also created a land bridge called Beringia connecting Siberia to Alaska, which was used by early people to migrate from Asia to North America. The first generations of these early people would have witnessed some of the changes in climate as Earth warmed up again and the ice sheets melted. They would also have seen young forests spreading northward, indicating natural reforestation. These shifts in landscapes took place before humans had any major effects on the larger environment.

When the Italian explorer Giovanni Caboto (John Cabot) arrived at the east coast of North America in 1497, he must have beheld a wonderful vista of forests still undisturbed by the large-scale colonization that would eventually follow. Colonization of the "new world" by Europeans didn't really take off for another 100 years, with the establishment of Jamestown in the colony of Virginia in 1607 and Plymouth in 1620. John Cabot, the settlers of Virginia, and the Pilgrims—who arrived in the famous *Mayflower* and settled in what would become Massachusetts—would have seen old-growth forests with trees hundreds of years old.

The sight may have been daunting as well, because much of the five million acres that would eventually become Massachusetts was thickly forested at the time with hemlock, red spruce, and black birch trees. Many of these and other mature trees, including sugar maples, red maples, and northern red oaks, would have been at least 27.4 m (90 ft) tall. Trunks of the old trees could easily have been 0.6–0.9 m (2–3 ft) in diameter, and there would have been large volumes of woody debris on the forest floor. Looking up to the tops of the trees, the settlers would have noticed gnarled crowns and a few openings in the canopy where trees had died of old age.

The Pilgrims who came aboard the *Mayflower* and the many groups that followed, including the Puritans who settled farther north, cleared sections of the forests to make room for their respective colonies and to have agricultural fields. Cleared areas also became pastureland to support animals the settlers brought with them on the ships. Their livestock—cows, pigs, chickens, goats, and sheep—needed areas to roam and feed. Along with fur pelts from beavers and other animals, fish and wood became important commodities for the New England colonies as they traded with Europe. Wood from the chopped-down trees also provided a steady supply of timber for building ships, houses, and furniture. The tallest species of trees, white pine—which can reach heights of 61 m (200 ft)—was mostly reserved for ship masts and was sought by England's Royal Navy.

As part of the Great Migration of Puritans, around 20,000 Europeans came to the colonies in the 1630s alone. The human population in North America grew and wide-scale deforestation occurred up through the mid-nineteenth century, by which time 50 percent of the roughly five million acres of Massachusetts were cleared (Dunwiddie 1993). The large temperate deciduous forest of the east coast of North America was not the only resource reduced; so too were the many animals that lost habitat space or were selectively hunted by the growing colonies. The demand for beaver pelts by hatters in London from the efficient hunters in the colonies led to the decline of beavers. White-tailed deer declined as well, and other animal species became locally extinct, including the wild turkey and the wolf. Other species that could utilize newly created open habitat—such as skunks, woodchucks, and cottontail rabbits—increased in number.

During the Industrial Revolution, large numbers of New Englanders who lived in rural agricultural areas moved to urban areas—abandoning approximately nine million acres of farmland across New England (Barraclough & Gould 1955). No longer maintained, the former farmlands became overgrown and changed into young forests in a process similar to what had occurred when the glaciers receded thousands of years before, except this time reforestation occurred more quickly because soil and seeds were already present.

Present-day Massachusetts is starkly different from the mature climax forest that covered it when the Pilgrims and Puritans first arrived. Tree surveys conducted throughout the state show that of the original five million acres of mature forests, only thirty-three stands remain, for a combined total of 1,119 acres (D'Amato et al. 1996). The surveyors located living trees that predated the arrival of the first settlers. For example, they found hemlock trees and red spruce trees that were over four hundred years old. Today, Massachusetts has regained some of its forests, with 64 percent of the state forested (Foster et al. 2006). Most of the forests (99 percent) are not considered old-growth forests because they have regrown since colonization, and consequently are not the same age and maturity as the original old-growth forests that have remained.

The outlook for Massachusetts' forests is somewhat positive because 1.1 million acres are now protected. Yet, on the negative side, another 1.1 million acres are already developed, leaving roughly three million acres undeveloped and unprotected. Deforestation again threatens the forests of Massachusetts, as seventy-eight acres are lost daily to development (Breunig 2008). This threat again challenges a state that has become the third most densely populated state in the country and one that has successfully regenerated a large percentage of its forests. Forests are worth protecting for many reasons, including 1) being carbon sinks in a world where atmospheric carbon is a problem; 2) providing habitat space for a diversity of animals; and 3) providing an improved quality of life for humans. One wonders what the landscape in Massachusetts will be like in the next twenty thousand years.

This story explains how ecosystems—a focus of this chapter—are not static and can be altered by natural and artificial forces. Massachusetts's forests provide one example amid many ecosystems that can be severely altered but can also recover. In this chapter, we also discuss terrestrial regions referred to as biomes, which have specific climates and community types, and aquatic environments referred to as life zones.

5.1 Ecosystem Structure and Function

Learning Objectives

1. Identify living and non-living components in a hypothetical ecosystem.
2. List goods and services provided by ecosystems.
3. Describe internal factors that lead to stability within an ecosystem, and external factors that can destabilize an ecosystem.
4. Explain the meaning of resistance and resilience in reference to aquatic and terrestrial ecosystems.

In this chapter, we further explore Earth's terrestrial and aquatic ecosystems. Each ecosystem, whether in northern North America, the Gulf of Mexico, or elsewhere, is a system consisting of a biological community and the community's physical environment (Arthur Tansley 1935). Scientists who study these diverse systems are called ecosystem ecologists. Their knowledge and skills are sought after by private agencies, federal and state governments, and universities. We begin with a review of ecosystem structure, goods, and services.

Ecosystem Structure, Goods, and Services: A Review

An ecosystem consists of one or more communities and the nonliving environment where those communities reside (see Chapter 3). Therefore, an ecosystem's structure is more complex than a community's because it contains living and nonliving components. The nonliving components of an ecosystem are the water (hydrosphere), soil particles and rocks (lithosphere), and air (atmosphere). The living components are the organisms, and like these, a healthy ecosystem requires a continuous source of energy to function.

Healthy, functioning ecosystems cycle matter and serve as throughputs for energy. These functions allow ecosystems to provide goods and services that benefit living organisms (see Chapter 1). Ecosystem goods are tangible benefits from ecosystems that include, for example, wood for construction and food for our kitchen tables. A little less obvious, ecosystems are also reservoirs for medicinal plants, which contain active ingredients for pharmaceuticals used to fight diseases.

Ecosystem services are intangible benefits from ecosystems. For example, ecosystems pollinate crops, provide pest control, create and stabilize soil, create raw materials, and maintain biogeochemical cycles. Human society depends on these services. For example, we depend on elements that cycle in and between ecosystems, such as carbon, nitrogen, phosphorus, and other elements that are essential for plant growth. Without the service of biogeochemical cycles, elements would be unavailable to plants for uptake.

Returning to the chapter's opening story, deforestation by early settlers in North America dramatically altered and even destroyed large forest ecosystems. With the removal of a forest, services provided by the forest cease. Nonexistent roots cannot stop soil erosion, and flooding is more likely to occur. An easily overlooked service from forests is the maintenance of good air quality. Forests filter the air we breathe by directly uptaking gaseous air pollutants such as ozone, sulfur dioxide, and nitrogen dioxide and by capturing particulate-matter pollution on plant surfaces (Nowak et al 2006; Nowak 2013). Trees in the United States alone, for example, are estimated to remove over 17 million metric tons of air pollution per year (Nowak et al. 2014). In addition, forests take up carbon dioxide and release oxygen. Deforestation also increases atmospheric carbon dioxide levels and therefore climate change because it releases carbon that had been locked in durable tree tissues, and reduces the amount of carbon dioxide that can be absorbed in the future. Probably the most intangible ecosystem services are spiritual benefits—those related to religion. Our knowledge of the many benefits of ecosystems encourages us to protect ecosystems. Some scientists have even attempted to measure the economic value of ecosystem services (see "Critical Thinking Activity: Economical Value of Earth's Ecosystems").

Critical Thinking Activity: Economical Value of Earth's Ecosystems

In 1997, Professor Robert Costanza led a team of researchers to assess the value of Earth's ecosystems and natural capital (Costanza et al. 1997). Natural capital refers to Earth's natural assets: soils, air, water, all living things, and geology. Accounting for inflation, their estimate is approximately $54 trillion. Many scientists and environmental ethicists have contested and questioned how an economic value can be assigned to systems that are priceless, sacred, and necessary for life. What do you think?

Assigning an Economic Value to Ecosystems

Think through how we might calculate the value of an ecosystem.

View in the online reader

Types of Ecosystems

There are many types of ecosystems on Earth, both terrestrial and aquatic. They differ in location, commonness, age, degree of openness, size, and species. Some such as caves are relatively isolated, whereas others such as grasslands or coral reefs are highly connected to other ecosystems. Each has its own group of adapted organisms, and many have well-defined boundaries such as the sharp delineation of a grassland with a forest, or the abrupt ending of a forest at the shore of a lake. Some ecosystems—particularly smaller ones and islands—are usually more fragile and have less ability to respond to disturbances. Terrestrial and aquatic ecosystems are further explored next.

Terrestrial Ecosystems

Any land system, no matter the size, that includes both a biological community and its physical environment qualifies as a **terrestrial ecosystem**. With this definition, an ecosystem is a very general term that can apply to the entire world or to any smaller system that still meets the definition. Even a single organism can be considered an ecosystem because it offers a defined habitat for a variety of microbes. It is easy to confuse the term *ecosystem* with *biome*—another ecological unit—because some scientists have suggested that biomes are ecosystems at the regional scale. Traditionally, *biome* refers to a land area characterized by a community or group of similar communities within a specific climate. Common terrestrial ecosystems include deserts, forests, grasslands, tundra, and taiga.

terrestrial ecosystem

A land system that includes both a biological community and its physical environment.

Critical Thinking Activity: Gaia Theory

Most ecologists think of the ecosphere as the top hierarchical level of ecology because it includes all living things, as well as their physical environment. Gaia theory (Lovelock 1989) has served to sway some ecologists to view Earth as a single macro-organism. If this level is accepted as well, then Earth would be another, more-complex level of ecology. Do you agree with this concept? What evidence is there to support the Earth as a living organism?

Among the many services they uphold, terrestrial ecosystems help to preserve healthy rivers and estuaries. Experiments at the Hubbard Brook Ecosystem within the White Mountain National Forest of New Hampshire documented how deforestation can change stream chemistry (Likens and Bormann 1975). In a large ecosystem experiment, researchers deforested one of the Hubbard Brook watersheds—the land area from which water drains into a stream (or river or lake)—to determine the effects of deforestation on a stream system. Leaching of soils increased and dissolved inorganic nutrient concentrations increased in the receiving stream by a factor of thirteen. This experiment documented the tight coupling between terrestrial and aquatic ecosystems. The Hubbard Brook ecosystem study continues today and is managed by the USDA Forest Service (see Figure 5.2).

FIGURE 5.2
The Hubbard Brook ecosystem in New Hampshire has been the site of large-scale ecosystem experiments for the last few decades. (A) Calcium is deployed by helicopter to determine its role in regulating forest and aquatic ecosystem functions. (B) A watershed has been deforested to determine its effects on stream chemistry.

Sources: Courtesy of Hubbard Brook Ecosystem, http://data.hubbardbrook.org/photos/picture.php?/199/; USDA Forest Service, Northern Research Station.

Aquatic Ecosystems

aquatic ecosystems

A body of water together with all of its biotic and abiotic components.

Lakes, rivers, estuaries, bogs, and oceans are all examples of **aquatic ecosystems**, which cover over 71 percent of the planet's surface and support the continuance of many ecosystem services essential for life and society. One of the most basic and underappreciated services of aquatic ecosystems, with the help of terrestrial ecosystems and the water cycle, is to continually provide fresh water. Another is the photosynthesis of countless phytoplankton. They are a source of much of the oxygen in our atmosphere (Field et al. 1998) and form the bases of aquatic food webs. Phytoplankton are eaten by zooplankton, which in turn are eaten by larger species, including fish. Up until the 1970s, the continued productivity of fish communities and their ability to recover from heavy fishing pressure was rarely questioned. However, as we will see in Chapter 10, since that time, this ecosystem service is straining, and it has become increasingly clear that the fishing industry's current practices are unsustainable (Pauly et al. 2005; Sumaila and Tai 2020).

Our understanding of the structure and function of aquatic ecosystems comes from conducting large-scale experiments in places such as the Experimental Lakes Area (ELA) in Northwestern Ontario, Canada. ELA has been the site of large aquatic ecosystem research since the 1970s. For example, Dr. David Schindler completed an experiment on one of the lakes, Lake 226, in which phosphorus was added to the entire lake (Schindler 1974). This and similar ecosystem-level experiments demonstrate the link between nutrient loads and phytoplankton blooms. Check out ELA's homepage and webcam to learn more about their current opportunities and activities to support ecological research and sustainable use of the environment. For instance, ELA scientists are currently studying the effects of silver nanoparticles on aquatic ecosystems. Silver nanoparticles are used as odor-fighting and antibacterial agents in socks and sports clothing.

Ecosystem Stability

Healthy ecosystems are resilient to normal, natural disturbances, which can take on many forms: windstorms, fire, floods, drought, lightning, and immigration of new species. Ecosystems can also recuperate from stress caused by human activities, but the speed of recovery depends on the type, level, and duration of activity. In the opening story, trees did eventually grow back in Massachusetts, a sign that even heavily stressed ecosystems may recover. What is it within an ecosystem that gives rise to resilience?

Stability does not arise from any single ecosystem component, and not all components of an ecosystem have equal weight in helping to maintain stability and resilience. Generally, the greater the number and type of living components—organisms—the more stable the ecosystem and the better it is at responding to natural disturbances and stress caused by human activities. One way to think about an ecosystem's stability in regard to its components is to compare the ecosystem to a plane, and the components of the ecosystem to the rivets holding the plane together. Any single rivet is not essential to a smooth flight, but the loss of a critical number of rivets can be devastating.

Ecosystem resistance is the property of an ecosystem that enables it to resist potential change caused by an external factor. One example of resistance is the buffering capacity of lake ecosystems, which helps to explain the varying responses of lakes to acid rain. Well-buffered lakes can absorb hydrogen ions in rainwater without changing their pH, until the molecules that bind to the hydrogen ions are no longer available. When this happens, the lake can no longer resist changes in its pH. If the inputs of hydrogen ions continue, the pH of the lake will plummet and aquatic life will suffer.

ecosystem resistance

A property of an ecosystem that enables the ecosystem to resist potential change caused by an external factor.

Sometimes, what may seem like a negative disturbance from a human perspective is a needed event for a natural ecosystem so that it can maintain normal functioning. Forest fires are an example of a useful disturbance for forest ecosystems, but they are considered harmful or deadly by people who live in or close to wooded areas. Forest fires remove underbrush, return nutrients to the soil, and remove diseased and dying trees. Healthy, mature trees can withstand small- and medium-sized fires, and the removal of dead branches and other accumulated debris from a forest floor helps to prevent or offset larger destructive fires. Some tree species such as jack pine depend on fire to open their cones, thereby releasing seeds to germinate the next generation. Jack pines don't grow well under low-light conditions, making the removal by fire of small plants and trees beneficial to this species. These and other slower-growing trees are given a chance of reaching maturity when smaller fires periodically remove the faster-growing species that might monopolize a stand of trees.

Key Takeaways

- Ecosystems have living and nonliving components.
- Ecosystems provide goods and services.
- Ecosystem goods are tangible products (i.e., wood from a forest).
- Ecosystem services (i.e., cycling of nutrients) are more intangible compared to ecosystem goods.
- There are many types of ecosystems, both terrestrial and aquatic.
- Healthy ecosystems are resilient to normal, natural disturbances.
- Generally, ecosystems with greater numbers and types of organisms tend to be more stable.

5.2 Introduction to Biomes

Learning Objectives

1. Explain how a biome is different from, yet related to, an ecosystem.
2. Discuss how the geographical location of a biome helps to shape its communities.
3. Identify examples of biomes in the lower forty-eight contiguous United States.

biome

A terrestrial region with a specified climate and community type.

Biomes are regions characterized by broad biological communities and distinctive climates in terrestrial areas (Clements 1916) (see Figure 5.3). Usually, biomes are described and classified by their dominant plant types and associated animal communities (Mucina 2019). Conveniently, biomes link all similar communities together across the world, so we can generate large-scale community patterns. We generally expect the same type of vegetation and climate in the same biome regardless of on which continent it is located. Each biome represents a set of communities around the world. For example, the community of trees in Massachusetts (opening story) contains different species than communities in central Europe, but they are in the same biome. There are similarities between an ecosystem and a biome, but an ecosystem also includes the physical environment, whereas a biome does not. This slight difference in definitions makes it possible to refer to a "desert ecosystem," implying a desert community and its physical environment, as well as "a desert biome," referring to all the deserts in the world and their dry climate. Specific biomes arise in specific locations because they are shaped by latitude, altitude, water abundance, temperature, and other environmental factors. Plant and animal species characteristic for each biome are evolutionarily adapted to environmental conditions that prevail in it (see Chapter 4).

FIGURE 5.3
Biomes are classified based on climate and dominant plant communities. They can be discontinuous and occur in different geographical locations.

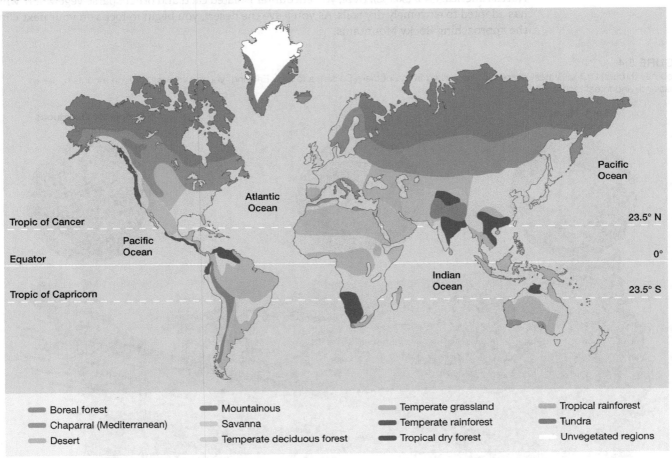

Sources: Joseph Shostell; © Shutterstock, Inc.

A Walk Through North America's Biomes

The biosphere has eleven generally defined biomes. A single biome may extend for thousands of miles in length or width, but throughout this vast range, the temperature, precipitation, and dominant vegetation are quite similar.

North America itself has a good representation of most of the world's biomes. If you were to walk from San Diego, California, on the west coast of North America, to Plymouth, Massachusetts, on the east coast, you would observe firsthand the transitions in climate, landscape, and biological community and pass through several different biomes (see Figure 5.4).

At the beginning of the journey, with the Pacific Ocean ecosystem at your back, you walk through a Mediterranean climate. Then you begin to scale the Sierra Nevada Mountains and observe your first mountainous biome. As you leave the scrub oak and California buckeye of the chaparral behind, you begin to witness a different dominant vegetation type of ponderosa pines, then red firs, and lodgepole pines. Then, at a higher elevation—at the tree line—there are no trees at all. Small shrubs dominate until there is no vegetation. All the while that you climb, the temperature drops and your views of ice and snow increase as you approach the highest elevation: 10,000 feet (3,050 m) or more, depending on where you choose to cross over.

On the leeward side of the mountains and as far as you can see, the view is drastically different because you are entering some of the driest and hottest desert biomes in the world. For example, your route may take you through Death Valley, which holds the record for high temperature in North America: 134°F (56.7°C). Here, you encounter isolated cacti and other sparse vegetation, which has adapted to extremely dry soils. As you leave the desert, you begin to focus on your next climb, the approaching Rocky Mountains.

FIGURE 5.4

A journey through United States' biomes. If you walked from Southern California to New England, you would pass through mountain, desert, grassland, and forest biomes.

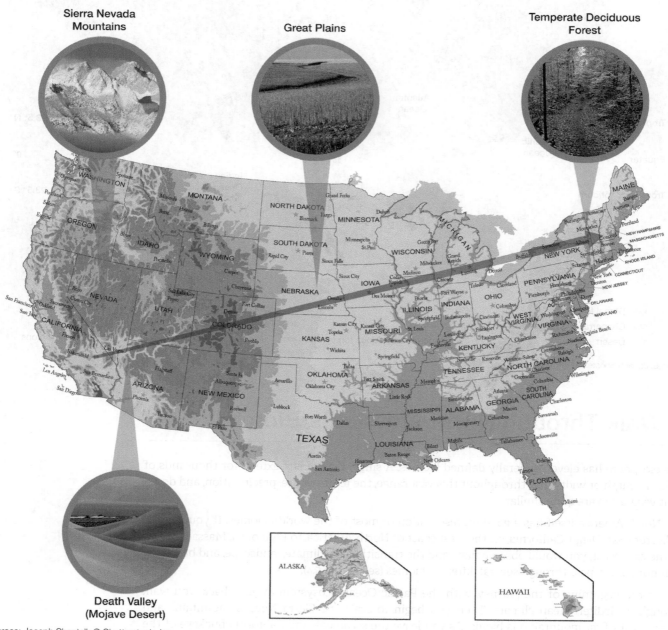

Sierra Nevada Mountains

Great Plains

Temperate Deciduous Forest

Death Valley (Mojave Desert)

ALASKA

HAWAII

Sources: Joseph Shostell; © Shutterstock, Inc.

Coming to the base of the mountains, you find a beautiful forest of pines, firs, and spruces. Undoubtedly, you experience unpredictable weather with high winds and precipitation as elevation rises with your climb. The last of the trees disappear at the tree line, but you continue to climb, passing over the 4,400 m (14,440 ft) summit to reach the other side. Bring your jacket because it is cold and there is snow and ice galore.

On the east side of the Rockies, you pass into grasslands—first a semidesert arid grassland, followed by a temperate grassland. These are the Great Plains of North America, extending over 500 mi (800 km) from west to east. Crossing the Mississippi River, you enter the eastern temperate forest, with its community of oaks, hickories, maples, and other trees—many of the same species that the early colonists saw. You cross one last mountain range: the Appalachians, older than its sister ranges in the west. As you traverse this mountain range, you may not even see a tree line, and the temperatures are not very low, because of Appalachia's lower elevation—a result of erosion over millions of years. More than likely, the temperate forest biome stays continuous throughout the rest of your journey to Plymouth, except for areas of deforestation caused by humans.

Key Takeaways

- Biomes are characterized by their biological communities and climate.
- The communities of a biome are adapted to the climate they live in, which varies with geographical location.
- The biosphere has generally defined biomes (e.g., desert, grassland).
- North America has a good representation of most of the world's biomes.

5.3 Terrestrial Biomes

Learning Objectives

1. List the world's general categories of biomes.
2. Explain why all forest biomes do not have the same types of communities and climate.
3. Describe how plants in grassland biomes have evolved differently from those in desert environments.
4. Explain how mountain biomes are representative of several other biomes.

In this section, we discuss the world's major terrestrial biomes in detail. Although there are eleven generally recognized biomes, you can think of them as various types of forests, grasslands, drylands, and mountains (see video link: " Earth's Biomes "). Their climate conditions reflect their geographical location (see Figure 5.5). To represent these climate conditions for individual biomes, we include with each biome figure a climate graph known as a climograph. Climographs indicate average temperatures and average amounts of precipitation for each month during a typical year. The climographs show in quantitative terms what we mean by warm or hot summers, a long or short rainy season, etc.

Earth's Biomes

Explore the world's biomes with Dr. Jessica Pamment of DePaul University.

View in the online reader

FIGURE 5.5

Differences in community structure among biomes reflect differences in temperature and precipitation. Note how each biome has its own unique range of temperature and precipitation, and some (e.g., desert) have a greater range of temperatures than others.

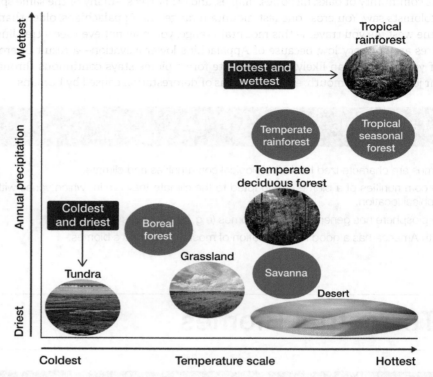

Source: Joseph Shostell; © Shutterstock, Inc.

Forest Biomes

The type of forest—temperate deciduous, temperate coniferous, mixed, boreal, or tropical—depends on overall precipitation, evenness of distribution, and temperature.

Temperate Forests

There are three general types of temperate forests: coniferous, deciduous, and mixed. Deciduous trees seasonally lose their leaves. Coniferous (evergreen) trees retain their needle-shaped leaves over the entire year. Mixed temperate forests are a combination of deciduous and coniferous trees. Which type of forest exists in a region comes down to temperature, overall precipitation, and consistency of precipitation. Coniferous forests are generally located in regions that receive less overall precipitation and have greater variability of precipitation, compared to regions with deciduous forests (Waring 2002). Most temperate coniferous forests receive an annual precipitation of between 25 cm (10 in) and 88.9 cm (35 in). However, coniferous forests can also exist in a range of climate habitats that have varying precipitation and temperature. For example, the temperate coniferous rainforests in the Pacific Northwest and Canada receive abundant rainfall of 366–426 cm (144–168 in) per year.

Temperate Coniferous Forests

Temperate coniferous forest biomes have large evergreen trees, variability in rainfall, warm summers, and cool winters.

    Location: The world's distribution of temperate coniferous forests includes the Pacific Northwest, parts of Central America, and Eurasia.

    Climate: Precipitation varies across this biome and is less toward the south. Summers are relatively dry.

    Communities: No other forests can compare to the gargantuan trees and biomass found in these forests (see Figure 5.6). Trees such as the California redwood can reach heights of over 91.4 m (300 ft)—at least 61 m (200 ft) taller than the temperate deciduous trees seen by the colonists in Massachusetts. Common species of these forests include cedar, fir, and redwood. Different from flowering trees, conifers have seeds stored within cones. Trees of coniferous forests are called "evergreen" because their leaves—shaped like needles—do not fall away from the branches before winter, keeping the trees green throughout the year. Having needles provides multiple benefits: trees reflect less radiation, undergo photosynthesis throughout the year, conserve water better, and dissipate heat well. Also, coniferous trees spend less energy on new leaf production; individual leaves may last three to forty years (Landsberg and Gower 1997). Brown bear, wolverine, and red fox are some of the many animals found in these forests.

    Human impact: Deforestation is the greatest issue with these forests.

temperate coniferous forests

A forest biome with large evergreen trees; variability in rainfall; warm summers and cool winters.

FIGURE 5.6
Temperate coniferous forests like this one near Portland, Oregon (A), experience warm summers and cool winters and are home to the spotted owl (B). Each of the world's biomes has characteristic temperature and precipitation patterns that can be visualized on a graph called a climograph (C). The climograph for this temperate coniferous forest in Oregon indicates abundant precipitation, but the amount varies greatly throughout the year with values lowest toward the end of the summer.

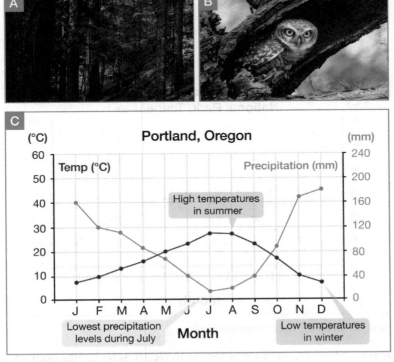

Sources: Joseph Shostell; © Shutterstock, Inc.; data from Meteoblue.

Temperate Deciduous Forests

Temperate deciduous forest biomes have broadleaf trees that lose all of their leaves seasonally, warm summers, and cool winters.

Location: The major regions of temperate deciduous forests are located in the eastern half of the United States, southwestern Ontario, the middle of Europe, and the extreme western sections of China and Russia. Smaller areas appear at the southern tip of South America, Japan, eastern Australia, and New Zealand.

Climate: These forests thrive in regions of distinct seasons, with warm summers and cool winters. Precipitation is high (75–150 cm per year or 30–59 in. per year) and fairly consistent throughout the year.

Communities: Temperate deciduous forests are dominated by hickory, oak, maple, beech, poplar, and other broadleaf hardwoods that lose all of their leaves in autumn (see Figure 5.7). During the winter, the trees are dormant because of a genetically programmed metabolic shutdown. Light penetrates to the forest floor, which has an accumulation of organic debris that contributes nutrients to the soil as it decays. You would expect to find black bears, wolves, mountain lions, raccoons, squirrels, chipmunks, skunks, opossums, and foxes, along with a diverse community of songbirds.

FIGURE 5.7
Temperate deciduous forests have trees that lose their leaves during the fall. These forests have fairly consistent precipitation throughout the year, but temperatures vary greatly, with warm summers and cold winters. A) Temperate deciduous forest of the Great Smoky Mountains National Park in Tennessee. B) Red foxes are some of the many animals found here. C) Climograph of temperate deciduous forests of the Great Smoky Mountain National Park.

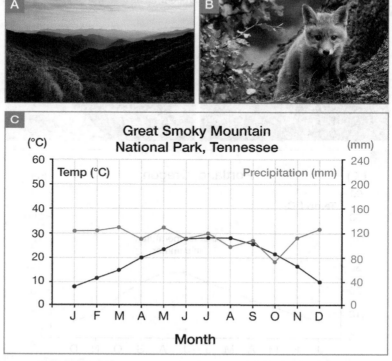

Sources: Joseph Shostell; © Shutterstock, Inc.; data from Meteoblue.

Human impact: Deforestation of these forests in North America has been an issue since the arrival of European settlers. Many of the originally cut forests have regenerated, but they have not yet reached their climax stage, and will not for another 150 to 200 years. Small, isolated towns in Wisconsin, by the names of Poplar and Maple, remind us of the abundance of some of the tree species of these forests. Over-hunting of select animal species such as the wolf has caused their disappearance from these forests and disrupted natural predatory–prey relationships.

Boreal Forests

Boreal forests are also known as taiga (a Russian word) or "spruce-moose" forests.

Location: Boreal forests make up the largest biome in the world, found in the northern hemisphere between or close to 45–67° latitudes in North America and Eurasia (see Figure 5.8). They lie just south of the tundra.

Climate: The climate in boreal biomes is very cold, with winters as long as six months. Summers are short, warm, humid, and rainy. Annual precipitation averages about 25–95 cm (10–37 in) per year with abundant snowfall, while the mean annual temperature ranges from –10°C (14°F) to –3°C (26.6°F) (Gauthier et al. 2015). Although this is a harsh environment, there is still ample water to support the growth of trees.

Community: The dominant tree types in boreal forests are pine, larch, spruce, hemlock, fir, and cedar. Some deciduous species are found as well, including maples, birch, and aspen. Evergreen or deciduous, the trees in this biome grow slowly due to the cold. The soil also tends to be nutrient-poor and acidic. Innumerable bodies of water—ponds, lakes, and acidic bogs—are spread out in this biome. Many animal species inhabit these forests, including wolves, lynx, wolverine, bobcat, bears, red squirrels, red deer, elk, and moose. A large number of migratory birds visit in the spring, but the area also supports nonmigratory birds such as owls and woodpeckers.

> **boreal forests**
>
> Also known as taiga or northern coniferous forest; the largest biome; very cold and long winters; located at high latitudes.

FIGURE 5.8
Boreal forests make up the earth's largest biome. They have extremely cold winters and receive less rainfall than other forested biomes. A) A boreal forest near Alaska. (B) The bull moose is the largest herbivore in boreal forests. This one is lying down and sleeping on the forest floor. C) A climate graph of boreal forests near Krasnoyarsk, Russia. Note the stark contrast in temperature between winter and summer with winter temperatures dipping into the double digits below 0°C (32°F).

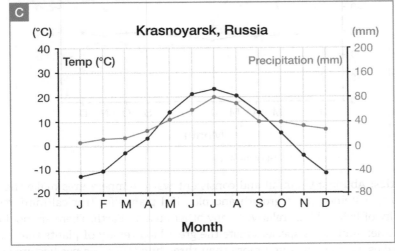

Sources: Joseph Shostell; © Shutterstock, Inc.; data from Meteoblue.

Human impact: Acid rain (see Chapter 10), global warming, and deforestation are major concerns for boreal forests. Increased air temperatures may push boreal areas farther northward. The wood of boreal forest trees was once considered inferior compared to wood of trees in more southern forests, but boreal forests are now being harvested for pulp and paper.

Tropical Rainforests

tropical rainforests

A biome that is warm year-round; high precipitation; high diversity and biomass; complex, multilayered forest; near the equator.

The key words to associate with **tropical rainforests** are *wet, hot, colorful,* and *diverse.*

Location: Tropical rainforests are located roughly between latitudes 28° north and 28° south, around the equator. They are found in Southern Asia and throughout Malaysia, Central America, most of northern South America, and mid-central/west-central Africa, as well as in islands in the Pacific Ocean, Caribbean Sea, and Indian Ocean.

Climate: Annual precipitation is high at 200 cm (80 in) per year or more, in some places exceeding 700 cm (275 in). Temperatures are always warm, generally 23–27°C (73–80°F). Within the understory, the air is humid, and light levels can attenuate down to about 1 percent near the forest floor.

FIGURE 5.9
The tropical rainforest biome receives more overall rainfall per year and more consistent rainfall than any other terrestrial area. It is also the most biodiverse biome, and temperatures here stay warm throughout the year. A) A tropical rainforest in Colombia. B) The jaguar is the apex predator in the Central and South American tropical rainforests. C) Climograph of tropical rainforests in Chiribiquete National Park, Colombia.

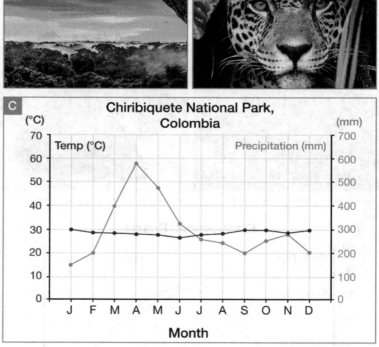

Sources: Joseph Shostell; © Shutterstock, Inc.; data from Meteoblue.

Communities: Abundant rainfall and consistent warm temperatures make the perfect conditions for rapid, sustained plant growth and plentiful plant life. Tropical rainforests have the greatest diversity of living things relative to any other area on Earth. There are no dominant tree species here; rather, numerous species create the great biodiversity of plants that exist here (see Figure 5.9). Studies have documented more than three hundred trees per hectare (2.5 acres) (Ter Steege et al. 2000). A variety of epiphytes—plants that grow on plants—occur here, including different vines, ferns, and mosses. Shallow roots and a large load of epiphytes cause some trees to fail, giving other trees the opportunity to take in additional sunlight and grow in the opening. Animal life is also diverse. Amphibians, birds, insects, and mammals are all well represented. Monkeys and many other animals use the assortment of flowers and fruits that are available throughout the year as a primary food source. Tropical rainforests are more complex than other biomes. Scientists have described four vertical layers of these forests, each with its own adapted community. Most of the nutrients in tropical rainforests are tied up in the living communities, leaving the soil nutrient-poor.

Human impact: The tropical rainforest is one of the most threatened biomes. The largest threat is continued deforestation for agriculture and other human activities. The nutrient-poor soils make for poor farmland because they can't sustain crops for long. As a consequence, farmers end up continually cutting trees to support their livelihood.

Tropical Dry Forests

Tropical dry forests are also referred to as tropical seasonal forests or tropical deciduous forests.

Location: Tropical dry forests are located approximately between 30°N and 30°S latitudes. Within this range of latitudes, they are found in northern Australia, the west coast of Central America, southwestern Asia, and the mideastern and southwestern parts of Africa (see Figure 5.10).

Climate: Tropical dry forests receive 25–200 cm (10–80 in) of rain per year and experience temperatures usually greater than 17°C (63°F). They have distinct dry and wet seasons, each several months long.

> **tropical dry forests**
>
> A forest biome with warm temperature and highly variable precipitation; several dry months and short wet season; trees are deciduous.

FIGURE 5.10
Tropical dry forests have large variation in precipitation during the year. Less rainfall and more unpredictable rainfall helps to explain why tropical rainforests such as the one shown in the photo (A) are less productive and less diverse compared to tropical rainforests. These forests experience a long dry season lasting for several months, followed by a wet season with abundant precipitation. (B) This can be seen in the climograph of a tropical dry forest in Guanacasta, Costa Rica.

 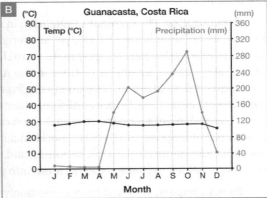

Sources: Joseph Shostell; © Shutterstock, Inc.; data from Meteoblue.

Communities: Plants and animals have adapted to the extreme variation in wetness throughout the year. Trees in tropical dry forests conserve water in storage areas of their roots and stems, and their roots are deeper than trees in tropical rainforests. These forests have about 50 percent fewer tree species, 50–75 percent less productivity, and significantly less biomass compared to tropical rainforests (Murphy and Lugo 1986). They are also not as complex and vertically layered as tropical rainforests, and their canopy height is roughly 50 percent of the height in rainforests. Some resident groups of animals, such as insects and amphibians, survive the dry seasons by decreasing their metabolic rate and burrowing into the mud. More mobile animals such as monkeys and birds move to wetter areas.

Human impact: The harshness of climate conditions, with long periods of dryness, make it difficult for tropical dry forests to withstand additional stress. Many of these forests have already been partly or wholly deforested and converted to cattle pasture and land for growing crops. Much of the wood removed is used as firewood; there is also a demand by industry for fine hardwoods such as mahogany. To balance out the deforestation pressure from humans, more trees need to be planted in these areas (Norman 1984).

Grasslands

All grasslands—prairie, steppe, or pampas—have in common the fact that they do not have enough precipitation to support trees. These biomes also typically have large variations in the amount of rain per month, and fires can occur during their drier seasons. Economically, they are significant to humans because of their rich soil, which is prized for agriculture and livestock. Grasslands cover a little more than 25 percent of Earth's land surface.

Savannas

savanna

A biome with scattered shrubs and isolated trees; warm temperatures; wet and dry seasons; covers about 45 percent of Africa.

Savanna biomes are known as the tropical grasslands.

Location: Savannas are located in Africa, South America, northern Australia, and India. Probably the most famous savanna is Africa's Serengeti, mostly in Tanzania, where millions of herbivores go on migrations. Africa has the world's largest savannas, which make up almost 50 percent of Africa's land mass.

Climate: Savannas receive an average of 50–150 cm (20–60 in) of rain per year, and they have consistent warm temperatures. Precipitation is uneven throughout the year, so there are distinct wet and dry seasons. During the rainy season, abundant rain falls and the air is humid, whereas in the dry season, non-adapted animals and plants would surely perish. Fire is common during the dry season.

Communities: The dominant vegetation in savannas is grass. The biome has insufficient water to support an abundance of trees, yet scattered, isolated trees and shrubs occur (see Figure 5.11). Larger plants tend to have long taproots, store their water in trunks, and lose their leaves at the end of the rainy season. Examples of trees in the African savanna are baobabs and the red-bark acacia. Frequent fires maintain a savanna's biodiversity and keep the area as a grassland (Staver et al. 2011). Fires prevent trees from establishing themselves in the savanna, keeping the surrounding forest at bay and maintaining the savanna's open canopy. The savanna in Africa supports the greatest abundance of large mammals in the world, including wildebeests, giraffes, zebras, lions, hyenas, and cheetahs. Elephants also inhabit savannas, and, through their ability to routinely snap and topple trees, have helped to change wooded areas into savanna.

Human impact: Africans have increasingly used part of the savanna for livestock, an unsustainable activity in this dry area that can cause desertification—the creation of desert.

FIGURE 5.11

The savanna biome has grass with scattered trees, dry winters (June–Sep), and warm summers. Its vegetation supports a diverse community of large mammalian herbivores and predators. A) Zebras in the savanna of Serengeti National Park, Tanzania. B) Based on the climograph, temperature varies little across months, whereas there are wide oscillations in precipitation.

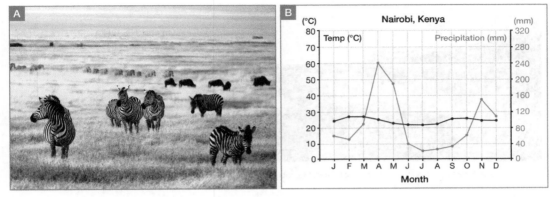

Sources: Joseph Shostell; © Shutterstock, Inc.; data from Meteoblue.

Temperate Grasslands

Overall, **temperate grassland** biomes are colder than the savannas, receive less precipitation, and also have more erratic precipitation.

Location: Temperate grasslands occur in North America between the Mississippi River and the Rocky Mountains in what is referred to as the Great Plains (see Figure 5.12). Similar grasslands are also found in Eurasia (the steppes), South America (the pampas), Australia, and southern Africa, roughly between 30° and 55° north and south latitudes.

Climate: Annual precipitation is usually around 25–75 cm (20–35 in.) and varies monthly. Summers can be rather hot (up to 100°F) and dry, whereas winters can dip to below 0°F.

Communities: The dominant type of vegetation is grass. Buffalo, purple needle, wild oats, and rye are some of the many varieties of grass found in the Great Plains. The taller grass species easily crest 1 m (3 ft) in height. This fairly flat region with rolling hills also has abundant and beautiful wildflowers—goldenrods, asters, and clovers. Primary production by the grasses supports a community of herbivores and indirectly carnivores, which are less diverse compared to animal communities in tropical forests. In North American temperature grasslands, we find animals such as bison, coyotes, and prairie dogs. A scarcity of trees and other aboveground shelters makes life challenging for both prey and predator species.

Human impact: Most of the original temperate grasslands have been transformed to some degree to support agricultural activities. Soils are nutrient-rich, dark, and usually several feet deep. The Great Plains are the origin of much of our grain in the United States and consequently many of the products in which wheat can be found. It has traditionally been tempting for farmers to over-farm, as they did in the 1930s. Over-farming is the excessive use of farmland to the point of land degradation. When this occurs, unprotected soils can be eroded by winds. Overgrazing by domesticated livestock has also been problematic for endemic species of grass, as has been the introduction of invasive grass species such as cheat grass. Over-farming and overgrazing are examples of non-sustainable activities in grass biomes that promote desertification.

temperate grasslands

A biome with grass as dominant vegetation; receives less water than forests; Great Plains in North America, steppes in Eurasia, pampas in South America.

FIGURE 5.12

The temperate grasslands in North America extend from the Rocky Mountains to the Mississippi River. (A) Notice the flatness and (at times) dryness of the Great Plains, and the Rockies far to the west. (B) The climograph indicates the temperature and precipitation in Omaha, Nebraska, hundreds of miles to the east of this scene but in the same biome. Temperature and precipitation show similar trends, both significantly higher in summer than winter.

 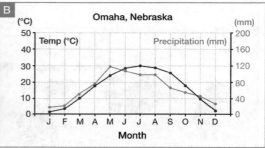

Sources: Joseph Shostell; © Shutterstock, Inc.; data from Meteoblue.

Chaparral

Chaparral (SHA-pa-RAL) consists of shrubland and small trees.

Location: Chaparral is located along the west coast of South America, the western tip of Australia, coastal areas of the Mediterranean, and the Cape Town area of South Africa.

Climate: Described as Mediterranean, the climate experiences mild, dry summers and wet winters. Temperatures usually range between –1°C (30°F) and 40°C (100°F) and average around 10°C (50°F). Droughts are common during the summer, as are fires (Hanes 1977). The winter season typically brings 65–75 cm (20–30 in) of rain.

Communities: Broad-leaved sclerophyllous vegetation is dominant in the chaparral. These plants, mostly evergreen shrubs, have hard, waxy leaves adapted to the periods of drought. Scrub oak, cacti, and poison oak are examples of plants found in this biome. Surviving plants are good at holding onto moisture in their leaves, and also have deep taproots that can access hard-to-find water during the summer. The olive industry in Spain has made good use of this biome. There, you can observe large tracts of land covered with olive trees (see Figure 5.13). Animals found within this biome include jack rabbits, mule deer, snakes, scorpions, coyotes, and lizards.

Human impact: Chaparral is the smallest of the world's biomes, so there is less room for error in conserving the chaparral compared to other biomes. People like the mild climate and have settled this biome in large numbers, such as in southern California. Natural wildfires that are needed to maintain the chaparral are usually suppressed to protect people and property, causing the accumulation of flammable woody biomass. Many chaparral species benefit from periodic fires, but frequent fires undermine the health of chaparral communities (Lippitt et al. 2013). Current studies are evaluating methods of reducing the chaparral biomass to preserve the biome, and also to prevent larger fires from erupting and harming people. For example, researchers have conducted studies on whether sheep and goats can forage on chaparral vegetation. Unfortunately, their findings show that the animals lost weight during their study, probably because of the poor nutritional quality of the plants (Narvaez et al 2011). A second threat to chaparral areas, especially in California, is the enrichment of nitrogen coming from human society. Excess nitrogen combined with climate change reduces biodiversity and promotes the conversion of natural chaparral communities to communities dominated by non-native grass species (Porter et al. 2012).

FIGURE 5.13
The chaparral biome, characterized by mild, dry summers and wet winters, is found in coastal Mediterranean areas, for which it is often described, but it exists on other continents as well. (A) In the image, the natural evergreen shrubs of the chaparral biome in Andalusia, southern Spain, have been largely replaced by groves of olive trees. (B) This can be seen in the climograph representing the chaparral biome in southern Spain.

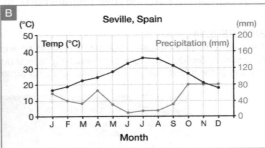

Sources: Joseph Shostell; © Shutterstock, Inc.; data from Meteoblue.

Tundra

Tundra, like taiga, is a Russian word. *Taiga* refers to the boreal forest biome, whereas tundra is a colder and more desolate biome.

Location: Most tundra is in the arctic, north of the taiga, found between 55–70°N latitudes, and makes up—in conservative estimates—10 percent of Earth's land surface (see Figure 5.14). The tundra spreads out in a belt across northern North America and northern Eurasia. A second type of tundra called alpine tundra is found in mountain areas.

Climate: Tundra is the coldest biome. It supports extremely long winters of up to ten months, making summers very short. Temperatures are usually between –40°C (–40°F) and 18°C (64°F), but can exceed (recently) 35.6°C (96°F) during the summer and dip down to –70°C (–94°F) in the winter. The scant precipitation of 15–25 cm (6–10 in) per year makes the tundra on par with desert biomes. Winters are not only cold with snow and ice, but also dark; many days are shrouded in almost complete darkness. Summers are the reverse, with days receiving long periods of sunlight. The long winters and short summers set up the unusual characteristic called **permafrost**, in which all but the surface layer of the ground is frozen year-round. During the winter, the entire ground is frozen solid.

Communities: Trees are rare in tundra because of low amounts of precipitation and because the frozen ground prevents the access of roots. Any trees that do exist are dwarf-sized, hugging the ground as an adaptation to the severe cold and wind. Dominant vegetation includes mosses, lichens, sedges, grasses, and dwarf shrubs. In summer, the sunlight heats up the top layers of the ground, melting snow and ice. Permafrost prevents the water from filtering into the ground, so it pools at the surface. Ponds, lakes, streams, and bogs all appear at this time, as do countless hordes of insects. Migratory waterfowl visit the tundra during the summer to feed on the abundant insect communities and reproduce. Arctic foxes, polar bears, wolves, caribou, and musk oxen exist here as well, as do lemmings and other rodents. Animals living in the tundra have evolved different characteristics for surviving in the extreme cold. For example, thick fur and fat keeps polar bears warm; burrowing into the ground allows lemmings to survive extremely harsh conditions; and glycerol in the tissues of insects keeps them from freezing solid.

Human impacts: The inhospitable conditions of the tundra make direct settling of the area by humans really of no concern. Real threats to the tundra are more indirect. For example, rising global temperatures from the burning of fossil fuels keep the tundra's ground thawed for longer periods than usual. An exceptional heatwave in 2021 brought in ground temperatures as high as 48°C (118°F). This section of the world is considered a reservoir of stored carbon and usually doesn't contribute to atmospheric carbon dioxide, as long as the carbon is not metabolically released by thawed bacte-

tundra

A treeless biome with low diversity; located north of taiga biome; extremely cold and harsh environment; has permafrost.

permafrost

Permanently frozen ground in the arctic tundra.

ria. Global warming is changing this scenario and thawing soil in the Arctic tundra (see Chapter 11). Other threats are mining and drilling operations. Unlike other biomes, the tundra responds slowly to disturbance because of slow decomposition rates and a short growing season. Another indirect effect from humans comes in the form of snow geese, which feed on crops farther south, increase their population size, and then migrate north to overgraze tundra areas.

FIGURE 5.14

The tundra biome extends across northern North America and northern Eurasia. A) Photo of tundra near Funäsdalen, Sweden. B) Musk oxen weighing several hundred pounds feed on lichens, willow shoots, shrubs, and grasses of the tundra. C) The tundra has cold long winters, little precipitation, and few trees.

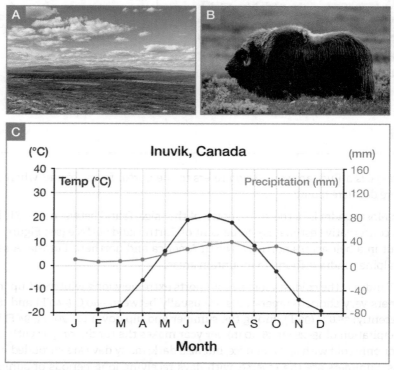

Sources: Joseph Shostell; © Shutterstock, Inc.; data from Meteoblue.

Deserts

desert

A biome with low precipitation; dry; can be either hot or cold.

Deserts make up about one-fifth of Earth's land surface. Several different types of desert exist, but regardless of where they are located, all have at least one characteristic in common—they are very dry.

Location: Deserts are found in Africa, southwest United States, northern Mexico, the west coast of South America, Australia, and parts of Asia (see Figure 5.15). Some of the largest deserts, such as the Sahara—close in size to the United States—lie between latitudes 15° and 35°, north or south of the equator. Some regions are deserts because they are on the leeward side of mountains, as is the case of the coastal desert in Chile, near the Andes. Other deserts are classified as cold deserts, such as the Antarctic.

Climate: On average, deserts receive 25 cm (10 in) or less of rain per year. Desert temperatures can vary tremendously. Most of us consider a desert to be always hot. Some are like this during the day, and then become cool at night because the low humidity and absence of clouds allow heat to radiate quickly from the ground upward to the atmosphere. However, other deserts, such as Antarctica, do not fit the profile of a hot desert, and instead are bitterly cold.

Communities: To survive in the driest biome of the world, plants and animals need to have specialized features. Plant vegetation usually grows close to the ground and is spread out, with more vegetation found in locations where more precipitation occurs. Desert plants have developed novel ways of accessing and conserving water. For example, desert plants can have large root systems, extending horizontally underneath the surface or deeply into the ground. When it does rain, expansive root systems near the surface can quickly take in water. The water is stored for later use by the plant during extended periods of no rain. Long taproots can access water far below the surface. The mesquite tree can have taproots up to 61 m (200 ft) long. Plant communities here have relatively low productivity relative to plant communities in other biomes, and they have a quick growth response when it does rain. Desert plants have also evolved modified hard leaves, such as spines, which inhibit grazing by herbivores. Cacti, prickly pears, yuccas, and turpentine bushes are some examples of desert plants. Animals tend to be small, active at night, and able to burrow. Lizards, snakes, kangaroo rats, and arachnids are common here.

FIGURE 5.15
Deserts make up the driest biome and are found on all of Earth's continents. They can be exceptionally hot during the day and cool at night. Deserts can also be found in brutally cold regions if the rainfall is less than 25 cm (10 in) per year. A) The photo shows a camel caravan going through the sand dunes in the Sahara Desert near Merzouga, Morocco. The Sahara, which makes up approximately 10 percent of Africa, is the world's largest hot desert. B) The elusive Mojave Desert tortoise, shown here, feeds on wildflowers, grasses, and cacti and spends about 95 percent of its time under ground. C) The climate graph shows the high temperatures and low precipitation of Las Vegas, Nevada, situated in the Mojave Desert.

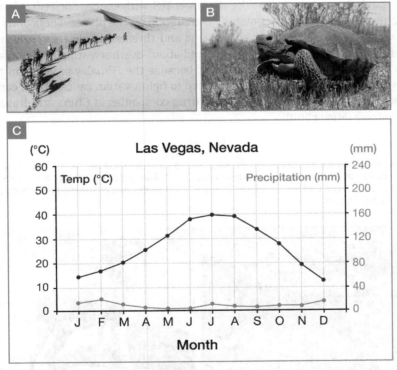

Sources: Joseph Shostell; © Shutterstock, Inc.; data from Meteoblue.

Human impact: Deserts are fragile because they respond slowly to disturbances. Off-road vehicles and grazing seem to be the larger threats to desert biomes. Phoenix and other large cities in desert areas can be stressful not only to the immediate environment, but also to other biomes because they drain water supplies hundreds of kilometers away. Rising air temperatures due to global warming will likely create new deserts, especially in areas where evaporation and precipitation are currently equally balanced (Bayram and Ozturk 2014).

When not careful, pumping of water out of the ground in dry areas results in the collapse or "falling" of land, a condition called subsidence. It is a serious environmental problem in Tucson and other desert areas where precipitation cannot match the water demands of a growing population.

Land around Tucson is dropping at a rate of 0.5 cm (0.2 in) every year, and there are visible cracks in the soil's surface, some 305 m (1,000 feet) long and 9.1 m (30 feet) deep.

Mountain Biomes

mountainous biomes

A biome with mountains; it can encompass multiple biomes because climate varies with altitude.

Mountainous biomes are complex because the same mountain can encompass multiple biomes. We have listed mountainous regions as a separate biome because they create islands of communities that, if not for a change in elevation, would be found only at other latitudes (see Figure 5.16).

Location: Mountain biomes are found on all continents and can extend for thousands of kilometers.

Climate: Temperatures decrease with elevation. In many ways, going from the base to the apex of a mountain is similar to moving from the equator to the North Pole.

Communities: Temperature and precipitation vary with elevation, so biological communities vary accordingly.

Human impact: Deforestation in mountainous areas destabilizes slopes and increases erosion. Depending on the location of the mountain areas, human populations may rely on them for a source of freshwater and mineral resources. For example, the Appalachian Mountain states support a vibrant coal industry, which provides the larger U.S. with energy. Society's mining of coal has also caused some of the worst environmental degradation on the planet. Thousands of coalmines, many now abandoned, pollute aquatic ecosystems and threaten biodiversity and human health (Voss and Bernhardt 2017). Concerns have appeared about overharvesting of yew plant species in mountainous areas. This is especially important because the Himalayan yew and the other ten species of yew contain a chemical called Taxol used to fight ovarian cancer. Taxol can now be produced synthetically or by cell culture, but some drug companies in China and India still harvest Taxol from yew trees (Mayor 2011).

FIGURE 5.16

The mountainous biome has a steep change in elevation over a relatively short distance. Climate varies with the change in elevation. A) Note that in this photo of the Canadian Rockies in Banff National Park, Canada, higher elevations do not support trees and are bare rock. B) Rams such as this one can move dexterously and elegantly over the rough mountain terrain.

Source: © Shutterstock, Inc.

Key Takeaways

- A biome is a terrestrial region with a specified climate and community type.

- There are eleven generally recognized biomes, including types of forests, grasslands, and deserts.
- Mountainous regions are complex because the same mountain can encompass multiple biomes.

5.4 Aquatic Life Zones

Learning Objectives

1. Describe how freshwater and saltwater life zones are similar.
2. Identify the four zones of lakes.
3. Explain why a river is considered a continuum.
4. Summarize why coastal life zones are more productive and have more species relative to the open ocean.

Aquatic areas are very different from terrestrial areas because they have abundant water and relatively stable temperatures. They are defined by their salinity, light levels, nutrient concentrations, and depth. Terrestrial regions were appropriately defined as biomes based on community type and climate. In the case of aquatic regions, the term *biome* is no longer applicable, and we instead use the term **life zone**.

Life zones provide several services we rely on. They recycle nutrients, create habitat for species, absorb carbon dioxide, treat wastewater, and moderate climate. We depend on life zones for transportation, fossil fuels, drinking water, recreation, irrigation of crops, electricity, food, and recreation. These values encourage us to monitor, study, and protect life zones, but with few fixed physical features, aquatic systems are more challenging to work with than terrestrial systems. In these systems, biologists must be creative to be able to contend with environmental conditions for which they are not adapted, and to successfully follow populations of aquatic species, which can move seamlessly across large areas.

life zone

A region of an aquatic system that is characterized by distinctive community, depth, and light levels.

Freshwater Life Zones

Freshwater life zones have a very low concentration of salt and take up only a small percentage of the world's water. They include ponds, lakes, wetlands, streams, and rivers, and are zones that most of us know well—or at least, observe on a weekly or daily basis. These systems are broken up into two types based on movement of the water. Lakes and other standing water bodies are lentic systems, whereas streams, rivers, and similar moving waters are lotic systems.

freshwater life zones

Aquatic areas with low concentrations of salt and which make up only a small percentage of surface waters.

Ponds and Lakes

Pond and lake zones are water-filled holes created by geological processes. Some are caused by glaciation and others—really deep lakes—by displacement of Earth's crust. Ponds are shallower and simpler than lakes and consequently have fewer habitat zones.

littoral zone

Shallow area at the periphery of a lake that contains rooted vegetation.

Lakes have four zones: littoral, limnetic, profundal, and benthic. The **littoral zone** (lit-er-uhl, see Figure 5.17) is shallow and at the periphery of the lake. Rooted aquatic vegetation is abundant. Submerged vegetation lies below the water surface, and other plants—emergent types, such as cattails and bulrushes—extend up above the water. Light easily penetrates to the lake bottom in a littoral zone, bringing in abundant energy for photosynthesis.

FIGURE 5.17

Each lake has distinct zones based on depth and plant life. Shallow areas where large plants grow make up the littoral zone. The open water area is the limnetic zone. The bottom of the lake is the benthic zone. Deeper lakes also have a profundal zone.

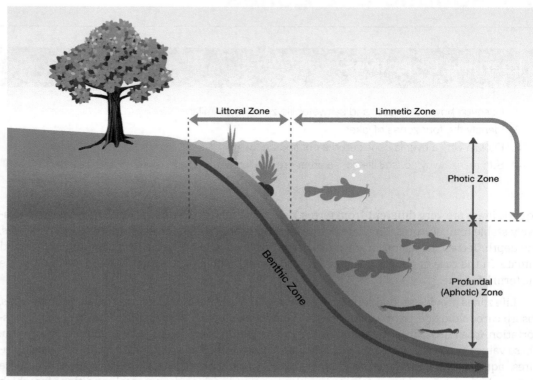

Source: © Shutterstock, Inc.

A little farther out from the shoreline begins the open-water **limnetic zone**—the upper part of the water column (see Figure 5.17). Its depth extends down to about the limits of light penetration, also referred to as the **euphotic zone** (you-FO-tic). Too deep for rooted vegetation, countless microscopic photosynthetic organisms—**phytoplankton**—float in the open water and undergo photosynthesis. Most of the lake's oxygen is produced here. A vibrant community of zooplankton are here as well, feeding on the phytoplankton and each other.

The **profundal zone** is found only in deep lakes and occurs directly beneath the limnetic zone. Very little light can be found here, not enough for photosynthesis. Oxygen concentrations are lower here compared to the limnetic zone. All energy that enters the profundal zone descends from above in the form of dead organic matter, which contains stored energy.

limnetic zone

The upper, open-water area of a lake. Light levels and oxygen concentrations are high.

euphotic zone

The layer of water closest to the surface that receives sufficient light for photosynthesis to occur.

phytoplankton

Microscopic photosynthetic organisms that live suspended in water.

profundal zone

The region found in deeper lakes between the limnetic and benthic zones.

At the bottom of lake is the **benthic zone** (see Figure 5.17). It also depends on matter that settles down from the upper zones. Many detritivores are found here, in addition to some predators. The animal community at this depth consists mainly of invertebrates. Crayfish, snails, and aquatic worms are common in this colder, low-oxygen environment. Dragonflies, damselflies, mayflies, and other insect larvae forms use the benthic zone as a habitat for the beginning stages of their life cycles. Fish can inhabit any of the zones and move among them.

Lakes, maybe even more so than rivers, are threatened by pollution. Pollutants accumulate over time and are not flushed out as they are in lotic systems.

Rivers and Streams

Rivers and streams are usually not as deep as lakes. They are also relatively thin and long, with a continuum of change from their headwaters—where they begin—to where they end (Vannote et al. 1980). At their headwaters they are cold, fast moving, and full of oxygen—wonderful for trout. Energy and matter in this upstream area come from leaves and other organic debris washed in from the terrestrial area. This surrounding terrestrial area that drains into the river is the watershed and is the reason why river systems are considered relatively open compared to lake systems. Downstream areas of rivers are deeper, wider, slower moving, and warmer. The fish community is different here, featuring smallmouth bass and a variety of sunfish, and even species such as sturgeon and huge channel catfish, especially in larger rivers. Vibrant fish communities also attest to the presence of zooplankton and phytoplankton communities in both small and large river systems. Rivers in low-lying flat areas can be heavily influenced by the floodplain because it acts as a filter by absorbing and storing water, nutrients, and sediments coming from the river channel. The floodplain also serves as a spawning ground for fish. Generally, a river possesses three sections: a source zone where it begins, a transition zone in the middle, and a floodplain zone in the last section before it empties into a larger body of water. The majority of human impacts on rivers come by way of the watershed.

Marine Life Zones

Saltwater areas, or **marine life zones**, cover 71 percent of Earth's surface. Ecologists classify them, using distance from shore and depth, into two types: coastal and open ocean. The **coastal zone** extends from the highest mark of the tide on the shoreline to the end of the continental shelf. This shallow (less than 100 meters deep) zone receives abundant sunlight and nutrients and is highly productive. Approximately 90 percent of marine species exist within the coastal zone even though it is much smaller than the open-ocean zone. Why is this zone so productive? Location is the answer. Living organisms require nutrients and energy, and coastal zones receive abundant matter (which contains nutrients and energy), both from rivers coming from terrestrial ecosystems and from deeper oceanic areas brought in by waves and tides.

Coastal Life Zones

The coastal zone includes areas close to the continental coast. In this section, we begin exploring the oceans by examining four of the coastal life zones: shorelines, estuaries, coral reefs, and barrier islands.

Shorelines lie between high and low tides and are also referred to as intertidal areas (see A in Figure 5.18). It is a stressful zone, with pounding waves followed by daily droughts when the tide goes out again. In order to survive, organisms burrow in the sediment or cling to rocks. Algae, sea urchins, starfish, and barnacles are all found here. Shore birds are common as well, and in some

benthic zone

Bottom life zone of a lake, ocean, or river.

marine life zones

Coastal and open-ocean areas.

coastal zone

Areas near the coast including shorelines, estuaries, coastal wetlands, mangrove swamps, salt marshes, mud flats, coral reefs, and barrier islands.

shoreline

Zone between high and low tides.

shoreline locations you'll even find walruses and seals. If you look in specific areas, you may be lucky enough to observe turtle nesting sites. Should you run into these nesting sites, be careful, because they are fragile and federally protected. The human impact on shorelines can be immediate and severe. For example, oil spills can wipe out established communities and lower diversity levels for years.

FIGURE 5.18
Examples of coastal life zones: (A) an intertidal zone in Oahu, Hawaii, and (B) a developed barrier island in South Beach, Miami.

Source: © Shutterstock, Inc.

estuaries

Zones of mixing between freshwater and saltwater in coastal areas.

coral reefs

Colonies of coral polyps that have symbiotic relationships with algae. The polyps lay down a calcium carbonate skeleton that increases in size yearly. They are located in warm, shallow areas of the tropics and subtropics.

barrier islands

Long sand islands off the coast of the mainland.

Estuaries such as Chesapeake Bay are a mixture of freshwater and saltwater, teeming with abundant life. They are part of the estuarine zone, which includes estuaries and coastal wetlands, both of which are valuable as spawning habitat for fish and also valuable to waterfowl for food, shelter, and breeding. Mangrove swamps are also good nursery areas for aquatic organisms; they consist of trees growing in shallow saltwater of the tropics, and they protect shoreline habitat.

Coral reefs and barrier islands also protect shoreline areas. **Coral reefs** are located in warm, shallow areas of the tropics and subtropics (see D in Figure 1.4). Not quite as diverse as tropical rainforests, coral reefs are complex systems with an impressive array of creatures and colors. Even if you are not a scuba diver or a snorkeler, you can still experience the world's coral reefs by watching *MacGillivray Freeman's Coral Reef Adventure*. I originally watched it while taking a break from snorkeling in Hanauma Bay, Hawaii. Request it at your school or local library and enjoy the sights, the sounds, and the scientists such as Jean-Michel Cousteau who visit and evaluate the health of the world's coral reef areas. Acclaimed Hollywood actor Liam Neeson narrates the movie.

Barrier islands are long sand islands off a continent's coast (see B in Figure 5.18). For example, there are barrier islands along the Atlantic coast stretching from New England through Florida. The Mayflower and other early adventurous ships would have had to pass through these islands to reach the mainland (see "Case Study: A Tale of Early North America"). Today, many of these barrier islands are heavily developed for tourism. Atlantic City is a wonderful example of this. A history of storms coming in from the ocean have shown us how vulnerable our developments can be to natural disasters, such as Hurricane Sandy in 2012 and Hurricane Irma in 2017. However, such knowledge does not seem to deter us from rebuilding in locations heavily damaged by hurricanes. Irma hit the Florida coastline as a category 4 hurricane and caused an estimated $50 billion in damage.

Open-Ocean Life Zones

The open ocean is divided into five life zones: neritic, euphotic, bathyal, abyssal, and hadal. The shallowest zone is the **neritic zone** (neh-RIT-ick), analogous to the littoral zone in lakes. It extends from the low-tide mark up to around 320 km (200 mi) outward, to the edge of the continental shelf (see Figure 5.19). A highly productive area, the neritic zone receives upwellings of nutrient-laden waters from the ocean floor, as well as influxes of nutrients brought by rivers from terrestrial ecosystems. Phytoplankton take up the nutrients and the sunlight that permeate the shallow waters. The healthy primary producers support higher trophic levels—consumers, including a fish community. Fishermen make a large percentage of their catch in the neritic zone. The neritic zone also receives the most pollutants from the concentrated human populations living along the coastline. Another term for the open ocean, away from coastal areas, that includes the entire water column from the surface to the benthic area is the **pelagic zone** (see video link: " The Open Ocean ").

neritic zone

Marine life zone analogous to the littoral zone in lakes, extending from the low-tide mark outward to the edge of the continental shelf.

pelagic zone

The entire oceanic water column, away from coastlines, from the surface to where the benthic area begins.

FIGURE 5.19
Oceanographers—scientists who study the oceans—divide the open ocean into five life zones: neritic, euphotic, bathyal, abyssal, and hadal.

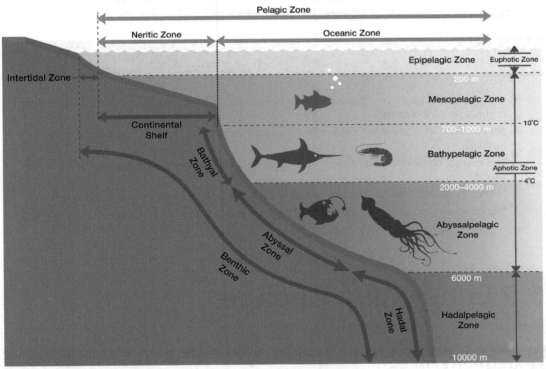

Source: © Shutterstock, Inc.

The euphotic zone is the layer of surface waters that receives sufficient sunlight for photosynthesis to occur. This zone includes the shallow neritic zone but also extends beyond the continental shelf, reaching depths of around 200 m (650 ft) in open-ocean waters (see Figure 5.19). A vast phytoplankton community of diatoms, dinoflagellates, and other groups are found in the euphotic zone, which covers 90 percent of the oceans' surfaces. Trillions and trillions of algal cells continually take in carbon dioxide and release oxygen from their photosynthesis activities. An acre of the euphotic zone is not as productive as an acre of a tropical rainforest, but the sheer enormity of the oceans makes the euphotic zone the greatest source of oxygen from any world ecosystem. Oxygen levels are high here, but nutrient concentrations are usually limiting, preventing the phytoplankton community from its true production potential. Wherever phytoplankton occur, zooplankton grazers appear, and then larger animals feed on the primary consumers. Swordfish, tuna, sharks, and other large, fast, predatory fish are found here. Only about 10 percent of commercial fishing occurs here.

The Open Ocean
Explore the life and structure of the open ocean.

View in the online reader

bathyal zone

Directly below the euphotic zone in marine ecosystems. A zone with little to no light.

abyssal zone

Life zone deep below the bathyal zone in marine systems.

hadal zone

Deepest part of the sea where deep ocean trenches occur; depths exceed 6,000 m (19,685 ft.).

deposit feeders

Aquatic organisms that feed on organic matter that has settled on the bottom.

filter feeders

Aquatic organisms that obtain their food by straining out suspended organic matter.

The **bathyal zone** (BATH-ee-el) is directly below the euphotic zone (see Figure 5.19). It has very little light, too little for photosynthesis. Because there are no photosynthetic organisms, production in the bathyal zone is the result of heterotrophic organisms that either consume and break down dead organic matter that sinks down from above or prey on other consumers. Shrimp and squid are some of the life forms found here.

The deepest zones are the **abyssal** (ah-BISS-el) and **hadal** (HĀ-dal)—zones very foreign to the average person, who needs light, warmth, and oxygen. No light penetrates to these great depths, pressure is extremely high, water is cold, and oxygen concentrations are low. Even these unforgiving conditions create opportunities for those animals who have adapted and survive here. Specialized **deposit feeders** (e.g., crabs, snails) and **filter feeders** (e.g., clams) can be found, relying on the organic matter falling from above. For species that can survive here, the sediments are rich with nutrients. Some organisms have evolved luminescent structures to attract mates, communicate, or fool predators.

Fissures in the ocean floor caused by geologic activity can spew out hot water and minerals. These areas, known as hydrothermal vents, support communities in otherwise low-biodiversity areas of the ocean floor. In a process called chemosynthesis, evolutionarily adapted bacteria and archaea utilize the energy stored within hydrogen sulfide molecules coming up through the fissures to drive the synthesis of sugar from carbon dioxide and water. These chemosynthetic microorganisms are the base of a diverse food web, which includes giant tube worms and clams.

Key Takeaways

- Unlike biomes, which are classified partly by climate, aquatic systems have abundant water and stable temperatures.
- Aquatic life zones are differentiated by factors such as depth, sunlight, and oxygen concentrations.
- The correct order of zones in lakes from deep to shallow is benthic, profundal, limnetic, and littoral.
- Neritic, euphotic, bathyal, abyssal, and hadal are the five life zones of marine ecosystems.
- Marine waters closest to the coastline are the most productive part of marine ecosystems.

5.5 Ecosystem Change

Learning Objectives

1. Explain why ecosystems change over time.
2. List the types of human activities that accelerate or decelerate succession of ecosystems.

Ecosystems can change in structure and function due to natural disturbance events, community succession (see Chapter 4), and human activities. In the opening story we described three examples of ecosystem change—the first due to glacial advancement, the second in response to deforestation, and the third after New Englanders stopped large-scale deforestation. The end result, either by glacial recession or by reforestation, was the re-establishment of a mature forest ecosystem. In order to get to this stage several successive stages took place. In this section, we explore the steps of ecosystem change from bare-ground areas to fully developed forests.

> ## Bringing It Closer to Home: No Ecosystem Is Permanent
>
> Your favorite lake, the park down the block, and the nearest forest were not always there. It took several steps, or stages, to become what they are today. Observe the small and large ecosystem surrounding your home and hypothesize as to what they were two hundred years ago, as well as what they will change into in the next two hundred years.

Mechanisms of Change

The glaciers that retreated in the opening story created a primitive underlying layer devoid of any evidence of earlier communities that existed prior to the advancement of the glaciers. A gigantic ice sheet is no longer present over New England for analysis, but we can study the movement of glaciers in more northern latitudes that are continually moving. Scientists interested in succession have studied the retreat of glaciers in Glacial Bay, Alaska (Crocker and Major 1955). By analyzing the distribution and type of communities at different distances from the receding ice, they have calculated that glacial ice moves approximately 100 km (62 mi) in 200 years. They determined this time span by assessing the age of trees at different distances from the ice. The youngest trees were those closest to the ice. No trees were found right next to the ice because the ground conditions are not suitable for most plants. The great weight of the glaciers scoured away the nutrient-laden soil, leaving behind a barren landscape. Besides glaciers modifying the physical environment, and hence ecosystem structure, colonizers do so as well. For example, pioneering colonizers fix nitrogen and help create a soil matrix capable of retaining water and hospitable to future colonizers (see Chapter 4). The ecosystem's community then changes from one composed of mosses and herbaceous species, to one of willows, alders, and eventually Sitka spruce and hemlock trees. During these changes in community structure, the soil gains nitrogen, changes pH, and even becomes more aerated and better able to hold water.

Aquatic ecosystems also undergo change and have communities that experience primary and secondary successions (see Figure 5.20). The same glaciers that changed the landscape of northern North America, leaving bare ground for new terrestrial systems to begin primary succession, also left behind newly formed lakes. Primary succession of these glacier-created lakes continues to this day, with the serial progression of their biological communities. What begins with succession of lake communities can transition into succession of terrestrial communities because over time a lake can fill with sediments and dry up. Secondary succession of aquatic systems occurs every time aquatic ecosystems recover from disturbances, natural or human-caused. For example, the removal of a reservoir dam allows a river ecosystem to return to its normal succession. Dredging of waterways may be beneficial for humans, but this act impedes and even reverses succession. In unimpeded natural succession, clear, deep lakes with few nutrients, referred to as **oligotrophic**, slowly convert to being turbid and shallow, with high nutrients. The increase of nutrients from low to high concentrations, called eutrophication, is expected and predicted, but can speed up in water bodies close to cities and towns.

oligotrophic

(In reference to a lake.) Characterized by a low concentration of nutrients and little primary production; usually clear and deep.

FIGURE 5.20

Ecosystems change due to many actions, such as glaciation, community succession, and deforestation. (A) For example, in time, a pond ecosystem fills with organic debris and becomes shallower and develops into (B) a marsh ecosystem. The marsh ages and converts into a (C) grassland. The grassland, if in an area with sufficient precipitation, will also slowly change. Shrubs and trees will begin to colonize the area until (D) a mature forest exists.

A	B	C	D
Pond	Marsh	Grassland	Forest

Source: Joseph Shostell; © Shutterstock, Inc.

Bringing It Closer to Home: A World of Forests?

In our discussion of succession, we saw how an aquatic system or terrestrial ecosystem is slowly converted into a climax forest ecosystem. If this is the case, why don't we observe forests everywhere we go? Why do lakes exist at all if they inevitably fill up with sediments and become prairies and then forests? Shouldn't everything in the environment be the same? Find a map of your state, and note the nearest lakes, rivers, and mountains as you contemplate an answer.

Disturbing one ecosystem inhibits its succession, but this disturbance may accelerate succession in a nearby ecosystem. This may be happening in the St. Clair Lake and Lake Michigan ecosystems (Quinn 1985). Evidence seems to suggest that dredging of the St. Clair River—doubling its depth compared to 1850s levels—has unintentionally exposed the riverbed to severe erosion. The effect is analogous to enlarging the drainage hole in a bathtub, in essence speeding the drainage of a body of water, or in this case prematurely lowering the levels of lakes Michigan and Huron. Whereas lowering has occurred in two lakes, there has been compensatory depth increases in Lakes St. Claire and Erie.

The Role of Succession and Climax

What is the role of succession and the climax community? As the environment changes, so does the community it supports. Species adapted to certain environmental conditions colonize first, and their presence alters the environment in a way that makes it hospitable for other species. In turn, the presence of new species in the community further alters the environment in a way that makes it hospitable for other new species, and so on. Nutrient-poor soil, for example, can become nutrient-rich, or a compacted airless soil can become aerated. Succession is not just about early-arrival species prepping for future-arrival species; community change is also the result of competition between the early- and late-arriving species. All of these changes lead to a climax community, dominated by trees.

Theoretically, a climax community exists indefinitely in a stable equilibrium until environmental conditions change. Even so, not all ecologists agree about the community end point. Some ecologists think only one climax community occurs, a concept called monoclimax theory. Other ecologists propose a polyclimax theory, which states that multiple outcomes can occur. In truth, as scientists, we may not yet fully understand succession events, in New England and elsewhere, because we have not directly observed the serial changes and recorded them. For example, maybe all of North America's biomes are still responding to glacial recession, and what we consider to be a climax community or climax ecosystem really isn't climax at all.

Key Takeaways

- Ecosystems can change in structure and function due to natural disturbance events, community succession, and human activities.
- Communities (living parts of ecosystems) undergo succession, leading to climax communities.

5.6 A Look to the Future: North America's Continued Change

Learning Objective

1. Think about past ecosystem changes in North America and predict the types of ecosystems that will exist in the coming decades, centuries, and millennia.

The opening story explains how ecosystems are altered by natural processes (e.g., glaciers) as well as artificial forces (e.g., deforestation). Here, at the end of the chapter, we reconsider the opening story and predict how North America's landscape and ecosystems may change in coming millennia. What would be a reasonable assertion? For some clues, we can turn to Eugene Odum's (1969) seminal paper on ecosystem development, in which he explains how communities modify the physical environment—meaning when community succession occurs, ecosystems change as well. A novel idea in the 1960s, he suggested the culmination of stabilized ecosystems, which, from time to time, are altered by disturbances. The severity of the effects—from minor change in ecosystem physical structure and temporary reversal of succession, to complete reshaping of physical structure and eradiation of communities—depends on the size and length of disturbance. We might find other clues in analyzing Earth's glaciations. So far, we have evidence of six major glaciation events, with the last one ending about 12,000 years ago. There is uncertainty as to how enhanced climate change due to society's activities may affect future glaciation cycles beyond continuing to diminish the size of the glacial ice sheets in Greenland and Antarctica (Archer and Ganopolski 2005, Herrero et al. 2014). What we do know is that community succession and biodiversity within ecosystems, and hence ecosystem structure and functioning, will continue to be affected by changing environmental conditions.

Key Takeaways

- North America's ecosystems will continue to change.
- Scientists are uncertain of how continued rapid climate change will affect long-term glaciation cycles.
- We expect future ecosystem structure to reflect community succession events, disturbances (natural and anthropogenic), and changing environmental conditions.

FIGURE 5.21 Visual Overview: Ecosystems and Biomes
Summarizing figure: Earth has ecosystems (5.1), biomes (5.2 and 5.3), and aquatic life zones (5.4). Like their communities, ecosystems undergo change (5.5) due to natural and artificial disturbances, and will continue to change for millennia to come (5.6).

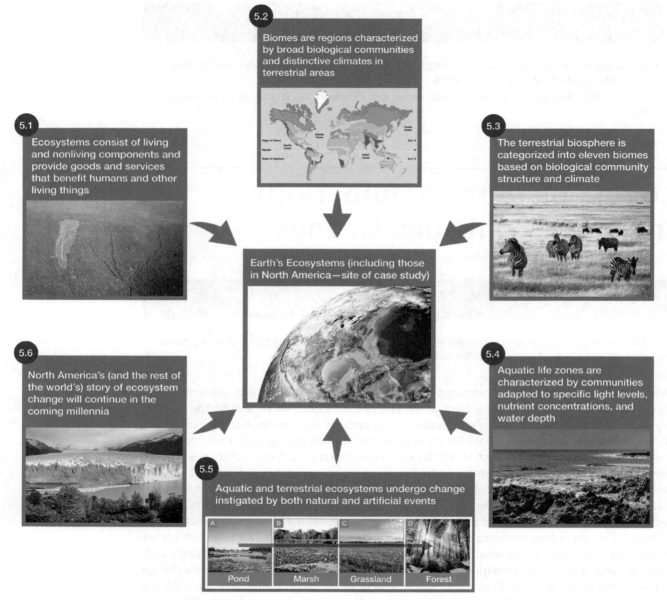

Sources: Joseph Shostell; See previous citations for image credits.

5.7 References

- Archer D., and A. Ganopolski. 2005. "A movable trigger: Fossil fuel CO_2 and the onset of the next glaciation." *Geochemistry Geophysics Geosystems* 6, no. 5: Q05003: https://doi.org/10.1029/2004GC000891.
- Atwater, T. 1970. "Implications of Plate Tectonics for the Cenozoic Tectonic Evolution of Western North America." *The Geological Society of America Bulletin* 81, no. 12: 3513–3536.

- Balmford, A., A. Bruner, P. Cooper, R. Costanza, S. Farber, R. E. Green, M. Jenkins, P. Jefferiss, V. Jessamy, J. Madden, K. Munro, N. Myers, S. Naeem, J. Paavola, M. Rayment, S. Rosendo, J. Roughgarden, K. Trumper, and R. K. Turner. 2002. "Economic reasons for conserving wild nature." *Science* 297: 950–953.

- Barraclough, S. L., and E. M. Gould Jr. 1955. Harvard Forest Bulletin No. 26. *Economic Analysis of Farm Forest Operating Units.* Petersham, MA: Harvard University.

- Bayram, H., and A. B. Ozturk. 2014. "Global climate change, desertification, and its consequences in Turkey and the Middle East." In: *Global Climate Change and Public Health, Respiratory Medicine* (Eds.: K. E. Pinkerton and W. N. Rom). Berlin, Germany: Springer Science+Business Media.

- Breunig, K. 2003. *Summary Report Losing Ground at What Cost? Changes in Land Use and Their Impact on Habitat, Biodiversity, and Ecosystem Services in Massachusetts.* Mass Audubon.

- Carroll, W. D., P. R. Kapeluck, R. A. Harper, and D. H. VanLear. 2002. "Background paper: historical overview of the southern forest landscape and associated resources." In: *Southern Forest Resource Assessment General Technical Report SRS-53* (Eds.: D. N. Wear and J. G. Greis). U.S. Department of Agriculture Forest Service, Southern Research Station.

- Clements, F. E. 1916. "The development and structure of biotic communities." In: *Ecological Society of America, New York Meeting, December 27–29, 1916.* Washington, DC: Ecological Society of America.

- Costanza, R., R. d'Arge, R. de Groot, S. Farberk, M. Grasso, B. Hannon, K. Limburg, S. Naeem, R. V. O'Neill, J. Paruelo, R. G. Raskin, P. Suttonkk, and M. van den Belt. 1997. "The value of the world's ecosystem services and natural capital." *Nature* 387: 253–260.

- Crocker, R. L., and J. Major. 1955. "Soil development in relation to vegetation and surface age at Glacier Bay, Alaska." *Journal of Ecology* 43: 427–448.

- D'Amato, A. W., D. A. Orwig, and D. R. Foster. 2006. "New Estimates of Massachusetts Old-growth Forests: Useful Data for Regional Conservation and Forest Reserve Planning." *Northeastern Naturalist* 13, no. 4: 495–506.

- Delcourt, P. A., and G. R. Delcourt. 1984. "Late quaternary paleoclimates and biotic responses in Eastern North Atlantic Ocean." *Palaeogeography, Palaeoclimatology, and Palaeoecology* 48: 263–284.

- Dunwiddie, P. W. 1993. "Survey of old-growth forests in Massachusetts." Unpublished report to the Massachusetts Natural Heritage and Endangered Species Program, Nantucket, MA.

- Earle, S. 2019. *Physical Geology, 2nd Edition.* BCcampus. Victoria, B. C.

- Field, C. B., M. J. Behrenfeld, J. T. Randerson, and P. Falkowski. 1998. "Primary production of the biosphere: integrating terrestrial and oceanic components." *Science* 281, no. 10: 237–281.

- Foster, C. W. 1998. *Stepping back to look forward: a history of Massachusetts forests.* Cambridge, MA: Harvard University Press.

- Foster, D., D. Kittredge, B. Donahue, G. Motzkin, D. Orwig, A. Ellison, B. Hall, B. Colburn, and A. D'Amato. 2006. *Wildlands and Woodlands: a vision for the forests of Massachusetts.* Petersham, MA: Harvard Forest, Harvard University.

- Gauthier, S., P. Bernier, T. Kuuluvainen, A. Z. Shvidenko, and D. G. Schepaschenko. 2015. "Boreal forest health and global change." *Science* 349: 819–822.

- Hanes, T. L. 1977. "California chaparral." In: *Terrestrial Vegetation of California* (Eds.: M. G. Barbour and J. Major). Hoboken, NJ: Wiley & Sons.

- Harper, R. M. 1918. "Changes in the forest area of New England in three centuries." *J. Forestry* 16, no. 4: 442–452.

- Herrero, C., A. García-Olivares, and L. Pelegrí. 2014. "Impact of anthropogenic CO_2 on the next glacial cycle." *Climate Change* 122: 283–298.

- Landsberg, J. J., and S. T. Gower. 1997. *Applications of Physiological Ecology to Forest Management.* San Diego, CA: Academic Press.

- Likens, G. E., and F. G. Bormann. 1975. "An experimental approach to New England landscapes." In: *Coupling of Land and Water Systems* (Ed.: A. D. Hasler). New York: Springer-Verlag.
- Lippitt, C. L., D. A. Stow, J. F. O'Leary, and J. Franklin. 2013. "Influence of short-interval fire occurrence on post-fire recovery of fire-prone shrublands in California, USA." *International Journal of Wildland Fire* 22, no. 2: 184–193.
- Mayor, S. 2011. "Tree that provides paclitaxel is listed as endangered." *BMJ* 343: 1023.
- Mucina, L. 2019. "Biome: evolution of crucial ecological and biogeographical concept." *New Phytologist* 222: 97–114.
- Murphy, P. G., and A. E. Lugo. 1986. "Ecology of tropical dry forest." *Annual Review of Ecology and Systematics* 17: 67–88.
- Norman, C. 1984. "No Panacea for the firewood crises." *Science* 226: 676.
- Nowak, D. J., D. E. Crane, and J. C. Stevens. 2006. "Air pollution removal by urban trees and shrubs in the United States." *Urban for Urban Green* 4: 115–123.
- Nowak, D. J., S. Hirabayashi, A. Bodine, and R. Hoehn. 2013. "Modeled PM2.5 removal by trees in ten U.S. cities and associated health effects." *Environ Pollut* 178: 395–402.
- Nowak, D. J., S. Hirabayashi, A. Bodine, and E. Greenfield. 2014. "Tree and forest effects on air quality and human health in the United States." *Environmental Pollution* 193: 119–129.
- Odum, E. P. 1969. "The strategy of ecosystem development." *Science* 164: 262–270.
- Pauly, D., R. Watson, and J. Alder. 2005. "Global trends in world fisheries: impacts on marine ecosystems and food security." *Philos Trans R Soc B Biol Sci* 360: 5–12.
- Porter, E. M., W. D. Bowman, C. M. Clark, J. E. Compton, L. H. Pardo, and J. L. Soong. 2013. "Interactive effects of anthropogenic nitrogen enrichment and climate change on terrestrial and aquatic biodiversity." *Biogeochemistry* 114: 93–120.
- Quinn, F. H. 1985. "Temporal effects of St. Claire River dredging on lakes St. Clair and Erie water levels and connecting channel flow." *Journal of Great Lakes Research* 11, no. 3: 400–403.
- Riddihough, R. 1984. "Recent movements of the Juan de Fuca plate system." *Journal of Geophysical Research* 89, no. B8: 6980–6994.
- Schindler, D. W. 1974. "Eutrophication and recovery in experimental lakes: implications for lake management." *Science* 184: 897–899.
- Staver, A. C., S. Archibald, and S. A. Levin. 2011. "The global extent and determinants of savanna and forest as alternative biome states." *Science* 334: 230–232.
- Sugden, D. E. 1977. "Reconstruction of the morphology, dynamics, and thermal characteristics of the Laurentide ice sheet at its maximum." *Arctic and Alpine Research* 9, no. 1: 21–47.
- Sumaila, U. R., and T. C. Tai. 2020. "End overfishing and increase the resilience of the ocean to climate change." *Front Mar Sci* 523 doi: 10.3389/fmars.2020.00523.
- Ter Steege, H., D. Sabatier, H. Castellanos, T. Van Andel, J. Duivenvoorden, A. A. De Oliveira. 2000. "An analysis of the floristic composition and diversity of Amazonian forests including those of the Guiana Shield." *Journal of Tropical Ecology* 16: 801–828.
- Voss, K. A., and E. S. Bernhardt. 2017. "Effects of mountaintop removal coal mining on the diversity and secondary productivity of Appalachian rivers." *Limnology and Oceanography* 62: 1754–1770.
- Waring, R. H. 2002. "Temperate coniferous forests." In: *Volume 2, The Earth System: Biological and Ecological Dimensions of Global Environmental Change* (Eds.: H. A. Mooney and J. G. Canadell). San Francisco, CA: John Wiley & Sons, Ltd.

CHAPTER 6
Human Populations

Case Study: China, Then and Now—Population Growth, Economics, and Limited Resources

In June of 2005, "barefoot lawyer" Chen Guancheng filed a class-action lawsuit against the Chinese government on behalf of women subjected to forced abortions and sterilizations due to the draconian One Child Policy (OCP). In short order, Chen was arrested, subjected to a trial with no due process, incarcerated for over four years, and afterward, placed under indefinite house arrest. Read about Chen's harrowing ordeal, escape, and flight to the United States Embassy in his book (Guancheng 2014).

Beginning in 1949, years before the OCP, Chinese citizens were encouraged to have large families. Couples commonly had, on average, seven children. As a result, China's population grew rapidly (see Figure 6.1). At this pivotal time in China's history, the new communist party drew on this growth, initiating an industrial campaign that transformed China and helped build a strong national economy. However, a population cannot grow indefinitely. By 1959, there were clear signs that China was outgrowing its food supply. Thirty million people died from starvation in just three years. This unprecedented famine and death amid continued population growth led Chinese leaders to set measures aimed at controlling population growth strongly and swiftly. The measures worked. For example, the OCP limited most families to just one child. This action had multiple consequences, but most important, it slowed population growth. By the 2010s, China's strong decline in population growth and dwindling workforce presented a new problem. How would China be able to continue to meet its ongoing goal of industrial and economic growth with a shrinking population? In 2016, China replaced the OCP with a Two Child Policy, and then in 2021 changed it again to a Three Child Policy because the Two Child Policy did not have the desired outcome. Couples are now encouraged to have three children. However, even with this encouragement, there has been no upsurge in the number of births because of high education costs, insufficient access to childcare, and inadequate maternity leave.

FIGURE 6.1
The China of the mid-twentieth century was very different than the China of today. China's population has grown by over 200 percent, and the Chinese enjoy healthier, longer lifespans. They have developed industrially, and to this day continue to build infrastructure to support their large population. A) China is no longer just known for historical monuments such as the Great Wall. B) China has experienced extensive industrialization and modernization, seen here at a shopping mall in ShenZhen and (C) a glass-bottom bridge in Zhangjiajie's National Forest Park.

Sources: © Shutterstock, Inc.; Sorbis/Shutterstock.com; u photostock/Shutterstock.com

China's current average number of children born per female (**total fertility rate**, or TFR) is well below replacement level, which is the number of children needed to replace the parent generation. Will China attempt a new strategy to increase population growth? If they do, what will it be?

Population growth and population size can also pose serious threats to the environment. China, for example, is the world's most populous nation, and also the greatest emitter of greenhouse gases. Because rapid climate change is a global concern, the global community has taken a keen

total fertility rate (TFR)
The average number of children born per female.

interest in China's population size and the effects of its activities on the environment. China's recent change of population growth plans and China's increased pollution emissions are alarming the international community. Will China continue to follow the growth mantra (*"Grow first and clean up later"*) when answering questions about environmental issues? They say they are just following the path laid out by Europe and the United States as these nations became industrialized. Even so, the world is more fragile today than it was during the time of the Industrial Revolution. Much of our planet is woefully damaged. Can the environment wait for China to finish growing before the cleanup begins?

6.1 Population Growth and the Environment's Health

Learning Objectives

1. Graph and summarize past, current, and predicted future global human population growth.
2. Compare and contrast population growth across geographical regions.
3. Describe the connection between population size and environmental degradation.

With or without the One Child Policy (OCP), China's population continues to grow, along with its consumption of food and natural resources. China knows from experience how a population suffers when its food supply is inadequate. In the early 1960s, during a time of high total fertility rate (TFR), China's food supply failed to keep pace with rapid population growth, causing massive famine across the nation. To meet its more recent population growth, China has sharply increased imports of soybeans, from about 490,000 metric tons in 1995 to over 92.5 million metric tons in 2020. China's consumption also reflects its rapid urbanization, rising middle class, and affluence. Evidence of air and water pollution in hundreds of cities in China supports what we know but do not want to believe: the environment does not contain an infinite supply of resources, nor can it effectively process society's pollution. Infinite population growth cannot occur in a finite world.

Earth's human population is now over 7.8 billion, and the number continues to increase. How large will it become, and what effects might a growing population have on our finite resources, environment, and standard of living? What factors affect population growth? At what population number do we become too numerous for our planet? These are the sorts of questions of interest to us within this chapter. Today's environmental problems are almost exclusively the result of humans' using Earth as a source to meet consumption needs and as a sink to absorb waste energy and pollution. In this first section on human populations, we analyze the size and growth of the global human population over time, discuss differences in these variables among geographical regions, and identify data linking human population growth to environmental degradation.

Our Population Has Grown Substantially in a Relatively Short Amount of Time

From a humble beginning in Africa 200,000 years ago, the human population has literally exploded in size to almost 7.8 billion today (see Figure 6.2) (Cann et al. 1987, McDougall et al. 2005). For much of our history our population was relatively small. We didn't reach our first million until around the end of the last ice age, 10,000–12,000 years ago, and not our first billion until 1830. Then the amount of time between each successive billion shrank as we moved into an exponential growth phase. One hundred years later, in 1930, we reached two billion, and then in only thirty years the population reached three billion (see Table 6.1). Since then, the time between successive billions has decreased to twelve years, and we are well on the way to eight billion. At the time of the printing of this book, 83 million people are added to the total every year. This continued growth over time explains why our population has grown 7,700 percent (7,700 times larger) since the last ice age, and why roughly 14 percent of all humans who have ever lived are alive today. Predictions by the United Nations suggest our population will grow to 11.2 billion by the end of this century. The main drivers of this growth are the greater numbers of people reaching reproductive age, a high TFR, and, to a lesser extent, migration. Although presently we continue to grow, our calculations of future growth indicate it will take longer to reach future billion milestones. Does this trend imply that we are approaching carrying capacity, just like other populations?

FIGURE 6.2
The human population has remained fairly small for most of its history except for the last two hundred years, when it rapidly increased in size. Each red dot represents the addition of one billion people.

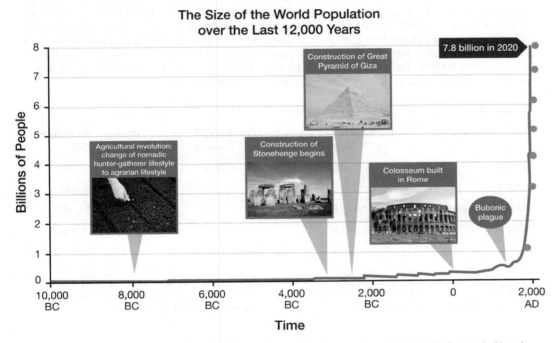

Sources: Joseph Shostell; data prior to 1950 from U.S. Census Bureau, https://www.census.gov/data/tables/time-series/demo/international-programs/historical-est-worldpop.html; Data from 1950 through today from U.S. Census Bureau, https://population.un.org/wpp/Download/Standard/Population/ Shutterstock, Inc.; Copycat37/Shutterstock.com

TABLE 6.1 Global Population Growth

Population Size	Year	Time to Reach Next Billion
100 million	500 BCE	—
500 million	1650	—
1 billion	1830	—
2 billion	1930	100 years
3 billion	1960	30 years
4 billion	1975	15 years
5 billion	1987	12 years

Population Size	Year	Time to Reach Next Billion
6 billion	1999	12 years
7 billion	2011	12 years
8 billion	2024 (projected)	13 years
9 billion	2039 (projected)	15 years
10 billion	2056 (projected)	17 years

Source: Data from the U.S. Census Bureau.

Critical Thinking Activity: Calculation of Doubling Time

In his book *An Essay on the Principles of Population* (1798), Thomas Malthus (1766–1834) warned of the dangers of sustained exponential population growth and the limits of agricultural yields and food supply. To avoid disaster, such as outstripping food supply, we study human populations and project future population growth. One method of analyzing population growth is by calculating a population's doubling time, which is the time needed for the population to double in size. Calculating doubling time allows a nation to determine whether it has sufficient resources for its future population. Usually, we use the rule of 70, in which we divide 70 by the population's growth rate. For example, if the growth rate for Nigeria is 2.6 percent, its estimated doubling time is 70 divided by 2.6, or 26.9 years. At a growth rate of 2.6 percent, Nigeria will double its population size in just under 27 years. Apply the rule of 70 to the growth rates of the countries listed in Table 6.2 and calculate their doubling times. Identify the country with the shortest doubling time. Why is there such a range of growth values?

TABLE 6.2 Using the Rule of 70 to Calculate Population Doubling Time

Country	Population Growth Rate	Doubling Time (Years)	Population Size in 2020
Nigeria	2.6	26.9	206,139,590
Niger	3.8	—	24,206,640
United States	0.7	—	329,484,120
China	0.6	—	1,402,112,000
India	1.1	—	1,380,004,390
Russia	0.1	—	144,104,080

Sources: Data from the United Nations, https://population.un.org/wpp/Download/Standard/Population/ and https://population.un.org/wpp/Download/Standard/Population/.

Population Size, Density, and Growth

The human population is unevenly distributed across the world. Differences in population density can be explained by proximity to environmental resources such as water, climate conditions, and developmental status of a country. For instance, people live in high population densities along coasts, near rivers, and in select countries. Today Earth has an average of fifty-seven people per square kilometer (km^2), up from 18.6 in 1950. More developed regions have lower population densities, around twenty-three people per km^2, whereas in poorer, less developed regions the average density is approximately sixty-eight people per km^2. Select countries within these categories can also have drastically different densities. For instance, within the group of developed countries, the United States has about thirty-three people per km^2 whereas Canada has four people per km^2. The world's highest population densities are 18,960 people per km^2 and 7,796 people per km^2, found in

Monaco and Singapore, respectively, yet these are not the countries with the largest populations. Densities don't always correlate with population size, as evidenced by both India and China's being the most populous nations but not the densest. In 2020, China and India each had a population size of about 1.4 billion.

Do the regions with the largest population sizes also have the highest population growth rates? Beginning with the most populous region, Asia contains 60 percent of the world's population and includes China and India (see Figure 6.3). Together, these two countries make up 37 percent of the total global population, and this region has the second-fastest growth rate. A comparatively less populated Africa holds 16 percent of the world's population and is experiencing the highest population growth rate, because twenty of the twenty-two countries with the highest TFRs are found here. Nigeria (TFR > 5) is already the largest African nation and is predicted to replace the United States as the third most populated country by mid-century. At the current growth rate of 2.49 percent per year, Africa will grow to an estimated 4.5 billion by 2100, at which point it will almost equal the entire population of Asia (4.8 billion). In comparison, Europe holds 10 percent of the world's population, but its population is declining because its TFR is less than **replacement fertility**. It is experiencing a negative growth of –.02 percent per year.

replacement fertility

The number children per female that survive to reproduction age and replace the two parents; usually considered as 2.1 after accounting for childhood death before the age of reproduction.

FIGURE 6.3
Some countries, such as China, India, and Nigeria, have disproportionately contributed to the global population—which continues to grow in size. A) A crowd in Mumbai, India's largest city. B) In areas of high population density, people develop inventive ways to travel.

Sources: sladkozaponi/Shutterstock.com; Malcolm P Chapman/Shutterstock.com

Population growth also varies by the developmental status of a nation. Developing countries have relatively high total fertility rates and high growth rates, and they typically have high poverty, gender inequality, poor education, hunger, and inadequate health care. Take, for instance, Niger, which has the highest TFR of any country (6.8 in 2020). Approximately 70 percent of its population is under the age of twenty-five, and there are few educational opportunities for women. With little education and few job prospects, financial independence is difficult, so Nigerien women tend to marry young and begin having children at an early age. While the legal age of marriage is fifteen, girls commonly marry at age twelve. About half of them have their first child at age sixteen. Therefore, initiatives to lower the TFR put forward for developing countries by the United Nations Population Fund (UNFPA) and other entities tend to be broad and include reproductive health, gender equality, and education, among other factors.

Is Human Population Growth the Root of Environmental Degradation?

Population growth and population size would not be disruptive to the environment if humans were to follow a strict sustainability agenda and live at or below carrying capacity. Even so, a cursory assessment of the global environment informs us of the difficulty of adopting a sustainable lifestyle. As a whole, humans have bitterly failed the challenge thus far. To keep up with the resource demands of our exploding population, we have converted large sections of the naturally biodiverse world into something else. Agricultural and grazing pastures now take up about 40 percent of Earth's ice-free land (Foley et al. 2005). The conversion is ongoing and involves both natural wetlands and forested areas. So far, we have drained roughly 50 percent of Earth's wetlands (Meyer & Turner 1992), and we are deforesting tropical rainforests at a rate of 55,000 square kilometers (21,236 mi^2)—an area more than twice the size of Massachusetts—every year (Keenan et al. 2015). On these lands, which now have low biodiversity, we disseminate a range of agrochemicals, including fertilizers and pesticides, which move into the hydrosphere. An influx of nutrients promotes eutrophication (see Chapter 10), thriving bacterial communities, and anoxic conditions. In turn, these changes damage water supplies, disrupt aquatic recreation, and destroy prime fishing habitats. Large "islands" of aquatic habitat in the oceans and lakes have succumbed to these changes and are now dead zones. One of the largest of these (there are over five hundred) dead zones is found in the Gulf of Mexico, near the mouth of the Mississippi River. Nitrogen loads contribute to this too, and phosphorus is part of the 200 million tons of fertilizers applied globally per year (FAO 2015). Society releases about 8.4 teragrams (≈9.3 million tons) of phosphorus every year (Lwin, Murakami, and Hashimoto 2017), more or less equal to the weight of ninety-three aircraft carriers.

As our pesticide use has increased and these chemicals have become ubiquitous in the environment, we have witnessed a downward trend in groups of non-targeted species such as amphibians (Brunelli et al. 2009) and pollinating insects. Pollination by animals is a key ecosystem service that is used by 90 percent of flowering plants (Ollerton et al 2011) and is instrumental in crop production for human consumption (Aizen et al. 2009). Loss of bees and other valuable pollinators puts global agriculture at risk (see Chapter 8).

Earth's water resources show other signs of strain beyond the influence of agrochemicals. Global water consumption (about 10,688 ± 979 km^3 per year; Jaramillo and Destouni 2015) far exceeds the total volume of water stored in all of Earth's rivers (2,000 km^3) and is over one-fourth of the available volume of water discharged (≈41,000 km^3 per year; Oki and Kanae 2006). Agriculture accounts for roughly 92 percent of our water footprint, and a relatively small number of countries take a disproportionately larger share of Earth's freshwaters. China, India, and the United States are the top users and together equal 38 percent of all consumed water. According to the United States Geographical Survey, mining efforts of subsurface water is the leading (80 percent) cause of subsidence in the United States. Subsidence, a serious issue in forty-five states, is the sinking or dropping of land surface, and it is the result of draining aquifers faster than they can be replenished.

Evidence of our non-sustainable lifestyles seems to abound, from giant masses of floating garbage in the oceans, to dissolved pollutants, to low abundance of fish. Even when we don't directly interact with other species, we still impinge on them indirectly. For example, few of us observe the critically endangered Southern Resident killer whale population of the northeastern Pacific Ocean, yet their population is waning because of contaminants, noise pollution, and overfishing of their favored prey (Lacy et al. 2017).

Evidence of our non-sustainable existence is also in the atmosphere, from high levels of anthropogenic greenhouse gases and consequent climate change, to acid rain, to smog. These are only a few examples of a lengthy list. All of these examples are evidence that we have not been living within our means. As financially prudent individuals, we plan ahead to afford vacations and to avoid spending more than we can afford. Applying these words of wisdom to sustainability, we should plan our activities accordingly and therefore avoid overspending our environmental currency. In other words, there is value in knowing both current and future consumption.

Key Takeaways

- The human population has grown substantially in a relatively short amount of time.

- There is a wide range in human population size, density, and growth across geographical areas.
- Africa is experiencing the world's highest rate of population growth.
- Evidence of our non-sustainable lifestyles abounds around us.

6.2 Benefiting from Knowledge about Population Characteristics

Learning Objectives

1. Recognize and explain the value of demographic data to cities and nations.
2. Analyze and interpret age and gender demographic data.

In our opening story, we learned about the challenges China now faces regarding its large population size and smaller workforce. In addition, we learned about global concern about China's rising pollution levels. Here, we continue with these thoughts and discuss the effects of a changing population structure on economic growth, health of the environment, and other factors. For example, China has enjoyed the dividends of a proportionately large labor force. However, this huge labor cohort is beginning to retire, which places China's economic ascent in jeopardy. There are not enough working-age replacements for the retirees. Astute governmental officials analyzed population data and predicted this upcoming economic problem.

Demography

Human populations are dynamic, which means they continuously fluctuate in size and structure. The large and important issues connected to these dynamics, such as economic productivity, food supply, and environmental sustainability, are some of the driving reasons why nations, states, and cities find value in monitoring and predicting changes in their population's size and structure. People who study population changes and who are interested in making predictions about these changes are called **demographers**. Demographers work in the field of **demography**—the statistical study of human populations. The prefix of demography, *demos*, means people. Demographic data inform us about the proportional sizes of a population's labor force, dependents, school age children, retirees, and those of reproductive age. As the relative proportions of a population change, so too do its capabilities and needs. Analysis of demographic data allows us to make predictions about the population's future structure and needs. With this information, we make decisions about health care, education, economic objectives, and even military strategy. For example, a larger work force provides a greater tax revenue to support a population's retirees and their needs. Alternatively, a predicted smaller labor force likely translates into a contracted economy.

A continuous analysis of demographic data is useful to ensure that the services, resources, and physical structure of a city adequately match its population size and composition. Even the initial development of a city relies on certain favorable conditions, including a good environment with clean water and hospitable climate, food supplies, and a secure social structure. A monitoring and maintenance of these elements also supports the long-term health of a city. Being able to predict

demographers

People who study the characteristics (growth, size, density . . .) of human populations.

demography

The statistical study of human populations.

how a population's composition, size, and consumption needs affect the environment is important too. Nations, cities, and the environment all win when societal structure supports a fully functioning natural environment. Society depends on a healthy environment to uphold ecosystem goods and services (see Chapter 1).

megalopolis

A very large metropolis; there are 10 million or more inhabitants.

Unanticipated population growth can have unfortunate consequences. A lack of appropriate planning to account for waves of immigrants, for example, will likely result in insufficient basic utilities (water, sanitation, trash removal) for some groups of people. There may be housing shortages, and possibly traffic congestion and unnecessarily high levels of atmospheric pollution if an appropriate transportation system is not established. In the worst-case scenario, a population grows with few or no basic services and joins the estimated 200,000 slum cities already in existence (Davis 2006). A great number of cities are trying to accommodate the influx of people taking part in global urbanization. For the first time in human history, there are more people living in urban rather than in rural areas. In 1950, only 29 percent of the human population lived in cities; today, 56 percent do, and by 2050 it will be 68 percent. In China alone, an estimated 100 million people have moved from rural agricultural areas to the bustling cities in the last ten years. Individual cities are absorbing hundreds of thousands of people in a very short period. Twenty-seven mega-metropolises, depending on how you demarcate city limits, are larger than New York City, North America's largest city. A mega-metropolis or **megalopolis** has 10 million or more inhabitants (see Chapter 17). No matter the size, every city generates waste and must deal with it efficiently, and hopefully sustainably. New York City's (unsustainable) solution is to transport a third of its 14 million tons of trash per year to landfills in upstate New York's Finger Lakes Region.

Age Structure of a Population

Collected census data are commonly organized into cohorts based on age and sex and then displayed in a histogram (see Figure 6.4). In this graphical format, large volumes of data can be interpreted quickly. For example, we easily discern the number of females within the age group of 0–4 at the bottom right of the graph in Figure 6.4. We expect a population graph, also known as a population pyramid, to become smaller toward the top, because fewer people make it to older age groups due to natural causes of death and accidents (see video link: "Analyzing Human Populations").

FIGURE 6.4
Population pyramids for Niger (A) and China (B) indicate population structure based on age and gender. Niger, in contrast to China, has a preponderance of its 2020 population in young age classes.

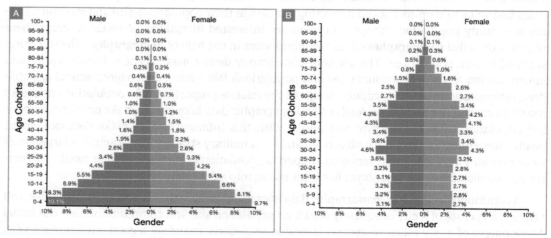

A population pyramid also portrays the number of young, as well as those of reproductive age. Within the United States, we use census data to make decisions about how to distribute hundreds of billions of dollars in federal funds each year. Similarly, states use these data to assist them in determining how to allocate funds for health care, roads, and education. Thus, a logical decision to accommodate populations with a disproportionately large cohort of young people would be to infuse monies into the educational system. In 2019, for example, the United States spent $752.3 billion on public school systems. About 87 percent of this amount covered teachers' salaries and day-to-day activities. Ten percent of the total amount covered new construction, improvements to existing structures, and large equipment expenses (USCB 2019). Therefore, a large influx of young people into a population can be demanding for cities, states, or nations that have a fixed number of schools and teachers, and a limited educational budget.

An analysis of population structure also provides information about the number of people in senior age groups. Having a large percentage of a population in older age groups can also burden a society because most of these people are retired. In the United States and many other countries, each retiree receives medical and other benefits that are provided by the working-age groups.

Shifts in a population's age structure can be detrimental to a society if those changes are not forecasted and planned for ahead of time. The baby boomer generation in the United States is an example of this. The baby boomer generation encompasses those people born following World War II, between 1946 and 1964, when there was a substantial rise in birth rates. Just between 1945 and 1946, the number of births increased from 2.9 million to 3.4 million, a 20 percent increase (Colby and Ortman 2014). The number of births in the United States peaked in 1957 to 4.3 million, and then dropped to a yearly average of 3.5 million after the baby boom ended. Because the birth rate fell after 1964, now there are fewer working-age adults to support a burgeoning population of retirees. Calculations indicate that this will be unsustainable in the long run because the U.S. Social Security system will run out of money before the next generation—the baby bust generation, born between 1965 and 1976—retires.

Analyzing Human Populations
Investigate the use of population pyramids in understanding historical population structure and in predicting future population growth.

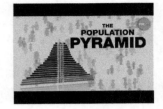

View in the online reader

We Use Age Structure Data to Make Predictions of Future Population Size

An analysis of current population age structure and the relative proportion of young also allows us to forecast future population size. For example, Figure 6.4 shows the age distributions of two different countries. In the case of Niger, a large percentage of the population is very young. Should most of these young survive and have children of their own, the population will dramatically increase. This is an example of **population momentum**. Unfortunately, the reality is that many of the children will not survive because the country will not have the infrastructure needed to support such a population increase, so they will experience poor living conditions, disease, and starvation. In contrast, in the case of China (see Chapter 6), young age groups are relatively small, indicating China's population will shrink in size. Back in 1975, over 40 percent of China's population was below the age of fifteen. China's population structure today is noticeably different, for now the value has dropped to 17.1 percent, and is predicted to drop to 13 percent by mid-century. As this transition occurs, China's aging population increases the proportion of the population over sixty-four years of age: from 3.9 percent in 1975, it is estimated to reach almost 31 percent in 2055. Are China's newly emerged economy and fragile social security system up to the task of supporting a large elderly population? China's small younger cohorts contrast with India's large ones, and explain why we predict India's population to surpass China's in the near future.

population momentum

Growth of a population due to an increase in the number of reproductive-age women who are having children.

Key Takeaways

- Demography is the statistical study of human populations.

- Collected census data are commonly organized into cohorts based on age and sex and then displayed in a histogram.
- A study of demographic data informs a nation about its population structure and future population size. With this information, they become knowledgeable about population needs and can make more meaningful decisions about health care, education, and economic objectives.

6.3 Biological Factors Affect Population Growth and Environmental Health

Learning Objectives

1. Explain the relevance of total fertility rate in predicting population growth.
2. Examine and describe how society has reduced infant mortality rates.
3. Detail the effects of lengthening human lifespan on the environment's health.
4. Discuss how family planning assists women and their families regarding the timing and number of pregnancies.

Population growth and, indirectly, our strain on the environment's health are to a large part driven by the number of people surviving to reproductive age, total fertility rate (TFR), migration (see Section 4), and affluence (see Section 5). Here, we discuss total fertility rate and its links to crude birth rate, crude death rate and replacement growth.

Global Total Fertility Rate (TFR) Is Declining

crude birth rate

The number of births per one thousand people.

Demographers often use TFR as a key statistic when discussing and predicting population growth (see video link: "Population Bombs and Low-Fertility Countries"). The **crude birth rate**, a measure of the total number of births per one thousand people, is another important statistic, but as a predictive number for growth, it is somewhat misleading because it represents men in addition to women. Our focus will therefore remain mostly on the female population. Since the early 1960s, the global TFR has dropped by 50 percent, from above 5 to less than 2.5, and even accounting for lag phases of momentum, the world's growth rate reflects this decrease (see Figure 6.5). When TFR reaches a replacement level (replacement-level fertility), the number of children who reach reproductive age is equal to the number of parents. In developed nations with low infant mortality, we use a replacement-level fertility of 2.1. The extra 0.1 accounts for child mortality—those who die before they reach sexual maturity, or children who are infertile or choose not to have children of their own. This means 100 out of every 2,100 births will not lead to future reproduction. Developing countries with poorer health services and living conditions experience higher childhood mortality rates and hence have higher replacement-level fertility values.

FIGURE 6.5

As long as total fertility rate (TFR) is above 2.1, the human population will continue to increase. (A) Globally, the total fertility (TFR) rate has decreased from a high of over 5 in the 1950s to 2.4 today. These data indicate a slowing of human population growth globally, but some geographical regions are experiencing an increase in growth. (B) Niger has the highest TFR (6.9) of any country. Only about 14 percent of Niger's land is arable (having soil suitable for crops); most of the country is covered by the Sahara Desert.

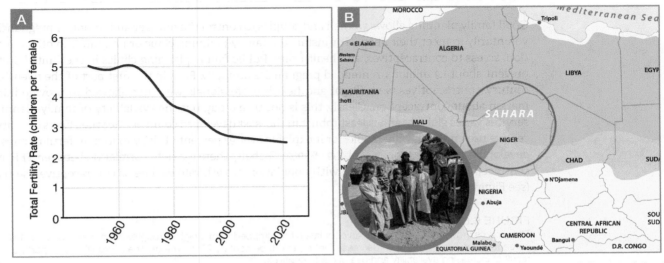

Sources: Joseph Shostell; data from https://ourworldindata.org/grapher/total-fertility-rate-by-world-region-including-un-projections-through-2100; © Shutterstock, Inc.; Katja Tsvetkova/Shutterstock.com

Right now, the United States has a TFR of 1.8, which by itself is insufficient to maintain its current population growth of 0.71. However, population momentum plus immigration combined with TFR continue to keep the United States in positive, albeit slow growth mode. In contrast, Niger has a TFR of 6.9, which means that, on average, females have about seven children during their lifetime. Niger experiences a very high population growth rate of 3.89 percent even accounting for large emigration numbers. Why didn't Niger's TFR follow the global declining trend, and what indirect affect does this high value have on Niger's environment? A combination of cultural and social practices, including social status linked to the number of children, polygamy, gender inequality, few educational opportunities for women, and religion, have made Niger resistant to adopting common methods of birth control. With every passing generation—from large cohort to the next large cohort—the amount of land inherited by a Nigerian becomes smaller. Therefore, subsistence farmers are forced to extract a living on smaller agricultural plots. In Niger, competition for environmental resources can be intense relative to countries of similar area and population size because over 80 percent of Niger is covered by the Saharan Desert. Access to water and arable land for farming are at the forefront of objectives for Nigeriens.

Population Bombs and Low-Fertility Countries

Listen to arguments for having fewer or more children and determine if we should be concerned about the rise or fall of total fertility rates.

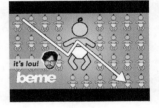

View in the online reader

Biological Constraints Limit the TFR

Biologically, the number of offspring a female can have depends on the age of sexual maturity, the length of gestation period, and the number of years from sexual maturity to menopause. Therefore, the **reproductive window** for a woman is, on average, from age twelve to fifty-one, a total of thirty-nine years. A pregnant woman falling within this window is physiologically committed to the developmental process and cannot be impregnated again. These biological conditions limit the number of children an individual woman can bear over the course of her lifetime. Many other factors affect the number of children a woman will have, and indirectly affect population growth. Family planning, education, women's rights, and financial independence are some of these factors.

reproductive window

A time in a woman's life from first reaching sexual maturity to menopause, on average between ages twelve to fifty-one.

Family Planning Helps to Reduce TFR and Control Population Growth

Good family planning allows women and couples to control the number and timing of pregnancies voluntarily to meet their needs. For instance, a family-planning clinic or program can offer education, access to contraceptives, and health care. Public family-planning clinics in the United States prevent about 1.9 million unintended pregnancies annually. Back in the first part of the twentieth century, contraceptives were illegal and health professionals were not allowed to provide information about contraception. Clearly, this is not true today, but the availability of family-planning services varies globally, and is least robust in the least developed countries. Yet the effects of contraceptive use on TFR is undeniable, for it explains over 92 percent of the variation in fertility rates in developing countries (Robey et al. 1992 & 1993). Globally, there is a tight correlation between TFR and contraceptive use, and TFR along with population growth rate decline as contraceptive use rises (see Figure 6.6).

FIGURE 6.6
The world's growth rate for the human population has dropped from a high of roughly 2.1 percent to about 1.0 percent today. It is projected to decrease further, to 0.5 percent by 2050. The decline in growth rate is partly a result of increasing availability and use of contraceptives.

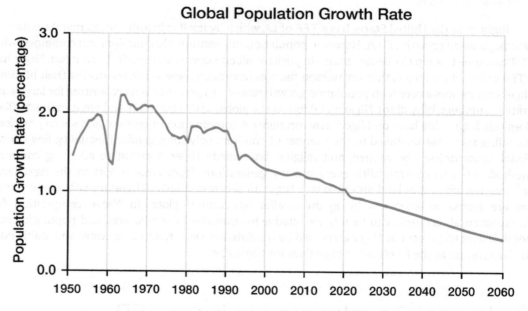

Source: Joseph Shostell; data from https://www.census.gov/data-tools/demo/idb/#/country?COUNTRY_YEAR=2022&COUNTRY_YR_ANIM=2022.

Per year, there are about 6 million pregnancies in the United States, and roughly half were unintended. At the global level, there are approximately 85 million unintended pregnancies each year, the majority due to lack of contraceptive availability and use, and a large percentage of these woman did not wish to be pregnant (Bellizzi et al. 2020; Sedgh et al. 2014). Access to reproductive education and materials (i.e., contraceptives) give women freedom of choice to reach their desired family size and to improve their health and that of their infants and families. Prevention of unintended pregnancies reduces women's exposure to potentially life-threatening events not of their choosing. Very young and older women are most at risk. Worldwide, each year 42 million women with unintended pregnancies choose abortion. About half of these women end up undergoing unsafe procedures, killing an estimated 68,000 women every year (Haddad et al. 2009). Access to reproductive education and materials also helps women to space out their children to at least three years, lowering the risk of infant death (Rutstein 2008). Planned birth spacing allows mothers to extend the overall time of breastfeeding per child and for the family to devote potentially limiting resources among fewer children.

Mortality

"All things that live will eventually die" (Kelly 2009). This powerful and accurate statement reminds us to incorporate death (mortality) in the calculation of population growth rate. In the simplest form of a population growth equation, population growth equals the number of births minus the number of deaths, over a given unit of time. A population only increases in size if the number of births exceeds the number of deaths assuming there is negligible emigration. Demographers use the **crude death rate** to describe mortality of a population. The crude death rate is the number of people who die per one thousand people. Advances in technology and medicine have helped to diminish infant mortality rates, and to substantially lengthen the average human lifespan.

crude death rate

The number of deaths per one thousand people.

Life expectancy—the average number of years a person is expected to live—can be significantly less in developing countries compared to developed countries. People in Niger, for example, have a life expectancy of fifty-four years, which is twenty-four years lower than the life expectancy in the United States. Why isn't life expectancy the same throughout the world? Poor sanitation and insufficient medicine contribute to high infant mortality and general loss of life. We also observe shorter life expectancy in those countries with less education and lower incomes (Crimmins 2021). Living to an older age also means, for many of us, more trips to the doctor and increased medical care. In our senior years we rely even more on health-care services. One indirect effect of a longer lifespan is an increase in medical waste. Every year the United States alone generates over 260 million tons of medical waste, up from 88 million in 1960. According to the United Nations, approximately 20–25 percent of medical waste is hazardous. There are infectious wastes that harbor a variety of pathogens, as well as chemical and pharmaceutical wastes, and radioactive wastes. Depending on the type of waste and location, it can end up in landfills, sewage systems, or, if incinerated, the atmosphere. Gone from sight only, incinerated waste is mobile, and under some circumstances is toxic and can enter the food chain. Medical waste incinerators release dioxins, heavy metals, particulate matter, and other pollutants.

life expectancy

The average number of years a person is expected to live.

Key Takeaways

- Global total fertility rate (TFR) is declining.
- TFRs are valuable in predicting population growth rates, but they are considered along with other important demographic information such as migration, population age structure, and infant mortality data.
- Biological constraints limit TFR.
- Family planning helps to reduce TFR and limit population growth.
- Life expectancy is not the same throughout the world.
- Differences in life expectancy are due to many factors, including varying access to clean water and medicine.

6.4 Social and Cultural Factors Affect Population Growth

In this section we consider social and cultural practices and how they influence TFR and therefore, indirectly, population growth and the health of the environment. Be careful to take a broad view of the data, for there are a number of factors working synergistically, such as education, health, equality, empowerment of women, and family planning. A study of these factors gives us cultural insight as to why some countries look favorably on children in the workforce, as well as why they strongly oppose the use of contraceptives.

Women's Empowerment Lowers TFR

The United Nations Charter calls for equality between men and women, but in reality gross inequalities exist in many countries. These inequalities occur in education, employment, family, law, and marriage, and they influence women's reproductive behavior and fertility. Specifically, the very number of children birthed by a woman (TFR) is strongly influenced by her status as measured, for example, by level of education obtained and employment outside the household. In addition, TFR tends to remain high in regions where sex discrimination policies are deeply rooted. A global recognition of these disparities (e.g., access to decent work and gender wage gaps) and a call for change can be traced to the UN's International Conference on Population and Development held in Cairo in 1993. From that point forward, human rights, human dignity, and women's empowerment became core pieces of sustainable development because sustainable development goals cannot be achieved under conditions of rapid population growth. Looking forward, the United States and the rest of the United Nations is working toward meeting seventeen sustainable development goals by 2030. One of those goals is gender equality, but because of the interconnected nature of these goals, each goal is affected by the other sixteen goals. Goals related to clean water (goal 6), clean energy (goal 7), and climate action (goal 13), for example, are dependent on improving gender equality. Remember that obtaining sustainable development goals improves prosperity for people and protects the environment.

Education of Girls and Women Reduces TFR

Patriarchal cultures, as found in China, India, South Korea, the Middle East, parts of Africa, and elsewhere, place greater value on males than females, and perceive females as having a lower status in society. Consequences of this gender inequality translate into fewer vocational opportunities for women and often relegates them to very traditional duties associated with the running of the house and raising of children. Such inequality strongly encourages women to be dependent on men. Male-dominated societies are correlated with women having little education, marrying early in life, and having a greater number of children over their lifetimes. We look to India as an example of a male-dominated culture (see video link: "Girls' Education in Rural India").

India's first prime minister, Jawaharlal Nehru, said, "You can tell the condition of a nation by looking at the status of its women." So true is this statement, for it places front and center the reason why India still struggles with stabilizing TFR. Low literacy rates, gender inequality, poor health, and poverty still plague the country, and are particularly egregious in some Indian states (see Figure 6.7). Over one-fourth of Indians can neither read nor write, and given India's population size, this translates into over 33 percent of the world's illiterate population. On the one hand, India has made huge strides forward from its literacy rate of 12 percent back in 1947, and yet today India's literacy rate (74 percent) is still lower than that for the world (about 80 percent). However, among women, the rate in India is only 65 percent, and drops much lower for some states, such as Bihar (51.5 percent). What explains this trend? Indian girls drop out of school in higher numbers than do boys. Insufficient school facilities combined with families stressing marriage rather than schooling for their daughters are common reasons why Indian girls drop out of school. Differences in literacy across states is partly explained by the financial investment of the state in their education system. The State of Kerala spends approximately $685 per student and enjoys a literacy rate of 92 percent, and its TFR (1.7) is well below replacement fertility. In contrast, Bihar only invests about $100 per student and has the highest TFR (3.3) of any Indian state.

Investing in education can provide more opportunities for women and reduce TFR. Data from other countries support the significant correlation between education and TFR. In Africa, TFRs are, on average, 5.4 among females who receive no education. Then, TFRs drop to 4.3 when they finish preschool, to 2.7 should they finish secondary school, and down to 2.2 if they attend college. These data strongly suggest the importance of education as an integral part of a strategic plan to control and reduce TFR and, indirectly, population growth.

Girls' Education in Rural India
Listen to social entrepreneur Safeena Husain discussing education in rural India.

View in the online reader

FIGURE 6.7
Literacy rate data are a good predictor of total fertility rates in countries. (A) For example, literacy rate data of Indian states generally associate smaller TFRs with higher literacy rates. (B) Students in rural India.

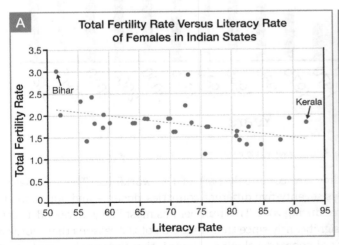

Sources: Data from Census of India 2021, https://censusofindia2021.com/literacy-rate-of-india-2021/; National Family Health Survey 2019–2021, http://rchiips.org/NFHS/factsheet_NFHS-5.shtml; CRS PHOTO/Shutterstock.com

Culture and the Ideal Number of Children

Developing and developed countries have different outlooks as to the ideal number of children per family and the role of children in the workforce. These opinions stem from cultural values. Generally, people in developing countries desire more children because they envision additions to the family as helpful, not harmful. For example, in sub-Saharan Africa, women on average desire to have more than four children. Extra children can offset child mortality and ensure that some children survive to adulthood. Traditional cultures in the sub-Saharan region of Africa consider having more children as being virtuous and even respectful to God (Seyoum 1998). This cultural thought helped Kenya to be, at one time, one of the fastest growing nations, not just in Africa, but in the world. By the early 1970s, Kenya's TFR had topped 8.1. Its TFR has dropped to 3.8 today, but its population is over 858 percent greater than it was in 1950 (see Figure 6.8).

FIGURE 6.8
Kenya has seen tremendous human population growth over the last few decades. Its population has grown from 6.1 million in 1950 to over 52 million today. From the 1950s through the 1990s, Kenyan women typically had more than seven children. Today the average is less than 4.

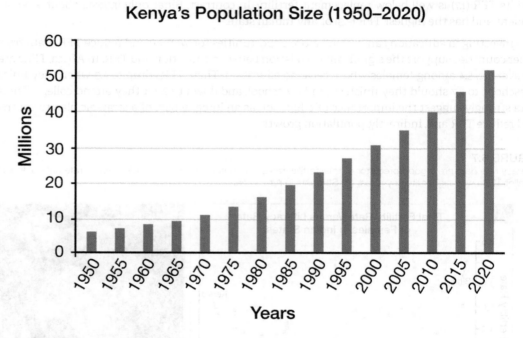

Source: Joseph Shostell; data from Worldometer, https://www.worldometers.info/world-population/kenya-population/.

In developing countries, children are commonly part of the workforce. The International Labour Organization, which surveys seventy-five different countries, documented approximately 247 million children in the workforce during 2002. This number has most likely increased, because the world's population has grown significantly since that time. One of the reasons that more children are seen as desirable in families of poorer developing nations is that they can be supplemental income earners. Stiff regulatory laws forbid child labor in the United States because it hinders their education, development, and future livelihood. Child workers have lower test scores, and they are less likely to advance in grade to complete their education (Orazem and Gunnarsson 2004). Most developed countries today, including the United States, perceive children in the workforce as a violation of children's rights (see Figure 6.9). However, historically, children in the United States played a large role in the workforce up until the passing of the Fair Labor Standards Act in 1938. The law limited the number of hours, set a minimum age of work, and set safety requirements for minors. Today, child labor is outlawed in most wealthy nations.

FIGURE 6.9
Children were a common part of the workforce in Europe and the United States until around 1940. A photo taken in 1909, showing two young boys at work in a mill in Macon, Georgia. Notice the unsafe conditions; for example, they are not standing on the ground. The first boy does not even have shoes to protect his feet.

Source: Hine, Lewis Wickes, photographer. *488 Macon, Ga. Lewis W. Hine 1-19-. Bibb Mill No. 1 Many youngsters here. Some boys were so small they had to climb up on the spinning frame to mend the broken threads and put back the empty bobbins. Location: Macon, Georgia*. United States Georgia Macon, 1909. Photograph. https://www.loc.gov/item/2018674998/.

Cultural Practices Can Affect Population Growth

China's draconian One Child Policy (OCP) prevented between 360 and 520 million births (Goodkind 2017), which is greater than the population size of the entire United States. Furthermore, when the calculation includes the removal of future population momentum, the prevented number will increase to one billion by 2060. In China's patriarchal society, and when it was still legal to use ultra-sound technology to determine sex, sex selected abortion occurred and females were aborted at a much greater number than males. Female infants were much more likely to be abandoned, given up for adoption, or even killed (infanticide) by their parents, in hopes the next child would be a male. This negative selection against females created a pronounced skewed sex ratio of 116 males born for every 100 females. A much larger differential occurred when comparing sex ratios of second and third children. A cultural preference for male children combined with the OCP has resulted in an excess of 34 million males, who may well never find a wife and have children. In China, these men are referred to as bare branches, because within the family tree they are dead ends—not producing any children to continue the lineage. A huge surplus of males is risky for society because it distorts the labor market and increases crime and prostitution. Marriage has become a social status, and there is fierce competition among Chinese men to attract a wife. To help correct the skewed sex ratio, the Chinese government launched the Care for Girls campaign in 2003. Couples with daughters receive a variety of benefits that are intended to change Chinese society's negative perception of having daughters. However, compensating parents for having daughters is having the opposite effect from what was intended, because it reinforces the idea that girls are less valuable than boys (Eklund 2011).

Migration Affects Population Size

Immigration and emigration also influence a population's size and its growth (see Section 1 and Section 4). **Immigration** is the movement of people into a population (see Figure 6.10). In contrast, **emigration** indicates the movement of people out of a population. These two processes may cause a population to grow even when birth rates are low, or to decline even if birth rates are high. People tend to emigrate for many reasons, including for improved living conditions, higher wages, freedom from persecution, better health, access to improved education, and to avoid environmental degradation. Currently about 3.3 percent of the global population, or roughly 260 million people, are international migrants. The United States is their main destination point, distantly followed by Germany, Russia, Saudi Arabia, and the United Kingdom. These migrants primarily come from India, Mexico, Russia, China, and Bangladesh, with roughly 50 percent of migrants emigrating from Asia. Generally, there is movement from underdeveloped nations to developed nations.

FIGURE 6.10
Immigration can play a significant role in contributing to a nation's population growth. A) In Tulsa, Oklahoma, immigrants take the Oath of Allegiance at a naturalization ceremony. B) Refugees from Syria and Afghanistan board a train in Munich, Germany.

Sources: Kim Kelley-Wagner/Shutterstock.com; Jazzmany/Shutterstock.com

Key Takeaways

- Women's empowerment and education are associated with lower total fertility rates, so they reduce population growth.
- Developing and developed countries have different outlooks as to the ideal number of children per family and the role of children in the workforce.
- Cultural practices can affect population growth.
- Sustainable growth and the environment's health are inextricably linked to issues of poverty, education, health, equality, and women's empowerment.
- Skewed sex ratios can be a repercussion of a patriarchal way of thinking.
- Migration affects population size.

6.5 Economic and Technological Factors Affect Population Growth Rate

What is the relationship between economics and population growth? Does economic development drive population growth? Does it lead to population control? Do technological factors affect population growth and the health of the environment? Here we navigate through economic and technological data and theories and attempt to address these types of questions, beginning with those relating to economics.

Economic Development and Population Growth

"It is impossible to draw any generalizations about the relationship between population growth and growth of economic wealth merely from history. Nor can we say that growth of a population stimulates growth of wealth, for in many cases, such as India, it has rather increased poverty" (Robinson 1996). What then, is the connection?

Our observations of established cities, with their industrialization and infrastructure that allows them to provide services and generate, ship, and accept products, suggests cities are good for the economy. Yet, rapid urbanization or population growth does not necessarily lead to economic prosperity. Bringing people into a city can lead to economic growth, but only under the right conditions. What are these conditions? For starters, we recognize the correlation between population growth and economic productivity. Rapidly growing developing countries have an incomplete infrastructure, and they are in the early stages of modernization, industrialization, and development of an educational system (Stycos 1977). In contrast, when urbanization occurs within the context of an established public transit system and educational system—two of many parts of a mature infrastructure—a growing population can be a net contributor to economic growth. A growing population and urbanization intensify the demand for products that, in turn, boosts sales and the local economy. So too, there is an expansion of health care, education, and other services required to meet the growing population's needs. Additional individuals also mean more laborers to work in the various sectors of the economy.

There is also a relationship between economic development and standard of living. Developed countries such as the United States, Western Europe, Japan, and Australia have well-established industries, with high-tech infrastructure and a high standard of living compared to developing and undeveloped countries (see Figure 6.11).

FIGURE 6.11

A map of the world's 2018 human development index (HDI). The HDI is a calculated value based on quality of life, standard of living, education, and literacy. It is an attempt to measure the well-being of people in their respective countries. The United States, Australia, Japan, Canada, Western Europe, and other industrialized areas have higher HDI values relative to developing or undeveloped countries.

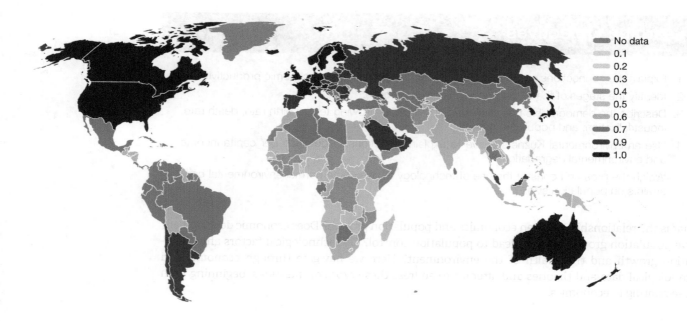

Source: Data from Our World in Data, Human Development Index, https://ourworldindata.org/human-development-index. [CC BY, https://creativecommons.org/licenses/by/4.0/legalcode]

The Demographic Transition Model

Today's rich, developed countries were not always rich, nor were they always developed. They went through successive stages called demographic transition (see Figure 6.12) (Notestein 1945). Stage one is the pre-industrial phase, a time of food shortage, no sanitation, primitive medicine, and malnutrition. The difficult conditions are reflected in high death rates and high birth rates. In the second stage, a transition to industrialization occurs, with general improvements in sanitation, health care, and food availability. These improvements result in a decline in death rates, but not in birth rates, as seen in Ghana and Kenya. Countries in this stage experience high growth rates. During the third stage, the industrial stage, a country is engaged in mature, full-swing industrial activities and has a sound industrial infrastructure. A country in this stage, such as Mexico or India, focuses more on parental care of children, education, and status of women, resulting in a decline in birth rate. Countries in phase three are experiencing slowly decreasing growth rates. Finally, the fourth stage—the post-industrial stage—shows zero or negative population growth. Germany and Bulgaria are examples of countries in stage four.

FIGURE 6.12
Countries go through stages of demographic transition as they move from pre-industrial to post-industrial stages of development. In stage one, birth and death rates are high. In stage two, when industrialization begins, economic benefits occur and the death rate declines. In stage three, the birth rate declines and the population growth rate slows. Stage four represents a post-industrial country that is experiencing zero or negative population growth.

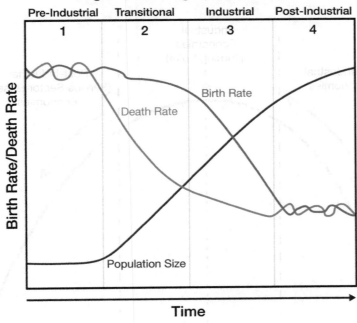

Source: Joseph Shostell

Do all countries go through demographic transition (see video link: "Demographic Transition")? The late influential American demographer Frank Notestein (1902–1983) rightly noted that death rates and birth rates decline with improved living conditions and better economic development. Countries that undergo a full demographic transition have an improved standard of living, increased survival of children, and more equal social status of women and men. Their citizens also have better access to and use of birth control. Not all countries undergo a demographic transition; instead, they become stuck in stage two, with high birth rates and low death rates. Improved health care has helped stem mortality in these countries, but their governments are struggling to meet the needs of their ballooning populations. Maybe they can't build schools fast enough, or roads, or even sewer systems. If their populations double in size, so too must their food supply, along with structures and roads (Ehrlich 1971).

How does a country get out of this demographic trap? Some population scientists, such as Lester Brown, suggest the solution is to provide family planning. Brown is a renowned environmental analyst who formed the Earth Policy Institute and authored *How to Prevent Environmental and Economic Collapse* (2010). According to Brown, this is the only way a country can take care of the real problem, which is a high birth rate.

Are economic growth and improved environmental health contradictory goals for a country? Based on Environmental Kuznets Curve theory, environmental degradation rises during a country's initial economic development; for example, beginning in the first stage of demographic transition (see Figure 6.13) (Grossman and Krueger 1995). Eventually, in the latter stages of demographic transition, a country improves its environmental awareness, develops more comprehensive environmental laws, enforces these laws, and more heavily invests in measures to protect the environment. Thus, an Environmental Kuznets Curve proposes lower environmental degradation when there is a high per capita income. Is this line of reasoning applicable to the United States and other developed countries? The quick answer is no and yes. America has a stable infrastructure and many

Demographic Transition
Explore the link between economic development and population growth.

View in the online reader

environmental protection laws, yet also has one of the highest per capita carbon footprints of any nation (see Chapter 1).

FIGURE 6.13
This is an Environmental Kuznets Curve showing a hypothesized relationship between environmental degradation and economic productivity.

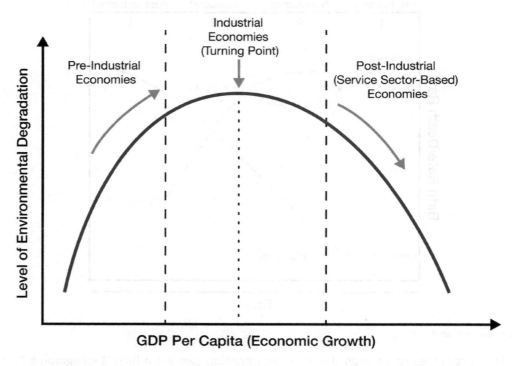

Source: Joseph Shostell

The IPAT Model

IPAT model

(I=PAT); A model that calculates environmental impact (I) based on population size (P), affluence (A), and technology use (T).

Our understanding about a carrying capacity value that allows for our preferred quality of life must consider the uneven environmental degradation by human populations. After all, a person from Niger and a person from the United States do not leave the same ecological footprints. The average American uses more energy, eats more food, uses more water, and creates more waste than the average Nigerian. This difference in use of resources and effect on the environment can be included in the calculation of a carrying capacity value. The **IPAT model** (I=PAT) developed by Paul Ehrlich and John Holdren leads us in the right direction (Ehrlich and Holdren 1971). Their model calculates environmental impact and accounts for a nation's affluence and technology use. The model was developed because the heaviest polluting nations are not always the most populous. In this simple equation, "I" equals environmental impact, "P" equals population size, "A" equals affluence as measured by consumption (per capita GDP), and "T" equals technology. A higher affluence and consumption helps to explain why a small population can cause large-scale environmental degradation.

Technology, Mortality Rates, and Lifespan

Application of new technologies in medicine, sanitation, irrigation, and other areas has mitigated disease and extended the average human lifespan. Today, for example, genetic testing is often used in diagnosis to determine whether the symptoms of an illness might be caused by a genetic disease. These tests can also be used as form of predictive testing and carrier testing. Predictive testing is useful because it helps you to know if you are at risk of developing symptoms of a genetic disease in the future. Carrier testing is valuable to people who are considering having children and who also have a family history of a particular genetic disease. Generally, these tests come with few risks because they only require a blood sample or a cheek swab. It wasn't long ago that people had not even heard about gene therapy as a way to cure genetic disorders. We have the technology and knowledge to provide vaccinations and to produce medicines needed to prevent disease and prolong life. Some of the newest advances in medical technology are the result of bioengineering. For example, one recent invention allows medications to be delivered by sound waves rather than by injection. Also, the resolution of imaging technologies has improved over the years, which allows better and more specific diagnoses, further lessening the need for performing life-threatening exploratory surgery.

China is using technology and engineering to solve a water shortage that has resulted from prolonged population growth. It initiated a grand-scale project to transport water thousands of kilometers from the south to 200 million people and their agricultural lands in the arid northern plains (see Chapter 6). However, solving one problem has exacerbated another. Now, water shortages will worsen in regions in the south. Environmental scientists worry about this strategy because it falls outside a pathway of sustainability and gives its beneficiaries a false sense of unlimited water. Redirecting water does not resolve the issue of nationwide demand for a limited resource. Thus, China has also reevaluated its water use efficiency and has set new goals. For irrigation, it is working toward improving efficiency by 23 percent above levels set in 2007; and it aims to reach this goal in 2030 (Zhao et al. 2014). This will reduce China's demand for irrigation water by 26 percent. It also aims to improve water efficiency across industries. Can China do it? Even if China, the United States, or any other country are able to reach their goals, a growing population will eventually outstrip any improvements in efficiency.

Key Takeaways

- Rapid urbanization or a growing population does not necessarily lead to economic prosperity.
- There is a relationship between economic development and standard of living.
- Countries go through successive stages called demographic transition.
- The demographic transition model shows a relationship between a nation's development and population growth.
- The IPAT model helps to explain the limitation of the Environmental Kuznets Curve.
- Application of new technologies in medicine, sanitation, irrigation, and other areas has mitigated the effects of disease and extended the average human lifespan.

6.6 Political Factors Affect Population Growth Rate

Learning Objectives

1. Identify political factors that incentivize families to have children.
2. Explain the spectrum of strategies that governments use to reduce population growth.

Governments can develop and enforce strategic policies to meet their population growth goals. They see an association of population size and structure with available environmental resources, public services, general infrastructure, labor-force size, productiveness of their economy, and even their military strength. Here we review examples of policies countries might use to regulate their population size—dividing the policies into two groups: those intended to reduce population growth and those intended to increase it.

Policies to Reduce Population Growth

Effective methods to control high population growth usually involve education to improve literacy, women's empowerment, and family-planning services. As seen in the opening case study, family planning can be mandatory, with stiff penalties levied against anyone who doesn't follow the law. However, unlike China, most countries allow their citizens to retain their reproductive rights and have the number of children they desire. Let us compare policies of the world's two most populated countries, China and India.

Political Control of Family Planning in China

In the opening story we learned about barefoot lawyer Chen Guancheng, who was prosecuted for speaking out against China's One Child Policy (OCP). To understand the development of the OCP as well as China's newer Two Child Policy (TCP), we take a historical approach using Chen as a point of reference.

Chen was born in 1971, well before the enactment of the OCP in 1979. It was a time when families typically had more children than Chinese families today. Between the 1960s and early 1970s, Chinese families, on average, had more than five children and often had more than six. Therefore, Chen's family of his parents, himself, sister, and five older brothers was not out of the ordinary. Mao was a strong proponent of high population growth and a large population, possibly because of the recent war with Japan and concern over a potential war between the United States and Soviet Union, and links to economic prosperity and production.

After Mao Zedong's death in 1976, the Chinese's Communist Party decided to aggressively curb population growth and therefore prevent overpopulation. They were concerned about pollution and the degradation of land, resources, and living conditions. Deng Xiaoping, who became the paramount leader of China in 1978, pushed several social and economic reforms and consequently boosted China's economy. The most controversial social reform was the One Child Policy, intended to control China's burgeoning population. Just as it sounds, the One Child Policy (1979–2015) limited Chinese families to one child, but the policy did not apply equally to all people across China. It was a controversial and very unpopular policy because it removed the reproductive rights of the individual and placed them into the hands of the state. Couples who followed the OCP needed to request permission to have a child, and if they abided by the policy, could receive priority in housing, a monthly subsidy, free medical care, additional vacation time, free tuition, and maternity leave. In contrast, there were strict penalties for having a second child. Large fines were imposed, along with increased taxes and even loss of employment. The most dehumanizing and barbaric part of the OCP fell on Chinese women, who were often forced to abort their second child and undergo sterilization, regardless of trimester and proximity to their due date (see "Bringing It Closer to Home: Acceptable Family Planning").

Bringing It Closer to Home: Acceptable Family Planning

The majority of Americans would strongly protest invasive state and federal involvement in the decision-making process of how many children we can have. Are there any conditions in which you would support mandatory family planning in your local community and nation? In consideration of basic human rights, equality, steady population growth, and limited resources, what would you recommend as an acceptable government plan to encourage families in your community to have fewer children?

China did reduce its TFR from a high of 6.4 in the mid-1960s to 1.7 today, but how much of this reduction is the result of the OCP remains unclear. TFR had already dropped to 2.94 by 1978, the year before the enactment of the OCP. Regardless, what has become evident, with sustained low TFR and China's aging population, is that China can no longer maintain a workforce large enough to support continued economic growth. Economic growth in China will decline 0.5 to 0.75 percent each year between 2020 and 2050. These predictions encouraged China to repeal the OCP (see Figure 6.14).

FIGURE 6.14
China rolled out its new Two Child Policy in 2016. In response, births rose by 7.9 percent, far less than the government had predicted. In the photo, taken in Beijing, a mother walks with her daughters.

Source: TonyV3112/Shutterstock.com

A Closer View of India

India is projected to surpass China in population size, which frankly seems amazing considering that India only has 2.4 percent of the world's land surface, about one-third the size of China. How is it possible for about 18 percent of the world's population to live in a relatively small area? Furthermore, India's population is unevenly distributed across its twenty-eight states and seven territories, with just eight states having roughly 52 percent of the total population. The most populated state, Uttar Pradesh, is only ranked twelfth in overall land size. At over 200 million people, this state has more people than all but the four most populated nations. What has the Indian government done to control population size?

India's population has grown by nearly 340 million in the last twenty years, and the government cannot build the infrastructure needed to meet the demands of all the additional people (see Figure 6.15). In fact, democratic India has performed a much poorer job of providing infrastructure such as basic sanitation compared with socialist China (Sen 2011). These failures by the government to keep pace with population growth have led to the development of densely packed urban areas where people lack basic services and slums proliferate.

FIGURE 6.15
A lack of access to clean water puts people at risk, as seen here in Kolkata, India, where a group of people wash themselves in the heavily polluted Hooghly River. Such sights indicate inadequate city infrastructure, overpopulation, and nonsustainability.

Source: Jan S./Shutterstock.com

The Indian government has tried different strategies to control population growth, and its fertility rate has steadily declined over the decades. Back in the 1960s, the government set a goal to bring down the crude birth rate from forty-one to twenty-five by the mid-1970s. An educational campaign ensued, but the country continued to grow faster than desired. Then, in 1975, the government declared a population state of emergency and began to enforce sterilizations, mostly in men, to slow down population growth. Over the course of two years, an estimated 6.2 million men were sterilized. Sterilizations are no longer enforced (and are now skewed toward women), but they have become the most common choice of birth control in India. A couple's decision on whether to undergo sterilization is often predicated upon if they already have children.

Part of the challenge for family-planning officials during the 1980s and 1990s was to overcome the cultural mindset of having multiple children, preferably sons who would assist the family in the long term. In traditional Indian culture, a daughter normally becomes an integrated part of her husband's family (Edmeades et al. 2011). Under these cultural constraints, financial incentives from the government have little influence on parents in limiting the number of their children. Women in India are less willing to use birth control until they have sons (Jayaraman et al. 2008).

Eventually, with strategic and persistent educational opportunities for women and broader acceptance and use of contraceptives, fertility dropped by over 63 percent compared to 1960. Now over eighteen of India's twenty-eight states are below replacement fertility level, and if the current trend continues, India's population will stabilize and even decrease.

Policies to Increase Population Growth

Not all countries have an overpopulation problem; in fact, some countries such as Canada and many in the European Union have the opposite dilemma and want to increase their population size. One common method for governments to promote population growth is to offer financial incentives for their current citizens to have children. For example, pregnant mothers in most countries have maternity leave and can take a leave of absence from their job without worrying about losing it. A well-established family-planning policy in the Czech Republic allows for leaves of up to three years. Moreover, many countries provide a paid maternity leave and give financial assistance to a mother or, in some cases, the father for periods of twelve weeks to well over a year. The federal government of the United States does not require companies to pay families during maternity leave. Still, select states—including New Jersey, Hawaii, and New York—do provide some financial assistance during this time. One protective measure for couples wanting children in the United States is the Family Medical Leave Act, passed in 1993. This act allows for twelve months of unpaid job-protected leave for family matters, including pre- and postnatal care and adoption. Families with children also qualify for a tax credit.

Alaska: Oil Money Revenue for Residents

In Alaska, each resident receives annual payments of $800 to $2,000 from oil revenues (see Figure 6.16). This financial return is from the Alaskan Permanent Fund, created in 1976 to ensure residents benefit from the drilling industry. And benefit they do, for a family of four—two adults and two children—can rake in $8,000! Those families with more children receive more oil-revenue money. Why do only Alaskans receive oil-revenue funds? One perception you might have on this policy is that it is unfair because all U.S. residents do not receive similar treatment. However, Alaska is unique because of its small population size and vast resources.

FIGURE 6.16
Every Alaskan citizen including these in Ketchikan (A) receives oil revenue annually. Amounts vary from year to year, but they are usually between $800 and $2,000. The money preferentially benefits families with more children. (B) The Alaskan pipeline.

Sources: Bob Pool/Shutterstock.com; © Shutterstock, Inc.

Governments Usually Establish Policies to Either Encourage or Prevent Immigration

Given that the United States is the main destination site of migrants, immigration can be a contentious subject, and may be either staunchly supported or bitterly opposed with each passing administration. Taking a positive stance, President George H. W. Bush said, "Today I am pleased to sign S. 358, the Immigration Act of 1990—the most comprehensive reform of our immigration laws in sixty-six years. This Act recognizes the fundamental importance and historic contributions of immigrants to our country. S. 358 accomplishes what this Administration sought from the outset of the immigration reform process: a complementary blending of our tradition of family reunification with increased immigration of skilled individuals to meet our economic needs." To President Bush and many others, skilled immigrants fill vacant positions and help fuel the economy. In contrast,

President Donald Trump took a forceful stance against immigration, and stated, "The United States will not be a migrant camp." President Trump perceived immigrants as potential terrorists and as competitors with Americans for jobs. Our stance reversed once again with the next administration, this time President Joseph Biden's.

Overall, every year, millions of people migrate to developed nations. Some developed nations, such as the United States, Italy, Spain, and Canada, take in hundreds of thousands of immigrants every year (see Figure 6.17). Why would countries do this in a time period when some people are worrying about overpopulation and limited resources? To answer this question, we will quickly review Canada's immigration program, which is based on the 2002 Immigration and Refuge Protection Act (IRPA). Canada's objectives for immigration are to contribute to economic development, reunite families, and protect refugees (CIC 2011). Canada sees people as resources themselves and even labels those with skills as "Economic Immigrants" who will contribute to the Canadian economy. Immigrants make up almost 22 percent the Canadian population. About 300,000 migrants arrive per year, which is equal to 0.8 percent of Canada's population of 38 million. This influx of people has dramatically increased the diversity of several Canadian cities. Toronto, for example, has become the most diverse city in the world, and by the mid-2030s will have first- and second-generation immigrants make up 80 percent of its population. Toronto's common descriptive slogan "Diversity Our Strength" nicely matches its population makeup.

FIGURE 6.17

The topic of migration policies can be contentious even within the same region of a country. A) A demonstration in Belgium to welcome refugees. B) On January 25, 2017, President Trump signed the Border Security and Immigration Enforcement Improvements executive order to extend and fortify the border wall between the United States and Mexico to prevent migrants crossing the border illegally. The photo shows a current border wall between Arizona and Mexico.

Sources: Alexandros Michailidis/Shutterstock.com; © Shutterstock, Inc.

The United States, since the late 1980s, has granted lawful permanent residence (i.e., a "green card") to over one million migrants per year. It is the influx of these migrants that drives population growth in the United States. By 2050, an estimated 82 percent of population growth in the United States will be due to immigration. The projection, much higher than today's, is not because of a large rise in immigration numbers, but rather to a diminishing fertility rate among American couples. Besides accounting for the impact of migrants themselves on population growth, their fertility rate affects future population growth.

Key Takeaways

- Governments can develop and enforce strategic policies to meet their population growth goals.
- Effective methods to control high population growth usually involve education to improve literacy, women's empowerment, and family-planning services.

- While some countries have an overpopulation problem, other countries have the opposite dilemma and want to increase their population size.
- Common methods for governments to promote population growth are offering financial incentives for their current citizens to have children.

6.7 A Look to the Future: Revisiting the Opening Story—China in the Crosshairs

Learning Objective

1. Review China's history of family-planning policies, population growth, and environmental issues, and offer a positive course of action to help regulate population growth and support sustainability in the future.

At the close of our discussion on population issues, we revisit the opening case study. China's One Child Policy (OCP) lasted for thirty-five years and ended in 2016, when they began the Two Child Policy (TCP). Concern over an aging population, strained pension plans, shrinking labor force, and decline in economic productivity overrode the issues of limited resources and environmental degradation. After a reflective analysis of the policy change a few years later, China considered new strategies. Repeal of the OCP and institution of the Two Child Policy (TCP) did not have the intended consequences. There was a spike in natalities in 2016 compared to the previous year, but many qualified Chinese couples did not elect to have a second child. Apparently, over 50 percent of reproductive-age couples in China only want one child. Other national statistics support a lower birth rate too. For instance, registered marriages are on the decline, while the opposite is true for divorces.

China's government reacted to the low response by implementing a new three-child policy in 2021 (see video link: "Three Child Policy"). The new policy is not popular among many Chinese mainly because raising children is expensive and living costs in China have been increasing. There are financial costs for education and childcare. In support of this family-planning policy, new proposals are being circulated for consideration, such as a new tax levied on all workers under the age of forty. These monies would go into a fund and be used to financially assist families who have more than one child. Deputy Huang Zihua to the National People's Congress proposes lowering the minimum age of marriage. Obviously, people do not have to be married to have children, but in China, having children is tightly associated with marriage because out-of-wedlock births are often discriminated against. Currently, men must be at least twenty-two and women twenty. The deputy suggests they be lowered to eighteen. She points out that eighteen is still older than the legal age of marriage in many other countries, including the United States. Opponents of the proposal say the move will decrease educational opportunities for women. As we predict the future of family planning and reproductive rights in China, what remains clear is the Communist Party's strong oversight of family planning.

Three Child Policy

For years, many Chinese families were restricted to having no more than one child. In 2016, this changed to two children, and in 2021 it changed to three. Watch this video to learn more about China's newest family-planning policy.

View in the online reader

Key Takeaways

- Nations will continue to strategize about the best ways to regulate their population size and population growth to meet their needs.
- The Chinese government has repealed the Two Child Policy and now encourages families to have three children. The government's goals are to maintain a strong workforce and sustain economic growth.

FIGURE 6.18 Visual Overview: Factors Affecting Population Growth
Summarizing figure: (6.1) Human population growth and consumption are linked to the environment's health. Demographic data (6.2) are useful to predict population growth, which is affected by (6.3) biological factors, (6.4) social and cultural factors, (6.5) economic and technical factors, and (6.6) political factors.

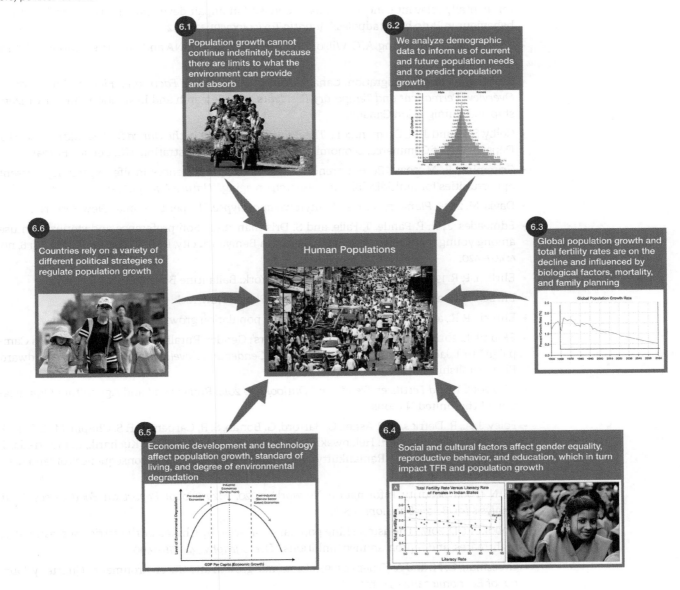

Sources: Joseph Shostell; See previous citations for image credits.

6.8 References

- Aizen, M. A., L. A. Garibaldi, S. A. Cunningham, and A. M. Klein. 2009. "How much does agriculture depend on pollinators? Lessons from long-term trends in crop production." *Ann Bot* 103: 1579–1588.
- Bellizzi, S., P. Mannava, M. Nagai, and H. L. Sobel. 2020. "Reasons for discontinuation of contraception among women with a current unintended pregnancy in 36 low and middle-income countries." *Contraception* 101: 26–33.

- Brown, L. 2010. *How to Prevent Environmental and Economic Collapse*. London: W. W. Norton and Company.
- Brunelli, E., I. Bernabò, C. Berg, K. Lunstedt-Enkel, A. Bonacci, and S. Tripepi. 2009. "Environmentally relevant concentrations of endosulfan impair development, metamorphosis and behaviour in Bufo bufo tadpoles." *Aquatic Toxicology* 91: 135–142.
- Cann, R., L., M. Stoneking, A. C. Wilson. 1987. "Mitochondrial DNA and human evolution." *Nature* 325: 31–36.
- Citizenship and Immigration Canada (CIC). 2011. *Canada Facts and Figures Immigration Overview Permanent and Temporary Residents 2010*. Research and Evaluation Branch, Citizenship and Immigration Canada.
- Colby, S. L., and J. M. Ortman. 2014. *The Baby Boom Cohort in the United States: 2012 to 2060*. U.S. Department of Commerce, Economics and Statistics Administration. U.S. Census Bureau.
- Crimmins, E. M. 2021. "Recent trends and increasing differences in life expectancy present opportunities for multidisciplinary research on aging." *Nature Aging* 1: 12–13.
- Davis, M. 2006. *Planet of Slums Shantytown apocalypse*. Harper Perennial. New York, NY.
- Edmeades, J., R. P. Pande, T. Falle, and S. Drishnan. 2011. "Son preference and sterilization use among young married women in two slums in Bengaluru city, India." *Glob Public Health* 6, no. 4: 407–420.
- Ehrlich, P. R. 1971. *The Population Bomb*. New York: Ballantine Books.
- Ehrlich, P. R., and A. Ehrlich. 1991. *Healing the Planet*. New York: Addison Wesley.
- Ehrlich, P. R., and J. P. Holdren. 1971. "Impact of population growth." *Science* 171: 1212–1217.
- Eklund, L. 2011. "'Good citizens prefer daughters': Gender, Rurality and the Care for Girls Campaign." In T Jacka & S Sargeson (Eds.), *Women, Gender and Development in Rural China*. Edward Elgar Publishing, Chewttenham, UK.
- FAO 2015. *World Fertilizer Trends and Outlooks to 2018*. Rome: Food and Agriculture Organization of the United Nations.
- Foley, J. A., R. Defries, G. P. Asner, C. Barford, G. Bonan, S. R. Carpenter, F. S. Chapin, M. T. Coe, G. C. Daily, H. K. Gibbs, J. H. Helkowski, T. Holloway, E. A. Howard, C. J. Kucharik, C. Monfreda, J. A. Patz, I. C. Prentice, N. Ramankutty, and P. K. Snyder. 2005. "Global consequences of land use." *Science* 309: 570–574.
- FSIN (Food Security Information Network). 2020. *2020 Global Report on Food Crises Joint Analysis for Better Decisions*. FSIN.
- Goodkind, D. 2017. "The astonishing population averted by China's birth restrictions: estimates, nightmares, and reprogrammed ambitions." *Demography* 54: 1375–1400.
- Grossman, G. M. and A. Krueger. 1995. "Economic growth and the environment." *Quarterly Journal of Economics* 110: 353–377.
- Guancheng, C. 2014. *The Barefoot Lawyer a Blind Man's Fight for Justice and Freedom in China*. New York: Henry Holt and Company.
- Haddad, L. B., and N. M. Nour. 2009. "Unsafe abortion: unnecessary maternal mortality." *Rev Obstet Gynecol* 2, no. 2: 122–126.
- Jaramillo, F., and G. Destouni. 2015. "Local flow regulation and irrigation raise global human water consumption and footprint." *Science* 350, no. 6265: 1248–1251.
- Jayaraman, A., V. Mishra, and F. Arnold. 2008. "The effect of family size and composition on fertility desires, contraceptive adoption, and method choice in South Asia." DHS working papers no. 40. Macro International, Calverton, MD.
- Keenan, R. J., G. A. Reams, F. Achard, J. V. de Freitas, A. Grainger, and E. Lindquist. 2015. "Dynamics of global forest area: results from the FAO global forest resources Assessment 2015." *Forest Ecology and Management* 352: 9–20.
- Kelly, J. 2009. *I Kill Giants*. Portland, OR: Image Comics.

- Lacy, R., R. Williams, E. Ashe, K. C. Balcomb III, L. J. N. Brent, C. W. Clark, D. P. Croft, D. A. Giles, M. MacDuffee, and P. C. Paquet. 2017. "Evaluating anthropogenic threats to endangered killer whales to inform effective recovery plans." *Scientific Reports* 7: 14119: https://doi.org/10.1038/s41598-017-14471-0.

- Lwin, C. M., M. Murakami, and S. Hashimoto. 2017. "The implications of allocation scenarios for global phosphorus flow from agriculture and wastewater." *Resources, Conservation and Recycling* 122: 94–105.

- Malthus, T. R. 1798. *An Essay on the Principle of Population, as it Affects the Future Improvement of Society with Remarks on the Speculations of Mr. Godwin, M. Condorcet, and Many Others.* London: J. Johnson.

- McDougall, I., F. H. Brown, and J. G. Fleagle. 2005. "Stratigraphic placement and age of modern humans from Kibish, Ethiopia." *Nature* 433: 733.

- Meyer, W. B., and B. L. Turner II. 1992. "Human population growth and global land-use/cover change." *Annual Review of Ecology and Systematics* 23: 39–61.

- Notestein, F. 1945. "Population: the long view." In: *Food for the World* (Ed.: T. Schultz). Chicago, IL: Chicago Press.

- Oki, T., and S. Kanae. 2006. "Global hydrological cycles and world water resources." *Science* 313: 1068–1072.

- Ollerton, J., R. Winfree, and S. Tarrant. 2011. "How many flowering plants are pollinated by animals?" *Oikos* 120: 321–326.

- Orazem, P., and L. V. Gunnarsson. 2004. "Child Labour, School Attendance, and Performance: A Review." *Iowa State Department of Economics Working Paper* No. 04001.

- Robey, B., S. O. Rutstein, L. Morris, and R. Blackburn. 1992. "The reproductive evolution: new survey findings." Baltimore, MD: Johns Hopkins University. Population reports, series M., 11.

- Robey, B., S. O. Rutstein, and L. Morris. 1993. "The fertility decline in developing countries." *Scientific American* 269: 60–67.

- Robinson, J. 1996. "Joan Robinson on population and development." *Population and Development Review* 22, no. 2: 359–364.

- Rutstein, S. O., K. Johnson, A. Conde-Agudelo, and A. RosasBermudez. 2008. *Further Analysis of the Effects of Birth Spacing on Infant and Child Mortality: A Systematic Review and Meta-Analysis.* Technical Consultation and Scientific Review of Birth Spacing, World Health Organization, Geneva, Switzerland.

- Sedgh, G., S. Singh, and R. Hussain. 2014. "Intended and unintended pregnancies worldwide in 2012 and recent trends." *Studies in Family Planning* 45, no. 3: 301–314.

- Sen, A. 2011. "Quality of Life: India vs. China." *Futurables* 380: 5–13.

- Seyoum, D. K. 1998. "Family systems in Ethiopia." In: *Handbook on Population and Family Line Education for Secondary School Teachers in Ethiopia* (Eds.: M. Ezra and S. G. Selassie). Addis Adaba, Ethiopia: Institute for Curriculum and Development Research.

- Stycos, M. 1977. "Population policy and development." *Population and Development Review* 3: 103–112.

- United States Census Bureau (USCB) 2019. 2019 Public Elementary-Secondary Education Finance Data.

- Zhao , X., J. Liu, Q. Liu, M. R. Tillotson, D. Guan, and K. Hubacek. 2014. "Physical and Virtual Water Transfers for Regional Water Stress Alleviation in China." *Proceedings of the National Academy of Sciences of the United States of America* 112, no. 4: 1031–1035.

CHAPTER 7
Preserving Biodiversity

Case Study: Plight of the Florida Manatee

One of the most docile, harmless marine mammals is the manatee (*Trichechus manatus*). This distant relation to the elephant really is a gentle giant. It hovers in shallow coastal waters and estuaries, feeding on vegetation up to eight hours daily to meet the demands of its rather massive body—averaging 500 kg (1,200 lbs) for adults, although its upper range can be up to three times this weight. At lengths of up to 4 m (13 ft), these creatures can really capture your attention should you be in the water in their vicinity. Yet there is no reason to fear these herbivores, should you be lucky enough to observe one. Forget about out-swimming them, for their normal sluggish manner belies an ability to swim at speeds of 18–25 km/hr, more than twice the speed of Olympian Michael Phelps's fastest sprint. Just enjoy their presence.

Manatees are a bit unusual in that they can inhabit both saltwater and freshwater systems, a distinction that classifies them as euryhaline. They avoid temperatures lower than 20°C (68°F) and are known to seek out warmer waters during the winter. In summer, they expand their range and are routinely found as far north along the Atlantic coast as Virginia. Their distribution also spreads west to the coast of Louisiana. However, from November through March, manatees shelter themselves in warm (72°F [22°C]) freshwater spring-fed areas within Florida and therefore have a contracted distribution range.

Tourists and tour companies understand the migration patterns of manatees and are known to frequent locations where manatees overwinter (see video link: "Manatees"). Some of Florida's state parks stay busy because of these friendly creatures. The Florida manatee is protected by both federal and state laws: the Marine Mammal Protection Act of 1972, the Endangered Species Act of 1973, and the Florida Manatee Sanctuary Act of 1978. Places such as Kings Bay are truly unique because humans can visit and observe manatees. At the time of the printing of this book, a person could observe many of the 500 manatees that overwinter in Kings Bay, a significant fraction of the approximately 6,000 estimated to be alive at that time.

 Manatees

Explore manatee refuge areas in Tampa, Florida.

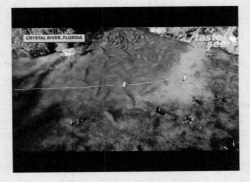

View in the online reader

Entrepreneurs have set up successful businesses that bring tourists to manatee-protected habitats such as the Crystal River National Wildlife Refuge. Perhaps even more interesting than the manatees themselves is the relationship between two somewhat opposing groups that both find value in healthy manatees—Florida State Park employees and tour company employees. The state park employees, along with volunteers like Art Jones of the local Rotary Club, help to monitor the refuge to ensure tourists do not contribute to the erosion problems around the natural freshwater springs. Captains anchor their large-sized pontoon boats right outside the spring areas. Then, they point their tourists—complete with snorkels, masks, fins, and cameras—in the direction their boats are not permitted to go, into the narrow river channel blocked by large vertical metal posts driven deep into the river bottom. Columns of snorkelers snake their way between the posts and enter the spring area, where they are permitted to swim and observe as long as they do not touch the land or any manatee. Amongst the seeming utter chaos of half-submerged tourists and hundreds of threatened manatees is the manatee kayak patrol. These skilled volunteers, with large manatee flags sprouted from the ends of their crafts, navigate among the snorkelers and serve as a constant reminder to the tourists of the regulations regarding the Florida manatee (see Figure 7.1).

FIGURE 7.1
Threatened manatees provide a challenge for wildlife managers attempting to protect them, because they inhabit areas close to dense human populations. (A) Near the Crystal River National Wildlife Refuge in Florida, snorkelers observe a manatee. (B) A close-up of a manatee.

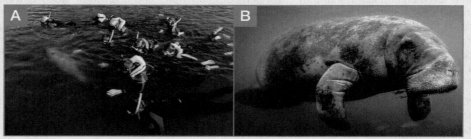

Sources: Ramos, Keith, Snorkelers swim with manatee, USFWS; © Shutterstock, Inc.

Manatees are such a large draw for tourists that their presence helps to drive the local economy. For example, Solomon et al. (2004) determined that in Citrus County alone manatees helped to create a financial benefit of over $9 million per year, with over $2 million coming just from **ecotourism** associated with Homosassa Springs State Wildlife Park. Corrected for inflation, this would be about $12.4 million today. How is so much money generated from one species? Money accrues through many activities, including jobs that require working directly with manatees, tourism, lodging, dining, and retail.

The Florida manatee provides one example among many species that are low in number and can easily be harmed by human activities. For example, of 6,373 manatee carcasses studied over a two-decade period, 1,877 had died from human-related causes, and 82 percent of these had died from being struck by a watercraft. These are high numbers, potentially very damaging to a threatened species. Moreover, manatee population growth is relatively slow, with females becoming mature at about four to five years of age and then having one offspring every three years, on average. Manatees and other k-selected species (see Chapter 4) certainly present challenges to wildlife managers trying to improve their conditions. True of all species, the manatee is not completely alone and, instead, interacts directly and indirectly with many species around it. In one example of their connection with other species, manatees recycle nutrients and drive primary production in estuarine areas. Their presence influences other species in their community. On a broader scale, manatees in southern Florida and South America are part of the **neotropical realm**, Earth's most biodiverse region.

When we take a biocentric approach (see Chapter 2) and begin to include the species of vegetation the manatees eat and the larger communities of organisms in those systems, we begin to consider biodiversity, which is the variety of life at all organizational levels, from genes through ecosystems. In this chapter, we discuss issues related to biodiversity, including ways to protect threatened species such as the manatee.

7.1 Defining Biodiversity

Learning Objectives

1. Summarize our process and progress in understanding global biodiversity.
2. Summarize Earth's biodiversity.
3. Identify Earth's biodiversity hotspots.

In the chapter opening story, we discussed the biology and status of the Florida manatee. The manatee is just one of many organisms that inhabit the environment and whose presence is included in the calculation of biodiversity. The Florida manatee, however, is not a distinct species; rather, it is one of two similarly structured subspecies of West Indian manatee. Each individual in the population of Florida manatees in Kings Bay has common features that have helped us classify the entire group as a subspecies, but each individual is unique and slightly different from those swimming around it. In this chapter, we begin a discussion about the meaning of biodiversity and geographical patterns of diversity, followed by discussions about its importance, human impacts on biodiversity, and efforts to preserve biodiversity.

We Are Still Counting Species

How many species are there? Dr. Camilo Mora of Dalhousie University contends that this is one of the most important questions to answer in science. After all, how are we to develop conservation plans to protect biodiversity when we are unsure of what we are protecting? So far, we have identified roughly 1.8 million eukaryotic species (see Chapter 3), just a fraction of the 5–100 million estimated to exist (see Figure 7.2). An amount of 1.8 million might seem small, relative to 100 million, but this is still a huge number. At one number per second, it takes about eleven days just to count up to one million. In other words, biologists have painstakingly observed, studied, categorized, and named each of these 1.8 million creatures, one at a time, at great expense—at an average cost of $48,500 per species (Carbayo 2011). Mora and his colleagues used a model to suggest that the overall number of eukaryotic organisms is less, roughly totaling 8.7 million (± 1.3 million) (Mora et al. 2011). Even if this smaller number is accurate, and considering the International Union for Conservation of Nature's (IUCN) acknowledgement of 1.8 million species catalogued in a central database, we still have not described the remaining 86 percent of land species and 91 percent of marine species. We have made the greatest achievement in taxonomy of plants, naming 72 percent of the 298,000 estimated species. Then, just when we thought we were finally making decent progress on identifying Earth's species, Drs. Kenneth Locey and Jay Lennon from Indiana University came up with a mind-numbing estimate of 1 trillion species (2016). Their calculation includes prokaryotes (bacteria and archaea) and eukaryotic organisms and is based on high-throughput sequencing, bioinformatics, and advances in computer technology. Based on their research, 99.99 percent of species remain undiscovered.

Our taxonomic efforts since Carl Linnaeus's death in 1778 have made slow progress in the identification of new species. Linnaeus—the father of taxonomy—identified and catalogued thousands of species. At our current rate of discovery (15,000 species a year) it will take hundreds of years to complete the task, even for the lower estimates of diversity, and almost 17 million years for the upper estimate. Why is the identification of new species moving along so slowly?

Progress could be greater, but scientists have their own biases and many choose to work with mammals rather than with invertebrates, or with eukaryotes rather than with bacteria. A breakdown of all taxonomists working with eukaryotes shows that about one-third work with vertebrates, one-third with plants, and one-third with invertebrates. The problem here is that vertebrates (see Table 7.1) only make up about 1 percent, at most, of the overall number of eukaryotic species, whereas plants make up about 10 percent of the total, and invertebrates are about 90 percent of the total. From this perspective, we can see that invertebrates are underrepresented in the field of taxonomy, and of course, microbes are even less represented. Another problem is that there are also a lot of unexplored or underexplored regions of Earth that likely contain many new species.

FIGURE 7.2

There are an estimated 8.7 million eukaryotic species on Earth, of which the vast majority are invertebrate animals such as insects. The Colombian shiny blue morpho butterfly (*Morpho cypris*) and the epiphytic bucket orchid (*Coryanthes macrantha*) are examples of insects and flowering plants, respectively.

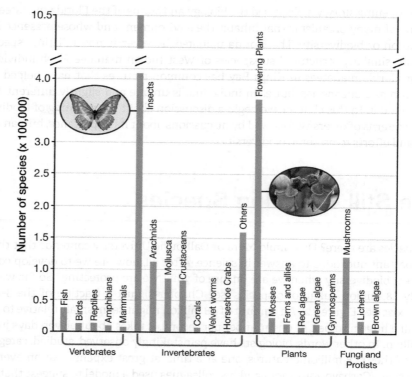

Sources: Data from IUCN Red List version 2021-3: Table 1a; © Shutterstock, Inc.

TABLE 7.1

A comparison of the number of estimated species across vertebrate categories (fish, birds, reptiles, amphibians, and mammals).

Animal Group	Number of Species
Fish	36,058
Birds	11,162
Reptiles	11,690
Amphibians	8,395
Mammals	6,578

Source: Data from IUCN Red List version 2021-3: Table 1a.

Biodiversity Varies Geographically

Species are not equally distributed across the world's surface; in other words, every species is not found in every habitat. Species are subject to natural selection forces and consequently those with the most helpful characteristics have a greater probability of surviving and having offspring. This process (see Chapter 4) gives rise to species that are adapted to a specific range of environmental conditions. For example, special water-saving adaptations allow cacti to survive in arid climates. Furthermore, large-scale variations in climate, available water, and other factors across the world limit the distributions of species.

Warm tropical areas with continuous rainfall throughout the year provide some of the highest values of species richness (see Chapter 5). Tropical rainforests of the Neotropics have the greatest known levels of species diversity of any ecosystem. Not too far behind, coral reef ecosystems also provide a stable habitat for many species. In many ways, biodiversity depends on environmental stability and decreases as needed resources becomes less abundant and environmental conditions become more erratic.

The Neotropics Supports the Highest Biodiversity on the Planet

Manatees represent one species inhabiting the coastal wetlands within the Neotropics, the most biodiverse region of the planet. The Neotropics is one of six biogeographical realms of the world, and includes South America, Central America, Southern Mexico, the Caribbean Islands, and southern Florida (see Figure 7.3). One of Earth's largest remaining wilderness areas, the Amazon, flourishes here, as do iconic predators such as the puma and jaguar. They are part of the Neotropics's astonishing array of species across taxonomic categories. Just considering bees, one taxonomic category of insects, there are an estimated 15,150 species! In the Neotropics, you can observe firsthand the greatest diversity of birds (Marra and Remsen 1997), freshwater fish (Toussaint et al. 2016), and epiphytic plants (Gentry and Dodson 1987), among other groups.

FIGURE 7.3
The Neotropics has the highest species richness of any of the six biogeographic regions. (A) This region includes Central America, South America, southern Florida, and the Caribbean Islands. (B) Perhaps the best-known iconic and endemic species in this region is the jaguar.

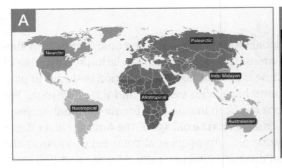 

Sources: Map of six of the world's eight ecozones from Ecozones [CC BY-SA 3.0 https://creativecommons.org/licenses/by-sa/3.0/deed.en], https://commons.wikimedia.org/wiki/File:Ecozones-2.svg]; © Shutterstock, Inc.

Biodiversity Hotspots

There are only a few wilderness areas left relatively unscathed from the presence of humans and their activities. In 2016, Dr. James Watson led a team of international scientists to map these locations. Only areas free of human influence and larger than 10,000 km² (3,861 mi²) qualified. They found that a mere twenty of the world's 195 countries contain 94 percent of these wilderness areas, and five of them hold 70 percent (Watson et al. 2018). One strategic conservation method to protect biodiversity is to focus on these five countries (see Figure 7.4). This is not the only group of scientists or environmental group to evaluate biodiversity across the world. Conservation International, a well-established environmental group, recognizes thirty-six biodiversity hotspots around the world, based on the preliminary work of Dr. Norman Myers (1988). Altogether, these thirty-six hotspots make up about 2.3 percent of the world's land, but they support more than 40 percent of known mammal, reptile, and amphibian species. To qualify as a hotspot, a location must have at least 1,500 endemic species of vascular plants, and its biodiversity must be threatened.

FIGURE 7.4
Five countries (marked with stars) contain 70 percent of the world's wilderness. These areas are important reservoirs of biodiversity.

Source: Joseph Shostell; © Shutterstock, Inc.

Several Hypotheses Describe Patterns of Global Biodiversity

Several factors help to explain the patterns of global biodiversity (see video link: "Patterns of Biodiversity"). Humans are one of these factors, as are natural factors such as latitude, time, size of area, and the frequency of natural disturbance. Time is a factor because evolution is always in play. The older the ecosystem, the longer its inhabitants have been evolving and adapting to it. For instance, the Amazon River Basin in South America has been in existence for about 11 million years (Figueiredo et al. 2009). Evidence from many studies suggests the old age of the Amazon River Basin makes it the primary source of diversity in the Neotropics (Antonelli et al. 2018). For this reason, the Amazon is often considered a cradle of biological diversity (Stebbens 1974, Moreau and Bell 2013). The high species richness is a result of a longer evolution time, compared to places such as North America, where many original populations were wiped out in periodic glaciation events. Species living in the middle and northern parts of North America have only been adapting to environmental conditions since the last glaciation event, which ended about 13,000 years ago. Species living in the Amazon have had no similar interruptions in their evolutionary history, so they have been evolving for millions of years (Wiens et al. 2011).

A second hypothesis to explain species richness relates to the size of an area, suggesting that larger areas have a greater range of habitats and consequently support more species. Although some data of insects support this hypothesis, we also know that the world's largest biome, the tundra, has a relatively low species richness. A third hypothesis suggests high species richness is due to droughts, floods, hurricanes, fires, landslides, and other natural disturbances. These disturbances seem to support both fast-growing colonizers that are poor competitors as well as slow-growing species that are superior competitors. As we can see, a combination of factors can drive biodiversity. Two additional factors are precipitation and temperature because biodiversity usually increases with each.

Patterns of Biodiversity
Listen to hypotheses about the patterns of global biodiversity.

View in the online reader

Key Takeaways

- We are still counting species.
- We are making progress in determining Earth's biodiversity, but the large estimated number of species suggests we will need hundreds of years to complete our cataloguing.
- Biodiversity varies geographically.
- The Neotropics supports the highest biodiversity on the planet.
- A higher percentage of global diversity is found in a relatively small geographic area.
- Several hypotheses describe patterns of global biodiversity.

7.2 Biodiversity Is Important

Learning Objectives

1. Explain how biodiversity is important to society and the environment.
2. Recognize the value of individual species in supporting ecosystem services.
3. Identify the categories of ecosystem services, which are upheld by biodiversity.

Biodiverse areas are reservoirs of genetic information essential to the health and functioning of species, communities, and ecosystems. Biodiversity maintains ecosystem services on which society and all life depend.

Biodiversity Benefits Populations, Communities, and Ecosystems

We can think about biological diversity at multiple levels, beginning with the population and continuing on to more complex entities—communities and ecosystems. At the population level, there is genetic diversity (see Chapter 4), which influences the potential for a population's long-term survival (Bouzat 2010). A population with a high level of genetic diversity enjoys multiple benefits from this diversity, such as a decreased susceptibility to disease and parasites (Ekroth et al. 2019). Biodiversity at the community level involves species richness and evenness and is the most commonly discussed aspect of diversity and the main focus of this chapter. More-diverse communities offer greater stability and resilience to environmental pressures. Each species of the community contributes to the functional diversity of communities and ecosystems (Tilman et al. 1997). For biodiversity of ecosystems see Chapter 5.

Healthy, Biodiverse Ecosystems Offer Goods and Services

Preserving biodiversity is important because every endemic species has a distinct and relevant role within an ecosystem. Only fully functioning and naturally biodiverse ecosystems maintain a full complement of free services, which fall into three general categories: provisioning, regulating, and cultural (see Chapter 1).

The manatee (see "Case Study: Plight of the Florida Manatee") is just one of many examples of endemic species, supporting ecosystem services. Manatees graze in shallow tropical waters and consume about 10 percent of their body weight per day. This means a 454 kg (1,000 lbs) manatee eats about 45 kg (100 lbs) of sea grass every twenty-four hours, and every ten days it will consume its weight in food. To test the effects of manatees on the Banana River ecosystem in Florida, Dr. Lynn Letebvre enclosed areas of seagrass, making them inaccessible to manatees, and then compared the growth, biomass, and diversity of the seagrass from these areas to seagrass communities grazed by manatees (Letebvre 2017). Manatees favored the superior competitor seagrass *Synringodium filiforme* over another seagrass species, *Halodole wrightii*. When manatees were excluded, *S. filiforme* slowly excluded *H. wrightii* and plant diversity declined. Therefore, manatees help to maintain healthy seagrass communities. This is important because seagrass communities have a number of functions. Seagrass has extensive root systems that stabilize the sea bottom and protect coastlines from ocean currents. Equally important, seagrass communities maintain water quality by absorbing nutrients from land areas. They create nursery areas for fish, so they are essential for commercial and recreational fisheries. In addition to stabilizing plant diversity through grazing, manatees play an important role in recycling and translocating nutrients, and therefore they are one component of biodiversity underpinning biogeochemical cycling. An established and maintained biodiversity preserves biogeochemical cycling (see Chapter 3).

Ecosystem Goods Are Tangible Materials

Foods, wood, wool, and medicines are just a few of the many ecosystem goods (see Chapter 1) we depend on (see Figure 7.5). Here we discuss one example, medicine, in more detail. Humans often turn to the rich biodiversity of Mother Nature for new pharmaceuticals. In fact, down the corridor from my office, a chemistry friend of mine has an entire research agenda focused on searching for and detecting potential anticancer compounds in plants. Table 7.2 does mention some of the more commonly known plants and their significance in medicines, but here we mention a widely used and relatively unknown compound, at least to the general public. It is found in horseshoe crab blood.

FIGURE 7.5

Society depends on a continual access to ecosystem goods. Examples of these goods are: (A) water, (B) timber, and (C) palm oil. Only healthy ecosystems can completely replenish these goods and maintain other ecosystem services. At times, society's demand exceeds the rate of renewal. In the case of palm oil, society's demand for this ecosystem good has resulted in deforestation and transformation of natural habitats to plantations, and consequently has reduced biodiversity (Iskandar et al. 2017) (D) Clotting factor from horseshoe crabs is an example of an ecosystem good used in medical research.

Source: © Shutterstock, Inc.

TABLE 7.2

Common pharmaceuticals and their source in the environment.

Source	Pharmaceutical/ Active Agent	Used to Treat/Function
Pacific yew (*Taxus brevifolia*)	Taxol, Baccatin, 10-deacetylbaccatin	Cancer (ovarian, breast, lung, pancreatic)
Periwinkle (*Catharanthus roseus*)	Vincristine, vinblastine	Cancer (Hodgkin's disease, non-Hodgkin's lymphomas, leukemia in children)
Yam (*Dioscorea spp.*)	Diosgenin (source of steroids)	Inflammation
Red peppers (*capsicum annuum*)	Capsaicin	Dermal and muscle pain; arthritis
Opium poppy (*Papaver somniferum*)	Codeine	Analgesic, antitussive

Every year, pharmaceutical companies harvest blood from over five hundred thousand horseshoe crabs inhabiting U.S. coastal waters (see D in Figure 7.5). Extract (limulus amebocyte lysate) from the blood is useful to human medicine because it is extremely sensitive to the presence of bacterial toxins (see video link: "Horseshoe Crab Blood"). Pharmaceutical companies use the extract to test the sterility of vaccines, drugs, and prosthetics to ensure drug and medical device safety for patients. Unfortunately, an estimated 15 percent (79,000) of the harvested horseshoe crabs die during the harvesting each year, from a combination of blood loss, handling, and transportation (Krisfalusi-Gannon 2018, Smith et al. 2020). Medicine would certainly be challenged without this species.

Biodiversity Helps Ecosystems to Regulate Climate

Regulating climate is an important ecosystem service, and like it or not, our climate is rapidly changing and will continue to do so as long as ecosystems are unable to absorb greenhouse gas emissions from society (see Chapter 11). The most abundant greenhouse gas is carbon dioxide, and therefore it is the one most often discussed. Ecosystems with their biodiverse communities play a role in climate regulation because they can either absorb or release carbon dioxide. Trees and other plants, for instance, undergo photosynthesis and remove carbon from the atmosphere and store it in tissue. One of the concerns with deforestation is the conversion of stored carbon in plants to atmospheric carbon. From a carbon perspective, some biomes and ecosystems sequester a greater concentration of carbon, and we keep a watchful eye on them to see if their biodiverse communities remain healthy. For example, the boreal biome covers about 17 percent of Earth's terrestrial area and contains more than 30 percent of all terrestrial organic carbon (Deluca and Boisvenue 2012). These forests in northern Canada and Russia combined with other forests absorb billions of metric tons of carbon every year. Additionally, boreal peatlands and frozen tundra soils are reservoirs of large quantities of carbon. However, as you read this text, permafrost in these northern biomes is thawing, and by the year 2100, Earth will have lost an estimated 9 million square kilometers (3.5 million mi^2) of permafrost soils. These areas will become sources rather than sinks of carbon, and thousands of years of carbon will be released in a very short period of time (Koven et al. 2011).

Biodiversity Affects Pollination

pollination

A process in flowering plants and cone-bearing plants in which pollen is transferred from the male part of a plant to the female part of a plant (ovule) of the same species.

Pollination is an indispensable ecosystem service strengthened by biodiverse communities. Of the roughly 290,000 flowering plants, 90 percent depend on insects, mammals, reptiles, birds, and amphibians as pollinators. About 99 percent of the pollinators are bees, moths, beetles, flies, butterflies, and other invertebrate species. Many flowers are visited by multiple pollinator species, which suggests that an overall abundance of pollinators is helpful in the reproductive success of flowering plants (Ollerton 1998). This is called generalized pollination. Studies by Scott Armbruster (2002) also suggest that specialized pollination is important too. In these cases, a plant species relies on just one or a handful of pollinator species for reproductive success, which suggests that a greater diversity of pollinators is helpful in successfully pollinating a diverse community of plants. Successful pollination can also depend on the diversity of functional groups within a pollinator community. A functional group of pollinators contains multiple species that share certain attributes, such as mouthpart length or body size (Gomez and Zamora 1999). Pollinators support 35 percent of food production across the world and can therefore have a considerable influence on food security and a powerful economic impact. Just within the United States, animal pollinators support a $29 billion agricultural industry, and of this amount, honeybees pollinate an estimated $15 billion worth of agricultural products. Certain crops such as almonds are almost completely dependent on honeybees. Do you like blueberries? This is but one example of crops and foods we enjoy and that are only produced with the assistance of pollinators (see "Critical Thinking Activity: Determining the Value of Honeybees").

Critical Thinking Activity: Determining the Value of Honeybees

FIGURE 7.6

Pollination of flowering plants is an important ecosystem service linked to food production. Maintaining a healthy diversity of pollinators including honeybees allows us to produce and enjoy vegetables, nuts, and fruits. Because these agricultural products have economic value, would not a honeybee have economic value as well?

Source: © Shutterstock, Inc.

Most of us enjoy blueberries. We can pop them one by one into our mouth, or enjoy their flavor in pies, muffins, Pop-Tarts, luscious jams, syrups, and assorted salads, among other possibilities. If blueberry orchards and foods with blueberries have economic value, so too do the honeybees (see Figure 7.6). This begs the question, what is the financial value of a single honeybee to the production of blueberries? To carry out this calculation, we first must answer a few questions related to honeybees and blueberries. We need to know how many flowers a honeybee visits during each trip from the beehive, the number of trips per day, and the number of days a honeybee lives. For our calculation, we will assume that successful pollination of a flower occurred during each visit to a flower, and furthermore, this translates into one blueberry. A honeybee visits between 50 and 100 flowers per trip and conducts a minimum of 12 trips per day. It continues this for the latter three weeks of its adult life. Combine this information with the cost of blueberries in the store. Multiply the number of flowers (75) by the number of trips (12) by the number of days (21) to arrive at 18,900. This is the number of blueberries. We'll divide this by 300 to help account for multiple bees pollinating the same flower (which can be up to 150 per flower per day; Aizen et al. 2014), a bee repeatedly visiting a flower, or the chance of a flower not producing a marketable blueberry (due to drought, frost injury, or pests). Because we know the price of blueberries at the local grocery store, we can determine the economic value in dollars of 63 blueberries. Keep in mind, that the price of fruit varies by location and time of year. For example, prices of blueberries in Minnesota range between $1.50 and $3.00 per pound during the summer. There are about 275 average-size blueberries per pint and 1.3 pints of blueberries weigh one pound. Given this information, 63 blueberries weigh 0.13 pounds (63 ÷ 275 ÷ 1.3 = 0.18). Based on these numbers, a single honeybee helps to produce 0.18 lbs of blueberries, which is equal to approximately $0.27 to $0.54 (0.18 * $1.50 = $0.27 and 0.18 * $3.00 = $0.54). Observe Table 7.3 below and complete the calculations for the value of a single honeybee for other fruits and nuts you enjoy. The final dollar amount only represents the pollinator in the context of an agricultural plant product and does not include the functional role of bees in other areas. For example, it does not include honey production, nor the importance of the insects in the food web. Although the number of flowers visited per bee varies across plants, assume they are similar to blueberries.

TABLE 7.3

Calculating the value of pollinators.

Fruit/Vegetable/Nut	Price ($) per Pound at Store	Value in Dollars of Individual Pollinator
Blueberries	$1.50 to $3.00	$0.27 to $0.54
Watermelons		

Fruit/Vegetable/Nut	Price ($) per Pound at Store	Value in Dollars of Individual Pollinator
Oranges		
Green beans		
Your favorite fruit		

Biodiversity Makes Life-Support Systems Possible

New evidence has come forward about a threshold level of biodiversity needed to maintain ecosystem services. When an ecosystem's biodiversity drops below this threshold, services are lessened. Scientists suggest a threshold value of 90 percent; that is, 90 percent of the biodiversity is intact (Newbold et al. 2016). As long as this is maintained, life-support systems are likely to continue (see Table 7.4).

TABLE 7.4
Ecosystem services essential for life.

Regulating weather	Decomposition of wastes
Soil formation	Pest control
Biogeochemical cycles	Disease control
Purification of air	Pollination
Purification of water	Disperse seeds
Detoxification of wastes	Protect against harmful ultraviolet rays

Biodiversity Supports Tourism

Healthy ecosystems with biodiverse communities are desirable locations for tourists to visit. Think of taking a walk through a national park, camping in your favorite campground, snorkeling in a coral reef ecosystem, or experiencing a fishing tour. In each case, biodiversity is an asset to the overall experience of the tourist. Biodiversity is not just an attractive feature in rural tourism where travelers seek the traditional outdoor adventure, spacious land, seclusion, or wildlife, but is also beneficial to urban tourism. City tourists might be drawn to museums, art galleries, and theaters, but they expect green spaces too. Today's sustainable-minded city planners purposely include green space and strive to enhance urban biodiversity. Green areas help to remove air pollutants and add pleasant vistas, among many other benefits. Globally, rural and urban destinations entice 1.4 billion people to leave their homes and explore a different part of the world each year (see Figure 7.7). Monies from tourists support one of the fastest growing economic sectors, which currently generates 10 percent of the world's gross domestic product (GDP).

FIGURE 7.7
When the appropriate consideration is given to traditional customs and equality for all, the involvement of local communities in ecotourism can protect biodiversity and native culture while infusing monies into the local communities. Here, in Sabah, Borneo, tourists are trying out bamboo rafts to experience daily activities of the indigenous population.

Source: Lano Lan/Shutterstock.com

Biodiversity Supports Indigenous Communities

All humans depend on ecosystem biodiversity, but some groups live closer to the land than others. About 50 percent of the global population has a livelihood directly dependent upon natural resources. Some subsist on the land and gather forest products, catch fish, or hunt game for consumption, trading, or selling. They live at or below poverty level, and their standard of living quickly erodes with loss of biodiversity.

Within this large group, indigenous peoples are especially at risk because a subsistence lifestyle is part of their cultural identity. Their sophisticated traditional economies are based on a high appraisal of Mother Nature's resources. The indigenous people have long historical ties with the land. Eons of living in a mutualistic relationship with the ecosystems they inhabit make them good examples of environmental stewards.

Biodiversity Has Intrinsic Value

Ecosystems and their components can have intrinsic value; that is to say, they have meaning and significance even without humans. The Society of Conservation of Biology states, "There is intrinsic value in the natural diversity of organisms, the complexity of ecological systems, and the resilience created by evolutionary processes." This ecocentric point of view (see Chapter 2) supports an intrinsic value of ecosystems.

A cultural ecosystem service is different from a strict intrinsic value because it adds the human element. In these circumstances, people might be somewhat removed from the environment, yet they still have an affinity for it and place value on it. For example, the knowledge that there are whales, dolphins, and Bengal tigers in the world pleases them, even though they will probably never touch one or even observe one.

Key Takeaways

- Biodiversity benefits populations, communities, and ecosystems.
- Fully functioning and naturally biodiverse ecosystems provide a full complement of ecosystem services, such as regulating climate, pollinating flowers, forming soil, and recycling nutrients.
- Biodiversity supports tourism and indigenous communities.
- Biodiversity has intrinsic value.

7.3 Biodiversity Threats, Decline, and Extinction

Learning Objective

1. Using the acronym HIPPCO, explain the linkages between anthropogenic environmental changes and loss of biodiversity.

Watson et al.'s publication, "Protect the Last of the Wild," drives home the reality of the current state of the global environment. Quite frankly, there is less of Mother Nature today than there was just a few years ago. As she dwindles, biodiversity suffers and we lose essential ecosystem services necessary for life and society. In this section, we discuss habitat loss, habitat degradation, and other factors threatening biodiversity that have pushed Earth into its sixth mass extinction event.

At the turn of the millennium, faced with exponential population growth, ascending consumption of environmental resources, and rising evidence of habitat loss and degradation, the United Nations called for a global assessment of ecosystems. Such an immense initiative was only made possible with the assistance of more than 1,360 experts and overwhelming support from membership nations. At a cost of $24 million, we became informed as to the health of and threats to Earth's many ecosystems. Reports of the assessments are available here. As a citizen of planet Earth, you have a right to access the information gathered, and thus be informed about threats and priorities in each of the world's regions: Africa, Asia, Latin America and the Caribbean (Neotropics), North America, and West Asia. Upon completion, the United Nations wrote, "The bottom line of the Millennium Assessment findings is that human actions are depleting Earth's natural capital, putting such strain on the environment that the ability of the planet's ecosystems to sustain future generations can no longer be taken for granted."

Beginning in 1997, the United Nations also began to publish a series of Global Environment Outlook reports, which are assessments of the state of the environment. These reports align with the mission of the United Nations' Environment Programme, established in 1972. The reports are made possible through a consultative, transparent process and are intended to assist governments to make informative and sustainable decisions about the environment. Each region receives its own assessment in the context of the UN's 2030 sustainable development goals (see Figure 1.18). There is a range of environmental threats, and they vary across regions. These primarily anthropogenic threats have raised the rate of species extinction 1,000 to 10,000 times above the natural rate.

Human Impact on Biodiversity (HIPPCO)

The main threats (abbreviated as **HIPPCO**) to biodiversity are habitat destruction (H), invasive species (I), population growth (P), pollution (P), climate change (C), and over exploitation (O) (see video link: "HIPPCO").

HIPPCO

An acronym for the six categories of human-induced threats to biodiversity. They are habitat destruction (H), invasive species (I), population growth (P), pollution (P), climate change (C), and over exploitation (O).

HIPPCO

Explore the threats to biodiversity.

View in the online reader

Habitat Loss

Habitat loss is the single greatest threat to biodiversity and ecosystems today. Evidence of this statement comes from many papers and assessment reports, such as the last Global Environment Outlook report of the Latin American/Caribbean (Neotropics) region. There, in the region of highest biodiversity containing 25 percent of Earth's tropical forests, land-use change is the foremost problem. Conversion of natural ecosystems to agricultural areas for the expansion of sugar cane, coffee, and soybean crops, and rearing of livestock, is a major issue. The 2005 Millennium Ecosystem Assessment Report gives us an estimate of the percentage of Earth's terrestrial biomes already converted for agricultural or other use. By 1990, we had already reduced six biomes by over 50 percent, two of these by over 66 percent (see Table 7.5). At the current rate of change, by 2050, we predict losses of two-thirds of six terrestrial biomes plus another biome reaching the 50 percent mark.

TABLE 7.5
Estimated loss of habitat in biomes by 1990 and estimated by 2050.

Biome	Fraction of Biome Lost by 1990	Estimated Fraction of Biome Lost by 2050
Mediterranean forests, woodlands, and scrub	2/3	>2/3
Temperate forest, steppe, and woodland	2/3	>2/3
Temperate broadleaf and mixed forests	>1/2	>1/2

Biome	Fraction of Biome Lost by 1990	Estimated Fraction of Biome Lost by 2050
Tropical and subtropical dry broadleaf forests	>1/2	>2/3
Flooded grasslands and savannas	>1/2	≈2/3
Tropical and subtropical grasslands, savannas, and shrublands	>1/2	>2/3
Tropical and subtropical coniferous forests	>2/5	>2/3

Source: Data from Millennium Ecosystem Assessment, 2005. *Ecosystems and Human Well-being: Synthesis*. Island Press, Washington, DC.

Habitat loss is one of the key threats to manatees as well (Reynolds and Odell 1991). As mentioned in the opening story, manatees are mostly herbivores and find refuge in natural spring–fed areas during winter. What they ingest depends on the location they inhabit and the time of year. For instance, during the dry season in South America, manatees increase their intake of mangrove leaves (Borobia and Lodi 1992). Unfortunately, by the end of the last millennium, we had already lost about 35 percent of mangrove forest areas (Valiela et al. 2001). Today, eleven of the seventy mangrove species are threatened with extinction. They are sought out and logged for fuel and timber or cleared for development (Polidoro et al. 2010). Loss of warm-water habitat to residential development also places manatees at risk. Without these natural areas, and given their thermal sensitivity, during the winter they either congregate in tenuous artificial areas created by effluent discharge from power plants, or instead perish in the cooler oceanic waters. For many species, it is the accumulated impacts of multiple threats that cause their demise. See "Bringing It Closer to Home: Estimating Habitat Loss" to evaluate habitat loss in your home community.

Bringing It Closer to Home: Estimating Habitat Loss

This activity calls for a thirty-minute stroll around your neighborhood; that is, if it is safe to do so. Take a notebook and writing utensil with you. As you leave the front door (time zero) of your residence, pause, and then do a 360° visual scan of your surroundings. Estimate the percentage of the land you observe as either natural or transformed and record the findings (see Table 7.6). Natural implies the presence of the original biome, maybe a forest or grassland. On the other hand, transformed reflects habitat loss. Pick a direction to walk away from your home and take a path that never crosses itself (or even comes close) and eventually ends back at your doorstep. Every five minutes, pause your walk and repeat your observations and recording until the table is filled. Summarize your findings. What do your observations tell you about the environment? For those of you living in the city, most if not all of the original biome has been transformed into impervious pavement, streets, and buildings. If you live on a college campus, you may observe some impervious structures, buildings and such, but perhaps also a fragmented forest, prairie, or other biome.

TABLE 7.6 Percentage of Land Transformed in Local Neighborhood

Time Interval	Percentage of Land in Natural State	Percentage of Habitat Loss
Beginning (time zero)		
5 min		
10 min		
15 min		
20 min		
25 min		
Average		

Invasive Species

The calculation of our environmental footprint (see Chapter 18) often does not account for the damage to biodiversity and ecosystems caused by invasive species, and yet they are the second greatest driver of human-caused extinctions (Bellard et al 2016). **Invasive species** have the potential to cause major ecosystem changes. Endemic species are not adapted to the presence of an invasive species, so they have no evolved defenses against them. Furthermore, predators of the invasive species may not exist, in which case there are no natural checks on their populations. For instance, the invasive catfish (*pterygoplichthys disjunctivus*), native to the Amazon River Basin, is an invasive species that disturbs the Florida manatee. This catfish attaches to manatees with its sucker mouth and proceeds to graze on algae growing on their skin. Underwater video shows manatees expending critical energy in winter trying to dislodge the fish (Gibbs et al. 2010). Travel to almost anywhere in the world and you may encounter an invasive species. There are African camels in Western Australia, North American beavers in Chile, zebra mussels from Eurasia in North American lakes and rivers, and rats on island archipelagos, just to name a few (see Figure 7.8). The last group has been particularly harmful to biodiversity on sub-Antarctic islands.

> **invasive species**
>
> An introduced species (not native to environment) that establishes itself, threatens endemic species and biodiversity, and has the potential to cause major ecosystem changes.

The ship rat (*Rattus rattus*), Pacific rat (*R. exulans*), and Norway rat (*R. nonvegicus*) species have successfully colonized and are flourishing on 90 percent of Earth's island archipelagos. Because rats were not present on the islands until they hitched rides on ships, endemic birds on the islands evolved in the absence of rats. Among their food sources, invasive rats prey on seabirds along with their eggs and chicks. This predatory interaction has placed many of the world's 328 seabird species at risk. Five species are already extinct, and roughly one-third are either threatened or endangered. A decline of seabird populations disrupts biogeochemical cycling because seabirds consume an estimated 7 percent of all oceanic production (Brook 2004). Healthy populations of seabirds spread this production as guano over intertidal areas, subtidal zones, and terrestrial systems, where it is used for primary production (Fukami 2006).

FIGURE 7.8

Tens of thousands of invasive Burmese pythons (Python molurus) have decimated biodiversity in the Florida Everglades. They consume a wide variety of animals from rabbits to coyotes to alligators. Several native mammal species are now locally extinct or close to it (Dorcas et al. 2012). Female pythons lay biannual clutches of up to one hundred eggs and will continue to do so through their two decades of life. Full-grown pythons like this one can reach lengths of up to twenty-five feet and have a girth as thick as a telephone pole. The United States spends $120 billion annually on managing and eradicating this and other invasive species.

Source: © Shutterstock, Inc.

Population Growth and Consumption

Every one of today's 7.8 billion people consumes environmental resources, and there are already observable signs of the negative effects of our nonsustainable lifestyles around us. Habitat loss and spread of invasive species are just two examples of observable signs, but we can also add pollution, climate change, and decreased abundance of wildlife to this list. Population growth exacerbates these threats because every additional person depends on and competes for a limited supply of environmental resources, and wants to enjoy the full extent of ecosystem services. In addition to clean air, everyone needs water to drink, food to eat, and a place to call home. All of us need water to stay hydrated, and food for energy, growth, and cellular repair, but exactly how much do we require on a daily basis? The average water intake per person per day varies between 2.7 and 3.7 liters (0.7 and 1.0 gal), and the recommended caloric intake per person per day is 2,000 kilocalories (kcal). For comparison, a medium-sized apple has about 72 kcal, a 20-ounce soda around 250 kcal, two tablespoons of peanut butter about 180 kcal, and a Big Mac, 540 kcal. If the human population continues to grow as predicted to 9.8 billion in 2050, it would take 7.4 billion Big Macs to meet their daily caloric needs. Of course, some diets are unsustainable, and in this case, sufficient pastureland would have to be made available for meat production (see Figure 7.9). Currently, over 40 percent of grain production either supports livestock or acts as a source for high fructose corn syrup.

FIGURE 7.9

The United States Department of Agriculture says the average American eats over 58 pounds (26 kg) of beef per year. Beef is more resource-intensive than plant-based foods as well as other animal-based foods. For example, significantly more land (graph, in green) and freshwater (graph, in blue) are needed to grow beef. Observe how greenhouse gas emissions (graph, orange/yellow) are comparatively much greater for beef as well. All data are per ton of protein consumed. Graph source: World Resources Institute.

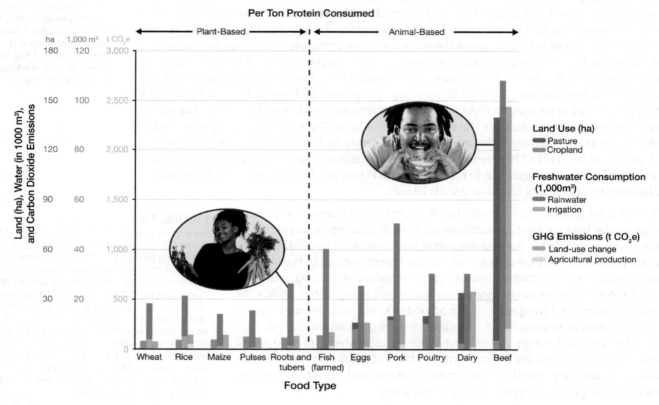

Sources: Adapted from "Animal-based Foods are More Resource-Intensive than Plant-Based Foods," World Resources Institute, April 20, 2016; © Shutterstock, Inc.

Pollution Negatively Affects Biodiversity

A broad definition of pollution incorporates any human-caused change in the environment that negatively affects environmental health. Therefore, and arguably, all the other factors of HIPPCO should be included under the category of pollution. Although this is true, here we narrow the topic to just two of the toxic pollutants regulated by the EPA—mercury and phosphorus. We will also discuss light and solid waste, giving examples of each and describing their connection to biodiversity.

Mercury

Mercury is one of the 187 toxic air pollutants regulated by the United States EPA (see Chapter 15). The predominant pollutant form of mercury comes from coal, in which it is a trace element. When coal is burned, elemental mercury is released as a vapor. Once airborne, this relatively non-harmful form of mercury can be dispersed for long distances and then deposited back to Earth's surface, mostly over the oceans. Microorganisms transform the inorganic mercury into a highly toxic form of mercury called methyl mercury. This form of mercury accumulates in microorganisms and progressively increases in concentration (biomagnification) within living tissues as it moves up to higher trophic levels of the food chain. Therefore, predatory animals such as tuna can sequester high concentrations of mercury over their relatively long lives, twenty to thirty-two years, depending on species and habitat. This is the reason why the United States Food and Drug Administration (FDA) recommends to not eat more than three ounces of white tuna per week.

mercury

A metal and toxin regulated by the United States EPA.

Phosphorus Loading from Society Threatens Biodiversity

Anthropogenic loading of nutrients into the environment causes excess eutrophication and threatens aquatic and terrestrial systems globally. In the natural environment, eutrophication is a normal process whereby an ecosystem becomes enriched with nutrients, followed by a response in plant growth. However, society's contribution of nutrients to the environment, known as **cultural eutrophication**, enhances eutrophication and reduces biodiversity.

cultural eutrophication

Eutrophication due to nutrient influx from human activities.

There are many examples of the large-scale negative effects of phosphorus pollution on biodiversity in different geographical locations, including aquatic and terrestrial areas. Some of the most biodiverse, rich terrestrial ecosystems have the lowest concentrations of phosphorus in the soil. In south west Australia, for example, phosphorus loading is one of the main threats to biodiversity because endemic plants are adapted to low-phosphorus conditions (Lambers et al. 2013). In high-phosphorus soils, non-native species easily outcompete endemic plants, so biodiversity declines. Research findings in Australia are supported by those in Europe. Although the average phosphorus concentrations in soil are naturally higher in Europe compared to Australia, elevated levels of phosphorus correlated with lower biodiversity. A group of researchers led by Dr. Tobias Ceulemans analyzed plant diversity and phosphorus concentrations in 501 grassland plots throughout Europe (Ceulemans et al. 2014). In their conclusion the researchers wrote, "Species richness was consistently negatively related to soil phosphorus." Therefore, to preserve biodiversity, it is essential to manage phosphorus. The authors hypothesized that biodiversity is lower with elevated concentrations of phosphorus because the excess phosphorus disrupts resource partitioning between coexisting plants. Plant growth is often limited by phosphorus availability and plants have evolved diverse adaptations to acquire phosphorus in phosphorus-poor ecosystems (Ceulemans et al. 2017).

In countless bodies of water, cultural eutrophication degrades water quality and causes community structural change (see Figure 7.10). As long as these nutrient loadings continue, we will observe algal blooms followed by decomposition of massive amounts of dead algae. The algae are decomposed by bacteria, which uptake all available oxygen in the water, thus creating dead zones no longer supportive of fish and other taxonomic groups dependent on oxygen (see Chapter 10). Biodiversity in these areas is extremely low.

FIGURE 7.10

In southern Florida, nutrients in the runoff from fertilized sugarcane fields, dairy farms, and septic systems have dramatically changed the plant biomass in Lake Okeechobee, Florida's largest lake. As a result, massive algae blooms (marked in green, yellow, orange, and red) cover the majority of the lake in summer. The nutrient issues of Okeechobee also propagate the formation of toxin-producing red algae blooms in coastal waters due to the diversion of lake water by the Army Corps of Engineers, therefore negatively affecting manatees and other species. Image source: NOAA taken by Copernicus Sentinel-3 satellite.

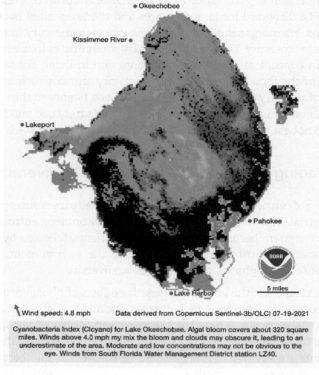

Cyanobacteria Index (CIcyano) for Lake Okeechobee. Algal bloom covers about 320 square miles. Winds above 4.0 mph my mix the bloom and clouds may obscure it, leading to an underestimate of the area. Moderate and low concentrations may not be obvious to the eye. Winds from South Florida Water Management District station LZ40.

Source: Courtesy of NOAA.

Garbage

All of us consume materials, use energy, and release waste. Individually, your generated waste is inconsequential to the normal functioning of large terrestrial and aquatic ecosystems. Rather, it is the accumulated waste of thousands, millions, and billions of people that overwhelms Mother Nature and threatens the ability of ecosystems to maintain ecosystem services. Heavily populated areas can generate large volumes of garbage. Chicago, for instance, produces close to 816,000 metric tons (900,000 tons) of garbage every year, and approximately 45 percent of this amount is hauled out of city limits to four landfills 160 kilometers (100 mi) away, two of them outside the state. These huge piles of refuse contain food wastes and other organic materials, and a long list of toxins harmful to life and biodiversity. To protect biodiversity, soil, and groundwater, in 1990 the EPA began to require landfills to have a nonporous clay barrier as well as a synthetic lining to inhibit the release of pollutants from the landfill to the surrounding environment. Even with these protective measures, landfills are significant sources of air and water pollution (see Chapter 16).

Light Pollution Threatens Biodiversity

"We'll leave the light on for you," is the ending phrase of every commercial for Motel 6. The advertisement is a reminder to us of the significance of light and how we can use it as a beacon to navigate our way out of the darkness. Although a company slogan, it pretty well sums up what society has done to Mother Nature (see Figure 7.11). Artificial light at night (ALAN) has doubled since the early 1990s and continues to increase (Koen et al 2018). The light disrupts circadian cycles, migration patterns, and the behaviors of nocturnal organisms. Birds that use moonlight and starlight for navigation fly off course due to city lights. Artificial light also disrupts the vertical migration behavior of zooplankton. In terrestrial systems, ALAN attracts nocturnal invertebrate pollinators and therefore interferes with pollination (Macgregor et al. 2015). There is now mounting evidence of ALAN's changing the structure of invertebrate communities (Davies et al. 2012) and affecting biodiversity. For example, Farnsworth et al. (2018) documented significant decreases of two groups of threatened invertebrate species in New Zealand within ALAN areas compared to control (no artificial light) areas. Researchers hypothesize that the light-avoidance behavior helps the insects to avoid nocturnal predators. ALAN offsets this anti-predator strategy. Studies like these encourage conservation biologists to closely monitor nocturnal mammals, birds, reptiles, and amphibians as they respond to lighter nights. One group of reptiles we pay close attention to is sea turtles. Hatchling sea turtles on beaches use moonlight reflecting off the ocean to determine the direction of the ocean and to navigate to the water's edge. Artificial lighting coming from buildings and streets near the shoreline easily distracts them.

FIGURE 7.11
A) Society floods the natural environment with artificial light, as seen here in a satellite image of the United States. This light (light pollution) disrupts nocturnal organisms and may influence community structure and biodiversity. B) During turtle nesting season, Fort Lauderdale turns off street lights near the beach.

Sources: NASA Earth Observatory/NOAA NGDC; Serenethos/Shutterstock.com

Climate Change Threatens Biodiversity

"There's one issue that will define the contours of this century more dramatically than any other, and that is the urgent threat of a changing climate." These were President Barack Obama's opening remarks when he addressed leaders at the United Nations Climate Change Summit in 2014. He was comparing the immediate challenges the world was facing. Terrorism, instability, inequality, and disease were all mentioned, but **climate change** was recognized as the most urgent threat. Climate change is the long-term change in the average weather patterns. Numerous studies support the existence of climate change, its threat to biodiversity, and how it is an indirect consequence of society's emissions of greenhouse gases (GHGs) (see Figure 7.12) (see Chapter 11). The primary source of the exponential growth of greenhouse gases is the combustion of fossil fuels to meet our energy needs. Another main source of carbon dioxide is deforestation. In this case, stored carbon in plant tissues is released. Trees that are cut down can no longer take up carbon dioxide from the atmosphere (Malhi and Grace 2000). If society continues to conduct activities as usual and maintain the current rate of greenhouse gas emissions, one-sixth of all species will likely become extinct in the coming decades (Urban 2015). Other scientists suggest a much higher rate of extinction.

climate change

The long-term change in the average weather patterns.

FIGURE 7.12

Based on direct measurements of the atmosphere, and on analysis of pockets of the ancient atmosphere preserved in ice cores, we know that the concentration of carbon dioxide in Earth's atmosphere has been increasing exponentially since the mid-1800s. Today, the atmosphere contains more carbon dioxide than at any other time in the last eight hundred thousand years—at least.

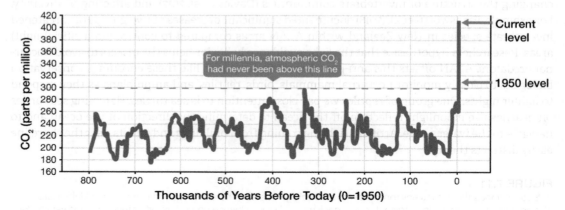

Source: Joseph Shostell; data from NASA.

Biodiversity suffers because greenhouse gases induce a cascading network of environmental changes, including trapping heat. Much of the trapped heat is absorbed by the oceans, warming up surface waters (Doney et al. 2012). In turn, the warming affects stratification (separation of the water into layers), mixing, currents, and general circulation patterns of the oceans. Availability of oxygen and nutrients become affected too, and therefore primary and secondary production are influenced. Warmer ocean water holds less oxygen than cold ocean water. According to the IUCN, the oxygen content in the oceans has already decreased by 2 percent since the middle of the twentieth century and is expected to decline by another 3–4 percent by 2100. Lower oxygen levels will affect the ability of many species such as Atlantic cod to meet their oxygen needs. Additionally, warmer surface waters are less likely to mix with deeper, nutrient-rich waters. As mixing declines, nutrients in the surface waters become scarce and phytoplankton productivity lessens. Water movement, temperature, and oxygen and nutrient content are important factors that shape the distribution patterns of species in aquatic areas. In addition, the environmental effects of global warming are unevenly distributed. For example, we are now witnessing the most rapid and profound changes in the polar and tropical regions, a consequence of warming surface waters. Biodiversity hotspots contain large numbers of endemic species with narrow distribution ranges, and are at high risk from these environmental changes (Lambers 2015). Hotspots in South America (Neotropics), Australia, and New Zealand are predicted to lose substantial numbers of species.

Species can have difficulty adapting to rapid environmental change. Most evolutionary adaption occurs gradually, over very long periods of time. If environmental change occurs too rapidly, there may not be enough time for this process to occur, and species unable to cope with the change will become extinct. Take, for example, food specialists, and those species adapted to a very specific habitat, or coevolved with another species. They may be at a higher risk of extinction relative to other species because their specialization on one resource may have come at the expense of losing traits required for utilizing a wider range of niches (Day et al. 2016; Haldane 1951). Species sensitive to higher temperatures may be able to survive by shifting their distributions, for example to higher elevations or poleward. Such shifts can be successful strategies if habitat space is available in the new territories.

What other environmental changes and threats to biodiversity might we expect from rising air temperatures? Perhaps the most obvious one is the loss of terrestrial habitats inundated by rising sea levels. Ice sheets are decreasing by 413 gigatons per year, and the Arctic sea ice is decreasing almost 13 percent per decade. These losses in ice because of melting result in the release of lots of water into the oceans and an increase of sea levels by 3.2 mm per year. Just how high will sea levels rise? As a possible answer we can compare today's sea level to the sea level during Earth's last interglacial period between 129,000 and 116,000 years ago when the West Antarctic ice sheet melted.

At that time, sea levels were up to 9 meters (29.5 ft) higher than they are today (Voosen 2018). Sea-ice habitat loss will place a considerable number of species at risk (see Chapter 11).

Overharvesting (Overexploitation)

Overexploitation is the harvesting of organisms above their rate of natural replenishment (see Table 7.7). This unsustainable practice threatens biodiversity and has already caused the extinction of many species, including the passenger pigeon, New Zealand's moas, and Madagascar's giant lemurs (see Chapter 2). According to the Food and Agriculture Organization of the United Nations (FAO 2009), overexploitation, in combination with climate change, is to blame for the decimation of 70 percent of Earth's wild fish stocks. Fisheries biologist Dr. Daniel Pauly states, "The world's marine fisheries resources are under enormous pressure, with global fishing effort exceeding optimum and sustainable levels by an estimated factor of three to four" (Pauly et al. 2002).

overexploitation

The harvesting of organisms above their rate of natural replenishment.

TABLE 7.7
Examples of species we overharvest, and in some cases obtain and/or kill illegally (poaching).

Taxa	Location	Threat	Status
Bluefin tuna (*Thunnus thynnus*)	Pacific Ocean	Overharvested	Endangered, population decreasing
Bengal tiger (*Tigris tigris*)	India, Bangladesh, Nepal, and Bhutan	Habitat loss, human–animal conflicts, poaching	Endangered, population decreasing
Black rhinoceros (*Diceros bicornis*)	Eastern and Southern Africa	Habitat loss, poaching	Critically endangered, population increasing
African elephant (*Loxodonta Africana*)	Sub-Saharan Africa	Habitat loss, poaching	Vulnerable, population increasing
Aloe spp.	Kenya	Habitat loss, climate change, overharvesting	Nine species are critically endangered, seven are endangered, four are vulnerable, three are threatened
Bornean orangutan (*Pongo pygmaeus*)	Borneo	Habitat loss, poaching, killed for bushmeat	Critically endangered, population declining
American manatee (*Trichechus manatus*)	Neotropics, Southeastern United States	Habitat loss, boat collisions, pollution, poaching, killed for meat	Vulnerable, population declining

Many nations see fishing as a critically important way to feed their growing populations. Fish are a great source of protein and essential micronutrients, but wild fish populations in the seas and inland bodies of water cannot match society's demand for fish. Fish consumption is increasing at a rate that outpaces human population growth by 100 percent. Collectively, the world's 4.6 million fishing vessels take in about 90 million metric tonnes (99 million tons) of fish each year. Asia maintains the lion's share of this fleet (75 percent). Intense fishing pressure and harvests above replacement levels threaten fish stocks in many locations of the world, but most greatly in the Mediterranean Sea, Black Sea, and the southeastern Pacific and southwestern Atlantic Oceans. On average, over 60 percent of the fish stocks in these areas are at risk from overharvesting. Today, global annual consumption of fish is about 170 million metric tons (187 million tons) per year, far more than what is captured from wild stocks. As consumption of fish continued to rise in the 1980s, aquaculture filled the gap in need. Now, almost 50 percent of the fish we eat comes from aquaculture facilities.

Poaching Harms Populations and Negatively Affects Biodiversity

poaching

The illegal hunting, capturing, or taking of wildlife.

Poaching is the illegal hunting, capturing, or taking of wildlife (see Figure 7.13). Illegal possession and trafficking of wildlife are supported by a sophisticated international network that involves many groups and more than 120 countries. In an average year, inspectors carry out 160,000 seizures and confiscate several thousand species. Numbers can be relatively high for a given taxonomic group, such as in the case of the 1,300 rhinos poached in 2015. Estimating the economic value of this black market is impossible, in part because of its non-transparency. Plus, how do we assess the value of an animal product such as a pelt that is later transformed into a designer handbag or a coat? Suggestions range from hundreds of millions to tens of billions each year.

FIGURE 7.13
Poaching of rhinos is mainly driven by the demand for their horns, which fetch around $60,000 per kilogram (2.2 lbs) on the black market. To prevent poaching of rhinos, a conservation team dehorns a rhino in Magaliesberg, South Africa.

Source: Snap2Art/Shutterstock.com

Of the thousands of wildlife species hunted, traded, and/or sold illegally, we mention just a few: manatees, African elephants, and vultures.

Despite laws that ban hunting of manatees in the Neotropics, these animals continue to be illegally hunted, traded, and consumed. After watercraft collisions, illegal hunting is the main threat to the Antillean manatee (*Trichechus manatus manatus*) in Belize. Based on interviews of indigenous communities of the Brazilian Amazon, Amazonians still hunt the vulnerable Amazonian manatees (*Trichechus inunguis*) today (Franzini et al. 2013). Their actions, which include trading of manatee meat, are currently illegal in Brazil. In order to protect manatees in these areas, new conservation plans will need to include the local indigenous communities.

A demand for ivory fuels the poaching of African elephants, and illegal killing frequently happens in national parks. In 2013, more than one hundred elephants were poisoned in Hwange National Park, Zimbabwe. Another ten were poisoned in 2017. These are examples of an increasingly popular method that poachers use to quietly take down large animals. Use of dilute sodium cyanide, paraquat—a powerful herbicide—and other poisons in poaching threatens elephants and harms biodiversity. A poisoned water hole can kill an entire elephant herd and a host of non-targeted animals too. Rotting elephant carcasses draw vultures and other scavengers that consume toxin-laden flesh and perish (Ogada et al. 2015). An estimated one-third of all vulture deaths are caused by poisoning. Seasoned poachers attempt to minimize any signals that might alert conservation officers to their presence. Recently, poachers have ratcheted up their killing of vultures to prevent the circling of vultures above elephant massacres. This pressure is pushing vulture species in Africa toward extinction.

Mass Extinction Events

Over the last 500 million years, Earth has experienced five mass extinction events (see Figure 4.7 and Figure 7.14). In these cases, the rate of extinctions spiked significantly above the "business as normal" or background extinction rate of 0.1–1 extinction per million species per year. To qualify as a mass extinction event, at least 50 percent of living species must become extinct within a relatively short period of time (Chen et al. 2012). All five of these cataclysmic events were induced by major environmental change—some combination of climate change and other factors such as volcanic activity, ocean acidification, continental movement, and asteroid strike (Clarkson 2015). We are witnessing a sixth mass extinction event taking place right now (Cafaro 2015). Human-induced environmental change has convinced scientists to refer to the current geological epoch as the **Anthropocene** (Crutzen 2002). Through a host of nonsustainable activities, we have decimated a huge proportion of our natural environment to devote to agriculture, mining, highway networks, and cities as well as polluted the atmosphere and hydrosphere.

Anthropocene

Name given to the current geological epoch and mass extinction event induced by human-caused environmental changes.

FIGURE 7.14
Earth has experienced at least five mass extinction events. In one hypothesis, evolutionary biologists contend that an asteroid struck the Earth approximately 65 MYA killing at least 70 percent of all life. In the illustration, a meteor is about to collide with Earth.

Source: © Shutterstock, Inc.

Key Takeaways

- The main anthropogenic threats to biodiversity are **h**abitat loss, **i**nvasive species, **p**ollution, human **p**opulation growth, **c**limate change, and **o**verharvesting.
- Use the acronym HIPPCO to remember the anthropogenic threats to biodiversity.

7.4 Saving Endangered Species and Preserving Biodiversity

Learning Objectives

1. Identify three instrumental national laws that protect biodiversity.
2. Determine the significance of international collaborations in protecting endangered species and biodiversity.
3. Explain how environmental scientists determine species.
4. Provide examples of the types of conservation actions that protect biodiversity.

Conservation plans rely on an assortment of methods to offset HIPPCO factors, and consequently protect endangered species and biodiversity. Conservation management plans might target endangered species or whole ecosystems, regions, or the entire world. In this section, we identify and explore powerful environmental laws and common strategies to protect biodiversity.

Environmental Laws Protect Biodiversity

One of the best ways to protect biodiversity is through legislation (see Chapter 2). Environmental laws help us to maintain a world capable of providing ecosystem services essential to all living things, including humans. Of the many environmental laws, we mention just a few broad-reaching ones intended to protect species and ecosystems. Close to the top of this list is the Endangered Species Act (see Chapter 2). The enactment of this law was in response to witnessed extinctions of fish, wildlife, and plants, and our realization that many species are at risk of extinction. With this law, the U.S. federal government formally recognized the aesthetic, recreational, scientific, educational, historical, and ecological values of species.

environmental impact statements

A description of the potential environmental impacts of a proposed federal activity on public lands.

One year earlier, President Richard Nixon also signed the Marine Mammal Protection Act (MMPA). Under this law, manatees, dugongs, and all other marine mammals are protected. Other laws target the issue of overharvesting oceanic fish. For example, in 1976, Congress passed the Magnuson-Stephens Act to appropriately manage marine fisheries in United States federal waters. The intention of this law is to prevent overfishing and to ensure a sustainable supply of seafood. Another far-reaching environmental protection law, the National Environmental Policy Act (NEPA), influences all federal activities. The purpose of NEPA is to integrate environmental values into government decision-making processes. Before a bridge or airport is constructed, or other federal government action can take place, an assessment must be completed that evaluates the potential environmental impacts of the proposed actions. These assessments are called **environmental impact statements** (EIS) and are shared with the public and all stakeholders.

In one example, the United States Fish and Wildlife Service (USFWS) and the Army Corps of Engineers completed an EIS of the potential harm of boat traffic to Florida manatees, in response to a lawsuit. Save the Manatee Club noted in their lawsuit that the number one human-related cause of manatee mortality was collisions with vessels, and the number of registered boats in Florida rose by 43 percent between 1993 and 2001, to 943,611 vessels. The final ruling regarding the suit states, ". . . the Plaintiffs charged that the Service issued biological opinions regarding applications for Corps permits that did not appropriately assess effects to manatees and critical habitat, in violation of the Endangered Species Act." As a settlement, the USFWS assessed the need for additional manatee refuge areas, and in the end designated thirteen manatee protection areas in eight Florida counties. In four of the areas, all waterborne activities are completely prohibited, whereas in the remaining nine, certain activities are either prohibited or tightly regulated. Where manatees are concerned, multiple environmental protection laws apply, including the Endangered Species Act of 1973, The Florida Manatee Sanctuary Act of 1978, and the Marine Mammal Protection Act of 1972.

The Wildlife Restoration Act (the Pittman–Robertson Act) is another important conservation law (see Figure 7.15) (see video link: "Who Pays For Wildlife Conservation?"). Signed by President Franklin D. Roosevelt in 1937, this law authorized the formation of the Wildlife Restoration Program. The Act supports management and restoration of wildlife with funds from excise taxes on the production of firearms, ammunitions, and archery equipment. Approximately 12.5 million hunters annually provide an average of $751 million, $606 million of which goes to fund the Wildlife Restoration Program (CRS 2019). This program was so successful that a similar law and program were suggested to protect America's fishing resources. The Sport Fish Restoration Act was passed in 1954, starting the Sport Fish Restoration Program. The program has permanent financial support because it receives tax funds from the purchase of fishing equipment and motorboats.

FIGURE 7.15

The Wildlife Restoration Act (WRA) supports taxes on firearm sales and archery equipment sales to fund conservation grants, hunter education, and the Wildlife Restoration Program (WRP). Because of the WRA and similar laws, we have seen successful recoveries of the (A) endangered Tennessee purple coneflower (*Echinacea tennesseensis*) and (B) threatened Louisiana black bear (*Ursus americanus luteolus*). Both species have been removed from the list of Threatened and Endangered Wildlife species.

Source: © Shutterstock, Inc.; Courtesy of the U.S. Fish & Wildlife Service.

International laws and treaties further support the protection of species, biodiversity, and ecosystems. Here, we mention four of the many international collaborations, beginning with the Convention on International Trade in Endangered Species (CITES). The aim of CITES is to ensure that international trade in wildlife does not harm the survival of species (see Chapter 2). As we have seen, the growing number of species faring poorly, extirpated, or even extinct helps explain the need for this international venture. But how does it work? Who is involved? There are now 183 participating countries, up from 80 in 1975. The framework of the international agreement stresses that each member should adopt its own domestic legislation in support of CITES. For the United States, the United States Fish and Wildlife Service (USFWS) is the administrative agency in charge of reviewing and approving trading permits regarding animal and plant species. The review and approval process allows the USFWS to determine that trade in particular species is legal and not detrimental to the species' survival in the wild. Decisions about whether or not to grant a permit begin by determining if the species is listed in one of three appendices by CITES. A permit may be granted for species on these lists if certain conditions are met (e.g., import of museum specimens). Roughly 5,800 animal species and 30,000 plant species are protected by CITES and are listed in these appendices. Appendix I lists those most endangered and threatened with extinction. The Bengal tiger, African elephant, black rhino, and Florida manatee are all on this list.

The establishment of the **Convention on Biological Diversity** demonstrates the focused effort of more than 178 governments to preserve biodiversity, act sustainably, and equally share in the benefits of natural goods. The Convention was one of the main agreements reached between nations at the 1992 Earth Summit in Rio de Janeiro. Projects set up in the spirit of the Convention exist around the world. Some address the need to grow food sustainably. In one example, in Mexico, farmers plant coffee trees interspersed among native plants in mixed tropical forests. Their objective is to grow and harvest coffee beans in a more natural setting, as an alternative to monocultures. Rather than spray pesticides to reduce pests, the farmers rely on natural biological pest control.

Our final two international collaborations were created for the protection of key taxonomic groups. One is the International Convention for the Northwest Atlantic Fisheries, which is an agreement among eighteen countries to assess and manage fish stocks in the Northwest Atlantic. The second is the Migratory Bird Treaty Act (MBTA), aimed at protecting thousands of bird species. Treaties with Japan, Russia, Canada, and Mexico extended the reach of the MBTA far beyond the United States, and it is credited for saving hundreds of millions of birds.

Conservation Protects the Environment

A conservation strategy supports the interaction of humans with the environment, but also stresses sustainability to protect the environment. This form of protection differs from preservation, which calls for a complete removal of humans from an area.

Conservation Begins with the Identification of Species

The development of advanced molecular techniques over the last three decades has revolutionized how we approach the identification of species. Today, it is common for ecologists to incorporate polymerase chain reactions (PCR) and other molecular genetic techniques into their research (see Figure 7.16). The technique begins with obtaining an extremely small sample of tissue—such as a drop of blood—from an organism, followed by the isolation and amplification of the DNA in it. The amplified DNA is run through an automated DNA sequencer, and the resulting DNA sequence can be compared with that of other organisms. As a general rule, individuals of the same species have more similarities in their DNA sequences than individuals of different species. Thus, if the new sequence is sufficiently different from that of all other known species, then the ecologist has probably discovered a new species.

In one way, this method is no different than comparing skull sizes and other characteristics that can be observed with the naked eye. However, DNA comparisons provide an advantage because many species are very difficult to distinguish by physical attributes alone, and some species have multiple forms, or morphs, that appear very different from one another. DNA comparisons also allow evolutionary biologists to estimate relative relatedness among different species. For example, in the case of the Florida manatee, physical differences backed up by DNA sequencing inform us that the Florida manatee is not a distinct species, but rather, is one of two similarly structured subspecies of the West Indian manatee.

Convention on Biological Diversity

An international collaboration of many governments to preserve biodiversity, act sustainably, and equally share in the benefits of natural goods.

Who Pays For Wildlife Conservation?

Learn about who pays for wildlife conservation in Wyoming and other states.

View in the online reader

FIGURE 7.16

Today's scientists often rely on advanced molecular techniques to reveal information such as a population's history and genetic variation. In the images, a chinook salmon is caught (A) and biopsied (B) for later genetic analysis in the laboratory.

Sources: Biologist holding a Chinook Salmon over the Yukon River, AK, USGS; Muscle biopsy sample from a Chinook salmon, AK, USGS.

Diets, Agriculture, and Biodiversity

We could very quickly reduce the wide-ranging negative effects of agriculture by opting to change our diets. Eradicating meat consumption would greatly reduce the amount of land devoted to agriculture. For instance, the average land area required for growing beef is over thirty-five times larger than the average land area needed to grow an equivalent weight in grains (Poore and Nemecek 2018). Our diet choices influence land use and can either increase or reduce threats to biodiversity. Is it possible to reduce the amount of land used in agriculture? The impetus for this question comes from the far-reaching and broad ecological impacts agriculture has on natural ecosystems. Not counting deserts and ice-covered locations, approximately 43 percent of the Earth's terrestrial areas now support agriculture. These agricultural areas are a source of pesticides, soil erosion, and greenhouse gas emissions, and require habitat space, high volumes of water, nutrients, and energy. A group of academic researchers took on this question and studied the relationships between ten different diet types and corresponding land use within the United States (Peters et al. 2016). Diets ranged from omnivorous types consisting of various percentages of meats and animal products to an exclusively vegan diet. As the average American diet becomes closer to vegan, more and more of the 299 million hectares devoted to grazing lands would be freed up and reconverted to natural ecosystems. With this diet choice, or at least closer on the spectrum to this choice, less land would need to be dedicated to support our food needs. The authors calculated that a shift in diet from meat-eating to vegan would reduce the requirement for agricultural land from about 1.08 hectares (2.67 acres) to 0.13 hectares (0.32 acres) per person. Some of the freed-up land could be used to grow food crops for a larger future population, or restored and set aside for strict conservation.

Community-Based Conservation

Despite international treaties, national laws, and greater public awareness of rising extinction rates and environmental degradation, ecosystems continue to lose biodiversity. A growing group of scientists, conservation groups, and governments suggest community-based involvement as a viable and complementary strategy to maintain long-term conservation of ecosystems. **Community-based conservation** projects involve and benefit local communities, and adhere to tenets of the Convention on Biological Diversity. A fine example of this local stewardship happens in Amboseli National Park in Kenya. The local community participates in the conservation efforts and also receives a portion of gate revenues. International tourists and wildlife explorers flock to this 10,000 km² (3,861 mi²) ecosystem to experience the rich diversity of large mammals. Strong com-

community-based conservation

Conservation that involves and benefits local communities, and adheres to tenets of the Convention on Biological Diversity.

munity conservation initiatives like this one at Amboseli National Park have helped Kenya to fend off more ivory poachers than has Tanzania.

Seed Banks Preserve Genetic Diversity

ex situ (off-site) conservation

Protection of an organism by moving it outside of its natural distribution.

Seed banking is a useful conservation strategy to protect natural biodiversity and genetic variation of seed-bearing plants. The method falls under the category of **ex situ (off-site) conservation**. Other examples of ex situ conservation are zoos, aquaria, laboratories, botanical gardens—anywhere we move organisms outside of their native range to help their species survive. Seed banking is advantageous over other ex situ methods. Seeds are relatively small, don't move, take little space, can endure lengthy periods of storage, and for the most part, are not labor intensive. In total, more than 7.4 million seed samples reside in seed banks around the world (see Figure 7.17). In 2008, Norway established and funded Svalbard, the largest secure seed storage facility in the world. Check Svalbard's current tally of seed deposits here.

FIGURE 7.17
Seed banks help to protect Earth's biodiversity. One of the world's largest is the Svalbard Global Seed Bank on Spitsbergen, an Arctic island in Norway. Many countries partner with Norway and store their seeds in the vault. The photo shows the entrance of Svalbard.

Source: © Shutterstock, Inc.

Captive Breeding Programs

Broad strategies in the protection of endangered species involve **captive breeding programs** (CBPs). A CBP serves as a source of captive-bred animals and plants that are then reintroduced into the wild. From the perspective of some, CBPs are a last resort for the salvation of a species, and yet there are many examples of species successfully recovering because of the intervention of a CBP. The aim of any CBP is to help reestablish a species that has become threatened or extinct in its native habitat. The Spanish National Research Council out of Almeria, Spain, runs one of many successful CBPs. For the last few decades, this CBP has focused on protecting ungulate species of North Africa. Today, several African countries have reestablished wild populations descended from this single CBP program.

captive breeding programs

A program used as a source of captive-bred animals and plants that are kept in controlled environments such as a zoo or wildlife reserve and then reintroduced into the wild. A CBP is considered a last resort to help recover an endangered species.

FIGURE 7.18
Captive breeding programs protect biodiversity. In one of the greatest success stories, the banning of DDT and the implementation of the peregrine falcon captive breeding program helped the peregrine falcon recover from the brink of extinction.

Source: © Shutterstock, Inc.

Captive breeding programs saved the peregrine falcon (see Figure 7.18). Widespread use of DDT following World War II decimated the peregrine falcon's population. DDT does effectively control insects but it also poisons peregrine falcons and causes thinning of their egg shells. As a consequence, egg shells crack during incubation. By 1964, ornithologists declared peregrine falcons absent from the eastern United States, a major section of its native range. The species became listed as endangered in 1970, and its future looked dire. A peregrine recovery plan began in 1975 with the objective of creating 175–200 breeding pairs in the Eastern United States. The basis of the program was to capture, breed, and release. By 1979, the goal of the recovery program was achieved, and by 1998, scientists proposed removing the peregrine falcon from the endangered species list because the peregrine's population had recovered. Rachel Carson's message about the negative effects of DDT, and the EPA's ban of DDT use in 1972, were instrumental in the success of released peregrine falcons. Without this communication and legislation, released peregrine falcons would have fared no better than their predecessors in a DDT-polluted environment.

Captive breeding programs alone are insufficient for species recovery and protection of biodiversity. The key to a CBP is the eventual release of reared animals into an environment where the animals can thrive. In many cases, habitat destruction, pollution, and other threats make reintroduction to native ranges impossible because released animals will not survive. Some captive breeding programs formally recognize this glaring problem. SeaWorld Parks & Entertainment have changed their approach to assisting manatees, now emphasizing rehabilitation and reintroduction rather than breeding. In response to questions about their role in breeding manatees, they state, "Zoological institutions in Florida are on a voluntary hold. Until the numerous problems are corrected in the manatee's environment, a breeding program will not be beneficial to them."

Setting Land Aside (Land Sparing) Protects Species

FIGURE 7.19

Land sparing is a common way to protect biodiversity. Crystal River is a National Wildlife Refuge in Florida intended to protect manatees and other species.

Source: K. Ramirez/Shutterstock.com

We set aside land and aquatic areas for protection to offset environmental degradation caused by HIPPCO factors (see Figure 7.19). Before we engage in this form of conservation, we first must consider competing theories as to the extent and type of natural areas to be set aside. These theories differ on the best way to protect the biodiversity of ecosystems. When we consider how to protect the biodiversity, questions arise. Are multiple areas needed? Should they be continuous? Are these areas completely apart from human interaction? Here, we compare two of these theories: 1) setting aside half of the world for non-human species, and 2) targeting diversity hotspots in multiple areas of the world.

A recently proposed strategy stresses the inability of ecosystems to recover while still enduring ongoing and increasing anthropogenic threats. In this version of setting land aside (land sparing), the percentage of land dedicated to non-humans is radically increased. The Nature Needs Half (NNH) and Half-Earth Project (Wilson 2016) movements suggest 50 percent of the world be allocated to humans and the remainder to all other life. These growing movements are based on three points. First, it is unethical to not share the Earth with other species. Second, current conservation efforts cannot stop the tide of rising extinction, and therefore current areas set aside are inadequate. Third, habitat loss is the main threat to biodiversity loss. Critics of the NNH ask what will happen to those indigenous peoples who utilize the land and must be displaced to appropriately remove all human influence? Other critics say it is an easy way to opt out of the complex sustainability thinking that is essential to solve the world's environmental problems. According to some critics, setting aside an area misses the point of sustainability, because business can go on as usual and the "solution" is separate from society. Others say that a 50 percent split is preposterous and unrealistic. Still others argue humans are from and in the environment, not separate. What do you think?

Part of our responsibility as global environmental stewards is to identify species at risk of extinction and then to assist in their recovery and protection. As just noted, the greatest single threat to species and biodiversity is habitat loss, the first part of HIPPCO. One conservation strategy, given this threat, is to prioritize those land and water areas with high biodiversity and then allocate the limited conservation funds available for the protection of these areas. Drs. David Olson and Eric Dinerstein (2008) suggest the protection of two hundred global spots selected as representatives of Earth's major habitats. They based their suggested areal units on ecoregions making up a set of natural communities, rather than on the territorial boundaries of countries. Just like pollution, species, communities, and ecosystems can cross national borders. Another group of researchers (Mittermeier et al. 2003) has a slightly different outlook on conservation, and suggests five priority areas where there is high biodiversity. These are Amazonia (in the Neotropics), Congo, New Guinea, the Miombo-Mopane Woodlands, and North American deserts. Furthermore, they call for proactive conservation by targeting twenty-four ecosystems that are greater than or equal to one million hectares and that have low human population densities (≤ 5 people per km^2).

All together, these ecosystems make up 44 percent of Earth's land. Naysayers and pragmatists ask how much this will cost and from where do the funds arise? We don't have solid answers to these questions, but we do have some estimates for the cost piece. Dinerstein et al. (2017) estimates a cost of $80 billion annually to conserve 50 percent of terrestrial areas, and another $19 billion annually to protect 10 percent of coastal and marine areas.

Key Takeaways

- Environmental laws protect biodiversity. Examples are the Endangered Species Act, Marine Mammal Protection Act, and the National Environmental Policy Act.
- International laws and treaties further support the protection of species, biodiversity, and ecosystems. Examples are CITES and the Convention on Biological Diversity.
- A conservation strategy supports the interaction of humans with the environment, but also stresses sustainability to protect the environment.
- Eradicating meat consumption would greatly reduce the amount of land devoted to agriculture.
- Community-based involvement is a viable and complementary strategy to maintain long-term conservation of ecosystems.
- Seed banks preserve genetic diversity of seed-bearing plants.
- Captive breeding programs serve as a source of captive-bred animals and plants to protect endangered species.
- Setting land aside (land sparing) mitigates the threat of habitat loss.

7.5 A Look to the Future: Expectations and Manatees

Learning Objective

1. Review the information of the chapter and hypothesize as to the manatee's future.

Maintaining and restoring biodiversity can be challenging because of its many potential obstacles. Yet given the importance of biodiversity and its links to our own welfare, we cannot afford to back down from our conservation efforts. Here, at the close of the chapter, we return to our opening story and discuss the future of manatees, and with them, biodiversity.

The Future of the Manatee: Revisiting the Opening Case Study

The Florida manatee and its sister subspecies, the Antillean manatee, face many threats. At the top of the list are collisions with watercraft, loss of warm-water refuge areas, and coastal development. Conservation efforts targeting the Florida manatee, including its classification as an endangered species, helped it to make a comeback. Today its population has recovered enough to be delisted, just like the Northern Rocky Mountain wolf. Groups such as the volunteer kayak patrol in the

Crystal River, who make sure tourists abide by regulations set up to protect the manatee, and the establishment of wildlife sanctuary areas have certainly helped in the manatee's recovery. Other conservation groups, such as Tampa Bay Watch, are also significant to the recovery efforts. Tampa Bay Watch's mission is to protect and restore the marine and wetland environments of the Tampa Bay Estuary. During an estuarine conference in 2012, I volunteered with other scientists to help restore Cockroach Bay, an ecosystem visited by Florida manatees, by planting more than ten thousand plants. More recently, Eckert College received funding from the Tampa Bay Environmental Restoration Fund to lead a study on the concentrations of microplastics in manatee guts and their habitats.

Recovery efforts for the Florida manatee are faring much better than attempts to help their close genetic relative—the Antillean manatee—in Brazil. This second subspecies is the aquatic mammal most threatened with extinction in Brazil. Its Brazilian population is estimated to be only about five hundred individuals. Herbicides and pesticides applied to monoculture sugarcane plantations are leaching into local waterways and harming manatees. Elevated concentrations of these chemicals can negatively affect the manatees' immune and urinary systems (De María 2021). Insecticides and herbicides are not the only threats to the Brazilian population. Anzolin et al. (2012) took tissue samples of the Antillean manatee and analyzed them for concentrations of heavy metals, comparing them to concentrations found in the Florida manatee. They determined that the Brazilian population has higher concentrations of aluminum, lead, cadmium, and tin—in some cases, up to twenty-three times higher. Elevated concentrations of these non-essential metals within manatees can have several negative effects on manatee health. The suspected origins of these heavy metals are the industries within the nearby city of Cabedelo.

Still, conservation efforts on behalf of the manatee have been under way in Brazil for some time. A conservation and management program called Projecto Peixe-Boi rescues orphaned manatee pups and cares for them until they are about six years of age. The manatees are then reintroduced to their natural habitat.

Clearly, manatees have a future in waters of North America and on other continents, and they are an example of one biological piece (one component) in complex ecosystems that we depend on for goods and services. Their continued existence influences nutrient dynamics in saltwater and freshwater areas, and indirectly affects the productivity of algal, plant, and fish communities. *Trichechus manatus* is just one of the many species threatened by habitat loss, invasive species, pollution, population (human) growth, and climate change (see Figure 7.20). Yes, these threats are daunting, but not insurmountable. Environmental legislation, habitat protection, and collaborative conservation networks among governments, conservation groups, and local indigenous communities are all helpful in protecting manatees and simultaneously maintaining biodiversity and ecosystem services.

FIGURE 7.20

All four species of manatees have a future as long as we continue to protect them against habitat loss, invasive species, pollution, a growing human population, and illegal hunting (HIPPO factors). A) An injured manatee. Observe the propeller cut marks down the length of his body and the large gash on the back. B) Signage to protect manatees from boat collisions. C) A young boy feeding lettuce to a manatee as part of an ecotourism experience in Mexico. The local community protects the manatees because they are a source of economic revenue, part of the local biodiversity, and have intrinsic value.

Sources: © Shutterstock, Inc.; Belikova Oksana/Shutterstock.com

Key Takeaways

- The manatee is one of many examples of species that positively affect the ecosystems they inhabit.
- The manatee's role in maintaining ecosystem services, and the very future of the species, depends on society's conservation efforts to reduce HIPPCO factors.
- The threats to manatees are not insurmountable, but it will take continued vigilance on our part to ensure a future that includes manatees.

FIGURE 7.21 Visual Overview: Preserving Biodiversity

Summarizing figure: Biodiversity (7.1) provides ecosystem goods and services (7.2), but is threatened by multiple factors (7.3). We have the capacity to protect biodiversity (7.4) thereby giving manatees (7.5) and other species a brighter future.

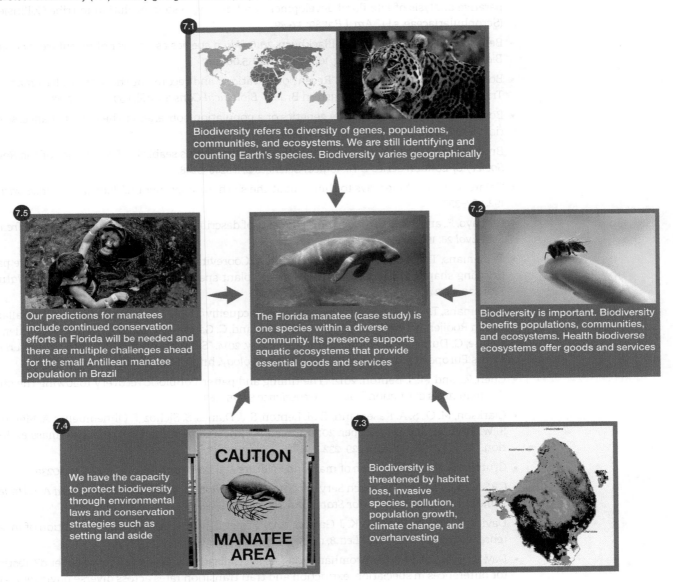

7.1 Biodiversity refers to diversity of genes, populations, communities, and ecosystems. We are still identifying and counting Earth's species. Biodiversity varies geographically

7.5 Our predictions for manatees include continued conservation efforts in Florida will be needed and there are multiple challenges ahead for the small Antillean manatee population in Brazil

The Florida manatee (case study) is one species within a diverse community. Its presence supports aquatic ecosystems that provide essential goods and services

7.2 Biodiversity is important. Biodiversity benefits populations, communities, and ecosystems. Health biodiverse ecosystems offer goods and services

7.4 We have the capacity to protect biodiversity through environmental laws and conservation strategies such as setting land aside

CAUTION MANATEE AREA

7.3 Biodiversity is threatened by habitat loss, invasive species, pollution, population growth, climate change, and overharvesting

Sources: Joseph Shostell; See previous citations for image credits.

7.6 References

- Aizen, M. A., C. L. Morales, D. P. Vazquez, L. A. Garibaldi, A. Saez, and L. D. Harder. 2014. "When Mutualism Goes Bad: Density-Dependent Impacts of Introduced Bees on Plant Reproduction." *New Phytologist* 204: 322–328.

- Antonelli, A., A. Zizka, F. A. Carvalho, R. Scharn, C. D. Bacon, D. Silvestro, and F. L. Condamine. 2018. "Amazonia is the primary source of neotropical biodiversity." *PNAS* 115, no. 23: 6034–6039.

- Anzolin, D. G., J. E. S. Sarkis, E. Diaz, D. G. Soares, et al. 2012. "Contaminant concentrations, biochemical and hematological biomarkers in blood of west Indian manatees: Trichechus manatus from Brazil." *Marine Pollution Bulletin* 6, no. 7: 1402–1408.

- Armbruster, W. S., C. P. H. Mulder, B. G. Baldwin, S. Kalisz, B. Wessa, and H. Nute. 2002. "Comparative analysis of late floral development and mating-system evolution in tribe Collinsieae (Scrophulariaceae, s.l.)." *Am J Bot* 89: 37–49.

- Bellard, C., P. Cassey, and T. M. Blackburn. 2016. "Alien species as a driver of recent extinctions." *Biology Letters* 12: http://doi.org/10.1098/rsbl.2015.0623.

- Borobia, M., and L. Lodi. 1992. "Recent observations and records of the West Indian manatee Trichechus manatus in northeastern Brazil." *Biological Conservation* 59, no. 1: 37–43.

- Bouzat, J. L. 2010. "Conservation genetics of a population bottlenecks: the role of chance, selection, and history." *Conserv Genet* 11: 463–478.

- Brook, M. de L. 2004. "The food consumption of the world's seabirds." *Proceedings of the Royal Society of London Series B-Biological Sciences* 271: s246–s248.

- Cafaro, P. 2015. "Three ways to think about the sixth mass extinction." *Biological Conservation* 192: 387–393.

- Carbayo, F., and A. C. Marques. 2011. "The costs of describing the entire animal kingdom." *Trends Ecol Evol* 26: 154–155.

- Ceulemans, T., S. Bodé, J. Bollyn, S. Harpole, K. Coorevits, et al. 2017. "Phosphorus resource partitioning shapes phosphorus acquisition and plant species abundance in grasslands." *Nature Plants* 3: 16224.

- Ceulemans, T., C. J. Stevens, L. Duchateau, H. Jacquemyn, D. J. G. Gowing, R. Merckx, H. Wallace, N. van Rooijen, T. Goethem, R. Bobbink, E. Dorland, C. Gaudnik, D. Alard, E. Corcket, S. Muller, N. B. Dise, C. Dupré, M. Diekmann, and O. Honnay. 2014. "Soil phosphorus constrains biodiversity across European grasslands." *Global Change Biology*. https://doi.org/10.1111/gcb.12650.

- Chen, Z., and M. J. Benton. 2012. "The timing and pattern of biotic recovery following the end-Permian mass extinction." *Nature Geoscience* 5: 375–383.

- Clarkson, M. O., S. A. Kasemann, T. M. Lenton, S. J. Daines, S. Sichoz, F. Ohnemueller, A. Meixner, S. W. Poulton, and E. T. Tipper. 2015. "Ocean acidification and the Permo-Triassic mass extinction." *Science* 348, no. 6231: 229–232.

- Crutzen, P. J. 2002. "Geologic of mankind." *Nature* 415: 23: https://doi.org/10.1038/415023a.

- CRS (Congressional Research Service). 2019. *Pittman-Robertson Wildlife Restoration Act: Understanding Apportionments for States and Territories* R45667.

- Davies, T. W., J. Bennie, and K. J. Gaston. 2012. "Street lighting changes the composition of invertebrate communities." *Biol Lett* 8, no. 5: 764–767.

- Day, E. H., X. Hua, and L. Bromham. 2016. "Is specialization an evolutionary dead end? Testing for differences in speciation, extinction and trati transition rates across diverse phylogenies of specialists and generalists." *Journal of Evolutionary Biology* 29: 1257–1267.

- DeLuca, T., H. and C. Boisvenue. 2012. "Boreal forest soil carbon: distribution, function and modelling." *Forestry* 95, no. 2: 161–184.

- De María, M., C. Silva-Sanchez, K. J. Kroll, M. T. Walsh, M. Nouri, et al. 2021. "Chronic exposure to glyphosate in Florida manatee." *Environmental International* 152: 106493.

- Dinerstein, E., D. Olson, A. Joshi, and C. Vynne. et al. 2017. "An ecoregion-based approach to protecting half the terrestrial realm." *BioScience* 67, no. 6: 534–545.

- Doney, S. C., M. Ruckelshaus, J. E. Duffy, et al. 2012. "Climate change impacts on marine ecosystems." *Annu Rev Mar Sci* 4: 11–37.

- Dorcas, M. E., J. D. Willson, R. N. Reed, R. W. Snow, M. R. Rochford, M. A. Miller, W. E. Meshaka Jr., P. T. Andreadis, F. J. Mazzotti, C. M. Romagosa, and K. M. Hart. 2012. "Seer mammal declines coincide with proliferation of invasive Burmese pythons in Everglades National Park." *Proceedings of the National Academy of Sciences of the United States of America* 109, no. 7: 2418–2422.

- Ekroth, A. K. E., C. Rafaluk-Mohr and K. C. King. 2019. "Host genetic diversity limits parasite success beyond agricultural systems: a meta-analysis." *Proc R Soc B* 286: 20191811.

- Farnsworth, B., J. Innes, C. Kelly, R. Littler, and J. R. Wass. 2018. "Photons and foraging: artificial light at night generates avoidance behaviour in male, but not female, New Zealand weta." *Environmental Pollution* 235: 82–90.

- Figueiredo, J. J. P., C. Hoorn, P. H. van der Vem, and E. F. Soares. 2009. "Late Miocene onset of the Amazon River and the Amazon deep-sea fan: Evidence from the Foz do Amazonas Basin." *Geology* 37: 619–622.

- Food and Agriculture Organization (FAO). 2009. *The State of World's Fisheries and Aquaculture 2008*. Food and Agriculture Organization of the United Nations.

- Franzini, A. M., N. Castelblanco-Martinez, F. C. W. Rosas, and V. M. F. da Silva. 2013. "What do local people know about Amazonian manatees? Traditional ecological knowledge of *Trichechus inunguis* in the oil province of Urucu, AM, Brazil." *Natureza and Conservacao* 11, no. 1: 75–80.

- Fukami, T., D. A. Wardle, P. J. Bellingham, C. P. H. Mulder, D. Towns, G. W. Yeates, K. I. Bonner, M. S. Durrett, M. N. Grant-Hoffman, and W. M. Williamson, 2006. "Above and below ground impacts of introduced predators in seabird-dominated island ecosystems." *Ecology Letters* 9: 1299–1307.

- Gentry, A. H., and C. H. Dodson. 1987. "Diversity and biogeography of neotropical vascular epiphytes." *Ann Missouri Bot Gard* 74: 205–233.

- Gibbs, M., T. Futral, M. Mallinger, D. Martin, and M. Ross. 2010. "Disturbance of the Florida manatee by an invasive catfish." *Southeastern Naturalist* 9, no. 4: 635–648.

- Haldane, J. B. S. 1951. *Everything Has a History*. London: C. Tinling and Company, LTD.

- Iskandar, M. J., A. Baharum, F. H. Anuar, and R. Othaman, 2017. "Palm oil industry in South East Asia and the effluent treatment technology—a review." *Environmental Technology and Innovation*. https://doi.org/10.1016/j.eti.2017.11.003.

- Koen, E. L., C. Minnaar, C. Roever, J. G. Boyles, E. L. Koen, C. Roever, and J. G. Boyles. 2018. "Emerging threat of the 21st century lightscape to global biodiversity." *Global Change Biology* 24, no. 6: 2315–2324.

- Koven, C. D., B. Ringeval, P. Friedlingstein, P. Ciais, P. Cadule, D. Khvorostyanov, G. Krinner, and C. Tarnocai. 2011. "Permafrost carbon-climate feedbacks accelerate global warming." *PNAS* 108, no. 36: 14769–14774.

- Lambers, H., I. Ahmedi, O. Berkowitz, C. Dunne, P. M. Finnegan, G. E. Hardy, R. Jost, E. Lalibertè, S. Pearse, and F. P. Teste. 2013. "Phosphorus nutrition of phosphorus-sensitive Australian native plants: threats to plant communities in a global biodiversity hotspot." *Conservation Physiology* 1: https://doi.org/10.1093/conphys/cot010.

- Lambers, J. H. R. 2015. "How will climate change affect global biodiversity?" *Science* 348, no. 6234: 501–502.

- Letebvre, L. W., J. A. Provancha, D. H. Slone, W. J. Kenworthy. 2017. "Manatee grazing impacts on a mixed species seagrass bed." *Marine Ecology Progress Series*. https/doi.org/10.3354/meps11986.

- Locey, K. J., and J. T. Lennon. 2016. "Scaling laws predict global microbial diversity." *PNAS* 113, no. 21: 5970–5975.

- Macgregor, C. J., M. J. O. Pocock, R. Fox, and D. M. Evans. 2015. "Pollination by nocturnal Lepidoptera, and the effects of light pollution: a review." *Ecol Entomol* 40, no. 3: 187–198.

- Malhi, Y., and J. Grace. 2000. "Tropical forests and atmospheric carbon dioxide." *Trends Ecol Evol* 15: 332–337.

- Marra, P. P., and J. V. Remsen Jr. 1997. "Insights into the maintenance of high species diversity in the neotropics: habitat selection and foraging behavior in understory birds of tropical and temperate forests." *Ornithological monographs* 48: 445–483.

- Millennium Ecosystem Assessment. 2005. *Ecosystems and Human Well-being: Synthesis.* Washington, DC: Island Press.

- Mittermeier, R. A., C. G. Mittermeier, T. M. Brooks, J. D. Pilgrim, W. R. Konstant, G. A. B. da Fonesca, and C. Kormos. 2003. "Wilderness and biodiversity conservation." *Proceedings of the National Academy of Sciences* 100: 10309–10313.

- Mora, C., D. P. Tittensor, S. Adl, A. G. B. Simpson, and B. Worm. 2011. "How many species are there on Earth and in the ocean?" *PLOS Biology* 9, no. 8: 21001127.

- Moreau, C. S. and C. D. Bell. 2013. "Testing the museum versus cradle tropical biological diversity hypothesis: phylogeny, diversification, and ancestral biogeographic range evolution of the ants." *Evolution* 67: 2240–2257.

- Myers, N. 1988. "Threatened biotas: 'Hot spots' in tropical forests." *The Environmentalist* 8: 1–20.

- Newbold, T., L. N. Hudson, A. P. Arnell, S. Contu, and A. De Palma, et al. 2016. "Has land use pushed terrestrial biodiversity beyond the planetary boundary? A global assessment." *Science* 353, no. 6296: 288–291.

- Obama, Barack "'No Nation Is Immune' to Climate Change" (speech, United Nations General Assembly Climate Summit, New York, NY, September 23, 2014).

- Ogada, D., A. Botha, and P. Shaw. 2015. "Ivory poachers and poison: drivers of Africa's declining vulture populations." *Oryx* 50, no. 4: 593–596.

- Ollerton, J. 1998. "Sunbird surprise for syndromes." *Nature* 394: 726–727.

- Olson, D. M., and E. Dinerstein. 2008. "The global 200: a representation approach to conserving the Earth's most biological valuable ecoregions." *Issues in International Conservation.* https://doi.org/10.1046/j.1523-1739.1998.012003502.x.

- Pauly, D., V. Christensen, S. Guénette, T. J. Pitcher, U. R. Sumaila, C. J. Walters, R. Watson, and D. Zeller. 2002. "Towards sustainability in world fisheries." *Nature* 418: 689–695.

- Peters, C. J., J. Picardy, A. F. Darrouzet-Nardi, J. L. Wilkins, T. S. Griffin, and G. W. Fick. 2016. "Carrying capacity of U.S. agricultural land: Ten diet scenarios." *Elementa Science of the Anthropocene* 4: https://doi.org/10.12952/journal.elementa.000116.

- Polidoro, B. A., K. E., Carpenter, L. Collins, N. C. Duke, A. M. Ellison, J. C. Ellison, E. J. Farnsworth, E. S. Fernando, K. Kathiresanh, N. E. Koedam, S. R. Livingstone, T. Miyagi, G. E. Moore, V. N. Nam, J. E. Ong, J. H. Primavera, S. G. Salmo III, J. C. Sanciangco, S. Sukardjo, Y. Wang, and J. W. H. Yong. 2010. "The loss of species: mangrove extinction risk and geographic areas of global concern." *Plos ONE*, e10095 5, no. 4: https://doi.org/10.1371/journal.pone.0010095.

- Poore, J., and T. Nemecek. 2018. "Reducing food's environmental impacts through producers and consumers." *Science* 360: 987–992.

- Reynolds, J. E., and D. K. Odell. 1991. *Manatees and Dugongs.* New York: Checkmark Books.

- Singh, R., P. R. Krausman, S. P. Goyal, and N. S. Chauhan. 2015. "Factors contributing to tiger losses in Ranthambhore Tiger Reserve, India." *Wildlife Society Bulletin* 39, no. 3: 670–673.

- Smith, D. R., J. J. Newhard, C. P. McGowan, and C. A. Butler. 2020. "The long-term effect of bleeding for Limulus amebocyte lysate on annual survival and recapture of tagged horseshoe crabs." *Frontiers in Marine Science* 7: 607668.

- Solomon, B. D., C. M. Corey-Luse, and K. E. Halvorsen. 2004. "The Florida manatee and ecotourism and toward a safe minimum standard." *Biological Economics* 50: 101–105.

- Tilman, D., J. Knops, D. Wedin, P. Reich, M. Ritchie, and E. Siemann. 1997. "The influence of functional diversity and composition on ecosystem processes." *Science* 277: 1300–1302.

- Toussaint, A., N. Charpin, S. Brosse, and S. Villéger. 2016. "Global functional diversity of freshwater fish is concentrated in the Neotropics while functional vulnerability is widespread." *Scientific Reports* 6: https://doi.org/10.1038/srep22125.

- Urban, M. C. 2015. "Accelerating extinction risk from climate change." *Science* 348: 571.

- Valiela, I., J. L. Bowen, and J. K. York. 2001. "Mangrove forests: one of the world's threatened major tropical environments: at least 35% of the area of mangrove forests has been lost in the past two decades, losses that exceed those for tropical rain forests and coral reefs, two other well-known threatened environments." *Bioscience* 51, no. 10: 807–815.

- Voosen, P. 2018. "Antarctic ice melt 125,000 years ago offers warning." *Science* 362, no. 6421: 1339.

- Walters, C., P. Berjak, N. Pammenter, K. Kennedy, and P. Raven. 2013. "Preservation of recalcitrant seeds." *Science* 339: 915–916.

- Watson, J. E. M., O. Venter, J. Lee, K. R. Jones, J. G. Robinson, H. P. Possingham, and J. R. Allan. 2018. "Protect the last of the wild." *Nature* 563: 27–30.

- Wiens, J. J., R. A. Pyron, and D. S. Moen. 2011. "Phylogenetic origins of local-scale diversity patterns and the causes of Amazonian megadiversity." *Ecology Letters* 14: 643–652.

- Wilson, E. O. 2016. *Half-Earth: Our Planet's Fight for Life*. London: Liveright Publishing.

CHAPTER 8
Agriculture, Food, and the Environment

Case Study: Two Farms with Different Strategies

Welcome to Molly and John Chester's sustainable farm—Apricot Lane Farms—in Moorpark, California. When John retired from filmmaking in 2010, he and his wife, Molly, decided to leave city life and begin to set up and manage a 214-acre farm. Unusually, the Chesters did not come from farming families, and they soon realized the mountainous task of fulfilling a dream to operate an environmentally sustainable farm. Their intent was to inspire the next generation, and to be a role model for farming methods that enhance the environment, wildlife habitat, and soil. They also wanted to produce marketable fruits and vegetables in a pesticide-free environment. Four years into their plan, they earned certification as an organic farm (see A in Figure 8.1).

FIGURE 8.1
Farms come in many types and sizes: (A) Food Bank volunteers pick carrots on a small organic farm in rural California. (B) A farmer sprays synthetic pesticides on his monoculture of corn in the rural Midwest.

Sources: Bill Morson/Shutterstock.com; © Shutterstock, Inc.

agricultural products

Corn, wheat, rice, beef, and other products that originate from farms.

In the beginning, the Chesters were confronted with the problems of farming nutrient-poor soil and irrigating a farm in a relatively dry chaparral biome. To offset both of these issues, the Chesters used cover crops that add nutrients to the soil and reduce water loss. A cover crop is a non-harvested crop used primarily to protect against soil erosion and improve soil health. Over the course of their first seven years, they incrementally lowered their water usage and increased the organic matter content of the soil. It took five years to become profitable. Today, they sell 250 types of fruits and vegetables and have over 800 animals. In 2018, to showcase their story and encourage other would-be farmers, John relied on his filmmaking knowledge and created a documentary about their experience titled *The Biggest Little Farm*. Apricot Lane Farms has also been highlighted by Oprah Winfrey on the daytime series *Super Soul Sunday*, shown on OWN. Listen to the Chesters describe their farming experience (see video link: "Apricot Lane Farms").

In contrast to the Chesters, Penelope and Oscar Alvarez run a 4,000-acre Midwestern farm (see B in Figure 8.1). It is eight times larger than today's average American farm, dwarfing the homestead farm Penelope's great-great-grandfather started back in 1880. Over the last 100 years, the Alvarez's farm has reduced the number of **agricultural products** they produce from five to just one: corn. Beginning in the late 1990s, they began to plant genetically modified seeds because the crops grown from these seeds were resistant to insects and tolerant to synthetic herbicides, and had significantly increased yields. Following the advice of neighboring farmers, they have steadily increased the application of nitrogen fertilizers. Their strategy includes irrigation to offset naturally dry conditions and recent droughts accompanying global climate change. They are still experimenting with the exact volume of water needed to maximize production, but initially calculated an amount of 1,350 L of water for every kilogram of corn produced (162 g/lb). Next year, the Alvarez family plans to expand into animal production when they acquire the adjacent 202-hectare (500-acre) beef farm.

 Apricot Lane Farms

Listen to the Chesters talk about their journey of growing food sustainably.

View in the online reader

Reflect on these two farms as you navigate through the various topics pertaining to agriculture.

8.1 Agriculture, Food Security, and Nutrition

Learning Objectives

1. Describe global patterns of food security.
2. Identify the factors that affect food security.
3. Define malnutrition and explain its causes.

food security

Consistent physical and economic access to sufficient, safe, and nutritious food to meet dietary needs for a healthy life.

A visit to the average American house in the morning would likely expose you to questions about food. How would you like your eggs? Toast with that? Grits? Orange juice? Milk? Everyone needs food, and sooner or later, we make our way back to the kitchen, grocery store, or restaurant to obtain more. Molecules in food provide a source of energy and are the building blocks in cellular repair and growth. Eggs, wheat in the toast, corn in the grits, oranges, and milk are examples of agricultural products that originate on farms such as those mentioned in the opening story. Our lives and health are improved with access to these products. In this section of the chapter, we first look into **food security**, or people's consistent access to sufficient, safe, and nutritious food; and second, we investigate the types and causes of malnutrition.

Supply and Access to Food Varies Globally

Globally, one in nine people (870 million) experiences chronic food insecurity and goes hungry. As defined by the United States Department of Agriculture, food insecurity is a household-level economic and social condition of limited or uncertain access to adequate food. Food insecurity exists in every nation, but it is more common in developing nations such as Sudan, Cambodia, and Vietnam, where 13 percent of people cannot fulfill their daily food needs and are therefore perpetually undernourished (see Figure 8.2). Two-thirds of this group is in Asia; in Southern Asia alone, approximately 280 million people go to bed hungry and do not know where they will find food the next day. Food insecurity can be exacerbated by conflict. For example, at the time of writing this book, Russia's ongoing war in Ukraine disrupts global exports of vegetable oils and wheat. Many of the developing countries that depend on these imports are experiencing food shortages.

FIGURE 8.2
Food insecurity exists in every country. (A) At a refugee camp in Somalia, children stretch out their hands to obtain food. (B) In the Bronx, NBA star Carmelo Anthony works with the anti-hunger organization Feed the Children to provide food. The South Bronx has the highest food insecurity rate in the United States (C) A food pantry on a college campus.

Sources: Sadik Gulec/Shutterstock.com; Jewjewbeed/Shutterstock.com; Kyle S Lo/Shutterstock.com

There is also evidence of unequal food security across the United States and other developed nations. For instance, 24 percent of Mississippians live in poverty and are food insecure. Good food security implies not only having access to food today, but also tomorrow, next week, and in six months. A growing number of Americans barely possess enough food for meeting their nutritional requirements today and are uncertain about their success in obtaining food tomorrow and further into the future. In this context, one out of six Americans experiences food insecurity (McMillan 2014). These people may very well be your neighbors in the inner city, in the suburbs, or the student sitting next to you in class (see "Bringing It Closer to Home: Food Insecurity on Campus"). Malnutrition, discussed next, is a result of food insecurity.

Bringing It Closer to Home: Food Insecurity on Campus

Food insecurity is a reality for millions of American college students today (USGAO 2018, THC-CCJ 2020). Does your college or university manage a food pantry on campus for the benefit of its students? Check to see if your campus has one, and if it does, determine who oversees it and where it is located. A well-run food pantry is easily accessible by students and is sufficiently advertised to the student population. Ask how students become informed about the food pantry. Then, visit the food pantry and ascertain the quantity and diversity of its staples. Canned goods have long shelf lives, but many have a high salt content. Eating high-salt foods once in a while is not harmful to you, but relying on a high-salt diet over weeks, months, and years is associated with high blood pressure. Does the food pantry have fresh vegetables? What about fresh fruit? Lastly, should your college campus fail to have a food pantry, one probably exists not too far from campus. Revisit the question about how students are informed about a food pantry, in this case to one off campus.

Malnutrition Affects Billions of People

macronutrients

Carbohydrates, fats, and proteins that make up a large percentage of our diets.

micronutrients

Nutrients that make up a small percentage of our diets; vitamins and minerals.

malnutrition

Deficiencies, excesses, or imbalances in a person's intake of nutrients.

marasmus

A disease caused by undernutrition; victims suffer from inadequate calorie and protein intake and experience dehydration, stomach shrinkage, diarrhea, and weight loss.

kwashiorkor

A disease caused by undernutrition; severe protein deficiency; symptoms of bulging abdomen, edema, and emaciation.

Our bodies require nutrients to maintain health, and we expect a normal diet to consist of macronutrients and micronutrients. **Macronutrients**—carbohydrates, fats, and proteins, grown on farms like the Chesters' and Alvarez's (opening story), make up the bulk of our diets. These molecules provide the energy we use to fuel a myriad of activities, including walking and studying. **Micronutrients** (vitamins and minerals) are the second part of a balanced diet, and compared to macronutrients make up a smaller part of the diet. Some of the more commonly known micronutrients are iron, zinc, calcium, iodine, and vitamins A, B, and C.

Malnutrition

Large segments of the global population experience **malnutrition**, which means their diets either have insufficient nutrients or an overabundance of them. Consuming too few nutrients—undernutrition—is a serious global problem. Over 800 million people suffer from chronic undernourishment, and more than two billion people have micronutrient deficiencies. Without the proper molecular building blocks for growth and tissue repair, people are underweight and more prone to infections. Acute undernutrition, which affects 50 million children under the age of five, causes wasting: a condition in which muscle and fat tissues of the body waste away. Two well-known diseases caused by macronutrient deficiency and most prevalent in food-insecure developing countries are **marasmus** and **kwashiorkor** (see Figure 8.3). Another 150 million children of the same age have stunted growth because they are undernourished. These children will not reach their potential height. Stunting is most prevalent in Africa and South Asia.

FIGURE 8.3

Consequences of acute undernutrition can be severe. (A) Victims of marasmus such as this little girl in Nepal suffer from inadequate calorie and protein intake. Dehydration, stomach shrinkage, diarrhea, and weight loss are symptoms. (B) Victims of kwashiorkor such as this boy in Venezuela suffer from severe protein deficiency. Symptoms include bulging abdomen, edema, emaciation, and fatigue.

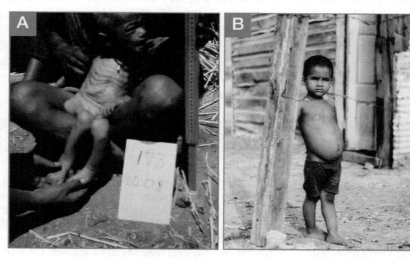

Sources: CDC/ Dr. Edward Brink; Nelson Bastidas/Shutterstock.com

Two Billion People Suffer from Overnutrition

Easy access to nutrient-poor food as well as to large quantities of food make it easy to overeat. Two billion people suffer from overnutrition, a type of malnutrition caused by an excessive intake of nutrients. Overnutrition is associated with heart disease, strokes, and diabetes. These are some of the leading causing of premature death, and yet, sadly, are preventable. Global incidences of obesity have tripled since 1975 and are most prevalent in higher-income regions.

Malnutrition and Environmental Degradation

Thousands of years ago, our ancient ancestors experienced malnutrition when they were unable to gather the quantity and/or diversity of foods containing the variety of minerals and vitamins needed for growth, development, and maintenance of their bodies. They were challenged to locate sufficient quantities of nutritious foods in a pristine environment. Today, we are faced with the added challenge of growing nutritious foods in increasingly degraded environments, and due to limited land resources, sometimes in naturally polluted areas (see Figure 8.4). There are many examples of how society's degradation of the environment has promoted malnutrition. Unclean drinking water and insanitary conditions due to pollution, for example, expose children to pollutants including fecal bacteria and other microbes. A consequence of this exposure is chronic inflammation of the intestine, which causes malabsorption of nutrients (Matariya et al. 2017).

FIGURE 8.4
The health of millions of people in Bangladesh is threatened by drinking (and irrigating crops with) arsenic-contaminated water. The World Health Organization calls this "the largest mass poisoning of a population in history." With 80 percent of Bangladesh dealing with arsenic contamination, there is a high probability that this rice field the two laborers toil in is contaminated with arsenic.

Source: Matyas Rehak/Shutterstock.com

Key Takeaways

- Supply and access to food varies globally.
- Food insecurity is more common in the least developed regions, but it exists in every country.

- Malnutrition affects billions of people.
- The two main categories of malnutrition are undernutrition and overnutrition.
- Pollution and other forms of environmental degradation promote malnutrition.

8.2 Today's Food Production Is Different from That of the Recent Past

Learning Objectives

1. Explain the primary differences between contemporary and historical food production.
2. Provide examples of traditional agricultural practices.
3. Compare and contrast organic and nonorganic farm practices.
4. Describe the global trend in animal production for food.

We depend on farmers to carry out productive harvests year after year so we can enjoy nutritious food and—for most of us—to be free of tending to the crops ourselves. The farmers' responsibility comes with many challenges. As a group, farmers need to produce more food for a population that is growing. Over the decades, and with new technologies and improved efficiency, the agricultural industry has dramatically increased food production; however, today's intensive farming has production limits, and there is strong evidence of unsustainability (see Figure 8.5). At some point, maximizing production on finite-sized agricultural lands just will not support the nutritional needs of a growing population. Furthermore, our gained knowledge of habitat degradation linked to common agricultural practices encourages us to question the method of irrigation and application of pesticides and fertilizers. Our task is to improve and maintain productivity without polluting the food we eat or diminishing soil fertility needed for future crops. In this section we discuss industrial and traditional food production methods.

FIGURE 8.5

Changes in farming practices in the United States (A) Since 1850, the total number of American farms has decreased from almost seven million to two million, but the average size of the remaining farms has increased. (B) Synthetic fertilizers and pesticides, technological advances, and genetic engineering have allowed agricultural productivity to triple since the 1950s.

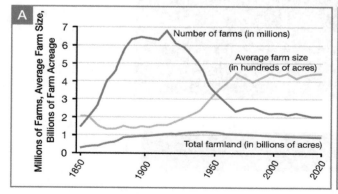

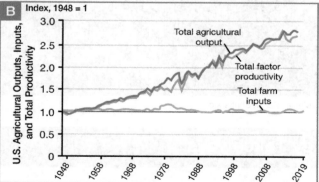

Sources: Joseph Shostell; data from USDA, Economic Research Service using data from USDA, National Agricultural Statistics Service, Census of Agriculture (through 2017) and *Farms and Land in Farms: 2020 Summary* (February 2021); data from the USDA.

Industrial Agriculture and the Green Revolution

The farms in the opening story are miniature relative to the world's mega-farms. Compare, for instance, the 800 animals on the Chesters' 214-acre farm to the 100,000 dairy cows maintained on Mudanjiang City Mega Farm in Heilongjiang, China. This farm is 22,500,000 acres and is larger than the state of South Carolina. China also manages the second-largest dairy farm, and Australia oversees the top eight cattle farms, each a few million acres in size. The largest crop farms tend to be much smaller—in the tens of thousands of acres. Today, the United States and many other countries practice industrial, intensive farming—reliant on large energy inputs to consistently produce high yields of crops (see Figure 8.6). In 2020 alone, the world produced an unprecedented 1,120 million metric tons (MT) of corn, 775 MT of wheat, and 505 MT of milled rice, numbers that just a few decades ago would have seemed unimaginable. Investments in agricultural research and development in the early 1950s proved to be worthwhile. For example, investments in hybrid corn research provided an estimated 700 percent return within a short time period (Jorgenson and Gollop 1992). With the help of improved technologies and new hybrid plants, U.S. productivity in the farm sector has tripled since the middle of the twentieth century. In fact, the second half of the last century was particularly amazing. Take, for instance, the dairy industry. In 1950, a single cow would produce 2,410 kg (5,314 lbs) of milk. By 2000, the average cow was producing over 8,256 kg (18,200 lbs) of milk! During that same time interval, corn yield increased from 39 bushels per acre to 153 bushels per acre. But just as U.S. agriculture developed and grew more profitable in the 1950s, other areas of the world such as China and India were experiencing human tragedy, with malnutrition and hunger commonplace.

The transfer of agricultural knowledge and agricultural practices from developed to developing countries, starting in the 1940s in Mexico, became known as the **Green Revolution** and helped to prevent billions of people throughout much of the developing world from dying of starvation. Dr. Norman Borlaug, a U.S. agronomist and geneticist, is often given credit for starting this revolution because of his work on the development of disease-resistant wheat (see Figure 8.7; Borlaug 1958). His work helped Mexico and India to go from being dependent on wheat imports to being wheat exporters. The new plant varieties matured more quickly and could grow at any time of the year—allowing farmers to have multiple harvests of the same crop in one year. These high-yield plants were supported by intense irrigation and fertilizer applications. Thus, the Green Revolution led to **high-input** agriculture, which relied on large energy inputs. Only a handful of different edible plants were then used—of all of the thousands available—essentially creating a monoculture agriculture system just like on the Alvarez farm (opening story). Biodiversity was lowered, and farmers added pesticides to compensate for monoculture crops' lower genetic diversity and hence greater susceptibility to pests (see monocultures in Section 4). Farmers on high-input farms add fertilizers to the soil too because intensive farming practices deplete soil nutrients. Obvious negatives to high-input agriculture are the need for irrigation, pesticides, and fertilizers, which have to be weighed against positive effects such as increased productivity, higher incomes for farmers, and lower food prices. Reduced food prices, for example, help people in poverty stay food-secure.

FIGURE 8.6

Industrial farming requires large energy inputs. Expensive machinery, fertilizers, and pesticides are routinely used in these large-scale farming operations. The photo shows sixteen combines mass-harvesting a field of soybeans in Mato Grosso, Brazil.

Source: Alf Ribeiro/Shutterstock.com

Green Revolution

A sharp increase in the production of wheat, rice, and other food grains in developing countries in the mid- and late twentieth century achieved by the use of chemical fertilizers, high-yield crops, and synthetic pesticides.

high-input

Also known as industrialized agriculture, an intensive production of crops and animals reliant on machines and large inputs of energy, inorganic fertilizers, synthetic pesticides, and water.

FIGURE 8.7
Dr. Norman Borlaug's work developing productive crop strains was instrumental in providing food to billions of malnourished people. In 2007, President George W. Bush congratulated Dr. Borlaug for his achievements in helping to stop world hunger. With the help of Dr. Borlaug and his new crop varieties, production of wheat increased sharply in Mexico and other developing countries.

Source: White House photo by Eric Draper.

Traditional Agriculture

In contrast to industrial agriculture, traditional agricultural practices require less energy input. Little if any capital is needed for these small-scale farms, which are usually run by individual families. Sometimes production is just at the subsistence farming level—providing only enough food for survival and not for the marketplace. Across the world, roughly 20 percent of our food supply comes from traditional agriculture, which is practiced by approximately 42 percent of our population—although to a much greater degree in developing regions such as Western Africa (Altieri 1999). Most people in these poor rural areas cannot afford complex, high-tech combines and other expensive equipment, and even if they could, the machines would not be of much use on the small plots of land farmed by individual families. They do rely on simple machines—tools such as the sickle—to cut and harvest crops by hand, a sign of how traditional agriculture is much more labor-intensive than industrial agriculture.

Polyculture

polyculture

More than one crop is grown on the same plot of land.

Traditional agriculture uses several types of growing techniques. One example, albeit a large category, is **polyculture**, in which more than one crop is grown on the same plot of land (Popanastasis et al. 2004). One form of polyculture is called intercropping or interseeding—literally planting seeds of different plants near each other. When done correctly, intercropping utilizes the strengths of different plant species and can assist in production efforts. One example is to plant corn and beans together (see video link: "Polyculture"). Corn has high nitrogen requirements, and the beans add more nitrogen to the soil, thus providing for the needs of corn with a natural product from beans (Cardoso et al. 2007). Intercropping is common in Latin America and Africa, but not in Europe or the United States, where industrial farming drives the agricultural industry. Polycultures also create habitat space for threatened wildlife (Wright et al. 2011).

Preserving Food Supply After Harvest

Polyculture
Learn about the benefits of growing multiple species of agricultural plants together.

Polyculture Garden

View in the online reader

So far, much of our discussion has centered on soil and crop productivity, but what about the next step—preserving the harvest until used by a consumer? Certainly, not all of the crops harvested make it to the dinner table. For example, in West Africa, an estimated 50 percent of fruits, vegetables, tubers, and roots, and 30 percent of food grains, are lost after harvest (Aworh 2008). Several factors are to blame for these losses, starting with poor harvesting practices and ineffective food processing. Bad roads, poor market practices, inadequate storage facilities, and an inefficient rail system are also to blame. If our goal is to provide more food to people, we should invest in better preservation techniques and other post-harvest activities rather than just in trying to grow more food.

Increase of Organic Agriculture

Every day we make decisions about which foods we want to purchase (or sometimes grow) to meet our nutritional needs, and at times we are presented with choosing between organic and nonorganic varieties. Apricot Lane Farms (opening story) spent years on earning an organic-certified label and is now part of the fastest-growing food sector in North America and Europe. Before a farm can earn this designation, it must pass an on-site inspection and several other steps in addition to paying hundreds to thousands of dollars in fees.

Organic farming has its origins in **humus** farming as well as in the persuasive writing of Lord Northbourne, who promoted the farm as a living organism rather than as a factory (Northbourne 1940; Paull 2014). Interest in organic farming in the United States really gained traction in the 1960s and 1970s with society's newly gained knowledge of pesticides and their potential negative effects on the environment (see Chapter 2). The organic industry expanded during the 1980s and 1990s, and given the growing interest of consumers in organic food and the existence of multiple certifiers of organic foods, there was a need to standardize this new segment of agriculture. Congress passed the Organic Foods Production Act of 1990. This law mandated the creation of the **National Organic Program** (NOP), overseen by the U.S. Department of Agriculture, to standardize the organic industry. For example, the Act requires clear labeling of organic foods. The Act also mandated the Department of Agriculture to develop a list of permissible and prohibited chemicals in organic agriculture. Pesticides and fertilizers can be used on organically grown crops, but they must be approved substances. Generally, natural pesticides are permissible, and synthetic ones are prohibited.

humus

The organic matter in soil.

National Organic Program

An agency within the U.S. Department of Agriculture that sets marketing standards and defines organic agriculture.

soil erosion

The breakdown, transportation, and redistribution of soil.

integrated pest management

An ecosystem-based strategy to manage pests through a combination of techniques that minimizes risks to humans, nontarget organisms, and the environment.

Organic foods still only make up a small percentage (about 6 percent) of the overall food sales in the United States. The mass majority of organic farmers are found outside of the United States, in low-income countries. Organic farming is more labor-intensive, and yields are 19–25 percent less than conventional methods. A large consumer demand and substantial price premium at the marketplace compensate for lower yields and make organic farms lucrative businesses, but is organic agriculture more sustainable? Yes, comparatively, organic farming lessens many of the environmental threats of conventional farming. Elevated humus content in organic soils generally improves water-holding capacity, so adding humus to soil often results in reduced water use (Lotter et al. 2009). The added humus also improves soil integrity and lessens **soil erosion**. Organic farmers typically use an **integrated pest management** (IPM) strategy to control pests (see Section 6). Such a strategy considers the potential impacts of pesticides on the environment and uses a combination of natural predators and, when appropriate, approved pesticides. Organic pesticides usually have a lower toxicity and lower persistence in the environment (Zehnder et al 2007). However, a lower toxicity can also encourage organic farmers to apply pesticides more frequently and in heavier concentrations.

Genetically Modified Crops

For thousands of years, we have modified plants through selective breeding to have the traits we desire; for example, size, taste, color, and resistance to pests. In the 1990s, we began to use genetic engineering to enhance and speed up the modification process (see A in Figure 8.8). It started the gene revolution in agriculture. Modern-day biotechnology gives us the ability to isolate DNA coding for a desired trait in one organism and then insert it into another. Farmers choose if they want to grow genetically engineered (GE) crops, and consumers decide if they want to purchase them in the store. Costs of more expensive GE seeds incurred by the farmer are eventually offset because GMO crops have higher yields and farmers end up with a greater profit (Klümper and Qaim 2014). For example, the Alvarez farm (opening story) spends roughly $50 more per acre to sow genetically modified seeds, at a cost of $200,000 for their entire 4,000 acres. As a result of using genetically engineered seeds, they have increased their yield per acre and, consequently, increased their profit by $140 per acre. This is a boost in annual income of $560,000. It is now commonplace for corn, soybeans, and cotton to have inserted genes that confer resistance to pests and herbicides. This is helpful to farming, because a farmer can spray herbicides on a cropland to inhibit the growth of undesired plants without harming the resistant crop. Still, there are many more varieties of unmodified crops, and farmers make decisions about the type of seeds they plant based on what is best for their farm, consumer demand, and what is approved by the federal government. Prior to commercial use of new GE seeds by farmers, the EPA completes an environmental impact statement to assess potential negative effects on the environment. All introductions of GE seeds are tightly regulated by USDA's Animal and Plant Health Inspection Services (APHIS).

Twenty-eight countries now grow GE crops, and a much greater number import GE products (see B in Figure 8.8). Because not every nation approves of growing or using GE crops, the international community created a regulatory framework for their international trade (FAO 2014). See Section 5 for the controversial issue surrounding the use of glyphosate-resistant crops.

FIGURE 8.8
Genetic engineering in agriculture. (A) The proportion of farmland devoted to genetically engineered crops has grown significantly since 1996. According to the United States Department of Agriculture, 92 percent of corn crops in the United States are genetically modified—more for soybeans (94 percent) and cotton (94 percent). (B) A small number of countries grow and produce the majority of genetically engineered agricultural products. The leaders are the United States, Brazil, Argentina, Canada, and India.

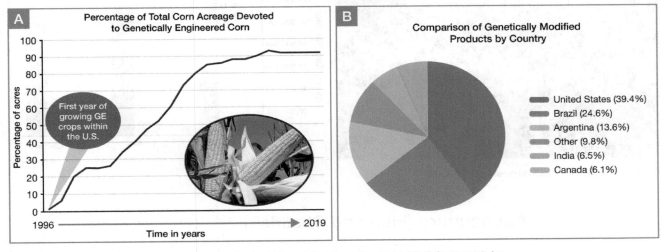

Sources: Joseph Shostell; data from World Trade Information Service, Volume 1, Part 1 and GeneWatch UK; © Shutterstock, Inc.

Animals as a Source of Food

How would you like your hamburger? Would you prefer chicken or pork? These types of questions are uttered with increasing frequency across the world. Access to beef, pork, and poultry is expected in developed nations, and as developing nations gain affluence, there is a transition in diet to include more animal protein. Society's desire for animal products is growing, and to meet the demand we must rear and manage large populations of animals. Currently, an estimated one billion cattle, 781 million swine, and 400 million chickens are found on farms worldwide. These and other livestock are the largest users of land resources. Over one-fourth of ice-free land is devoted to livestock grazing, and about one-third of cropland produces feed for these animals.

With a greater demand for animal products, society has increasingly transitioned from a traditional animal agricultural approach of maintaining a diffuse population of animals grazing freely, to the use of intensive rearing under restricted housing conditions (see Figure 8.9). Predictions suggest we will have to increase animal production by 70 percent to 100 percent by 2050 to satisfy the need of a larger global population and the transition to a proportionately greater meat-based diet. See Section 4 for environmental concerns about animal production facilities.

FIGURE 8.9

Animal production facilities like this one (A) help to provide (B) the millions of tons of animal products we consume each year.

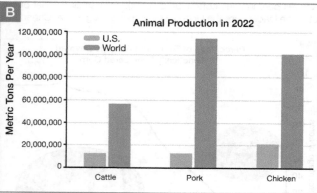

Sources: © Shutterstock, Inc.; Joseph Shostell; data from USDA.

Aquaculture (Fish and Shellfish)

aquaculture

The farming of aquatic organisms.

Fish offer another protein-rich source of food. They contain essential fatty acids, minerals, and vitamins, and people are eating more fish every year. Since the early 1960s, consumption of fish has grown twice as fast as human population growth. One of the first major dilemmas faced by the fishing industry was to figure out how to meet a demand that had exceeded what natural waters could provide. Global fish production is now over 170 million tons per year and roughly half of this amount comes from **aquaculture**—the farming of aquatic organisms. This massive growth is now labeled as the blue revolution. Other sectors of the agricultural industry are also affected by growth in aquaculture. For example, about 25 percent of aquafeed consists of soybeans. Therefore, projected growth in aquaculture to 109 million tons by 2030 will also require greater production of soybeans. Water, fertilizers, pesticides, and land space to grow soybeans, by default, become part of the sustainability discussion when considering aquaculture.

Key Takeaways

- Within the United States, farms have increased in size, crop diversity has decreased, and there is a greater dependence on mechanization, technology, genetically modified seeds, synthetic fertilizers, and pesticides.

- Traditional agricultural practices require less energy inputs than industrial agriculture, and are usually run by individual families.

- A large percentage of harvested crops is lost and never makes it to the kitchen table.

- Certified organic farms do not use synthetic pesticides or synthetic fertilizers, and typically are more labor intensive, have smaller yields per unit area, rely more on integrated pest management (IPM), and support a greater diversity of crops.

- Our use of genetically modified crops has increased agricultural yields and farmers' profits.

- Globally, there is an ongoing increase in demand for animal food products.

- Roughly half of global fish production comes from aquaculture.

8.3 Healthy Soils Lead to Healthy Crops

Learning Objectives

1. Classify and describe soils based on soil texture and soil structure.
2. Identify and describe the main soil horizons.
3. Compare and contrast methods of soil formation.
4. Explain how soil type affects permeability and crop performance.

Successful agricultural ventures, such as Apricot Lane Farms (see "Case Study: Two Farms with Different Strategies"), depend on healthy, nonpolluted soil, which has natural nutrients, water, and vibrant fauna and microbial communities. Without these elements, growing of crops and rearing of livestock cease. Thus, we begin this section with a discussion of soils, which can take hundreds of years to form a layer just a couple of centimeters (<1 in) thick.

Soil is essential to the majority of our crops. Exceptions to this would be aquaponics and **hydroponics**, two farming practices that rely on water rather than soil as the growth medium. Here we tease apart the connection between soils and crops, and explore soil formation, structure, and type. Let us begin with defining soil.

An agronomist, a scientist who studies soils, will tell you, "Soil isn't dirt." They are correct, because **soil** is a mixture of minerals, water, decaying organic matter, rock fragments, and gases. Healthy soil also contains an active community of bacteria, fungi, insects, worms, protists, and other taxonomic groups. Bacteria are part of the rich, biodiverse microbial community that affects nutrient and water cycling and soil structure stability. The fauna of the soil community move through the soil in search of food and in doing so mix the soil and recycle nutrients. Tunnels they create serve as holding spaces for gases and water and facilitate drainage.

hydroponics

Growing plants without soil in nutrient solutions.

soil

Earth's unconsolidated land surface consisting of a mixture of minerals, water, decaying organic matter, rock fragments, air, and an active community of bacteria, fungi, insects, worms, and protists.

Scientists and Farmers Describe a Soil by Its Texture and Structure

To the nonfarmer, soil texture and structure may seem to refer to the same thing, but in actuality, they are two related but different properties of soils. **Soil texture** refers to the relative proportions of sand, silt, and clay particles (see A in Figure 8.10), whereas **soil structure** refers to the arrangement of soil particles into groups called aggregates. It is the combination of soil texture and soil structure that determines a soil's degree of permeability and water-holding capacity, which in turn affects pH and nutrient availability (see Section 3, later this section).

soil texture

The relative proportions of sand, silt, and clay particles in soil.

soil structure

The spatial arrangement of soil particles into groupings (aggregates).

FIGURE 8.10

Soil. (A) A soil-texture diagram showing relative amounts of sand, silt, and clay particles in twelve types of soil. (B) A soil profile. Horizon O consists of fallen leaves and other organic debris; Horizon A is topsoil, which is rich in decayed organic matter.

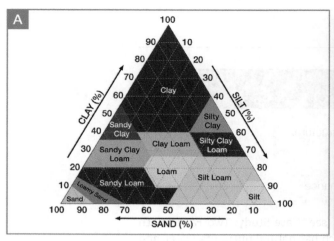

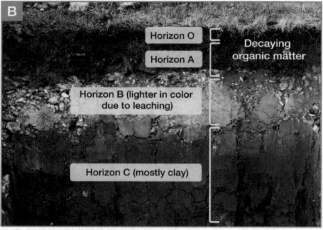

Sources: Joseph Shostell; © Shutterstock, Inc.

soil profile

Sequence of horizontal layers (horizons) in soil.

horizon

A horizontal layer of soil that has a unique chemical, physical, and sometimes biological composition.

Soil structure and texture change with depth. A **soil profile** depicts this vertical change and breaks soil into a series of horizontal layers called **horizons**, each with a unique chemical, physical, and sometimes biological composition (see B in Figure 8.10). Soil profiles often have at least three general horizons: surface (A), subsoil (B), and substratum (C), with these divided into smaller horizons. There may also be a top surface layer (O) composed of decaying organic matter. The quality and quantity of the topsoil is critical to farmers because it correlates with crop productivity. Underneath the top layer is the subsoil, consisting of some organic material, but mostly clay and minerals. Further down is the partially altered geologic material of the substratum from which the soil horizons form. Lastly, beneath the substratum lies solid bedrock.

Soil Forms Slowly

Soil formation occurs with the assistance of the material from which soil originates, in addition to climate, topography, biota, and time. All soils originate from parental material and are classified according to origin and how they are transported. The parental material is the most important factor to the development of soil because it provides the raw material that is acted upon by other factors. There are many examples of parental materials, including granite—a common bedrock in the continental United States—and basalt, developed from slow-moving lava flows and found in Hawaii. Dead plants combined with other decaying organic matter is another form of parental material. Once weathered, the parent rock and decaying organic material can also be transported by wind, water, and gravity to new locations. The parental material of soils therefore includes bedrock as well as what was transported, such as materials carried by glaciers (glacial till). In addition, parental material includes accumulations of dead plants. This variation in parental material is reflected in the texture and nutrient content of the soil that formed from it. For example, there is wind-deposited soil, referred to as loess, in the Central and Northeast United States. Loess soils are extremely fertile because they tend to be well-aerated, contain nutrients, and have a good supply of water (Catt 2001).

We focus on the type of parental material and how it develops because this helps to explain the properties of soils. As an example, wind is a good separator of particles based on size, because it transports silt great distances relative to much heavier sand. Water also separates out silt, clay, and sand particles by size. The percentage of the abundance of silt, clay, organic debris, and sand affect porosity, filtration of water, and water-holding capacity.

Soil Type, Permeability, and Crop Performance

What type of soil does corn favor? Are there certain soil conditions desirable for growing soybeans? Answers to these types of questions help us to have success in farming. Soil type affects permeability, water retention, nutrient content, pH, and, consequently, crops. The most challenging soils to farmers are those with exceedingly high or low permeability because they may lead to conditions of too little or too much water, pH extremes, and compromised nutrient availability.

Most crops can survive in a range of soil types, but each crop has a particular optimal range of nutrient, water, pH, and other environmental conditions. Farmers may gripe when confronted with a heavy clay soil because its pore spaces are small, the clay particles stick to each other in clumps, and water drains poorly from it. To improve soil fertility, farmers may plant cover crops, and over the course of a few years, the small pore spaces get bigger, and air and water move more easily through the soil. In contrast, sandy soils have large pore spaces and experience rapid water drainage, and therefore water may drain too rapidly past roots for them to absorb enough of it. Moreover, heavy rains and rapid drainage tends to transport essential nutrients downward in a process called **leaching**, which also increases soil acidity. Conversely, in drier regions where soils receive little rain, nutrients are not leached and soil is alkaline.

The vast majority of crops exhibit normal growth in the pH range of 6 to 7.5. Outside of this range, there is reduced uptake of multiple nutrients. Crop roots take up nutrients from soil when they are dissolved in solution, and these nutrients can be bound and insoluble at high or low pH. For example, phosphorus is bound to aluminum and iron at low pH, and bound to calcium at higher pH (Brady and Weil 2008). Low pH (below 6.0) is also harmful to beneficial Rhizobium bacteria associated with legumes like beans. In addition, low pH increases the solubility of aluminum and manganese, causing toxicity issues for plants. No matter the type of soil, productive farmers regularly check soil pH and try to maintain it within an optimal range. They may add a liming agent to raise pH to help offset acidification caused by harvesting, decaying organic matter, and inefficient use of nitrogen fertilizer.

leaching

Loss of dissolved substances, including nutrients, from soil.

Key Takeaways

- Soil texture refers to the relative proportions of sand, silt, and clay particles.
- Soil structure describes the formations of particles into larger structures called aggregates.
- The three main soil horizons are the topsoil (A horizon), subsoil (B horizon), and substratum (C horizon).
- Soil forms slowly.
- Soil formation begins with weathering of bedrock in addition to decaying organic matter. Particles of the original material are often transported to new locations to form various mixtures of soil.
- Every soil has distinctive properties of texture and structure that in turn influence soil porosity, drainage capabilities, pH, nutrient availability, and in the end, crop performance.

8.4 Environmental Problems of Farming

One of the steps in creating a sustainable society is recognizing the methods of growing food that contribute to environmental degradation. In this section, we explore the effects of monocultures, species introductions, irrigation practices, fertilizer use, meat production, and industrial farming on the environment.

Monocultures and Habitat Loss Threaten Biodiversity

overgrazing

Grazing that surpasses the ability of grazed plants to replace their lost tissues.

All areas with croplands were originally natural habitats used by multitudes of flora and fauna. As long as these croplands exist, biodiversity will be depressed and different from the natural environment. Agro-ecosystems (cultivated ecosystems) now cover over one-third of Earth's land surface (FAOSTAT 2016), and the percentage continues to increase. Within the United States, about 1.2 billion acres (45 percent) are devoted to growing crops (18 percent) and raising domestic livestock (27 percent). Almost all of the once-diverse prairie grasslands our ancestors witnessed have been completely transformed by crop production and **overgrazing** by livestock. Several taxonomic groups have suffered from the loss of this natural habitat space. For example, grassland birds in the Midwest have declined in some areas by as much as 91 percent (Sauer et al. 2008). While the total farmland area in the United States today is fairly stable from year to year, it is sharply increasing in other parts of the world. The last pristine areas of the tropical rainforests in South America—described as the heart and lungs of the planet—are deforested at an estimated rate of 600 million trees per year (Ometto et al. 2011). Since 1990 we have lost an estimated 420 million hectares (1 billion acres) of forests globally (FAO 2020). The main driver of this loss is agriculture.

Estimates of global species losses due to deforestation from agriculture combined with other forms of habitat degradation range from a few thousand to more than 100,000 per year (Sodhi et al. 2009). These estimated losses mostly include species that were never scientifically described (see Chapter 7). The large differences in estimates are a result of calculations based on species-area relationships (i.e., larger areas have more species), and the great variation in number of species per unit area globally. Demand for agricultural products like palm oil, sugar cane, and rubber drives deforestation. Tropical Asia, Central America, and South America are all experiencing deforestation to expand monocultural croplands. In Borneo, the third largest island in the world, 50 percent of all deforestation is associated with the development of oil-palm plantations. Similarly, the Cerrado region in Brazil, which supports an estimated 160,000 species of plants and animals, is disappearing at a rate of about 6 hectares (14.8 acres) every minute, or 3.2 million ha (8.2 million ac) per year (see Chapter 9). Agricultural land is replacing Cerrado's forests. These forest losses are causing an alteration of the Cerrado's water cycle, a key ecosystem service (Spera et al. 2016). During the dry season, monoculture crops recycle 60 percent less water than native vegetation. The recycling refers to water drawn in by the roots of plants, used by the plants, and then released into the atmosphere.

Agriculture threatens biodiversity in many geographical locations outside of South America as well. The Green Revolution increased the crop yield per acre for crops in India, Mexico, and many other developing countries and simultaneously accelerated the loss of biodiversity and created many environmental problems. In Haryana, India, for example, yearly yields of food grain per hectare increased from 0.63 tons in the mid-1960s to 1.37 tons by the early 1990s (Singh 2000). By 1999, mechanization and new plant varieties dependent on additions of fertilizers, pesticides, and heavy irrigation increased grain production close to 300 percent, and by 2018, to 400 percent (see Figure 8.11).

FIGURE 8.11
The Green Revolution in India increased food production four-fold. (A) In the graph, the first bar represents food production in the mid-1960s, prior to the Revolution. All numbers are in millions of metric tons per year. (B) In the image, a worker in rural India carries sugarcane. Note that the agricultural intensification has been a two-edged sword: Food production is higher, but natural biodiversity has declined, the water table has risen, waterlogging occurs frequently, and there is evidence of water contamination by fertilizers and pesticides.

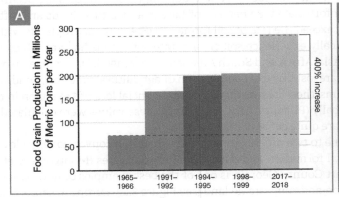

Sources: Joseph Shostell; data from Singh, R. B. 2000. Environmental consequences of agricultural development: a case study from the Green Revolution state of Haryana, India. *Agriculture, Ecosystems and Environment* 82: 97–1033; RAMNIKLAL MODI/Shutterstock.com

Over the last two hundred years, farming has substantially changed in North America as well. The number of farms has steadily declined from 6.8 million to about 2 million, and, simultaneously, the average American farm has grown in size. Mechanization is commonplace, and contemporary farms such as the Alvarez's (opening story) offer fewer types of agricultural products. Whole farms specialize in one or just a few crops, which means hundreds to thousands of acres can be planted with just a single species. These monocultures come with a price to the environment. In the short term, they have higher yields that maximize profits, but crop, animal, and plant diversity all suffer in the long term. Modern farm crop varieties—many genetically modified—require large volumes of water, heavy nutrient additions, and routine pesticide applications.

After decades of agricultural intensification, there are signs of long-term damage to the environment and declines in soil fertility. There is also evidence that the Green Revolution did not benefit all members of society equally. Different from the transformation of rural economies in Latin America and Asia, in sub-Saharan Africa (Dawson et al., 2016), a subsistence way of life was disrupted and poverty for many was exacerbated.

The trend of farms to specialize in fewer agricultural commodities also threatens food security. Monocultures can produce greater yields, yet they are also more susceptible to pests and diseases. The problem is that all of the plants in a monoculture are genetically identical, so all are identically susceptible to the same fungal and bacterial diseases, and vulnerable in the same way to the same agricultural pests. In monocultures, there is nothing to interrupt the spread of disease and pests to every susceptible plant, so an entire crop can be devastated and the farmer will be left with nothing to sell. Alternating rows with different crops (a polyculture) provides a natural break that can slow or stop the spread of a pathogen or pest. Not only is crop diversity important, but the presence of certain weed species either within or adjacent to croplands also has benefits. Weeds offer food and refuge for pollinators (Nicholls and Altieri 2013).

Soil Erosion

Civilizations will rise or fall depending on the quality of their soil (Scholes and Scholes 2013). Just as rich fertile soil is favorable for strong crop yields and bolsters food security, degradation of soil leads to food insecurity and civil strife. Therefore, if you consider food to be important, then so is the protection of the quality and quantity of soil. Deforestation, poor land management, and certain agricultural practices—including tilling—enhance soil erosion, which is the breakdown, transportation, and redistribution of soil. Soil erosion and soil formation are natural processes, and, when balanced, soil quantity is maintained. Parental rock converts to soil at an average rate of about 1 ton per hectare per year ($ha^{-1} yr^{-1}$) (Troeh and Thompson 1993). Comparatively, this is greater than the rate of natural erosion in forested areas (0.004–0.05 tons $ha^{-1} yr^{-1}$; Roose 1988). Under these conditions, and if there are no other external factors, and assuming these numbers are accurate, soil forms faster than it erodes. Unfortunately, 80 percent of Earth's agricultural lands are suffering from soil erosion, and the rates exceed the rate of soil formation (Speth 1994). Croplands within the United States and Europe typically experience soil erosion rates of 17 tons $ha^{-1} yr^{-1}$, which are notably lower than rates found in Asia, Africa, and South America (Barrow 1991). On average, an estimated 75 billion metric tons of soil are lost due to a combination of agricultural practices, wind, and water. Putting this in economic terms, these losses equal a yearly financial loss of $44 billion in the United States, and $400 billion globally (Pimental et al. 1995). Since these values were calculated in the mid-1990s, the dollar amounts are quite conservative for today.

Loss of soil due to erosion is one to two orders of magnitude greater in conventionally plowed croplands relative to the rate of soil formation and background erosion rates (Montgomery et al. 2007). Providence Canyon in Stewart County, Georgia, is one of the best examples of how poor soil management accelerates soil erosion and ruins arable land (see Figure 8.12). European settlers who came to the area in the 1820s quickly cleared mixed forests of pine, hickory, and oak trees. They plowed the open areas, and on sloped terrain they plowed vertically rather than following the contours of hills. Gullies of 0.6–1.2 m (2–4 ft) formed within the first years, and these widened, deepened, and lengthened every year. Valuable topsoil washed away with each rain and made its way to the Chattahoochee River. Some of the gullies are now over 46 m (>150 ft) deep, are 91 m (>300 ft) wide, and over 0.8 km (0.5 mi) long. In 1971, Providence Canyon became a state park, and today it is advertised as one of the six wonders of Georgia. The site is beautiful to see, but also a stark reminder as to the effect of poor land management (see video link: "Providence Canyon"). Soil erosion is also attributed to desertification, overcultivation, overgrazing, and deforestation, all discussed next.

Providence Canyon
Tour Georgia's Providence Canyon and learn about one of the world's worst soil erosion problems caused by unsustainable farming methods.

View in the online reader

FIGURE 8.12
Providence Canyon in Georgia is a reminder of the power of erosion that can occur with nonsustainable farming practices. This photo shows an area of about 450 hectares (1,000 acres); observe the size of the gullies.

Sources: Joseph Shostell; © Shutterstock, Inc.

Desertification

Globally, drylands cover about 41 percent of the world's land surface. These are fragile environmental areas vulnerable to climatic variations and human activities. Drylands are being degraded (**desertification**) and they are expanding. Back in the 1970s, desertification meant an expansion of deserts, but today it refers to degradation of arid, semi-arid, and dry sub-humid land areas. By the end of this century, drylands are predicted to expand by as much as 23 percent. Expansion will occur unequally across geographic regions because desertification is intertwined with climate conditions, human activities, and social issues. Some of the greatest desertification will occur in developing areas, but both modern agriculture in developed countries and low-tech agriculture in developing countries can accelerate desertification.

Unsustainable irrigation practices can contribute to the process of desertification. In dryland areas, where evaporation exceeds precipitation, inappropriate irrigation can cause **salinization**. When this happens, some of the irrigated water evaporates, leaving behind salts in the upper layers of soil. An accumulation of salts in soil decreases soil fertility. Heavily irrigated soils can have issues with **waterlogging** due to poor drainage. In this case, water saturates the soil and there is insufficient oxygen between soil particles for plant roots. Drylands can also be degraded by overgrazing, overexploitation of wood, and uncontrolled use of fire.

desertification

Degradation of arid, semi-arid, and dry sub-humid land areas.

salinization

The salt concentration of soil increases; this can be an effect of irrigating crops.

waterlogging

Saturation of soil with water; occurs in poorly drained soils with over-irrigation.

Overcultivation Leads to Soil Loss

In farming, cultivation refers to the preparation of the land for growing crops, and it involves the breaking up of soil with, for example, a hoe or a plow. This is known as tilling and can easily increase the rate of soil erosion if not done carefully (see Figure 8.13). Overcultivation, also referred to as overtilling, puts a demand on producing crops that outpaces soil formation.

FIGURE 8.13
Overcultivation: (A) Overtilling and (B) overgrazing are examples of actions leading to soil erosion and decreased productivity of the land.

Sources: Joseph Shostell; © Shutterstock, Inc.; Image courtesy of the USDA-NRCS.

Overgrazing Leads to Soil Erosion

Overgrazing occurs when grazing surpasses the ability of the plants to replace their lost tissues. A rancher may, for example, mistakenly keep a herd in a pasture that is too small. Should overgrazing continue, the grazed plants weaken and become poorer competitors with less edible vegetation (weeds) and more easily succumb to disease (see Chapter 9). Compared to sustainable grazing, overgrazing easily leads to higher water runoff and increased soil losses (Kairis et al. 2015). Introductions of nonendemic species—discussed next—can reduce biodiversity and facilitate soil erosion as well (Berendse et al. 2015).

Invasive Species Affect Agriculture

Invasive species pose a global threat to agriculture. An invasive species is a nonnative organism whose introduction causes harm to the environment or society (see Chapter 7). Their ability to cause damage stems from the lack of coevolved predators in their new location. Of the 12,000 nonindigenous species detected in Europe, approximately 10–15 percent are considered invasive, and cause an estimated $12 billion in damage per year, much of it affecting the agriculture industry. What about beyond Europe? An international group of researchers from Australia, United States, and New Zealand analyzed 1,297 invasive species in 124 countries and determined their routes of dispersal and potential risks to countries (Paini et al. 2016). The largest agricultural producers—the United States and China—are at greatest risk from invasive species, but are also more likely to have the financial resources to control them. Each year, the United States loses an estimated $40 billion from damaged crops and decreased forest production (Pimentel et al. 2005). Estimated costs reflect the value of the lost crops plus the measures used to control the invasive species. Developing nations are most at risk because they are less likely to possess the resources to successfully deal with invasive species. These same nations are disproportionately more dependent on agriculture. Algeria, Sudan, and other sub-Saharan African nations are considered to be at greatest risk.

Back at the Alvarez farm (opening story), invasive European starlings (*Sturnus vulgaris*) steal animal feed and damage ripening corn. This widespread and abundant black songbird consumes crops on millions of farms in the United States, Canada, Cuba, Australia, South Africa, and New Zealand. Within North America, the European starling population has surged from sixteen pairs released in New York City in the late 1890s, to 200 hundred million today. The most popular explanation as to why they were intentionally released relates to William Shakespeare. Apparently, a New York fan of Shakespeare wanted to introduce European starlings to North America because they were mentioned in the first part of Shakespeare's *King Henry IV*. Although well-intended, one person's actions indirectly led to huge agricultural and financial losses in several countries. Just within the United States, this robin-sized bird causes agricultural losses worth an estimated $800 million each year. History is rife with invasive species introductions; some, like the European starling, are intentional, whereas others are accidental (see Figure 8.14).

Invasive species disrupt agriculture in other areas of the world as well. Their disruptions are on the rise, principally due to human population growth and globalization. In the Middle East, invasive weeds reduce alfalfa yields by almost half (Khalil et al. 2017). African bees introduced to Brazil in 1956 to improve honey production have hybridized with native bees and have spread up through Central America; today these Africanized bees are now found in Florida, Texas, New Mexico, Arizona, and other southern states. How they disrupt the honey industry is uncertain, but African bees are more defensive and swarm more readily—making them a threat to people and a fair number of other animals.

FIGURE 8.14

Invasive species destroy crops. A) The invasive cottony cushion scale (*Icerya purchase*) as shown here on a lemon tree leaf, almost collapsed California's entire citrus industry back in 1868. B) The Asian giant hornet (*Vespa mandarinia*) is a new threat to North American honeybees and therefore honeybee-pollinated crops and the honey industry. Coevolved Asian honeybees defend their colonies by applying animal feces outside of their nest entrances (Mattila et al. 2020). The feces act as a deterrent to the Asian giant hornet. European honeybees lack similar anti-predatory defenses because they have not coevolved with the Asian giant hornet. In the photo, the USDA attached a radio tag to this Asian giant hornet and then followed it back to its hive in Blaine, Washington. They destroyed the hive before it could produce mated queens and start additional colonies.

Source: © Shutterstock, Inc.

Irrigation, Mining for Water, and Draining of Aquifers

Of the vast volume of water on Earth, only about 0.003 percent is available to us as freshwater. How does our level of use compare to what is available? And, to what extent does agriculture play a role? Society's consumption is about 10 percent of the annual discharge from all of the world's river systems. In this light, it appears that our demand is much lower than the freshwater available to us. The remaining 90 percent of the water (the buffer) is available for use, but the water must be shared with other life forms as well as ecosystems to maintain essential ecosystem services. Another issue is that water resources are not equally distributed globally and do not correlate well with the distribution of people. Dense concentrations of people found in some cities already overburden the scarce water resources of the local environment. How far we can edge into the 90 percent buffer without damaging ecosystem services is unclear. As new information comes forward about humanity's global water footprint, we expect our calculated estimates of where we are in the buffer zone to change (Jaramillo and Destouni 2015).

irrigation

The watering of land for agriculture.

dryland farming

The nonirrigated cultivation of crops.

Globally, agriculture accounts for about 70 percent of groundwater use. The percentage moves into the 90s in developing regions and can be much lower in developed regions. Within the United States, about 45 percent of groundwater we withdraw is used for agriculture, much of it for **irrigation**—the watering of land for agriculture. According to the United States Department of Agriculture, when groundwater and surface water are jointly considered, agriculture accounts for approximately 80 percent of water use.

How do these withdrawals of water match with the natural replenishment rate? Aquifers may take thousands of years to replenish, and we are pumping water from these deep pools daily to support agriculture. As one old American farmer said, "There are just too many straws in a small cup." The cup is in reference to the aquifer, and the straws represent drilled wells. His analogy is fairly accurate, because the number of wells in America's largest aquifer, the Ogallala (see Chapter 10), increased substantially after World War II.

The Ogallala aquifer underlies 450,657 km² (174,000 mi²) of the U.S. Central Plains and spans eight states, from Texas in the south to South Dakota in the north. Regardless of the Ogallala's immense size, there is ample evidence of it draining faster than it is replenishing. In some areas—such as Kansas—the water has dropped below drilled wells (>45.7 m [150 ft]) and farmers have no alternative but to either abandon their way of life or convert to **dryland farming**. Based on water-mining rates, the longevity of the Ogallala aquifer is in question (see Chapter 10).

Currently, we rely on irrigation to increase crop yields. Withdrawing water from the ground (mining water) is not irresponsible, but it is irresponsible to pump water unsustainably—removing water faster than it can be naturally replenished.

Just how much water is used by croplands? There is a different answer for each crop type. As an example, one to three tons of water are used to grow 1 kg (2.2 lb) of cereal. In another example, 15 tons of water are used to produce 1 kg (2.2 lb) of beef. As you can see, solutions to reduce water demand include a switch from an animal-based to a plant-based diet.

One of the negative side effects of irrigation farming is salinization. It is a condition in which irrigated water evaporates, leaving behind salts originally dissolved in the water. Over time, salts build up in the soil and impede the movement of water from the soil to plant roots. Salinization is a common problem in semi-arid regions where poorly drained soils are heavily irrigated. As soil salinity increases, soil fertility plummets.

Future projections of growth in population size indicate further aggravation of the water situation in the years to come. Furthermore, water withdrawal is growing at 1.7 times the rate of population growth. It would seem that we have our work cut out for us! Solving the issue of increasing food supply without overstressing natural replenishing rates is key to human survival. As discussed next, water is also linked to other environmental problems, such as runoff carrying nutrients to water resources off the farm.

Croplands Are Sources of Nutrients

Croplands are sources of nutrients to the rest of the environment. Each year, American farmers collectively apply over 12.2 million kg (≈ 27 million lb) of nitrogen and 4.3 million kg (9.5 million lb) of phosphorus to their farmlands. Nutrient additions—i.e., fertilizers—do improve the fertility of soils and thus can benefit crop productivity, but not all fertilizers have the same positive effects. There are two groups of fertilizers: organic—materials such as manure that come from living things, and inorganic—extracted, processed, or synthesized compounds sold large-scale on the commercial market. Inorganic fertilizers principally have only two or three of the nutrients (nitrogen, phosphorus, and potassium) plants need for growth, and there is no organic matter to replenish any soil that might have eroded away. Soils with lower organic content are less able to retain water, so any added nutrients can easily be leached out to become part of runoff and carried to local streams and lakes and even as far away as coastal waters (see Figure 8.15). On a short-term basis, inorganic nutrient additions are helpful to croplands, but on a long-term basis they are insufficient to provide the full complement of nutrients plants need—especially micronutrients and organic matter, which are eventually depleted. Use of inorganic nutrients also depends on large energy inputs needed for extraction, processing, or synthesis of nutrient compounds.

FIGURE 8.15
Land areas and water areas are interconnected and thus influence each other. For example, nutrients such as nitrogen originating from land eventually will make their way through runoff to local streams and then large rivers. The United States Geological Survey tracks these sources of nitrogen, as shown in this map. Notice two large sources of nitrogen: cropland (in yellow) and manure (in orange).

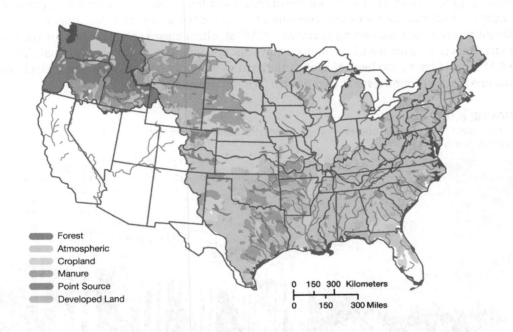

Forest
Atmospheric
Cropland
Manure
Point Source
Developed Land

0   150   300   Kilometers

0   150   300   Miles

Source: National Water-Quality Assessment Project, USGS, https://water.usgs.gov/nawqa/home_maps/nutrients_streams.html.

Environmental Issues with Meat Production

Raising beef, pork, and chicken unsustainably causes a host of environmental problems. Unless the livestock are naturally fed and kept in sparse populations, livestock operations can have all of the same environmental issues as cropland farms plus those associated with working with livestock. A far greater land area is required to produce animal meat relative to the same weight in crops. Therefore, relative to cropland farms, animal operations have a much larger carbon footprint. To accommodate areas needed for animal husbandry and growth of crops for feed, livestock operations are dependent on a very large surface area that directly conflicts with natural habitat space and biodiversity. Nutrient accumulations, antibiotic use, methane production, and burning of fossil fuels also must be considered when measuring the full effects of raising livestock. From an energy-efficiency perspective, raising livestock for food doesn't make much sense. An average of 90 percent of the energy is lost with each energy transformation up the food chain (see Chapter 2). People can receive the necessary calories from plants alone to meet their dietary needs, but there is a large group of people who prefer the taste of meat. And yet, within the livestock category there is a range of energy conversion efficiencies. Beef has the lowest caloric conversion rate from animal feed to consumed meat. A little less than 3 percent of calories consumed by cattle in the feed become part of their tissues (Shepon et al. 2016). The efficiency in caloric conversions increase to 9 percent and 13 percent for swine and poultry, respectively. If everyone in America switched from a beef to a poultry diet, we could meet the caloric demands of another 120 million people without increasing the surface area needed for producing food.

Concentrated Animal Feeding Operations

Global consumption of beef, pork, and chicken is possible because of the millions of farms dedicated to animal production across the world. In the United States, we classify any facility in which livestock are confined for at least forty-five days as an animal feeding operation (AFO). These facilities are quite numerous—far outnumbering cities and towns. Nationally, we have approximately 450,000 animal feeding operations compared to 35,000 cities and towns. Just under 20,000 AFOs are concentrated animal feeding operations (CAFOs), which means they have at least 1,000 animal equivalents (see Figure 8.16). One animal equivalent is equal to 1,000 pounds of animals. Therefore, a CAFO could have 1,000 head of beef cattle, 2,500 swine, or 125,000 chickens. The United States is just one of many countries that have animal feeding operations.

FIGURE 8.16
Concentrated animal feeding operations like this one generate large volumes of wastes that end up in river systems, lakes, and oceans.

Source: © Shutterstock, Inc.

AFOs offer an immense benefit for society, for they provide a source of eggs, milk, and meat. However, AFOs, and CAFOs in particular, are a source of environmental pollutants,s such as the 1.1 billion tons of manure generated each year.

Animal operation facilities in the United States generate over 6 million kg (13.2 million lb) of nitrogen and close to 2 million kilograms (4.4 million lb) of phosphorus each year from manure and urine. When not captured and recycled, these nutrients eventually move into local streams and rivers and make their way to larger bodies of water. Release of nutrients here drives algae overgrowth, which reduces the water's oxygen content and causes dead zones to appear (see Chapter 10).

Wastes from AFOs contain more than just nutrients, for there are also hormones, cleaning agents, greenhouse gases, and pathogens. Such wastes are partially to blame for cultural eutrophication, enhanced climate change, water pollution, air pollution, and general habitat destruction. Because AFOs are the origin of pollutants that enter waters, they are required to possess a National Pollutant Discharge Elimination Systems Permit. Under the Clean Water Act, it is unlawful to discharge a pollutant from an AFO into navigable waters unless a permit is obtained.

Industrialized Farming and Climate Change

All of the environmental problems mentioned so far are magnified by industrialized farming. In addition, industrialized farming is one of the main drivers of human-caused climate change. Here, we tease apart the connection between farming and climate change. In the opening story, we recognized the transformation of the Alvarez farm in size, specialization, and dependence on genetically engineered seeds, large-scale machinery, synthetic fertilizers, and irrigation. The direction of this transformation leads to industrialized farming, characterized by high-yielding plants and animals, large-scale monocultures, and high densities. These high crop yields are unnatural and only possible with continued anthropogenic inputs of matter and energy. Industrialized farming drives climate change. Farms are responsible for an estimated 10 percent of global greenhouse gas (GHG) emissions (IPCC 2007).

This value does not include any initial deforestation and drainage of peatlands that might occur to create farmlands. These changes release stored carbon in plants and the soil and convert natural ecosystems that are sinks for carbon dioxide into net generators of this greenhouse gas. Massive inputs of energy are required to produce synthetic fertilizers and pesticides, and additional energy is needed for mechanized irrigation. The majority of this required energy comes in the form of fossil fuels, which when burned release GHGs. There are also emissions associated with running large farm machinery and the transportation of agricultural products from farms to factories and grocery stores. Livestock operations are particularly high users of energy, for they depend on crop farms and also require energy for heating, lighting, ventilation, and additional transportation (Koneswaran and Nierenberg 2008). In all, global food-related emissions of GHGs contribute an estimated 21–37 percent of total anthropogenic emissions (Rosenzweig et al. 2020).

Key Takeaways

- Cultivated ecosystems cover one-third of Earth's land surface and depress biodiversity.
- Desertification is the degradation of arid, semi-arid, and dry sub-humid land areas.
- Overcultivation, farming vertically on slopes, and overgrazing promote soil loss.
- An invasive species is a nonnative organism whose introduction causes harm to the environment or society. Invasive species cause the loss of billions of dollars in agricultural products each year.
- Mining water for irrigation can remove water from aquifers faster than the replenishing rate.
- Continued irrigation and overirrigation can cause waterlogging and salinization.
- Animal-feeding operations use vast amounts of water and habitat space and are a continued source of greenhouse gases, nutrients, and various chemicals and pathogens, all of which make their way into the environment.

8.5 Pests and Pesticides: Weighing the Pros and Cons

Learning Objectives

1. Analyze international pesticide data to understand differences in pesticide use among countries and over time.
2. Describe how pests become resistant to pesticides.
3. Summarize the scientific evidence of pesticides' not reaching their target organisms.
4. Explain how to assess a person's exposure to pesticides.
5. Identify the benefits and drawbacks of using pesticides.

As long as there has been farming, humans have been trying to control pests to protect their crops. For instance, the Sumerians applied sulfur compounds to control insects thousands of years ago. These compounds were examples of pesticides, substances used to kill pests (insects, pathogens, and weeds). However, the golden age of pesticides didn't occur until around the 1960s. Within the United States, pesticide use has grown considerably over the past seventy years. In 1952, only 5–10 percent of all the acreage planted in corn, wheat, and cotton in the United States was treated with pesticides, but by 1980, the percentage had become 90–99 percent. The quantity of pesticides farmers apply to their fields depends on crop type. Here in the United States, corn receives close to 40 percent of the total pesticides used, followed by soybeans (22 percent), potatoes (10 percent), cotton (7 percent) and wheat (less than 5 percent).

Three examples of commonly used pesticides are atrazine, chlorpyrifos, and glyphosate. A quick assessment of just one of these pesticides helps us to gain an understanding as to the sheer size of the pesticide industry, the number of different products they market, and the overall quantity of pesticides released in the world yearly. Just consider the broad-based herbicide glyphosate, used to control broadleaf weeds and grasses. This single pesticide is an active ingredient in over 750 products, and 826,000 tons are applied worldwide every year.

Globally, today we dispense over 4.1 billion kg (9.0 billion lb) of pesticides each year to manage pests and to increase harvest yields and agricultural product quality (see video link: "Pesticides"). In the end, more food is available and farmers earn a higher income. Society's use of pesticides varies geographically and has changed over time (see Figure 8.17). For its role, the United States uses about 10 percent of this total, a distant second to the largest user—China, at 43 percent—but still significantly more than entire regions such as Africa, which uses only 2.5 percent. How do the benefits of using pesticides (increased quantity and quality of agricultural yields) compare to the negatives, described next?

Pesticides
Are pesticides safe? Listen to a summary of our pesticide use and decide for yourself.

View in the online reader

FIGURE 8.17

Pesticide use. (A) Global use of pesticides has increased overtime. (B) In the photo, a worker without protection gear sprays pesticides on pineapples. (C) Pesticide use varies geographically (numbers indicate tons of pesticide consumed in 2019).

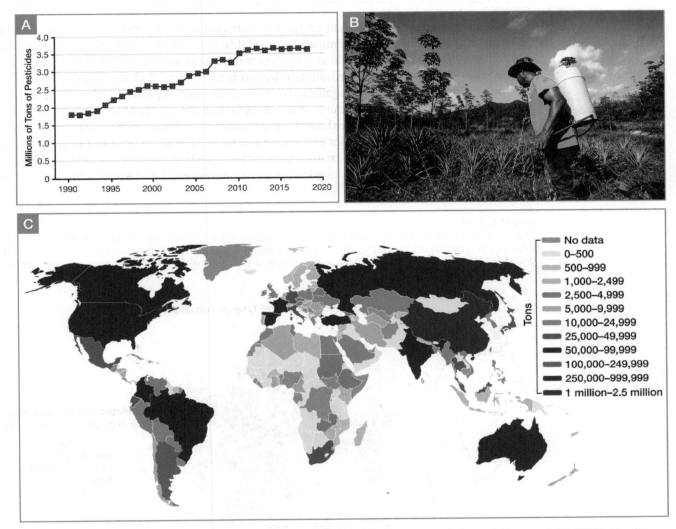

Sources: Joseph Shostell; Data from Our World in Data, Pesticides consumption, https://ourworldindata.org/pesticides#pesticide-consumption. [CC BY, https://creativecommons.org/licenses/by/4.0/legalcode]; Hanafi Latif/Shutterstock.com

Resistance to Pesticides

Continued use of pesticides results in **pesticide resistance**. With each application of pesticide, susceptible pests die and leave resistant organisms (i.e., superweeds) behind to give rise to the next generation. Pest populations quickly become resistant. Ultimately, the farmer must change pesticides because the original pesticide is no longer effective in controlling pests. There are, however, methods to reduce pesticide resistance. Farmers might plant a peripheral row of nonsprayed crop to act as a refuge for some of the pests they are trying to eliminate. Survivors from the refuge area reproduce with resistant biotypes and in doing so create pesticide-susceptible offspring. In this way, farmers delay the rate of pesticide resistance. Another way to reduce pesticide resistance is by frequently changing management practices and not relying solely on pesticides.

pesticide resistance

Genetic ability of a pest to survive exposure to a pesticide.

Most Pesticides Never Reach Their Targets

Somewhere between 90–99.9 percent of applied pesticides do not reach targeted organisms and therefore may accumulate (bioaccumulation) in wildlife, fish, and other beneficial components of ecosystems (Pimental 1995; Pimental and Burgess 2012). We can assess the threat of a pesticide to nontargeted organisms and the environment by considering its persistence, mechanism of transport, and ability to magnify (biomagnification) in the food chain. A pesticide's chemical properties and physical transport processes inform us as to how far it might travel and where we might expect concentrations to be high. Pesticides have different modes of transport in the environment. One of the most common mechanisms is for pesticides to move into the air by volatilization (fumes from spraying), or through windblown dust and soil particles. Once in the air, the pesticides can be transported to urban areas and other nonagricultural ecosystems (see Figure 8.18) (Foreman et al. 2000; Chang et al. 2010).

FIGURE 8.18
Atrazine, one of the most common herbicides used in the United States The National Resources Defense Council reported the presence of atrazine in approximately 75 percent of stream water in the United States, 40 percent of groundwater samples collected from agricultural areas, and a high percentage of drinking water samples. Atrazine has been banned in Europe since 2003.

Estimated Agricultural Use of Atrazine, 2019

Estimated use on agricultural land, in pounds per square mile

- <2.93
- 2.93–17.39
- 17.40–63.35
- >63.35
- No estimated use

Source: Pesticide National Synthesis Project, USGS, https://water.usgs.gov/nawqa/pnsp/usage/maps/show_map. php?year=2016&map=ATRAZINE&hilo=L.

Pesticides Harm Non-targeted Species

According to the United Nations, an estimated 200,000 people die from toxic exposure to pesticides every year, and up to another 41 million people have adverse reactions to exposure. Cancer, hormone disruption, developmental disorders, sterility, Alzheimer's disease, and Parkinson's disease have all been linked to chronic exposure to pesticides. Agricultural workers are one subset of the larger population that is routinely exposed to pesticides by the initial spray, drift, or through direct contact with crops and soils that have been sprayed. Incomplete health and safety training and inadequate safety gear are part of the problem. Risk of pesticide exposure also varies among work groups. Migrant workers are often subjected to a greater risk because of language issues. Children, a large work group in developing countries, are at high risk of pesticide poisoning because they have relatively little experience and are more sensitive to toxins than adults. A full measure of the effects of pesticides on human health must also include the 250,000–375,000 who die from intentionally ingesting pesticides annually (Dawson et al. 2010).

Pesticides Harm Bees

Bees fare poorly with pesticide use (Woodcock et al. 2017). Because they play a crucial role as pollinators, their recent declines are of immense interest to us and relate directly to food security (see video link: "Pesticides and Bees"). Researchers, for example, have linked the use of neonicotinoids to reduced overwintering success, lower colony reproduction, and drop in queen production (Woodcock et al. 2017; Whitehorn et al. 2012). This group of pesticides also reduces survivorship of bees through weakening their ability to locate and return to their hives (Henry et al. 2012). Neonicotoids are not the only group of pesticides to threaten bees. New evidence suggests the pesticide methoxyfenozide—long considered safe for beneficial insect species—significantly affects honeybee flight activity and thermoregulation (Meikle et al. 2019). The pesticides mentioned here are just some of the thousands of pesticides currently used on a variety of crops in over fifty countries. Based on research conducted by the United States Geological Survey (USGS), we have direct evidence of bees, being exposed to insecticides (Hladik et al. 2016). USGS scientists captured native bees and then analyzed the bees for the presence of insecticides. They found eighteen different pesticides in the bees. Evidence of bee exposure to insecticides also shows up in the honey they produce and the honey products we purchase (Song et al. 2018).

Pesticides Harm Amphibians

A large and growing contingent of research studies indicates pesticides are a contributing factor in why an estimated 40 percent of amphibians are threatened with extinction (IUCN 2021). Findings indicate inhibited amphibian larval growth and development, damage to the thymus gland (Hayes et al. 2006), and increased susceptibility to the fungus *Batrachochytrium dendrobatidis*, an exceptionally lethal pathogen to amphibians worldwide (Buck et al. 2015). Learn about sustainable methods to manage pests and grow food in Section 6.

Pesticides and Bees
Listen to Purdue University Extension discussing the link between pesticide use and bees.

View in the online reader

Decisions about Whether or Not to Use Pesticides

There is evidence of pesticides negatively affecting human health. Peer-reviewed papers began to link the presence of chlorpyrifos, an organophosphate pesticide, to neurological impairments in children. A brain-imaging study conducted by the Columbia Center for Children said, "Even low to moderate levels of exposure to the insecticide chlorpyrifos during pregnancy may lead to long-term irreversible changes in the brain structure of the child" (Rauh et al. 2012). Although a string of studies supported the connection between chlorpyrifos and human health, the Environmental Protection Agency (EPA) refused to change their policy regarding use of this pesticide. At the time, EPA Director Scott Pruitt elected to postpone a decision about a potential ban until 2022. In response to this decision and the disclosure of support of the executive government for this decision, the chairperson of the EPA Science Review Board testified on Capitol Hill. Dr. Deborah Swackhamer stated, "The scientific foundation must be free of politics and must be robust." In her opinion, and for the safety of the public, the government should never control science, but should robustly review scientific data and use it to make decisions about policy. In this case, a good many scientists did not agree with the EPA's decision. Nevertheless, the scientific community values the presence of the EPA because the EPA has had a long history of protecting the environment and human health.

Chlorpyrifos is not the first pesticide to be supported by industry but criticized by scientists. Dichlorodiphenyltrichloroethane (DDT) has a similar but more popular and contentious story. Entomologists in America and England became aware of the success of DDT at killing common pests during field trials, and DDT was adopted for use by the military during World War II to protect Allied troops against typhus and malaria. Postwar, use of DDT expanded to residential communities and agriculture. DDT remained popular into the early 1960s, until the publication of Rachel Carson's book *Silent Spring*, which described the dangers of pesticides. The 1.5 million published and sold copies of *Silent Spring* sparked a national discussion about pesticides and helped launch the environmental movement of the 1960s and 1970s. DDT became banned in 1972 and is now listed as a probable carcinogen to humans. The title *Silent Spring* also highlights the detrimental effects of pesticides like DDT to wildlife (see Chapter 2). We now understand the biomagnification of DDT up the food chain and its disruption of calcium metabolism and consequent egg-thinning in predatory birds.

Why do farmers continue to use pesticides despite the mounting evidence that pesticides have negative effects on the environment (Zaller and Brühl 2019) and human health (Parent et al. 2009)? This seems like a reasonable question, doesn't it? However, the question itself is a little misleading since it makes some assumptions about farmers, collection and dissemination of data (the evidence), and the process of science (see "Critical Thinking Activity: Conflicting Messages about Glyphosate"). In short, reasonable and ethical people, farmers included, avoid products when confronted with clear, concise information indicating their threat to human health. The term *evidence* in the initial question is in reference to data generated in scientific studies, and these studies take time and can have conflicting conclusions. Once a collection of studies is complete and there is a clear data trend, recommendations go forward. Unfortunately, the effects of particular pesticides on human health may not be initially known, but when substantial evidence is revealed, governmental policy can and should change to effectively protect people and the environment. There can be exceptional cases of policy resistance by the government, even when confronted with new information, such as in the case of chlorpyrifos.

Critical Thinking Activity: Conflicting Messages about Glyphosate

Who are we to believe when there are mixed messages in the news about the safety of pesticides? The International Agency for Research on Cancer and the U.S. Environmental Protection Agency have given conflicting messages about the risk of glyphosate, which is routinely applied as a pesticide to GE crops (see Table 8.1).

TABLE 8.1 Conflicting Messages about the Risk of Glyphosate

Governmental Agency	Message about Glyphosate
International Agency for Research on Cancer, an agency of the World Health Organization (WHO)	Glyphosate is a probable carcinogen.
World Health Organization/Food and Agricultural Organization panel	"Glyphosate is unlikely to pose a carcinogenic risk to humans through the diet."
Environmental Protection Agency	"Glyphosate is not likely to be carcinogenic to humans at doses relevant for human health risk assessment."

A true evaluation of a compound for its toxicity on life is achieved through experimental research and a repeat of this research over time. We may not elect to conduct the experiments ourselves, but as mindful citizens we can access research results on peer-reviewed platforms. Access your school's library and read papers by Guilherme et al. (2010), Mesnage et al. (2015), and Andreotti et al. (2018) and come to your own conclusion.

Key Takeaways

- Farmers use pesticides to control pests and boost crop yields.
- Farmers use a variety of methods to control pests, but one of the most common ones is pesticide use.
- Farmers receive information about pesticides from multiple sources, which may not always agree on the benefits and drawbacks of pesticide use.
- Continued use of pesticides causes pesticide resistance.
- Most pesticides never reach their targets.
- Pesticides harm nontargeted species.

8.6 Practicing Sustainable Agriculture

Learning Objectives

1. Analyze conventional farming methods and identify areas to improve sustainability.
2. Explain how the diversification of agricultural crops protects food security and biodiversity.
3. Illustrate techniques and/or structures beneficial to reducing soil erosion and soil loss.
4. Identify methods to use less fertilizer on farm fields.
5. Examine sustainable options for farmers to reduce their energy use. Consider direct and indirect uses of energy.
6. Summarize the methods of growing meat sustainably and recognize their limitations.
7. Examine and describe techniques to manage pests with less pesticides relative to conventional farming.
8. Compare and contrast sustainable methods to grow crops, taking into account scarcity of water, geographical location, irrigation possibilities, and crop type.

It is possible to grow food sustainably without converting additional natural ecosystems to agriculture. Sustainable agriculture addresses the full complement of HIPPCO threats (habitat destruction, invasive species, population growth, pollution, climate change, and over exploitation) to biodiversity (see Chapter 7). In this section, we look into the value of diversification over monocultures, and at methods to improve soil quality and simultaneously reduce the use of synthetic fertilizers and energy. We also explore sustainable ways to grow meat, control pests, and efficiently meet the water demands of crops.

Diversify Agricultural Crops

Sustainable farming supports crop diversification globally and locally. We accomplish this, in part, by expanding the number of plant species we cultivate worldwide. Such an action moves society away from almost exclusive dependence on a minority of the 6,000 plant species humans have cultivated throughout history and more strongly supports natural biodiversity, Indigenous cultures, and more balanced nutrition. Locally, we replace segregated fields of monocultures with polycultures. Implementation of this action takes advantage of a mixed crop's collective resistance to pests and diseases and therefore lessens the "need" for pesticides. Sustainable farming also includes integrated agriculture. In this case, different types of farms (i.e., animal vs. crop) are combined to some degree to share common goals, minimize wastes, improve soil quality, and enhance production levels.

Consumers have the power to encourage agricultural diversification. Be curious about the foods you eat, and when the opportunity arrives try something new. Support locally grown foods and communicate your tastes to farmers. When society's food preference changes, farmers can adjust their crops and adapt to the new demand.

Sustainable Management of Soils

Farmers who develop a sustainable farming strategy see the "big picture" and understand the links among fertilizer use, soil erosion, degradation in soil quality, and eutrophication. These farmers use a number of strategies to reduce nutrient losses that contaminate local water bodies, and to maintain soil quality. The aim is to improve the efficiency of delivering nutrients directly to plant roots and to minimize the loss of nutrients to the watershed (Bley et al. 2017). A beneficial nutrient management strategy begins with adding the right amount of fertilizer to the crops grown. Year-round ground cover and low- or no tillage in combination with windbreak barriers of trees and shrubs (shelterbelts) minimize soil erosion, and therefore reduce the loss of nutrients to local waterways (see Figure 8.19). Cover crops have the added benefit of feeding the soil's microbial community with organic matter. Consistent addition of organic materials also improves water retention of the soil—lessening the need for irrigation. When nutrient additions are deemed necessary, natural organic matter serves as the preferable option over synthetic fertilizers, because organics offer a stronger support of the microbial community. On sloped lands, a sustainable strategy calls for contour farming (recall Providence Canyon).

FIGURE 8.19
Sustainable agricultural practices like these protect the quantity and quality of soil. (A) In Russia, a line of trees (a shelterbelt) at the edge of an agricultural field protects against soil erosion. (B) A crop of soybeans thrives in a no-till farm field in Minnesota. (C) In Vietnam, farmers maintain rows of rice along the contours of mountain slopes (contour farming).

Source: © Shutterstock, Inc.

Optimize Energy Use Efficiency and Reduce Energy Use

Energy use is costly for the farmer and the environment. On average, about 15 percent of a farmer's expense is attributed to energy use, and most farms are significant sources of carbon dioxide emissions from fossil-fuel burning to run machinery. The aim in sustainable farming is to rely less on fossil fuels (direct and indirect uses) while still sustaining harvest levels (see Figure 8.20). Since 1981, the Rodale Institute in Kutztown, Pennsylvania, has documented how organic farming reduces energy usage relative to conventional farms. Their organic fields of corn use 63 percent less energy and have healthier soil with improved filtration and carbon stores. By rotating crops and using biological control, the farmers control pests without synthetic pesticides. This in itself saves money for the farmer—increasing profit margins—and the environment does not incur pollution from the manufacturing of pesticides, which requires energy-intensive inputs. Rotating crops and using cover crops further translates into lower energy usage because manufactured fertilizers become unnecessary. Nitrogen fertilizer production uses large amounts of energy and can be greater than 50 percent of a farm's total energy use (Woods et al. 2010).

FIGURE 8.20
Examples of sustainable farming strategies that reduce GHG emissions and control pests. (A) Use of renewable energy. (B) Organic farming requires less energy and doesn't rely on synthetic pesticides or fertilizers. (C) Use of natural predators to control pests. The photo shows a ladybug (*Rodolia cardinalis*) preying on a cottony cushion scale (*Icerya purchase*). (D) Produce sold locally.

Source: © Shutterstock, Inc.

The cost benefits of no-till farming are well documented. Less fuel is used, and the farmer saves precious time and protects against soil erosion. According to the USDA, no-till farming uses 15.1 liters (4 gallons) of diesel fuel per acre each year compared to the 22.7 liters (6 gallons) required for conventional till farming. If the Alvarezes (opening story) practiced no-till farming, they would save about $10,500 each year. U.S. farms currently practicing no-till farming are saving 1.7 billion liters (282 million gallons) of diesel fuel annually, which translates into 3.1 fewer million metric tons of greenhouse gases released into the atmosphere. Correctly matching a farmer's needs to machinery type is another way to increase energy efficiency. For example, using a 150-horsepower tractor when only a 70-horsepower tractor is needed doubles fuel costs and greenhouse gas emissions.

Farms can also offset their demands for energy and simultaneously lessen greenhouse gas emissions by installing windmills or solar panels. When appropriate, farms can choose to have an anaerobic digester as another source of energy to transform organic matter into electricity. An anaerobic digester uses anaerobic bacteria to break down animal manure and other organic matter in the absence of oxygen. Dairy farms, with their high volume of manure, are great locations for anaerobic digesters. A digester receiving manure from 2,000 cows can provide a continuous source of energy for approximately eighty average American homes.

Grow Meat Sustainably

To be clear, farmers can grow animal meat sustainably, and therefore it is a myth that animal agriculture has to be destructive. Society doesn't have to stop eating meat to save the planet. The vocal statements by the famous economist Lord Stern and others about the destructive nature of animal agriculture are true in the sense of how the majority of animal meat is produced today. The real issue is the abundance of livestock and the rate of reproduction required to meet society's desire for meat. A lack of sufficient available land and water makes it unfeasible for everyone to have a predominantly meat-based diet. Then, what is recommended? Eating less meat is helpful, and choosing chicken over beef leaves a smaller carbon footprint. In the end, eating meat can be sustainable, but all of us can't eat a high volume of meat daily. The question becomes, "How is it possible to grow meat sustainably?" One option is to raise pasture-fed livestock and avoid intensive animal production facilities. Another is to integrate crop and livestock systems as they did in test trials in West Texas. Texas has long been known for raising cotton and livestock, but traditionally these are seen as two separate systems, each with its own demands for nutrients and land. With an integrated systems approach, the two systems merge and share nutrient and land resources. For example, animal manure is not wasted; instead, it serves as a fertilizer for cotton.

Lab-grown (cellular agriculture) meat may provide a future source of sustainable and ethically grown animal-derived products; however, this is still an emerging field, and currently overly energy-intensive and cost-prohibitive at the commercial level (Post 2014; Pandurangan and Kim 2015). See video link: "Lab-Grown Meat".

🎥 **Lab-Grown Meat**

Hear about the scientific breakthrough of growing meat in a lab.

View in the online reader

Reduce Use of Pesticides

A logical pathway toward sustainable control of pests probably begins with a reduction of pesticide use. French researchers analyzed data collected from 946 nonorganic commercial farms and determined that 77 percent of these farms could reduce pesticide use without negatively affecting profitability or productivity (Lechenet et al. 2017). Furthermore, almost 60 percent of the surveyed farms could slash pesticide use by 42 percent without influencing profitability or productivity, and a large number of farms would actually see an increase in profits because they would remove the costs of the pesticide and its application. Therefore, and quoting the French research team, "pesticide reduction is already accessible to farmers."

One option for farmers is to adopt an integrated pest management strategy (IPM). An IPM approach aims to manage pests (insects, weeds, and pathogens) and minimize risks to humans, nontarget organisms, and the environment. It begins with the identification of potential pests and understanding their biology and natural environmental factors that control them. After this assessment, a farmer may conclude that a particular pest does not pose a significant risk to the crops and can be tolerated. In an IPM approach, if a pest does qualify as a significant risk, a combination of techniques to manage the pest are considered, such as biological control of an insect pest with natural predators and planting several varieties of a crop (see D in Figure 8.20). In two of many examples, parasitic wasps called *Trichogramma*, raised from eggs in a laboratory, have proved helpful in controlling infestations of the sugar cane borer and the European corn borer. Without some form of control, these infestations can cause significant losses of sugar cane and corn crops. Biologic control has been a very effective way to control problematic nonnative (exotic) insects. Since the late 1880s only a minor number of environmental problems have resulted from the more than 5,000 species introductions that have occurred to control insects and mites in 196 countries (Bale et al. 2008). Although introductions of exotic species are usually not recommended because of their potential threat to native species, targeted introductions of an exotic species' natural predator can be helpful to prevent further destruction. In these cases the exotic predator population rises and falls with its harmful prey population.

Part of IPM may also include cultural and mechanical controls and, when deemed necessary, chemical control. In cultural control, a farmer may attempt to disrupt a pest's habitat in and near the crop. Possible strategies are harvesting a crop before a pest arrives or adjusting the density of crop to change the humidity conditions within the planted area. Certain humidity conditions may select for or against a pest species.

Most nations regulate the use of pesticides in agriculture. In the United States, several laws authorize the Environmental Protection Agency (EPA) to cover this responsibility. For example, as part of its broad authority, the EPA establishes maximum pesticide residue limits in foods and also regulates the distribution, sale, and use of pesticides. Furthermore, the EPA sets safety tolerance limits and considers the susceptibility of children to pesticides. It also conducts periodic reviews of registered pesticides. When new scientific data about a pesticide comes forward indicating significant danger to humans or the environment, the pesticide can be deregistered and banned from use. This was the case of DDT, once celebrated for its ability to control insects, but then later banned because of toxicological effects. The EPA's review process has been instrumental in helping to remove dangerous chemicals from use, but the review process does not always have effective outcomes, as in the case of chlorpyrfos.

Sustainable Irrigation

A key goal of sustainable irrigation is to not remove water faster than the environment's natural replenishing rate. Drip irrigation, the recommended method to optimize water use, delivers water directly to crop roots. In drier areas, such as in Arizona, western Texas, and Egypt, subsurface drip irrigation will further protect against evaporation of water into the overlying dry air. Studies conducted by soil scientists on broccoli and seedless watermelon crops indicate a reduction in water use by up to 25 percent when using subsurface drip irrigation compared to furrow irrigation, as well as significantly greater crop yields (see Figure 8.21; Thompson et al. 2002). Another strategy—dryland farming—is electing to not irrigate, but instead to grow crops adapted to the natural environmental conditions.

FIGURE 8.21

Farmers can choose from a variety of methods to water their crops. Common methods such as furrows (A) and sprinkler systems (B) are not as efficient as drip irrigation (C). Dryland farming (not shown) does not rely on any irrigation.

Source: © Shutterstock, Inc.

Key Takeaways

- To grow foods more sustainably, we need to enhance our protection of soils, rethink how we raise livestock, and lessen reliance on synthetic fertilizers, nonrenewable energy sources, pesticides, and irrigation.
- A diversification-of-crops strategy supports polyculture farming, a greater variety of crops, and integrated agriculture.
- To reduce erosion and prevent soil loss, farmers use no-till farming, contour farming, cover crops, and shelterbelts.
- To minimize the loss of nutrients to the watershed, farmers only add nutrients when needed, practice reduced or no-till farming, erect shelterbelts and buffer zones, and use organic rather than synthetic fertilizers.
- To reduce fossil-fuel use, farmers lessen reliance on synthetic pesticides and fertilizers, use the right-sized tractor, sell locally, refrain from tilling, recycle manure, control pests biologically, use cover crops, and use renewable energies.
- In order to produce meat sustainably, animals are kept at low densities to not overcome nature's ability to provide needed resources and also absorb wastes. Thus, a main issue is finite land space.
- Agricultural pests can be sustainably managed by adopting an integrated pest management strategy.
- Sustainable farming does not remove water faster than nature's replenishing rate. Example strategies are drip irrigation, subsurface drip irrigation, and dryland farming.

8.7 A Look to the Future: Revisiting Apricot Lane Farms

Learning Objective

1. Compare and contrast the sustainability of Apricot Lane Farms with that of the Alvarez farm.

Together, we can follow sustainable agricultural principles to meet the food needs of tomorrow's larger population without unduly threatening biodiversity and natural ecosystems. This is a reasonable challenge, for we have the appropriate capabilities and resources. The answer must effectively consider and solve issues of soil erosion and nutrient loss, energy use and climate change, the scale of meat production, pest management, and overuse of water. An increase in the efficiency of the agriculture industry is part of the solution, but this alone is insufficient to move agriculture fully into the category of sustainability. There also must be a fundamental change in how we grow food, and then as consumers, a behavioral change in what we eat and where we purchase our food.

Revisiting Apricot Lane Farms

As we end this chapter, we return to the opening story of two farms. Apricot Lane Farms has developed and maintained a strong sustainable strategy. In contrast to monocultural farms like the Alvarez's, they have diversified and refrained from using synthetic fertilizers and pesticides. If possible, everything is generated and used within the farm itself. Manure is used as fertilizer, and a nurtured biodiversity helps to control pests naturally with no chemical applications. In brief, the Chesters' labor-intensive farming methods have eliminated some of the largest environmental issues of conventional agriculture: cultural eutrophication caused by synthetic fertilizers, soil erosion due to tilling, killing beneficial organisms due to pesticide pollution, and biodiversity loss because of monocultures.

Is Apricot Lane Farms the face of the future farm? They are one of a growing number of farms that are organic certified and regenerative organic certified (ROC), which means they prohibit the use of synthetic fertilizers, GMOs, and chemical pesticides. Additionally, the added ROC indicates they support the humane treatment of animals and development of healthy soil, and promote social justice and good working conditions for farm workers (see Chapter 2). Of course, just growing sustainable plant- and animal-based foods is insufficient alone, for food must be accessible to people. Remember, a large percentage of global crops are wasted due to storage, preservation, and transportation issues. Apricot Lane Farms' strategic location just outside of Los Angeles allows for easy, quick, and economical transport of agricultural products to local farmers markets, grocers, and restaurants throughout Los Angeles and Ventura counties in California. Book a tour of the Chesters' farm and observe this progressive farm for yourself, or apply for one of their six month internship positions aimed at training future farmers.

Key Takeaways

- We have the capability and resources to follow sustainable agricultural principles and meet the food needs of tomorrow's larger population without unduly threatening biodiversity and natural ecosystems.

- A sustainable future involves a fundamental change in how we grow our food and behavioral changes in what we eat and where we purchase our food.

- Apricot Lane Farms (ALF) has implemented sound sustainable strategies (such as no-till farming and using manure as fertilizer), setting them apart from the Alvarez farm. ALF is a completely organic farm and does not use synthetic pesticides, genetically modified seeds, or synthetic fertilizers.

FIGURE 8.22 Visual Overview: Agriculture, Food, and the Environment
Summarizing figure: We depend on agriculture to provide food for our growing population (8.1 and 8.2). Thus, we have a vested interest in giving attention to all facets of food production, from maintaining soil quality (8.3) to delivery of food to our tables. Soil erosion (8.4), synthetic fertilizers, and pesticides (8.5) that contaminate the environment, and other issues are effects of producing food nonsustainably. Sustainable farming practices (8.6 and 8.7) offer solutions to these issues. We can meet our current food needs without hurting future generations or the environment.

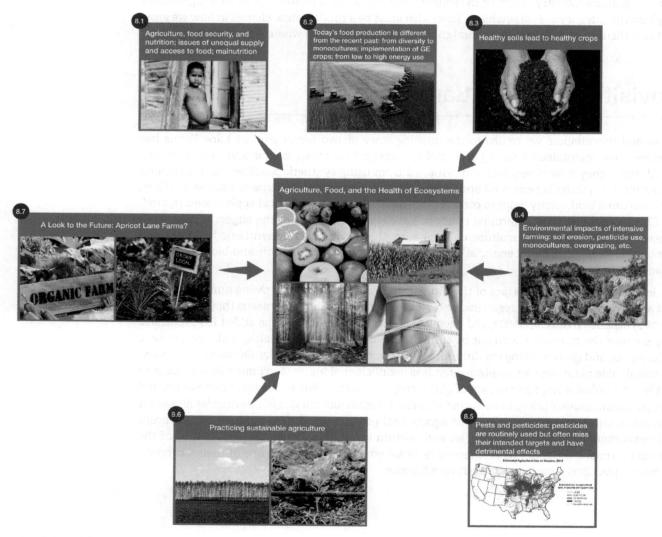

8.8 References

- Altieri, M. A. 1999. "The ecological role of biodiversity in agroecosystems." *Agricultural Ecosystems Environmental Journal* 74: 19–31.

- Andreotti, G., S. Koutros, and J. N. Hofmann. 2018. "Glyphosate use and cancer incidence in the agricultural health study." *Journal of the National Cancer Institute* 110, no. 5: 505–509.

- Aworh, O. C. 2008. "The role of traditional food processing technologies in national development: West African experience." In: *Using Food Science and Technology to Improve Nutrition and Promote National Development* (Eds.: G. L. Robertson, and J. R. Lupien). International Union of Food Science and Technology.

- Bale, J. S., J. C. van Lenteren, and F. Bigler. 2008. "Biological control and sustainable food production." *Philos Trans R Soc Lond B Biol Sci* 363, no. 1492: 761–776.

- Barrow, C. J. 1991. *Land Degradation*. Cambridge, UK: Cambridge University Press.

- Berendse, F., J. van Ruijven, E. Jongejans, and S. Keesstra. 2015. "Loss of plant species diversity reduces soil erosion resistance." *Ecosystems.* https://doi.org/10.1007/s10021-015-9869-6.

- Bley, H., C. Gianello, J. da Silva Santos, and P. L. Roldão Selau. 2017. "Nutrient release, plant nutrition and potassium leaching from polymer-coated fertilizer." *Rev. Bras. Cienc. Solo.* 41: e0160142.

- Borlaug, N. E. 1958. "The impact of agricultural research on Mexican wheat production." *Transactions of the New York Academy of Science* 20: 278–295.

- Brady, N. C., and R. R. Weil. 2008. *The Nature and Properties of Soils, 14th Edition*. London, UK: Pearson.

- Buck, J. C., J. Hua, W. R. Brogan III, T. D. Dang, J. Urbina, R. J. Bendis, A. B. Stoler, A. R. Blaustein, and R. A. Relyea. 2015. "Effects of pesticide mixtures on host-pathogen dynamics of the amphibian chytrid fungus." *PLoS One* 10, no. 7: e0132832. https://doi.org/10.1371/journal.pone.0132832.

- Cardoso, E. J. B. N., M. A. Nogueira, and S. M. G. Ferraz. 2007. "Biological N2 fixation and mineral N in common bean-maize intercropping or sole cropping in southeastern Brazil." *Experimental Agriculture* 43, no. 3: 319–330.

- Catt, J. A. 2001. "The agricultural importance of loess." *Earth–Science Reviews* 54, no. 1–3: 213–229.

- Chang, F., M. F. Simcik, and P. D. Capel. 2010. "Occurrence and fate of the herbicide glyphosate and its degradate aminomethylphosphonic acid in the atmosphere." *Environmental Toxicology and Chemistry* 30, no. 3: 548–555.

- Dawson, A. H., M. Eddleston, L. Senarathna, F. Mohamed, I. Gawarammana, S. J. Bowe, G. Manuweera, and N. A. Buckley. 2010. "Acute human lethal toxicity of agricultural pesticides: a prospective cohort study." *PLoS Med* 7, no. 10: e1000357.

- Dawson, N., A. Martin, and T. Sikor. 2016. "Green revolution in sub-Saharan Africa: implications of imposed innovation for the wellbeing of rural smallholders." *World Dev* 78: 204–218.

- Elliott, J., M. Glotter, A. C. Ruane, K. J. Boote, J. L. Hatfield, J. W. Jones, C. Rozenzweig, L. A. Smith, and I. Foster. 2017. "Characterizing agricultural impacts of recent large-scale US droughts and changing technology and management." *Agricultural Systems* 159: 275–281.

- Food and Agriculture Organization of the United Nations (FAO). 2014. *Genetically Modified Crops*. United Nations.

- Food and Agriculture Organization of the United Nations (FAO). 2016. *Food and Agriculture Organization of the United Nations—Statistics Database*. http://faostat3.fao.org/.

- Food and Agriculture Organization of the United Nations (FAO). 2017. *Food and Agriculture Organization of the United Nations—Statistics Database*. http://faostat3.fao.org/.

- Food and Agriculture Organization of the United Nations (FAO). 2020. "The State of the World's Forests." *Forests, Biodiversity and People.* https://doi.org/10.4060/ca8642en.

- Foreman, W. T., M. S. Majewski, D. A. Goolsby, F. W. Wiebe, and R. H. Coupe. 2000. "Pesticides in the atmosphere of the Mississippi River Valley, part II—Air." *The Science of the Total Environment* 248: 213–216.

- Guilherme, S., I. Gaivão, M. A. Santos, and M. Pacheco. 2010. "European eel (Anguilla anguilla) genotoxic and pro-oxidant responses following short-term exposure to Roundup—a glyphosate-based herbicide." *Mutagenesis* 25, no. 5: 523–530.

- Hayes, T. B., P. Case, S. Chui, D. Chung, C. Haeffele, K. Haston, M. Less, V. P. Mai, Y. Marjuoa, J. Parker, and M. Tsui. 2006. "Pesticide mixtures, endocrine disruption, and amphibian declines: are we underestimating the impact?" *Environmental Health Perspectives* 114, no. 1: 40–50.

- Henry, M., M. Béguin, F. Requier, O. Rollin, J. F. Odoux, P. Aupinel, J. Aptel, S. Tchamitchian, and A. Decourtye. 2012. "A common pesticide decreases foraging success and survival in honey bees." *Science* 336: 348–350.

- Hladik, M. L., M. Vandever, and K. L. Smalling. 2016. "Exposure of native bees foraging in an agricultural landscape to current-use pesticides." *Science of the Total Environment* 542: 469–477.

- IPCC. 2007. "Mitigation of Climate Change: Contribution of Working Group III to the Fourth Assessment Report of the Intergovernmental Panel on Climate Change." In: *Climate Change 2007* (Eds.: B. Metz, O. R. Davidson, P. R. Bosch, R. Dave, and L. A. Meyer). Cambridge, United Kingdom and New York: Cambridge University Press.

- IUCN. 2021. "Red list of threatened species." https://www.iucnredlist.org (accessed February 5, 2021).

- Jaramillo, F., and G. Destouni. 2015. "Local flow regulation and irrigation raise global human water consumption and footprint." *Science* 350, no. 6265: 1248–1251.

- Jorgenson, D. W., and F. M. Gollop. 1992. "Productivity growth in U.S. agriculture: a postwar perspective." *Journal of Agricultural Economics* 74, no. 3: 745–750.

- Kairis, O., C. Karavitis, L. Salvati, A. Kounalaki, and K. Kosmas. 2015. "Exploring the impact of overgrazing on soil erosion and land degradation in a dry Mediterranean agro-forest landscape (Crete, Greece)." *Arid Land Research and Management* 29: 360–374.

- Khalil, M., A. Alghamdi, S. Sharawy, and N. I. Al-Dremly. 2017. "Screening of weeds and their effect on alfalfa (*Medicago sativa*)" 87, no. 11: 1565–1571.

- Klümper, W., and M. Qaim. 2014. "A meta-analysis of the impacts of genetically modified crops." *PLoS ONE* 9: e111629. https://doi. org/10.1371/journal.pone.0111629.

- Koneswaran, G., and D. Nierenberg, 2008. "Global farm animal production and global warming: impacting and mitigating climate change." *Environmental Health Perspectives* 116, no. 5: 578–582.

- Lechenet, M., F. Dessaint, G. Py, D. Makowski, and N. Munier-Jolain. 2017. "Reducing pesticide use while preserving crop productivity and profitability on arable farms." *Nature Plants* 3: 17008. https://doi.org/10.1038/nplants.2017.8.

- Lesk, C., P. Rowhani, and N. Ramankutty. 2016. "Influence of extreme weather disasters on global crop production." *Nature* 529: 84–87.

- Lotter, D. W., R. Seidel, and W. Liebhardt. 2009. "The performance of organic and conventional cropping systems in an extreme climate year." *Am. J. Alternative Agr.* 18: 146–154.

- Matariya, Z. R., K. K. Lodhiya, and R. G. Mahajan. 2017. "Environmental correlates of undernutrition among children of 3–6 years of age, Rajkot, Gujarat, India." *Journal of Family Medicine and Primary Care* 5, no. 4: 834–839.

- Mattila, H. R., G. W. Otis, L. T. P. Nguyen, H. D. Pham, O. M. Knight, and N. T. Phan. 2020. "Honey bees (Apis cerana) use animal feces as a tool to defend colonies against group attack by giant hornets (Vespa soror)." *PLoS One*. https://doi.org/10.1371/journal.pone.0242668.

- McMillan, T. 2014. "The new face of hunger: millions of working Americans don't know where their next meal is coming from." *National Geographic Society* 226 (2): 66.

- Meikle, W. G., V. Corby-Harris, M. J. Carroll, M. Weiss, L. A. Snyder, A. D. Charlotte, E. Beren, and N, Brown. 2019. "Exposure to sublethal concentrations of methoxyfenozide disrupts honey bee colony activity and thermoregulation." *PLoS One* 14, no. 3. https://doi.org/10.137/journal.pone.0204635.

- Mesnage, R., M. Arno, M. Costanzo, M. Malatesta, G. E. Séralini, and M. N. Antoniou. 2015. "Transcriptome profile analysis reflects rat liver and kidney damage following chronic ultra-low Roundup exposure." *Environ Health* 14, no. 70. https://doi.org/10.1186/s12940-015-0056-1.

- Montgomery, D. R. 2007. "Soil erosion and agricultural sustainability." *Proceedings of the National Academy of Sciences of the United States of America* 104, no. 33: 13268–13272.

- Nicholls, C. I., and M. A. Altieri. 2013. "Plant biodiversity enhances bees and other insect pollinators in agroecosystems. A review." *Agron. Sustain. Dev.* 33: 257–274.

- Northbourne, L. 1940. *Look to the Land.* London, UK: J. M. Dent and Sons.

- Ometto, J. P., A. P. D. Aguiar, and L. A. Marinelli. 2011. "Amazon deforestation in Brazil: effects, drivers and challenges." *Carbon Management* 2, no. 5: 575–585.

- Paini, D. R., A. W. Sheppard, D. C. Cook, P. J. De Barro, S. P. Worner, and M. B. Thomas. 2016. "Global threat to agriculture from invasive species." *PNAS* 113, no. 27: 7575–7579.

- Pandurangan, M., and D. H. Kim. 2015. "A novel approach for in vitro meat production." *Microbiol Biotechnol.* 99: 5391–5395.

- Parent, M. E., M. Desy, J. Siemiatycki. 2009. "Does exposure to agricultural chemicals increase the risk of prostate cancer among farmers?" *Mcgill J Med* 12: 70–77.

- Paull, J. 2014. "Lord Northbourne, the man who invented organic farming, a biography." *Journal of Organic Systems* 9, no. 1: 31–53.

- Pimental, D., C. Harvey, K. Resosudarmo, K. Sinclair, M. McNair, S. Crist, L. Shpritz, L. Fitton, R. Saffouri, and R. Blair. 1995. "Environmental and economic costs of soil erosion and conservation benefits." *Science* 267, no. 5201: 1117–1123.

- Pimental, D. 1995. "Amounts of pesticides reaching target pests: environmental impacts and ethics." *Journal of Agricultural and Environmental Ethics* 8: 17–29.

- Pimental, D., R. Zuniga, and D. Morrison. 2005. "Update on the environmental and economic costs associated with alien-invasive species in the United States. *Ecol Econ* 52, no. 3: 273–288.

- Pimental, D., and M. Burgess. 2012. "Small amounts of pesticides reaching target insects." *Environ. Dev Sustain* 14: 1–2.

- Post, M. J. 2014. "An alternative animal protein source: cultured beef." *Annals of the New York Academy of Sciences* 1328: 29–33.

- Rauh, V. A., F. P. Perera, M. K. Horton, et al. 2012. "Brain anomalies in children exposed prenatally to a common organophosphate pesticide." *PNAS* 109, no. 20: 7871–7876.

- Riegler, M. 2018. "Insect threats to food security Pest damage to crops will increase substantially in many regions as the planet continues to warm." *Science* 361: 846.

- Roose, E. 1988. *Conservation Farming on Steep Lands.* Ankeny, IA: Soil and Water Conservation Society.

- Rosenzweig, C., C. Mbow, L. G. Barioni, et al. 2020. "Climate change responses benefit from a global food system approach." *Nature Food* 1: 94–97.

- Sauer, J. R., J. E. Hines, and J. Fallon. 2008. *The North American breeding bird survey, results and analysis 1966–2007. Version 5.15.2008.* Laurel, MD: UGS Patuxent Wildlife Research Center.

- Scholes, M. C., and R. J. Scholes. 2013. "Dust unto dust." *Science* 342: 565–566.

- Shepon, A., G. Eshel, E. Noor, and R. Milo. 2016. "Energy and protein feed-to-food conversion efficiencies in the US and potential food security gains from dietary changes." *Environmental Research Letters* 11. https://doi.org/10.1088/1748-9326/11/10/105002.

- Singh, R. B. 2000. "Environmental consequences of agricultural development: a case study from the Green Revolution state of Haryana, India." *Agriculture, Ecosystems and Environment* 82: 97–103.

- Sodhi, N. S., B. W. Brook, and C. J. A. Bradshaw. 2009. "Causes and consequences of species extinctions." In: *The Princeton Guide to Ecology* (Eds.: Levin, S. A., S. R. Carpenter, H. C. J. Godfray, A. P. Kinzing, M. Loreau, J. B. Losos, B. Walker, and D. S. Wilcove). Princeton, NJ: Princeton University Press.

- Song, S., C. Zhang, Z. Chen, F. He, J. Wei, H. Tan, and X. Li. 2018. "Simultaneous determination of neonicotinoid insecticides and insect growth regulators residues in honey using LC-MS/MS with anion exchanger-disposable pipette extraction." *J Chromatogr A* 1557: 51–61.

- Spera, S. A., G. L. Galford, M. T. Coe, M. N. Macedo, and J. F. Mustard. 2016. "Land-use change affects water recycling in Brazil's last agricultural frontier." *Global Change Biology*. https://doi.org/10.111/gcb.13298.

- Speth, J. G. 1994. *Towards and Effective and Operational International Convention on Desertification*. United Nations, NY: International Convention on Desertification.

- The Hope Center for College, Community, and Justice (THCCCJ). 2020. *Real College 2020: Five Years of Evidence on Campus Basic Needs Insecurity*. Philadelphia, PA: Temple University.

- Thompson, T. L., T. A. Doerge, and R. E. Godin. 2002. "Subsurface drip irrigation and fertigation of broccoli: I. Yield, quality, and nitrogen uptake." *Soil Sci. Soc. Am. J.* 66: 186–192.

- Troeh, F. R., and L. M. Thompson. 1993. *Soils and Soil Fertility, Edition* 5. New York: Oxford University Press.

- United States Government Accountability Office (USGAO). 2018. *Food Insecurity Better Information Could Help Eligible College Students Access Federal Food Assistance Benefits*. GAO-119–95.

- Whitehorn, P. R., S. O'Connor, F. L. Wäckers, and D. Goulson. 2012. "Neonicotinoid pesticide reduces bumble bee colony growth and queen production." *Science* 336: 351–352.

- Woodcock, B. A., J. M. Bullock, R. F. Shore, M. S. Heard, M. G. Pereira, J. Redhead, H. Ridding, H. Dean, D. Sleep, P. Henrys, J. Peyton, S. Hulmes, L. Hulmes, S. Sárospataki, M. Edwards, E. Genersch, S. Knäbe, and R. F. Pywell. 2017. "Country-specific effects of neonicotinoid pesticides on honey bees and wild bees." *Science* 36, no. 6345: 1393–1395.

- Woods, J., A. Williams, J. K. Hughes, M. Black, and R. Murphy. 2010. "Energy and the food system." *Philosophical Transactions of The Royal Society B* 365: 2991–3006.

- Wright, H., R. Iain, and P. M. Lake. 2011. "Agriculture—a key element for conservation in the developing world." *Conservation Letters* 5, no. 1: 11–19.

- Yang, T., J. Doherty, B. Zhao, A. J. Kinchrla, J. M. Clark, and L. Hi. 2017. "Effectiveness of commercial and homemade washing agents in removing pesticide residues on and in apples." *J. Agric. Food Chem.* 65, no. 44: 9744–9752.

- Zehnder, G., G. M. Gurr, S. Kühne, M. R. Wade, S. D. Wratten, and E. Wyss. 2007. "Arthropod pest management in organic crops." *Ann. Rev. Entomol.* 52: 57–80.

CHAPTER 9
Sustainable Management of Forests, Grasslands, and Protected Areas

Case Study: The Significance and Plight of the Amazon–Cerrado Region

In 2013, a doctor in the Netherlands observed a remarkable pattern of pea-sized scars on a patient. Upon inquiry of their origin, the patient responded that they were from his participation in a Kambô ceremony when he lived in the Amazon (Brave et al. 2014). Each mark was a deliberate wound and a reminder of the potent effects of a giant tree frog's (*Phyllomedusa bicolor*) secretion, which is directly applied during the ceremony. While its famed healing powers have yet to be validated by science, Indigenous communities such as the Matses of the Amazon have harvested the white secretion for hundreds of years. This secretion is just one example of what makes this species unique, and like all of the region's species, the giant tree frog has a specialized set of characteristics, biology, and behavior. The giant tree frog and the Indigenous communities are two of countless elements of the immense Amazon–Cerrado region—equal in size to almost 90 percent of the contiguous United States (see Figure 9.1). This vast region spreads across nine South American countries and contains multiple biomes, such as the tropical rain forest of the Amazon and the savanna of the Cerrado.

FIGURE 9.1
Tucked away in the Amazon and Cerrado is an unusual array of creatures, from the giant monkey frog (A) to the Brazilian tapir (B) and the anaconda (C).

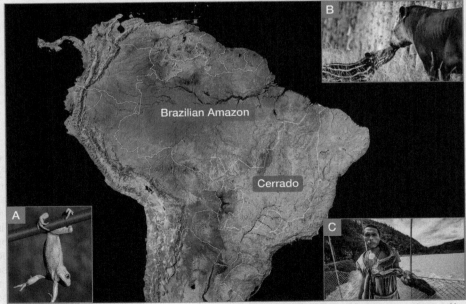

Sources: © Shutterstock, Inc.; Mapping the Amazon, NASA Earth Observatory, https://earthobservatory.nasa.gov/images/145649/mapping-the-amazon.

Besides being a home to the most biodiverse forests and grasslands (Da Silva et al. 2005; Lewinsohn and Prado 2005) on the planet, this region has a profound influence on continental- and global-scale water and carbon cycles as well as climate (Ellison et al. 2017; Ellison 2018). Each tree, bush, and blade of grass in this vast region offers shade from solar radiation and releases water into the atmosphere. Collectively, hundreds of billions of trees—each transpiring up to 100 liters of water per day—help generate a prodigious volume of water vapor, which benefits agricultural production in far-off Asia and even North America's Mid-west.

FIGURE 9.2
Deforestation of the Brazilian Amazon and Cerrado is primarily attributed to expanding agriculture such as soybean fields. Brazil is the leading exporter of soybeans and most are destined for China, the world's largest importer. Soybeans are used in animal feed for poultry, cattle, chickens, and aquaculture. (A) Pristine (left) and deforested (right) amazon rain forest in Mato Grosso, Brazil. (B) Deforestation of the Brazilian Amazon. (C) Brazilian soybeans ready for packaging and shipping.

Sources: Joseph Shostell; © Shutterstock, Inc.; data from Observacao da Terra, http://www.obt.inpe.br/OBT/assuntos/programas/amazonia/prodes

Undeniably and unfortunately, these benefits are weakening due to habitat destruction in support of a growing agricultural industry (see Figure 9.2) (see video link: "Beef Grown in the Amazon"). Long has the world recognized deforestation in the famous Amazon, but the global community rarely discusses the Amazon's neighbor—the Cerrado, where 50 percent of natural habitat has already been transformed to support croplands and livestock fields (Roche et al. 2011). How have we reached this point? With 60 percent of the Amazon and almost all of the Cerrado located in Brazil, protection or devastation of these areas depends mainly on a single country. Deforestation in the Brazilian Amazon peaked in the 1990s and early 2000s, and then declined by a concerted effort of the Brazilian government and international pressure. Brazil targeted soybeans, because one million hectares of natural habitat of the Amazon had been converted to soybean fields in just five years (2001–2006). The Soy Moratorium, which was signed in 2006, prohibits the selling of soybeans from areas deforested after July of 2006. In response, expansion of new soybean fields into the Amazon dropped to less than 1 percent (Gibbs et al. 2015), but ratcheted up in the Cerrado, which was not included in the agreement (Soterroni et al. 2019). Environmental organizations and companies have called for Brazil to protect the Cerrado, but there is doubt that Brazil will support this and other policies to protect the environment while Jair Bolsonaro remains as president. Since taking office in 2019, President Bolsonaro has dismantled environmental protections and deforestation has significantly increased.

 Beef Grown in the Amazon

Listen to a reporter as she investigates the animal industry in the Amazon.

View in the online reader

In this chapter, we investigate the management of forest lands and grasslands—noting environmental problems and sustainable solutions. Humankind can't afford to lose these ecosystems, for they provide services we need for survival. The chapter also covers national parks and wilderness areas set aside for the benefit of people today and future generations.

9.1 World Forests: Description, Problems, and Sustainable Management

Learning Objectives

1. Summarize the size, characteristics, and distribution of Earth's forests.
2. Identify the main threats to forests.
3. Describe five examples of managing forests sustainably.

The opening story about the Amazon–Cerrado region informs us of the value of natural ecosystems as well as the consequences of poor land management. Deforestation is one of many examples of nonsustainable practices driven by a complex network of factors. Cattle ranching, crop farming, infrastructure development, and mining all play roles in the destruction of old-growth forests. Who is ultimately responsible for deciding how these lands are used? Control falls under the umbrella of ownership, laws, and enforcement of those laws. In the case of Brazil, there are strong environmental laws, such as requiring landowners to reserve up to 80 percent of their land for native vegetation, but these laws are weakly enforced, or not enforced at all, in the case of Bolsonaro. In this section, we focus on the world's forests, their environmental problems, and management solutions.

Forests cover a relatively small percentage of Earth's surface (about 8 percent), yet have a pronounced effect on biodiversity, biogeochemical cycles, climate, and society. They hold the vast majority of terrestrial species and contain many of the world's biodiverse hotspots, where large numbers of endemic species are threatened. The world's forests store an estimated 296 billion tons (296 gigatons) of carbon and absorb 2 billion tons of carbon dioxide each year. Their ability to sequester and absorb carbon means they play a powerful role in the mitigation of climate change. Furthermore, tree roots impede soil erosion and help to retain nutrients. Forests also have an integral role in the hydrological cycle, especially in tropical climates. Water, taken in by roots, moves vertically upward within trees and eventually evaporates from leaves, adding moisture to the atmosphere. In the case of large tropical rain forests such as the Amazon, generated moisture can influence ecosystems thousands of kilometers away. Along with fresh water, forests offer clean air and a number of products useful to society. Trees, for example improve air quality by absorbing air pollutants (Nowak 2002). Roughly 25 percent of the global population—including the rural poor—depends on forests for their livelihood (Munang el al. 2011). We would be hard pressed to find anyone who doesn't benefit from at least one of the many forest commodities. In total, forest commodities contribute $450 billion to the global economy each year. They are also home to hundreds of Indigenous peoples, such as the Matses (see "Case Study: The Significance and Plight of the Amazon–Cerrado Region").

Overview of World Forests

What are forests, where are they located, and how large are they? Not all trees are part of a forest. According to the Food and Agricultural Organization (FAO), a group of trees taller than 5 m (16.4 ft), covering an area greater than 0.5 hectares (1.2 acres), and with a canopy covering more than 10 percent of the ground, qualifies as a forest.

forest zones

Land covered fully or partially by trees; forest zones: tropical, subtropical, temperature, and boreal.

Nearly 4 billion hectares (9.9 billion acres) of diverse forests are spread across the globe, covering one-third of all land (see Figure 9.3). They are distributed unevenly, with almost 70 percent in just ten countries, and more than 50 percent in just five (see Table 9.1). Following criteria proposed by FAO, forests are classified according to zones based on climate, which is, in part, an outcome of distance from the equator (Iremonger and Gerrand 2011). The four major **forest zones** are tropical, subtropical, temperate, and boreal (taiga) (see Figure 9.3). See Chapter 5 for a review of forest biomes. Of these, the tropical is the most diverse. Located closest to the equator, it has conditions of warm temperatures, high precipitation, and a lack of seasonal variation in day length (twelve hours year-round). These conditions are ideal for dense plant growth and support the development of a large variety of ferns, mosses, and other plants beneath the forest canopy.

Tropical rain forests (see "Case Study: The Significance and Plight of the Amazon–Cerrado Region") are home to millions of species (Gallery 2014). Giant tree frogs, jaguars, and howler monkeys are just a few of the species we expect to find here. Adjacent to the tropical forests are the slightly cooler subtropical humid forests and subtropical dry forests.

The comparatively less biodiverse temperate forests are found between approximately 25° and 50° latitude in each hemisphere, in cooler climates with less precipitation. Hardwood oaks, maples, beech, and other deciduous trees dominate here and provide habitat space for bears, deer, foxes, owls, and an assortment of small mammals. Temperate forests are common in Japan, North America, and Eurasia. Soils in these forests are typically well developed and nutrient rich, a clear distinction from the tropics, where soils are often nutrient poor due to abundant rainwater leaching away the nutrients (Dalling et al. 2016). Historically, large numbers of people have settled in temperate forests.

FIGURE 9.3
Approximately 29 percent of the Earth's surface is land (A), and of this, an estimated 30 percent is covered in forests (B). Based on ecological zones, tropical forests make up the greatest percentage of total forested area.

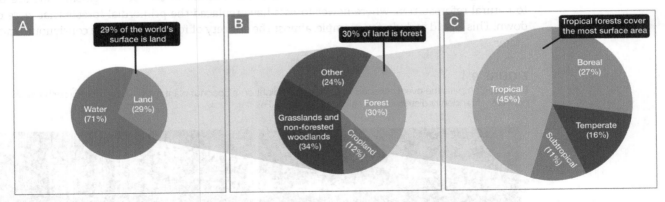

Sources: Joseph Shostell; "How Much Water is There on Earth?" by Water Science School, November 13, 2019, https://www.usgs.gov/special-topics/water-science-school/science/how-much-water-there-earth#:~:text=About. 71 percent of the,percent of all Earth's water; Table on page 5 within the following reference: FAO. 2011. The State of the World's Land and Water Resources for Food and Agriculture Managing Systems at risk. The Food and Agriculture Organization of the United Nations and Earthscan; FAO. 2020. The State of the World's Forests Forests, Biodiversity and People. Food and Agriculture Organization of the United Nations. (see figure 7 on page 18.).

TABLE 9.1
Top ten forested countries.

Rank	Country	Forest Area (ha)	Percentage of Land Area	Percentage of Global Forested Area
1	Russian Federation	815,312,000	50	20
2	Brazil	496,620,000	59	12
3	Canada	346,928,000	38	9
4	United States	309,795,000	34	8
5	China	219,978,000	22	5
6	D.R.C.	126,155,000	67	4
7	Australia	134,005,000	16	3
8	Indonesia	92,133,000	53	2
9	Peru	72,330,000	58	2
10	India	72,160,000	24	2

Source: Data from FAO 2020; https://www.fao.org/state-of-forests/en/.

Boreal forests of conifers and evergreen trees stretch between 50° and 60° northern latitude, enduring even colder temperatures and receiving less precipitation than temperate forests. These conifer and evergreen forests, distributed in Canada, Alaska, Scandinavia, and Siberia, provide habitat space for a faunal community of moose, deer, bears, caribou, wolves, rabbits, birds, and rodents. Lower light intensity, long, cold winters, and short growing seasons make it difficult for these forests to regenerate after deforestation. While not commonly inhabited by people due to cold temperatures, society does threaten boreal forests with mining of iron, coal, and natural gas. Loggers initially ignored boreal forests, at least relative to other forests, because the trees were more widely dispersed and their wood less desirable.

The vast majority of forested area (93 percent) is still natural (see Figure 9.4). Planted forests make up the remaining 7 percent of the total forested area. These include intensively managed forests called plantations that are composed of one or two tree species of similar age. Approximately one-fourth of natural forests are still primordial, which means they have been left relatively untouched by society. Their intactness is more due to inhospitable climate or difficult access than conservation efforts. Boreal forest in the northern parts of Canada and the Russian Federation are primordial, as are large tracts of tropical forests in Brazil, Indonesia, and Papua New Guinea. Of course, as accessibility to these forests improves with additional roads, these forests become increasingly threatened. The other three-fourths of natural forests at the global scale are due to natural reforestation, where newer forests have replaced the primordial forests that were cut down. This would include, for example, almost the entirety of forests within the contiguous United States.

FIGURE 9.4
Forests. Compare the evenly spaced trees of equal height on a coconut plantation (A) to an old-growth forest consists of randomly distributed trees of various sizes (B).

Source: © Shutterstock, Inc.

Problems and Challenges Facing World Forests

Forests have successfully evolved and adapted to natural, slow environmental change since their beginnings, some 400 million years ago. They have contracted and expanded their distributions in response to climate changes. In addition to global-scale drivers of change, forests also have the capacity to adequately respond to and regenerate from losses caused by tornados, fires, and other relatively small-scale drivers of change. As we discuss next, problems arise whenever the rate of environmental change exceeds a forest's ability to adapt.

Over the last few hundred years, forests have been forced to contend with a growing human population, and, unfortunately, forests are in jeopardy. Three major anthropogenic factors threatening forests today are deforestation, climate change, and acid rain.

Deforestation

Since 1990, the total forested area in the world has dropped by 4.2 percent, from 4.24 billion hectares (ha; 10.47 ac) to 4.06 billion ha (10.03 ac) (FAO 2020). Part of these losses include a 2.5 percent global reduction in primordial forests. Of the four climate domains, the tropics is experiencing the highest rate of deforestation (see "Case Study: The Significance and Plight of the Amazon–Cerrado Region"). Brazil, for example, lost 1.1 million ha (2.7 million ac) in 2020 (Silva-Junior et al. 2021) (see Figure 9.5).

FIGURE 9.5
Between 1990 and 2020, global forest area decreased by 4.4 percent. Forest area trends are broken up by continent and decade and indicated by colored histograms (shades of green = gain, shades of red = loss). Bold numbers indicate total forest area for each continent (M = millions). The highest rates of deforestation are in South America and Africa.

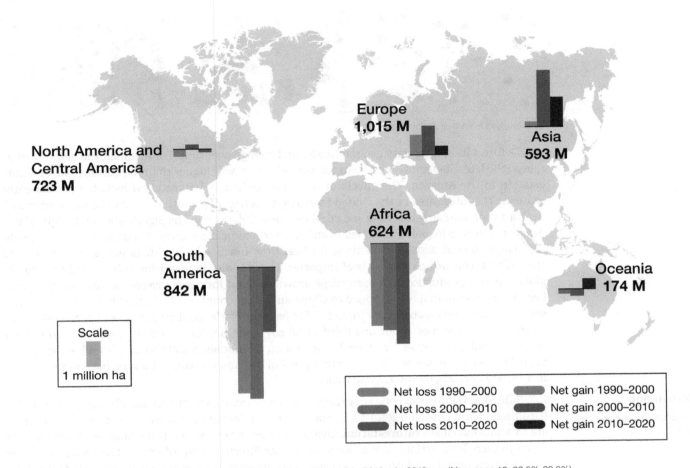

Source: Joseph Shostell; © Shutterstock, Inc.; data from FAO, https://www.fao.org/3/ca8642en/ca8642en.pdf (see page 10: 32.5%-30.8%).

There are three main types of deforestation: clearcutting, selective cutting, and slash-and-burn (see Figure 9.6). **Clearcutting** is the easiest and most devastating type of deforestation because it removes all trees, regardless of size, over an entire area. Only tree stumps, an assortment of crushed vegetation, and bare soil remain. Deforestation at this scale requires harvesters, huge bulldozers, and other heavy machinery to cut down, move, and haul away trees. Afterward, soil erosion becomes a problem and the soil in the denuded landscape moves unimpeded into local streams via runoff. Biodiversity plummets on the land and in the streams. Another form of deforestation is **selective cutting**. In this practice, also known as selective logging, only a few trees are removed from an area, with the intention of leaving the rest untouched. This form of deforestation can also cause extensive destruction of a forest (Asner et al. 2005). On average, loggers practicing selective cutting of marketable tree species in the dense Amazon end up severely damaging up to thirty trees for every tree they remove. Why is this? Part of the answer is the thickness of the forest and the network of strong, tangled vines connecting trees together. The third form of deforestation—**slash-and-burn**—is a form of agriculture practiced for centuries, and commonly used by subsistence farms today. The process begins with the farmer cutting down all of the trees and shrubs in a small area (the slashing). Then the farmer burns the cut foliage and plants crops on the cleared terrain. In nutrient-poor tropical areas, crop production is strong for a couple of years and then quickly wanes because the crops have absorbed most of the nutrients in the soil. In a few years, the farmer moves to another section of land and repeats the process in a continual cycle.

clearcutting

A form of deforestation; all trees are removed from an area.

selective cutting

A form of deforestation in which a few trees are removed from an area.

slash-and-burn

Cutting down trees and other plants followed by burning; a common agricultural practice for subsistence farmers.

FIGURE 9.6

Logging methods. (A) Clearcutting removes all trees in an area. Selective-cutting methods include (B) shelterwood harvesting, in which unhealthy trees (in yellow) are targeted and removed, and (C) strip-cutting, in which trees are removed in narrow strips, leaving the majority of the forest intact and able to regenerate itself.

Sources: Joseph Shostell; © Shutterstock, Inc.

Deforestation rates vary geographically and change over time. For instance, the deforestation rate in the late nineteenth century in the United States, was higher than the current rate of deforestation in the Amazon. The effects of this unprecedented deforestation included permanently reducing the forest area of the United States by 30 percent. In South America, the main drivers of deforestation are cattle ranching and croplands (see "Case Study: The Significance and Plight of the Amazon–Cerrado Region"), both tied to animal production and international commerce (Fearnside 2017; Nepstad et al. 2006). The demand for beef from Brazil—the world's largest exporter—comes from China, the world's largest beef importer. There is also demand for animal feed to support global animal production. Soybean crops grown on land formerly covered by primordial forests become part of animal feed shipped to China and other countries. In fact, all but 2 percent of the soybeans produced globally are intended for feed for cattle, poultry, swine, and fish (Goldsmith 2008). China consumes about one-third of all soybeans produced each year to feed 440 million swine as well as its other livestock. Deforestation in Indonesia (681,000 ha [1.7 million acres] per year), Peru, and Ecuador is driven, in part, by global demand for palm oil, a versatile substance used in a variety of foods, cosmetics, and fuels.

reforestation

The action of regenerating a forest.

Subtropical forests experience extensive forestry management and are often treated as a crop (Drummond and Loveland 2010). Large tracts of forest are deforested and then allowed to regenerate in a process called **reforestation**. Overall, 30 percent of forests in the subtropics are cut and regrown each decade (Hansen et al. 2013). Temperate forests undergo deforestation as well, but they are being reforested at a faster rate. These forests are increasing in size by an average of 2.7 million ha per year (6.7 million acres) (Keenan et al. 2015).

Boreal forests are the least settled forested zone, and overall the least disturbed. Deforestation occurs in boreal forests, but the overall change in forested area at the national level is small. In Canada, boreal forests are relatively intact with about 80% unfragmented by roads. A different story continues to develop in northern Europe, where boreal forests are more intensively managed. The largest losses of boreal forests are occurring in Russia from clearcutting and high-intensity selection logging to meet wood demands in China and Japan (Mayer et al. 2005). In addition, human-caused fires have significantly contributed to deforestation of boreal forests in Russia (Achard et al. 2008). For example, two megafires within one nine-year period there deforested 22 million ha (54.4 million acres), an area larger than the state of Utah. However, as we discuss next, climate change is the greatest threat to boreal forests.

Climate Change

Climate change may well prove to be the single greatest environmental issue for forests and the world throughout the twenty-first century. With warmer atmospheric temperatures comes an increase in length of growing season and likelihood of droughts. Higher temperatures mean more carbon dioxide is released naturally, accelerating the cycle of global warming. Distributions of forests and individual tree species will shift to reflect the new temperatures and rainfall patterns (see Figure 9.7). Generally, cold-tolerant species will shift further northward, unless they are in mountain biomes, where they can shift to a higher elevation. For instance, within the Eastern United States, we predict forests dominated by maple, beech, and birch to be replaced by forests with oaks, pines, and hickory. Climate change also brings irregularity and extremes swings in precipitation patterns, and with this, periods of flooding and drought. Because of this, we predict a continued increase in the severity and frequency of forest fires (Halofsky et al. 2020). Warming of boreal forests and associated peatlands where large volumes of carbon are stored will further contribute to the release of carbon into the atmosphere. Northern peatlands in Canada and Russia currently sequester 25 percent of the Earth's entire soil carbon (McLaughlin and Webster 2014).

Climate change is also fostering the spread of destructive insects from southern to northern areas. For example, southern pine beetles have moved northward and are killing pine trees in the upper Midwest through to Nova Scotia. Colder weather use to kill the larvae of these beetles and hold their spread northward at bay. This is no longer true, and the once protected northern pine trees are dying.

FIGURE 9.7

Climate change will alter the distribution and composition of forests around the world. These graphs show the composition of forests in the eastern United States in (A) 1990 and (B) 2100 (predicted).

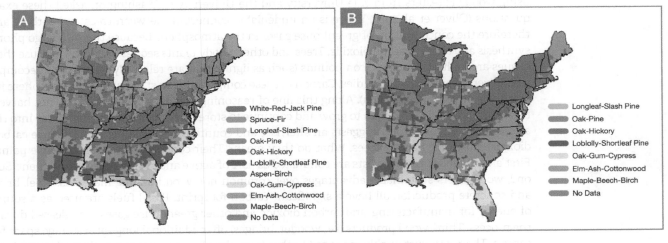

Source: USGCRP (2009).

Acid Rain

Forests also succumb to the effects of acid rain generated indirectly from the burning of coal, oil, and natural gas (see Chapter 3). Acid rain acidifies soils, leaches soil nutrients, and impedes tree growth. Trees in areas that receive acid rain are more vulnerable to winter freezing and other stressors. One observable sign of a tree stressed from acid rain is the yellow color of its leaves, or in the case of evergreens, reddish-orange colored needles. Over time, whole groves of trees and forests can perish from acid rain (see Figure 9.8).

FIGURE 9.8

Acid deposition acidifies soils and degrades the health of forests. The photo shows a formerly healthy forest in western Germany that perished from acid rain.

Source: © Shutterstock, Inc.

Sustainable Forestry Management

Sound forestry management begins with at least a basic understanding of the characteristics of a healthy forest. Identifying factors that degrade forest health is equally important. In this section, we discuss some management solutions to the main issues facing forests today. Keep in mind that as living, dynamic systems, forests—healthy forests—are expected to change naturally and undergo succession, and therefore not all change is negative. However, one concern of **foresters**—scientists who manage forests—is that forests encumbered by multiple pressures, including deforestation, climate change, fires, pests, disease, and acid rain, eventually lose the ability to rebound from disturbances, and then they fail.

Harvest or Not Harvest?

What is the best way to reduce carbon emissions and protect biodiversity? Is the answer to stop using wood? Foresters from Yale University and the University of Washington asked these exact questions (Oliver et al. 2014). There is an undeniable connection between trees and carbon, and therefore the concentration of greenhouse gases in the atmosphere, because trees undergo photosynthesis and absorb carbon dioxide. Trees and other woody plants sequester carbon because their tissues are built with organic compounds (such as lignin) that are relatively resistant to decomposition even after the organism dies. Carbon in these compounds can stay out of the atmosphere for hundreds of years (Ziekus 1981). Along this line of reasoning, it makes perfect sense to not harvest trees, but rather to allow them to grow and continue to store carbon, preventing its release into the atmosphere. Oliver's group suggests an alternate and counterintuitive approach to reduce carbon dioxide emissions: harvest trees. What do they mean? Their conclusion rests on multiple points. First and foremost, tree harvests are conducted as part of active and sustainable management. Second, wood offers sustainable advantages over common nonwood building materials. Steel, brick, and concrete production all have a significant carbon footprint. Fossil fuels are used as a source of energy for manufacturing, and carbon dioxide and other greenhouse gases are released during the process. Third, wood products (i.e., wooden bridges) offer additional long-term storage space for carbon. Therefore, sustainably managed timber farms by way of their trees and wooden products can end up sequestering more carbon compared to similar-sized unharvested forests. Dr. Chadwick Oliver's research group estimates that using wood instead of common building supplies could save up to 31 percent of global carbon dioxide emissions. In their view, and those of many other scientists, society could sequester carbon in wooden bridges and wooden buildings. Based on these findings, wooden structures may well be more abundant in the larger infrastructure (predicted to triple in size by 2050) of tomorrow's society.

Sustainability Through Certification

Forests are dynamic and can regenerate sections lost to deforestation. Foresters of sustainably managed forests take into account the ability of a forest to regrow and the multiple stressors placed on a forest. They ensure the rate of deforestation does not exceed the natural rate of reforestation. As consumers, how do we determine if the wood we use is sustainably grown? This is the role of the Forest Stewardship Council (FSC). They are an international nonprofit group that has already certified over 190 million hectares of forests in over eighty countries. FSC works with companies and scrutinizes their supply chains to ensure forests remain thriving environments. Their motto is "forests for all forever." The FSC is neither a supplier nor a buyer. They assess the quality of forestry management, and will only certify the forest if the management adheres to FSC's set of requirements. Multilevel criteria are required of forest operations in order to receive FSC certification of their products. Consumers can look for the FSC label when shopping for wood products.

Legislation Helps to Protect Forests

We—society and foresters—save and sustainably manage forests by developing and then following management plans. To help in this regard, Congress passed the National Forest Management Act in 1976. It is the main federal law that concerns the governance of national forests. This law builds upon and amends the Forest and Rangeland Renewable Resources Planning Act of 1974. It requests the Forest Service—the overseer of national forest lands—to develop management plans for each of its forests and then monitor and manage them so they are maintained in both size and composition. All national forests are therefore assessed for need of reforestation as well as the degree of potential pest infestations. The Act also promises annual funding to the Forest Service in the amount of $200 million to fulfill these responsibilities. Finally, the Act mandates the Forest Service to produce and present to Congress an annual report describing the health of national forest lands.

Another important Act is the Lacey Act of 1900, which prohibits the trade of illegally acquired wildlife. In 2008, the U.S. government passed amendments to the Lacey Act that made it illegal to import timber and wood products illegally obtained outside the United States Since these amendments took effect, imports of illegally obtained wood have declined by an estimated 44 percent.

International Sharing of Resources and Collaborations

International collaborations help in the conservation of forests. Here, we discuss global forest assessments, the REDD Program, debt-for-nature swaps, and corporate zero deforestation pledges.

Sharing of Forest Data Is Essential

Meaningful sustainable solutions to forest issues draw from historical and contemporary global forest data. When Rafael Zon and William Sparhawk published their seminal assessment of the world's forests in 1923, they set a baseline for future foresters and the world to follow (Zon and Sparhawk 1923). Thankfully, in 1948, the Food and Agriculture Organization of the United Nations (FAO) continued the process and has published assessments of the world's forests every five to ten years. The scope and content of the reports have evolved, and the reported data have become more reliable over time. Current assessments include satellite data, cover 88 percent of global forests, and report on forested area, volumes, growth rates, and other useful data. Our awareness of the state of forests and how they are changing is a result of these international collaborative reports. We now know the densities and species compositions of forests, globally. Moreover, through a long-term monitoring process, we can analyze and even predict trends.

Wealthy Countries Finance the Protection of Forests in Poorer Nations

In general, richer, higher latitude nations are seeing forest gains, and poorer tropical countries are enduring the greatest forest losses. These contrasting trends are troublesome, but new partnerships have developed to assist low-income countries in forest management. Back in 2008, the United Nations launched an international program called the Collaborative Program on Reducing Emissions from Deforestation and Forest Degradation in Developing Countries (UN-REDD). Emissions are part of the title because approximately 17–20 percent of global carbon emissions arise from deforestation and forest degradation. The program offers financial incentives for developing countries to lessen deforestation and carbon emissions. Within REDD there is the REDD plus (REDD+) initiative, which extends beyond deforestation and forest degradation to the sustainable management of forests, biodiversity conservation, and the lives of local peoples (see video link: "Saving Forests"). For example, one project in the Peruvian Amazon encourages local farmers to sign conservation agreements not to expand coffee plantations into the surrounding forests. Farmers who participate in the program receive an assortment of benefits that depend on needs, such as a stove for cooking and assistance to improve crop yields.

🎥 **Saving Forests**

Listen to a strategy of saving forests in Uganda.

Rebecca Tavani

View in the online reader

Debt-for-Nature Swap

Forests are also protected through debt-for-nature swap agreements. In this case, developing countries exchange their financial debt for the protection of forests. For example, the United States cancelled $21 million of Brazil's debt in exchange for the protection of Cerrado's forests (see "Case Study: The Significance and Plight of the Amazon–Cerrado Region") and coastal rain forests. As part of the agreement, Brazil invested a small proportion of the original monies owed into local conservation efforts. Just targeting the environment and not the local people is insufficient, because over the decades we have learned of the links between quality of life, poverty, and environmental protection. Therefore, the investment is also intended to improve the livelihoods of the people living in the threatened forests. Hundreds of millions of dollars in debt-for-nature swap agreements protect threatened ecosystems around the world. There are, however, limitations to debt-for-nature swaps. Nature swaps are effective at lessening the rate of deforestation, but these bilateral agreements, such as between the United States and Brazil, are often not sufficient to totally prevent deforestation (Sommer et al. 2019).

International Corporations and Countries Are Pledging Zero Deforestation

What is the most efficient way to stop deforestation? For the Amazon and Cerrado ecosystems, the main drivers of deforestation are demands for meat, soybeans, and palm oil (opening story). In this light, forest destruction is really a fault of commerce and economics. Taking this into account, international companies that control supply chains can have a powerful influence on forestry management. These companies can leverage their size and established connections with buyers and consumers to pressure ranchers and farmers to abide by sustainable principles. So far, about 450 companies have pledged to curb forest degradation this way. These pledges, such as Brazil's Soy Moratorium, often occur through consumer pressure on companies (Heilmayr et al. 2020). In this case, Walmart, McDonalds, and other large companies pledged not to purchase products containing soy grown on recently deforested lands of the Amazon. The decision has a top-down effect, influencing the large distribution company Cargill and the farmers who are no longer incentivized to clear forests to grow soybeans. As a result, deforestation of the Amazon linked to soy production decreased significantly. Because the Soy Moratorium only applies to the Amazon, soy production continues to cause deforestation in the Cerrado.

Fire and Salvage Logging

Forests ecosystems benefit from regular, low-severity surface fires that eliminate organic debris (i.e., leaf litter) on the forest floor. The debris is highly flammable, so the accumulation fuels high-intensity fires, which get hot enough to kill even the largest trees in a forest. Under controlled conditions, forest managers may intentionally start a fire (prescribed fire) to remove organic debris and prevent the development of high-intensity fires. Today, prescribed burns are regularly used in forest management.

Before 2000, salvage logging—the removal of logs from a burned area—was thought to be beneficial to natural reforestation. However, research now documents that this action can significantly reduce the development of new seedlings, an important step in forest recovery (Donato et al. 2006). In addition, salvage logging can also have negative effects on water quality, soil, and biodiversity (Smith et al. 2012; Malvar et al. 2017; Leverkus et al. 2018). Updated review of research findings like these helps us to formulate new management plans for forests.

We Can Harvest Trees Without Clearcutting

Earth has never had unlimited resources. We have come to better understand this fact as our population size has steadily increased. Clearcutting, for example, is no longer accepted as a universal practice. No, the human population has surged in size, and the only way to protect forests is to develop and implement forest management plans that offer alternatives to clearcutting. Four alternatives are selective cutting, strip cutting, shelter wood cutting, and seed tree cutting (see Figure 9.6). In selective cutting, loggers only cut down individual trees and leave the remaining forest intact. **Strip cutting** removes a narrow strip of trees, essentially leaving a corridor. **Shelter wood cutting** is a very different approach because the emphasis is on cutting dead and less desirable trees. This management strategy leaves the healthiest trees in the forest. Finally, **seed tree cutting** removes almost all of the trees within an area. The few remaining trees (seed trees) act as sources of seeds to help regenerate the forest.

Inga Alley Cropping

What is the best approach to protect old-growth forests, reforest, and support agriculture? Foresters of tropical regions grappled with this question, mainly because tropical forests are yielding to agriculture and local peoples' desire to improve their livelihood. One answer in Central and South America is Inga alley cropping—the planting of crops between rows of Inga trees (Leblanc and McGraw 2004) (see Figure 9.9). Inga are fast-growing trees native to Central America and South America and have a number of beneficial qualities. They are adapted to the acidic soils of tropical forests and are also leguminous, so they fix nitrogen (see Chapter 3). At the beginning of the agricultural season, when the farmers plant corn and beans, they also prune back the canopy of the Inga trees. Prior to this, the Inga's thick leaves created a thick canopy, shading the crop area. The pruned leaves and smaller branches are laid on the ground to prevent the growth of weeds. Weeds are therefore not a problem, and the farmers do not need to use pesticides. Nitrogen and phosphorus retained in the leaves act as fertilizer for the crops, which means the farmers do not spend time or money on fertilizers. This also means that farmers don't need to slash-and-burn more tropical forest every few years because of nutrient-poor soil. The Inga trees are planted about 4 m (4.4 yd) apart. After the trees are pruned, sunlight reaches the soil and the crop seeds germinate. At the end

strip cutting

A form of deforestation in which trees are harvested in narrow strips.

shelter wood cutting

A type of logging/deforestation targeting dead trees and undesirable trees.

seed tree cutting

A form of deforestation in which almost all of the trees are removed from an area. The few remaining trees are allowed to reseed the cleared area.

of the season, the crops are harvested, and the Inga trees are allowed to regrow their canopy, and then the entire process is repeated each year. Inga alley cropping is sustainable.

FIGURE 9.9

Inga alley cropping is a sustainable method to grow crops without deforestation. Cash crops are grown between rows of Inga trees. The trees are pruned before each growing season and allowed to regrow their canopies between crop seasons. (A) Inga trees with full canopies when no crops are planted. (B) Inga trees are pruned and crops are planted between trees. (C) Crops grow and are harvested. (D) Canopies of Inga trees begin to regrow after crop harvest.

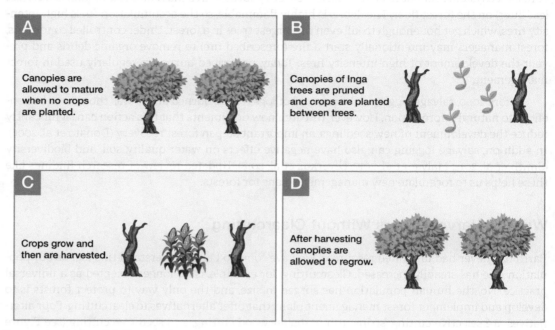

Sources: Joseph Shostell; © Shutterstock, Inc.

Reforestation of the Planet Is Needed

Reforestation can restore the world's cleared forests wherever land has not been permanently altered. Thanks to the ability of trees to regenerate growth, they are renewable, and with assistance they can once again populate landscapes. Forest acreage is increasing in some parts of the world, particularly in Asia, Europe, and North America. Large increases in Asia are primarily due to strong reforestation programs. China's Grain for Green program increased China's overall forested area by 32 percent—over 28 million ha (69 million acres) (Hua et al. 2018). The policy called for farmers to plant trees in cropland and scrubland areas; in return, they received money. Dr. Fangyuan Hua of Cambridge University acknowledges the gain in trees but questions their value as equal to naturally grown forests. Almost 50 percent of the farmers participating in the green program only plant one tree species. The end result is a large monoculture of trees unable to support high levels of biodiversity, and at greater risk from pests, invasive species, and disease. Growth of forests in North America and Europe are largely attributed to natural growth of temperate and boreal forests.

There are also success stories of reforestation on other continents, including heavily deforested Africa. Probably the most famous project began with the efforts of one person, **Wangari Maathai** (1940–2011). She founded the Green Belt Movement and encouraged the recognition and active involvement of women in society and environmental conservation. To date, the Green Belt Movement has planted over 51 million trees in Kenya. For her exceptional contributions to sustainable development, democracy, and peace, Wangari was awarded the Nobel Peace Prize in 2004.

Wangari Maathai

2004 Nobel Peace Prize laureate; environmental activist who started the Green Belt Movement and among her many sustainable efforts spoke against the use of plastic bags.

Key Takeaways

- Approximately 30 percent of terrestrial areas are covered by forests; they are distributed unequally because of natural climate conditions and human activities. The largest intact forests are found in the tropics and boreal zones.
- Three major anthropogenic factors threatening forests today are deforestation, climate change, and acid rain.
- Clearcutting is a nondiscriminate lumbering practice that removes all trees from an area, making it very difficult for a forest to regenerate.
- There are a variety of initiatives that help protect forests, including certification of forest products, forest protection laws, wealthy country financing of conservation efforts in developing countries, debt-for-nature swaps, government and corporate pledges of zero deforestation, Kenya's Green Belt Movement, and China's Grain for Green program.
- Forest managers have several options for sustainably harvesting wood from forests. The commonality among these options is harvesting wood in a way that allows the forest to regenerate. Examples are selective cutting, strip cutting, and shelter wood cutting.

9.2 World Grasslands: Description, Problems, and Sustainable Management

Learning Objectives

1. Summarize the extent and characteristics of global grasslands.
2. Discuss the quality of grassland areas and the threats these areas face.
3. Identify strategic and sustainable management methods of grassland areas.

Vast open space is a common feature of Earth's various grassland ecosystems, from the tropical savanna of the Cerrado (opening story), to the prairies of the Midwest, to the highlands of Ethiopia. Grasslands also provide habitat space for many endemic and threatened species. Perhaps one of the most unusual creatures is the gregarious, lip-smacking, and highly vocal gelada, or bleeding-heart monkey (*Theropthecus gelada*), of Ethiopia (see G in Figure 9.10). Scientists think this chatty Old World monkey, with its repertoire of barks, high-pitch squeals, and grunts, might provide answers to our questions about the development of speech (Bergman 2013). The grassland ecosystem where the geladas live is one example of Earth's diverse grassland ecosystems. In this section, we present an overview of global grasslands, the threats they face, and their sustainable management.

FIGURE 9.10

The world's grasslands (in yellow) are found on all continents save Antarctica. Examples of grassland types include A) Great Plains of North America, B) Eurasian steppe, C) Mongolian steppe, D) Pampas of South America, E) Cerrado, F) Tropical savanna, G) Montane savanna, and H) Savanna of Australia.

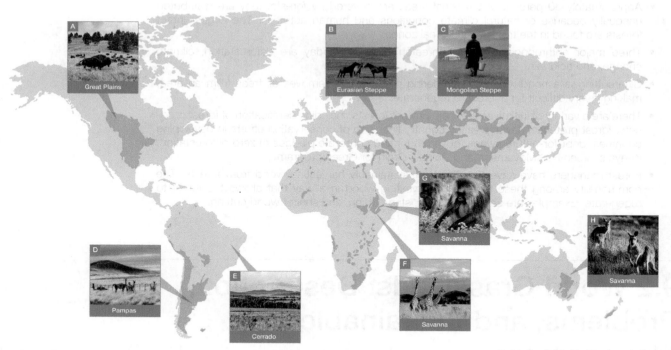

Sources: Joseph Shostell; © Shutterstock, Inc.; data from Grassland, NASA Earth Observatory, https://earthobservatory.nasa.gov/biome/biograssland.php.

Overview of Grasslands

Grasslands, first described in Chapter 5, make up at least 25 percent of the world's land surface and are found in geographical locations that receive less precipitation than required by forests, and more than found in deserts. Some scientists estimate that the overall extent of global grasslands is as high as 41 percent (White et al. 2000). Differences in estimates are due to the definition of a grassland and whether only naturally developed (old-growth) grasses are considered or if grasses in deforested areas are as well. Here, we only consider naturally developed grasslands and define grasslands as biomes with grasses as the dominant type of vegetation. This definition disqualifies tundra areas, which have grasses equally dominant with flowering plants, herbs, mosses, shrubs, and lichens. The grasslands occur on all Earth's continents except for Antarctica and can have nutrient-rich, fertile soils often used in support of agriculture. The savannas of sub-Saharan Africa and South America (such as in the Cerrado), the Great Plains of North America, the Steppes in Eurasia, and the Pampas in South America are all examples of grasslands (see Figure 9.10). Most of these areas are fairly flat, but some have a rolling terrain. All are of great importance to society and the larger environment.

rangelands

A combination of grasses and other plants and shrubs used for grazing.

According to the Food and Agriculture Organization (FAO) of the United Nations, grasslands are linked to the livelihoods of approximately 800 million people across the globe. Similar to other biomes, grasslands provide goods and services we and other living things need. Grasslands are a goldmine of society's main food staples. Wheat, rye, barley, millet, oats, and other grains grow here, and these crops support small subsistence farmers and large commercial farms alike (see Chapter 8). These lands include pasturelands with domesticated forage plants to feed livestock too, and are therefore instrumental in the production of meat, milk, leather, and wool. Grasslands are also part of **rangelands**, which contain a combination of natural grasses, as well as other plants and shrubs used as a food source by natural and livestock grazers. At a larger scale, grasslands provide a number of ecosystem services, including soil generation, watershed protection, protection against soil erosion, maintenance of biodiversity, dispersion of seeds, and mitigation of droughts and floods. They also serve as reservoirs for about one-third of all carbon on land (terrestrial carbon), which means their presence and storing capacity help to mitigate climate change.

What do grassland ecosystems look like? What would you observe should you visit one? Probably the first noticeable characteristic is the height of the grasses, anywhere from one to seven feet (0.3–2.1 m). In other words, standing amid the grasses, you may be completely camouflaged and only observe blades of grass, quite a different feeling from standing on a recently mowed yard in the suburbs. The wide diversity of grasses hides and provides habitat for a variety of herbivores and predators. Think of a cheetah on the hunt in the tall grasses of sub-Saharan Africa, or a bison laying in the grasslands of the Midwest. You may hear or smell these creatures, or only sense the wind rushing along the tops of the grass. The two main kinds of grasslands are tropical grasslands and temperate grasslands. Each supports an assemblage of species adapted to local environmental conditions. The tropical savanna of Africa supports gazelles, giraffes, zebras, wildebeests, and other large mammals. There is a different view amid the temperate grasslands of North America, where you may encounter a bison, badger, coyote, fox, or prairie dog, maybe even see a golden eagle. At the right time of year, you cannot miss the thousands of species of wildflowers. The most extensive grasslands are in Asia and sub-Saharan Africa. Grasslands adapt to long-term climatic conditions, and their extent, structure, and composition are maintained by fire, drought, and the presence of grazers.

Problems and Challenges Facing World Grasslands

Grasslands face a number of anthropogenic threats. Conversion to agriculture, livestock grazing, desertification, urbanization, fragmentation, and invasive species all negatively affect grassland and rangeland systems. Over 50 percent of soil in grasslands is degraded, and 5 percent is severely degraded as a result of anthropogenic pressures.

Grasslands like the tallgrass prairies of North America are some of the most threatened systems of the world (McLaughlin et al. 2014). The majority of these prairies were converted to croplands by the early twentieth century, and now a good percentage of the nation's food is cultivated here. Destruction of natural grass habitat destroys the homes of natural plants and animals, driving their population sizes down and confining them to isolated areas that still have intact grassland. In particular, native birds in these systems are in peril (Sauer et al. 2011), and mammal numbers have plummeted well below those described by Lewis and Clark. Tallgrass prairies once held huge herds of bison and pronghorn, along with robust populations of elk, grizzly bears, wolves, black-tailed prairie dogs, and North American beavers. No, not any more. The population of North America's fastest animal, the pronghorn, shrank from an estimated 30–60 million in the early 1800s to about 13,000 by 1915 due to loss of habitat, unregulated hunting, and fencing. The fencing is not an issue for grasses, but it threatens the migrations of pronghorn. Bison experienced a similar decline due to hunting during the same period; their population decreased from 40–60 million to less than 2,000 (see Figure 1.9). Today, with the help of conservation efforts, pronghorn and bison numbers are 800,000 and 500,000 respectively, still substantially less than their population sizes in precolonial America.

Overgrazing Degrades Grasslands

Natural grazers stimulate growth and promote plant biodiversity, but ill-managed domestic livestock can do the opposite, causing erosion and potentially eradicating grasses and other vegetation completely. Grasslands are challenged by overgrazing by livestock, which is a serious problem in the United States and other countries (see Figure 9.11). Roughly 55 percent of pastureland in the United States is overgrazed, and as a result is experiencing soil erosion. Wild herds, such as the historic herds of bison in the Midwest or the more current wildebeest herds in Tanzania, migrate across grasslands as needed—facilitating new growth of plants by their grazing and deposited manure. Corralled livestock do not have this opportunity unless an educated rancher rotates his/her livestock routinely among several separated pastures—allowing each area time to recover from grazing.

FIGURE 9.11
Overgrazing and urbanization are examples of threats to grasslands. (A) Soil erosion caused by overgrazing. In (B) and (C), satellite photos from NASA of the capital of India, New Delhi, taken in 1989 and 2018 respectively, show the conversion of grasslands (green) into streets, buildings, and parking lots (darker areas). By 2018, the once-separate cities of Bahadurgarh, New Delhi, and Ghaziabad grew and merged into one large city.

 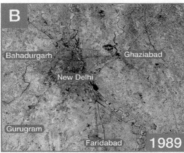 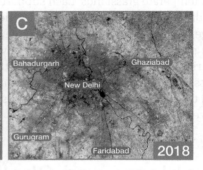

Sources: © Shutterstock, Inc.; Joseph Shostell; Urban Growth of New Delhi, NASA Earth Observatory, https://earthobservatory.nasa.gov/images/92813/urban-growth-of-new-delhi.

Urbanization Threatens Grasslands

More people live in urban areas today than ever before (see Chapter 17). This increasing urbanization trend has created some special challenges for conservation managers trying to protect grasslands. These lands (see Figure 9.11) have historically been the easiest to settle because there were few trees to remove, and they contained productive soil. Furthermore, urbanization tends to be long lasting, no matter where it occurs in the world. What we are seeing today in the North American Great Plains is the engulfment of the few remnants of prairies left untouched from agricultural expansion (McKinney 2002). Given the projected growth of the human population in the savanna of sub-Saharan Africa and accompanying urbanization in the coming decades, strong sustainable management plans are essential for the survival of these grassland systems. Urbanization is associated with other threats to grasslands, including roads and agricultural fields.

Other Threats to Grasslands

Fragmentation of grasslands and natural rangelands is due to roads, agriculture, and fencing. Each of these structures breaks up the natural flow of the landscape and hinders the movements of free-ranging wildlife. Fencing, for example, threatens the mobility and survival of large grassland mammals such as the endangered Prezewalski's gazelle in China (Zhang et al. 2014) and the cheetah in Namibia (Marder et al. 2008). Another main threat to grasslands and rangelands is invasive species. Take, for example, the introduction of cattle (*Bos Taurus*) and horses by Europeans settling in the Pampas of Argentina in the fifteenth century (de Villalobos and Salba 2010). The number of cattle and horses thrived in the new environment and grew in number from a few thousand to 48 million by 1700 (Crosby 2004). Grazing and trampling by their herds is considered to be one of the main reasons why all but one-fourth of the native grasslands species within the Pampas grasslands had disappeared by the early twentieth century (Schmieder 1927). European settlers also introduced pigs (*Sus scrofa*) to the Pampas. Pigs, in particular, are disruptive to grasslands because of their behavior of repeatedly pushing their snout into the ground (soil rooting) in search of food. Rooting behavior modifies the structure and composition of grass communities (Seward et al. 2004). Thousands of other exotic species including exotic grasses have been introduced into grassland and rangeland systems.

Similar to invasive animals, invasive grasses can negatively affect native grassland diversity. For example, Kentucky bluegrass has spread through the prairies of North Dakota and South Dakota. Where Kentucky bluegrass has become the dominant species, the diversity of native grasses has decreased dramatically (DeKeyser et al. 2013). In another example, invasive African grasses in the Cerrado (see "Case Study: The Significance and Plight of the Amazon–Cerrado Region") release allelopathic chemicals that inhibit the growth of other grass species (Barbosa et al. 2008). Invasion of nonnative grasses can also reduce the ability of grasslands to store carbon (Koteen et al. 2011). Therefore, their introductions in grassland systems can be indirectly linked with climate-change issues.

Sustainable Grassland Management

Based on the ecosystem services and goods they provide, grasslands and rangelands have great value to society and the world (see video link: "The Value of Grasslands"). Sustainable management of these systems ensures their continuation for the benefit of all. Here, we discuss the sustainable management of grasslands and rangelands pertaining to the issues of grazing, climate change, exotic species, and other key environmental issues.

Delineation of ancient grasslands and rangelands is a good start. Once identified and mapped, they can be adequately protected from conversion to forests. In today's push for reforestation, grasslands can easily be mistaken for a byproduct of deforestation. It is time for scientists to develop an updated status of the grasslands in the same way foresters produce a global assessment of the world's forests every five to ten years. These data and their analyses set the course for management decisions.

One of the common questions about the management of grasslands and rangelands deals with the role of grazers: specifically, whether grazing is harmful or beneficial. Natural endemic grazers in normal densities facilitate plant growth and are beneficial to plants. Plant biodiversity is maintained, and nutrients from large mammal grazers fertilize the landscape. Furthermore, areas with grazers have higher soil organic carbon and greater root biomass (Wilson et al. 2018). Maintaining a proper balance of grass community and livestock through use of **rotational grazing** and other techniques helps to prevent grassland degradation (Galt and Holecheck 2000). Rotational grazing is a commonly used practice to prevent overgrazing and allows for postgrazing recovery. Farmers and ranchers who use this strategy subdivide their pasture and then rotate the livestock sequentially among the pastures (see Figure 9.12).

The Value of Grasslands
Explore the grasslands of eastern Africa.

View in the online reader

rotational grazing

Subdivision of a pasture and then rotation of livestock sequentially among the subpastures in order to allow grazed vegetation to recover.

FIGURE 9.12

Rotating livestock among fields is one sustainable grazing strategy to avoid overgrazing and allow grazed grasses to recover. Livestock might be moved daily, weekly, or longer depending on the density and type of livestock.

Source: © Shutterstock, Inc.

To adequately understand and protect against large-scale threats to grasslands and other biomes, we find it helpful to think across a large spatial scale (landscape scale), and to do this we form partnerships. In 2009, the United States initiated a network of twenty-two regional conservation entities called landscape conservation cooperatives (LCC). The intention was to better prepare for threats such as climate change. One immediate outcome of this initiative was the formation of the Great Plains Landscape Conservation Cooperative Steering Committee, which identified three priority areas: grasslands, prairie rivers, and wetlands. It is a very wide-thinking, well-rounded group represented by several governmental agencies, the National Audubon Society, and NextEra Energy Resources. Since 2010, they have directed millions of dollars of funds to improve conservation efforts in the Great Plains. In contrast to President Donald Trump's efforts to eliminate this network, President Joe Biden invests in and uses landscape-scale platforms like LLC to reach his goal of conserving 30 percent of America's lands. Partnership between governments, companies, and farmers can also support sustainable farming to protect against loss of grasslands. Environmental scientists, for instance, are calling for the expansion of the Soy Moratorium to include the Cerrado, which continues to lose native grasslands to agriculture (opening story).

Fire is a tool in grassland and rangeland management (see Figure 9.13). It removes standing dead vegetation and undesirable plants, and releases nutrients to assist new plant growth. Grasses respond well to fire (fire adapted) because they have extensive root systems under the surface of the ground. After a fire, grasses resprout from their roots. Prescribed burning in Uganda, for example, removes acacia bushes that are encroaching into rangeland areas (Sabiiti 1986). Fire can also be used to limit the spread of invasive grass species. In North Dakota, prescribed fires are used to reduce invasive Kentucky bluegrass (*Poa pratensis*). These prescribed burns are typically more successful in the early spring after the invasive grass has greened, but before the emergence of native grasses.

FIGURE 9.13
Prescribed burns remove dead plants, recycle nutrients, inhibit invasive plants, and improve natural biodiversity. (A) A firefighter uses a prescribed fire to manage rangeland vegetation. (B) New grass sprouts after a prescribed burn.

Source: © Shutterstock, Inc.

Critical Thinking Activity: Grazing Subsidies

Read through and evaluate the arguments for and against grazing subsidies. After weighing the evidence, decide which one you support, or provide an alternative viewpoint to this highly contentious debate.

Against Grazing Subsidy

"There is an unfair grazing practice occurring mostly in eleven western states where ranchers are permitted to have their livestock use federal lands at the cost of federal tax dollars. A paltry few livestock owners (21,540 or about 2.7 percent) are provided with grazing permits, which cost approximately $1.35 per cow per month, far less than the true cost of using the land—creating a huge financial burden for taxpayers (Glaser et al. 2015). This payment is grossly unfair to the bulk of other farmers not given access to these lands and who have to pay about $30 per cow per month to use other lands. Therefore, the permittees are receiving a subsidy, certainly an unfair advantage over natural competition and again, one at the expense of the taxpayer. This is not a small financial amount, but equals an estimated average of $150 million each year. The grazing fees—about $22.3 million per year on average—are not sufficient to cover these costs, and over a period of ten years, the federal government loses over $1.25 billion. Why do we support such an unethical practice?"

For Grazing Subsidy

"Livestock grazing on federal lands is needed for proper management of wildlife habitat, and because the very structure of grassland areas is maintained by grazing. Grazers help to increase the diversity of plant species by cropping down superior competitors, thus allowing the lesser ones to remain in the community. Many studies indicate the value of having a predator present, even a grazer, to increase biodiversity. In the case of federal lands, livestock have thankfully filled the open niche space created by the loss of millions of bison that used to wander through and graze in the Great Plains. Without these livestock on federal lands, biodiversity would surely decrease. Therefore, ranchers play a crucial role here in having their livestock help to appropriately manage federal lands. Furthermore, these actions by ranchers should be supported financially because they are providing a service to the public who own these lands. Yet, groups lobby politicians to penalize the very farmers who are acting as environmental stewards. Why is this? Grazing subsidies are essential because they help us to manage expansive grassland areas that we would find nigh impossible to manage ourselves—at least not without a huge infusion of funds—much greater than any nominal funds given to support farmers that have livestock grazing on federal property."

Key Takeaways

- Grasslands make up at least 25 percent of Earth's land surface. They receive less annual precipitation than forests, but more than deserts, and provide key ecosystem services and goods, including but not limited to pollination, food production, foraging area for livestock, biodiversity, and carbon storage.
- Grasslands face a number of anthropogenic threats. Conversion to agriculture, overgrazing, desertification, urbanization, fragmentation, and invasive species all imperil grasslands.
- There are many strategies to sustainably manage grasslands, such as 1) delineation and monitoring of grasslands and rangelands, 2) rotation of livestock between fields, 3) creation of environmental laws and enforcement of those laws, 4) prescribed fires, and 5) formation of conservation partnerships.

9.3 Wilderness and Wilderness Management

Learning Objectives

1. Explain why some federal lands receive a wilderness status.
2. Identify two major challenges for wilderness managers.
3. Discuss the value of ecotourism to wilderness areas.

wilderness areas

Federal lands afforded the highest level of protection and kept in a fairly primitive state.

As you read these words, consider where you are. Take away the walls of your room and the floor beneath your feet. Erase the buildings, roads, the bridges, and the old rusty hinge on the door. Remove the hum of the electrical grid and the mechanical sounds of jackhammers and squeals of tires. Eliminate the repugnant smells of sewers and car exhaust. Remove everything of human origin and focus on what remains. Can you sense an environment devoid of human intervention? What does this primitive and exceedingly rare environment look like? Does it have an aroma? What does it feel like to be within this primitive environment? In this section, we examine untamed sections of land called **wilderness areas** set aside for protection.

Overview of Wilderness Areas

Wilderness Act

Established the National Wilderness Preservation System.

In 1964, President Lyndon B. Johnson signed the **Wilderness Act** to create the Wilderness Preservation System, a special system designed to set aside federal lands and to offer these lands the highest form of federal protection (see A in Figure 9.14) (see video link: "Wilderness Act"). Many Americans feel that the next generation receives the hand-me-downs of our environmental problems—not at all fair for people yet unborn and who never contributed to these problems. Here, in the case of wilderness areas, we, in essence, pass down things yet unworn—in the condition in which we, ourselves, first received them. Under the Wilderness Act, wilderness areas are generally open to the public, although there are many restrictions. You can, for example, hike, fish, and hunt, but vehicles are prohibited, as are commercial activities, commercial timber harvesting, and human infrastructure. Livestock grazing and mineral development are also authorized with special conditions.

FIGURE 9.14

Wilderness areas: (A) Mount McKinley in the Denali Wilderness area of Alaska is just one of many examples of the majesty of nature worth preserving for the enjoyment of future generations. (B) More federal areas can receive this same protection by going through a straightforward process as shown here. Congress receives and reviews proposals for new wilderness areas. Should they approve, the proposal is then sent to the president to be either approved or vetoed.

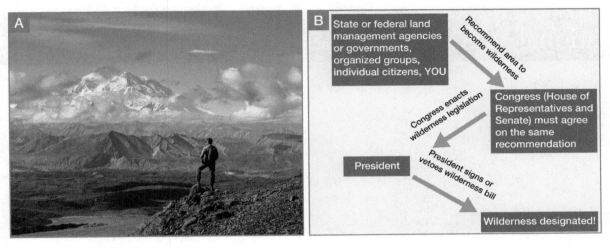

Source: © Shutterstock, Inc.; Joseph Shostell

How do lands become designated as wilderness? Federal lands can be recommended as a wilderness area to Congress (see B in Figure 9.14). With the approval of Congress and the president, more wilderness areas can be added. By signing the Wilderness Act, President Johnson immediately created 3.7 million ha (9.1 million ac) of wilderness—the first designated wilderness area of America. Since that time, new wilderness areas have been designated, and the total has grown to 44 million ha (109 million acres). The National Wilderness Preservation System now includes 765 wilderness areas that are managed by the Bureau of Land Management, Fish and Wildlife Service, Forest Service, and National Park Service (see Figure 9.15). There are promising signs that another 1.5 million acres of public lands will soon be designated as wilderness as a result of a new bill titled The Protecting America's Wildernesses and Public Lands Act and President Biden's ambitious plan to conserve 30 percent of U.S. lands and waterways by 2030 (see "Bringing It Closer to Home: Appreciating Wilderness Areas").

Wilderness Act

Listen to why the Wilderness Act is one of our country's greatest conservation laws.

View in the online reader

Bringing It Closer to Home: Appreciating Wilderness Areas

There is a good chance you haven't visited a wilderness area yet. After all, only about 5 percent of the United States is designated as wilderness, with about half located in Alaska. In this exercise, you have the opportunity to see and hear people give their testimonies of their experiences in these lands. Click here to watch recordings from the National Park Service's Wilderness Webisode Series. Your objective is to ascertain why these people were moved to record their experiences. Then, ask yourself which wilderness area most interests you and why. You could, for example, choose to visit the small 2.2 ha (5.5 acres) Pelican Island Wilderness in Northern Florida or the 3.6 million ha (9 million ac) Wrangell Saint Elias Wilderness in Alaska. They are both beautiful and wild!

FIGURE 9.15

U.S. wilderness areas are managed by multiple federal agencies (see map and legend). Visitors are required to follow strict regulations in order to protect natural habitat space, quietude, and biodiversity. If you are planning to explore a wilderness area, leave drones and bicycles at home because neither are permitted.

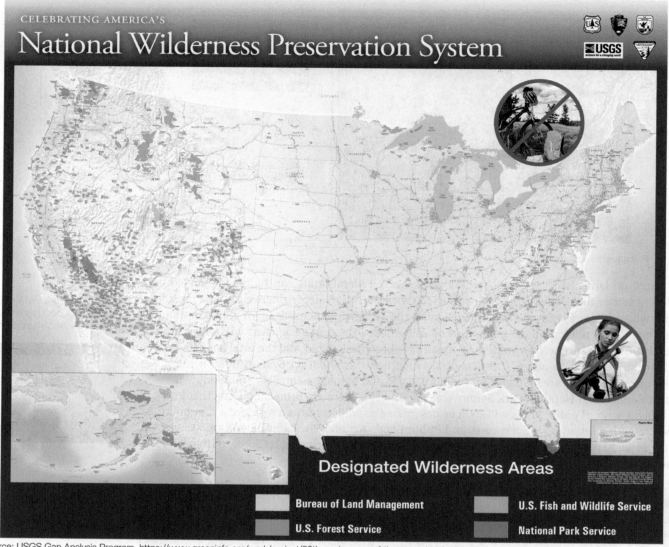

Source: USGS Gap Analysis Program, https://www.greeninfo.org/work/project/50th-anniversary-of-the-us-national-wilderness-preservation-system; © Shutterstock, Inc.

Problems and Challenges Facing Wilderness Areas

Wilderness areas are afforded the highest protection of our federal lands, but they still are exposed to some of the same threats facing nonwilderness areas. Climate change, invasive species, overuse, mineral exploration (see below), livestock grazing, and pollution are examples of threats to wilderness areas.

Greenhouse gas emissions are causing climate change, which is influencing all of Earth's ecosystems, no matter their location or category of protection. Thus, as surface air temperatures have increased, droughts and floods are becoming more common, and we observe a greater intensity of fires in grassland and forest systems (Abatzoglou and Williams 2016; Fried et al. 2004). As mentioned earlier, plant and animal communities in these systems will change, and, when possible, species will shift northward. In time, whole wilderness areas may contain entirely different biomes and species. Invasive species previously held to lower latitudes will continue to migrate northward as well.

Within wilderness areas, we expect to see few if any people, and we hope those people abide by the regulations (see Figure 9.15). Many, but not all, visitors follow these rules, and on occasion people's choice of activities can disrupt threatened and endangered species as well as visitors who seek solitude and quiet adventure from human civilization. One rather recent problem involves drones. They are considered a motorized vehicle and are therefore prohibited in wilderness areas; that is, if they are launched from within the park. Because of their remoteness, wilderness lands can also be sites for growing illegal crops. One of the more recent cases occurred in 2019 within Sequoia National Forest, a designated wilderness area. In this single incident, law enforcement officers confiscated over 1,800 marijuana plants.

Mining and livestock grazing threaten wilderness areas. Mining is permissible in wilderness areas where valid claims preceded wilderness designation. Strict regulations do apply, however. Grazing is expressly included in the Wilderness Act as a special provision. Some doubt the Act would have passed through Congress if livestock grazing weren't permitted. Improperly managed livestock can lead to overgrazing, and livestock are a visual blight to the raw, natural beauty of wild areas.

The largest anthropogenic threats to wilderness areas originate from activities conducted outside of them: some nearby, and many tens, hundreds, and even thousands of kilometers in the distance. Pollution, in its various forms, is a major problem. Heavy metals, volatile organic compounds, persistent organic pollutants (POP), nitrogen oxides, and other toxic pollutants travel by air across great geographical distances (see Chapter 1). The incineration, for example, of plastic in Hazard, Kentucky, releases dioxin, a cancer-causing POP that can travel as far as the Arctic National Wildlife Refuge wilderness area in Alaska. Combustion of coal for energy releases mercury into the atmosphere that later falls on terrestrial and aquatic ecosystems, where it accumulates in food chains. The highest concentrations of mercury within tissues are found within long-lived carnivorous animals such as shark, tuna, and polar bears. As a consequence of mercury pollution, there are fish consumption advisories in most states and wilderness areas. Burning fossil fuels also emits nitrogen oxides and sulfur dioxide, which combine with water and form acid rain. All 64,900 ha (160,300 ac) of Mount Zirkel Wilderness are negatively affected by acid rain. Acid rain destroys fish habitats in streams and lakes and kills terrestrial vegetation. Light and sound pollution also disrupt wilderness areas. Artificial light from cities interferes with the nocturnal movements and behaviors of species. For example, artificial light disrupts migrating birds that use the stars for orientating at night (McLaren et al. 2018). Artificial light also disrupts the movement of marine creatures. A group of researchers from Norway determined that vertical migrations of tiny marine creatures (zooplankton) are disrupted by artificial light (Ludvigsen et al. 2018). Under natural conditions, in the early morning, the zooplankton move to deeper water farther away from the light to avoid predators, and then in the night, migrate back to the surface. When the Arctic zooplankton are exposed to artificial light at night, they do not migrate to the surface. Sound is another form of pollution that unsettles wildlife in wildernesses areas. For example, wildlife in Utah's Zion National Park began to avoid areas when the numbers of visitors and vehicles spiked. Zion National Park is somewhat of an exception among wilderness areas because it does have roads.

Sustainable Management of Wilderness Areas

Management plans for wilderness areas reflect the intention of the Wilderness Act. The objectives are to preserve and protect lands in their natural condition, but also to make these areas available for the enjoyment of current and future generations. Additionally, a wilderness area is supposed to stay in a primitive state, so humans are only welcome as visitors. These directives present wilderness managers with the awkward decision of either engaging in active management versus acting as an observer. Should they, for example, attempt to halt the migration of species due to climate change, or instead chronicle the changes in community structure and biome type? The management responsibilities of a wilderness area fall to whichever federal government unit had jurisdiction of the land before its new designation. Therefore, the Forest Service, Bureau of Land Management, United States Fish and Wildlife Service, and National Park Service all make management decisions concerning wilderness areas. It is rare indeed when wilderness managers embark on a restoration project. When the officers located marijuana in the Sequoia National Forest (see above), they removed toxic pesticides in addition to the marijuana plants. Management actions also aim to protect and recover threatened and endangered species. They conduct fish stockings, wildlife transplants, and control the access of visitors.

What about the protection of wilderness areas from global- and continental-scale threats? The interconnected nature of ecosystems and the movement of pollutants across large distances present environmental problems beyond isolated wilderness areas, states, and countries. In 2009, the United States, Canada, and Mexico formed the North American Intergovernmental Committee on Cooperation for Wilderness and Protected Areas Conservation. The group works together on environmental issues that transcend any one or two countries. One of their products is a compilation of all the protected and managed conservation areas across North America. All three countries are also members of the United Nations and promote environmental conservation globally.

Key Takeaways

- The Wilderness Act supported the creation of the Wilderness Preservation System, in which federal lands are set aside and offered the highest form of federal protection.
- Wilderness areas are exposed to some of the same threats facing nonwilderness areas, such as climate change, invasive species, pollution, and livestock grazing.
- Wilderness areas provide valuable services and support biodiversity. By protecting them, we allow for the continuation of these services for the benefit of future generations.

9.4 National Parks and Preserves

Learning Objectives

1. Identify the various categories of National Park Service lands.
2. Explain how natural and human-caused factors threaten National Park Service lands.
3. Provide example solutions to threats of NPS lands.

The establishment of Yellowstone as the first national park in America in 1872 was the beginning of the National Park System, although at the time we did not know it, because the National Park Service would not be created for another forty-four years (see Figure 9.16). To be designated as a national park, a land area must be considered of such value—notably scenic or environmentally significant—to be given a special type of protection. In 1916, President Woodrow Wilson signed the act to create the National Park Service.

FIGURE 9.16
On March 1, 1872, Yellowstone became America's first national park. Geysers such as Old Faithful, shown here, are one of the main attractions for visitors.

Source: © Shutterstock, Inc.

What America started began a domino effect around the world, such that other countries began to establish their own national park areas. Canada soon followed with labeling the beautiful Banff as a national park in 1885, followed by Japan and Mexico, and then soon more than one hundred nations had their own national parks.

Overview of National Parks and Preserves

Views of the Grand Canyon or Old Faithful or giant sequoias are the images we conjure up when we consider lands of the National Park Service (NPS) (see video link: "Sequoias and Canyon"). What is less known is that national parks are only one among many land designations under management of the NPS. Examples of other categories are national monuments, national preserves, national cemeteries, and national memorials. Although they differ greatly in content and size—being a cemetery or canyon or as small as a single house—all are considered of value to the American people (see Figure 9.17). All states but Delaware have land managed by the NPS. Worldwide, there are approximately 1,200 parks or preserves (see "Bringing It Closer to Home: Exploring NPS Lands").

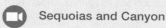 **Sequoias and Canyon**

Take a tour through Sequoia and Kings Canyon National Parks.

View in the online reader

FIGURE 9.17
National Park Service sites vary greatly. Compare (A) the Thaddeus Kosciuszko National Memorial (TNM) in Philadelphia, which is 0.008 ha (0.02 acres), with (B) the Wrangell-St. Elias National Park and Preserve (WNPP) in Alaska, which encompasses more than 5.3 million ha (13 million acres). TNM preserves the house where Thaddeus Kosciuszko lived. Kosciuszko was an important engineer during the American Revolution.

Sources: Beyond My Ken Wikipedia [CC BY-SA 4.0 (https://creativecommons.org/licenses/by-sa/4.0/), https://commons.wikimedia.org/wiki/File:Thaddeus_Kosciuszko_National_Memorial_301_Pine_Street.jpg; © Shutterstock, Inc.

Bringing It Closer to Home: Exploring NPS Lands

The National Park Service currently manages 398 units (different land areas), and the number continues to grow over time. These units can be monuments, battlefields, parks, etc., and are found in abundance in almost all U.S. states. Check out the NPS's website here and determine which NPS unit is closest to where you live. The website allows for the selection of individual states and then displays a map of the state and surrounding region, identifying the location of all NPS units. Is one close to where you live? Click on an individual NPS unit to learn more about what you can explore. Remember, your tax dollars support the management of these areas.

Problems and Challenges Facing National Parks

There are several challenges to effectively managing NPS areas, and most also pertain to other government lands as well as those that are privately owned. Additionally, all of the problems that NPS managers try to solve fall into two categories, those caused by nature or those caused by humans. We begin by briefly discussing three examples of natural problems in NPS areas, followed by discussions of the major problems linked to human activities.

The top three natural issues facing the NPS are invasive insects, general management of wildlife, and control of nonendemic plants and animals. Insect pests such as the gypsy moth, which defoliated around 13 million acres of hardwood in the 1980s, threaten some of our national parks today, including Isle Royale National Park in Michigan. Stressed, defoliated trees die and then increase the likelihood of forest fires, thus creating another management issue. A bit unusual for flying pests, only the male gypsy moth can fly, which means its spreading can be slow; that is, unless strong winds blow females to neighboring trees, or people accidentally transport gypsy moth egg sacks on their clothes or other belongings to new areas. The gypsy moth provides a good example of all three management problems because it is also an invasive species, and as such it disrupts the distributions of native butterflies and moth species.

At the forefront of human-caused problems for NPS lands are air pollution, climate change, development, and water issues. Air pollution, a topic of Chapter 11 and usually known to occur in cities, has begun to imperil national parks (see Figure 9.18). Wildlife and humans have many of the same needs, including access to clean air. Global climate change, the result of burning fossil fuels, will create hardships for biomes in general, because their presence is dependent on precipitation and temperature. During natural temperature changes, biomes adapt and change their ranges accordingly (see Chapter 5). However, NPS lands are locked, and although their organisms might migrate to new areas, the land or water areas are concretely defined. It remains unclear how NPS managers will deal with the issue of climate change.

FIGURE 9.18
Shenandoah National Park in clear and smoggy conditions. Air pollution is becoming a problem for some of our National Park Service lands because it is harming wildlife.

Good visibility day | Poor visibility day

Source: NPS, https://www.nps.gov/subjects/air/visibility.htm

Adjacent development can also be a source of problems for NPS areas. Lake Clark National Park and Preserve in Alaska is being threatened by a proposed mine that would be about 22.5 km

(14 mi) southwest of its border. Groups of concerned citizens have requested the EPA to use its authority under the Clean Water Act to prohibit the proposed work. Initial studies indicate that the proposed mine will negatively affect the park and salmon habitat. To create the mine, an estimated 1,619 ha (4,000 ac) of wetlands and 34 km (21 mi) of salmon streams would be destroyed. In addition, the mine would produce over one billion tons of toxic mining wastes that would need to be stored long term adjacent to Lake Clark National Park and Preserve.

National Park Service lands are chronically underfunded, which creates a backlog of upkeep projects. Museum artifacts are not catalogued, roads are not upgraded, and buildings are not repaired—to name a few of the constant financial demands bearing down on the NPS. Approximately half of the $9.5 billion shortfall is needed for road repair work alone. Overcrowding is another national park problem. Dealing with overcrowding can be difficult, and visitors coming from urban areas prefer to not have hordes of competitor visitors nearby, because this can detract from the park experience (see Figure 9.19). The Great Smoky Mountain National Park is the most visited of all U.S. parks; it receives between 250 to 300 million visitors each year. Such a great number of people creates an additional challenge for NPS employees trying to balance visitations with preservation. The challenge is not just the crowding, but also the people's trash and the pollution from cars. Visitors may also consume limited water resources and, when not closely supervised, can easily trample on sensitive vegetation.

FIGURE 9.19
Tourists crowd a cliff in Zion National Park. Overcrowding can detract from a visitor's positive experience in a national park. Managing crowds can also be challenging for NPS employees.

Source: trekandshoot/Shutterstock.com

Sustainable National Park Management

Finding solutions to the problems facing national parks and similar areas will be difficult because some problems do not originate in the parks. How does one control activities outside parklands? Also, the very reason we set aside some of these areas—for the enjoyment of Americans—can create problems such as overcrowding. It would not be reasonable to prevent everyone from entering a national park, but it would be reasonable to limit the number of people that can be in the park at any given time, and limit the types of activities—such as the use of motorized vehicles, which we already do in some areas. Sometimes, a solution to one problem will solve a second problem. For example, reducing the number of roads in parks to save on upkeep funds also limits human access to some park areas—thus lessening the potential for overcrowding. Increased fees for park entry would also help to offset funding issues, but then again, citizens argue that national parks, monuments, battlefields, etc. are owned by the public and should be accessible to them and should be free, or only a nominal cost.

Any NPS containing wildlife will pose extra challenges to manage, because wildlife are not static and can overpopulate the finite size of the designated area. This is especially true for larger mammals and birds that have large territory ranges. At the extreme, for example, are international parks with elephants in India and Africa. Elephants are the draw for visitors, but if not carefully managed, an elephant population will outgrow a park's carrying capacity. The elephants can then quickly overeat their natural food supply, at which point their population would be in danger of collapsing. How do park managers prevent overcrowding of wildlife? Game managers may, for example, choose to shoot some of the elephants—referred to as **culling**—thereby saving the herd as a whole (Van Aarde et al. 1999). Passive management along with 7 percent average yearly population growth can quickly lead to food shortages and huge losses from the resulting starvation. In this case, what may be the correct management decision to save a herd may be seen as intolerable or inhumane to those who have little understanding of population growth and limited habitat size. The Kruger National Park in South Africa has been in the international spotlight over the last three decades for trying to control the size of their elephant herd within the park. Closer to home, we have similar problems with wolves, grizzly bears, and bison whose populations outgrow the boundaries of our national parks.

> **culling**
>
> Killing off of some of a population to reduce the population's size.

Each park or preserve area is unique with its particular wildlife and terrain, but there are some common management strategies helpful to every area set aside for preservation. First, the establishment of a management plan is essential, as is the determination of the area's biological diversity and its unique land features. Also, it is important to have flexible enough plans be able to successfully solve yet unforeseen problems, and also to network with managers of other parks who are dealing with their own park problems.

The United Nations Environment Program and the IUCN have been instrumental in helping to create a global database of protected areas (UNEP 2018). Their work reaches across political boundaries and focuses on the protection of land as well as water resources. In their last document, published in 2018, they estimated that the current 238,563 protected areas cover at least 20 million km^2 (7.7 million mi^2) of land, equivalent to almost 15 percent of Earth's terrestrial area. Next, we return to the opening story of the Amazon–Cerrado and predict its future.

Key Takeaways

- The National Park Service oversees many types of sites in addition to parks, including monuments, preserves, lakeshores, seashores, wild and scenic riverways, historic sites, memorials, battlefields, cemeteries, recreation areas, and parkways.
- Air pollution, invasive species, water shortages, development, and climate change negatively affect national parks.
- National Park Service lands are chronically underfunded and often overcrowded.
- There are some common strategies for managing national park lands. They include establishment of a flexible management plan, determination of biological diversity, recognizing unique land features, and networking.

9.5 A Look to the Future: Sustainable Use of Forests and Grasslands

Learning Objective

1. Reflect on habitat destruction and sustainable management of the Amazon and Cerrado and then hypothesize about the future of these ecosystems.

At the close of the chapter, we return to the opening story about the Amazon–Cerrado region. The future of its biodiverse forests, grasslands, and waters depends on ceasing the conversion of natural habitat to croplands and rangelands and preventing illegal logging and mining operations. Inga alley cropping, enforcement of environmental laws, and Brazil's Soy Moratorium extended to the Cerrado offer solutions, as does the involvement of consumers who can make decisions about purchasing sustainably grown products. Of equal importance are the hundreds of Indigenous tribes who have lived in harmony with the natural biodiversity of this region for millennia. Tribes have successfully opposed corporations attempting to explore and strip their home of natural resources. The lands and species who live there have great cultural value and spiritual importance, and not until recently have conservation proposals recognized the relationship between Indigenous cultures and biodiversity. A new conservation concept now comes from the Sarayaku people of the Ecuadorian Amazon that may fundamentally change the world's view of conservation. To the national and international communities, they proposed Kawask Sacha, which recognizes the Amazon forest as a conscious living thing with rights. The purpose of this proposal is to create a new international category of conservation based on the sophisticated cohesiveness among Indigenous cultures, landscapes, and the species who share this space with them. Global acceptance of this new concept will certainly brighten the Amazon's future.

However, the immediate future of Brazil's Amazon–Cerrado is looking dire. Brazil has some of the most stringent environmental laws in the world, but they are not adequately enforced. Under President Bolsonaro's leadership, environmental protection of this vital region worsened. He slashed the budget of Brazil's environmental enforcement agency's (IBAMA) by 25 percent, making it even more challenging to monitor illegal logging activities. In a reversal of the trend before he took office, deforestation rates increased by 30 percent in 2020. A global community waits in anticipation to see if degradation of Brazil's Amazon–Cerrado will continue to escalate. We hope not. There are solutions; we just hope they are implemented while there is still time. Over half of the Cerrado is already gone, and an estimated 17–20 percent of the Amazon as well (see video link: "The Cerrado's Future"). Will newly elected Lula da Silva (elected in 2022) reverse or continue Bolsonaro's environmental policies?

The Cerrado's Future
Listen to Mongabay discussing new approaches to save the Cerrado's reptiles.

View in the online reader

Key Takeaways

- Scientists have identified the major threats to the Amazon and Cerrado and proposed management solutions to these threats. Brazil's Soy Moratorium, use of Inga alley cropping, involvement of conscientious-minded consumers, and the Kawsak Sacha proposal all provide hope for a positive prognosis.

- However, the immediate future of Brazil's Amazon–Cerrado is looking dire due to inadequate enforcing of environmental laws, and actions of President Bolsonaro's administration.

FIGURE 9.20 Visual Overview: Sustainable Management of Forests, Grasslands, and Protected Areas
Summarizing figure: We acknowledge and understand land degradation issues (i.e., deforestation in the Amazon [9.5]) and strive to sustainably manage (9.1) forests, (9.2) grasslands, (9.3) wilderness areas, and (9.4) national parks for the benefit of ecosystems, all life, and society.

Sources: Joseph Shostell; See previous citations for image credits.

9.6 References

- Achard, F., H. D. Ece, D. Mollicone, and R. Beuchle. 2008. "The effect of climate anomalies and human ignition factor on wildfires in Russian boreal forests." *Phil Trans R Soc B* 363: 2331–2339. https://doi:10.1098/rstb.2007.2203.

- Barbosa, E. G., V. R. Pivello, and S. T. Meirelles. 2008. "Allelopathic evidence in Brachiaria decumbens and its potential to invade the Brazilian cerrados." *Braz Arch Biol Technol* 51: 825–831.

- Bergman, T. J. 2013. "Speech-like vocalized lip-smacking in geladas." *Current Biology* 23, no. 7: PR268–R269. https://doi.org/10.1016/j.cub.2913.02.038.

- Crosby, A. W. 2004. *Ecological Imperialism The Biological Expansion of Europe, 900–1900.* Cambridge, UK: Cambridge University Press.

- Dalling, J. W., K. Heineman, O. R. Lopez, S. J. Wright, and B. L. Turner. 2016. "Nutrient availability in tropical rain forests: the paradigm of phosphorus limitation." In: *Tropical Tree Physiology, Tree Physiology 6* (Eds.: Godstein, G. and L. S. Santiago). Cham, Switzerland: Springer International Publishing.

- Da Silva, J. M. C., A. B. Rylands, and G. A. B. Da Fonseca. 2005. "The fate of the Amazonian areas of endemism." *Conservation Biology* 19, no. 30: 689–694.

- DeKeyser, E. S., M. Meehan, G. Clambey, and K. Krabbenhoft. 2013. "Cool season invasive grasses in Northern Great Plains natural areas." *Nat Areas J* 33: 81–90.

- De Villalobos, A. E., and S. M. Zalba. 2010. "Continuous feral horse grazing and grazing exclusion in mountain pampean grasslands in Argentina." *Acta Oecologica* 36, no. 5: 514–519.

- Donato, D. C., J. B. Fontaine, J. L. Campbell, W. D. Robinson, J. B. Kauffman, and B. E. Law. 2006. "Post-wildfire logging hinders regeneration and increases fire risk." *Science* 311: 352.

- Drummond, M., and T. Loveland. 2010. "Land-use pressure and transition to forest-cover loss in the eastern United States." *Bioscience* 60: 286–298. https://doi.org/10.1525/bio.2010.60.4.7.

- Ellison, D. 2018. *Background Analytical Study 2 Forests and Water*. United Nations Forum on Forests. United Nations.

- Ellison, D., C. E. Morris, B. Locatelli, et al. 2017. "Trees, forests and water: Cool insights for a hot world." *Global Environmental Change* 43: 51–61.

- Fearnside, P. 2017. "Deforestation of the Brazilian Amazon." *Oxford Research Encyclopedia of Environmental Science*. https://doi.org/10.1093/acrefore/9780199389411.013.102.

- Food and Agriculture Organization of the United Nations (FAO). 2020. *Global Forest Resources Assessment 2020 Key Findings*. Rome: United Nations.

- Fried, J. S., M. S. Torn, and E. Mills. 2004. "The impact of climate change on wildfire severity: a regional forecast for northern California." *Climatic Change* 64: 169–191.

- Gallery, R. E. 2014. "Ecology of tropical rain forests." In: *Ecology and the Environment* (Ed.: Monson, R. K.). New York: Springer.

- Galt, D., and J. Holechek. 2000. "Grazing capacity and stocking rate." *Rangelands* 22: 7–11.

- Glaser, C., C. Romaniello, and K. Moskowitz. 2015. "Costs and Consequences The Real Price of Livestock Grazing on America's Public Lands." Tucson, Arizona: Center for Biological Diversity.

- Goldsmith, P. D. 2008. "Economics of soybean production, marketing, and utilization." In: *Soybeans Chemistry, Production, Processing, and Utilization* (Eds.: Johnson, L. A., P. J. White, and R. Galloway). Amsterdam, Netherlands: Elsevier.

- Halofskyet, J. E., D. L. Peterson, and B. J. Harvey. 2020. "Changing wildlife, changing forests: the effects of climate change on fire regimes and vegetation in the Pacific Northwest, USA." *Fire Ecology* 16, no. 4. https://doi.org/10.1186/s42408-019-0062-8.

- Hansen, M. C., P. C. Potapov, R. Moor, M. Hancher, S. A. Turubanova, A. Tyukavina, D. Thau, S. V. Stehman, S. J. Goetz, T. R. Loveland, A. Kommareddy, A. Egorov, L. Chini, C. O. Justice, and J. R. G. Townshend. 2013. "High-resolution global maps of 21st-century forest cover change." *Science* 342: 850–853.

- Heilmayr, R., L. L. Rausch, J. Munger, and H. K. Gibbs. 2020. "Brazil's Amazon soy moratorium reduced deforestation." *Nature Food* 1: 801–810.

- Hua, F., L. Want, B. Fisher, X. Zheng, X. Wang, W. Y. Douglas, and D. S. Wilcove. 2018. "Tree plantations displacing native forests: the nature and drivers of apparent forest recovery on former croplands in southwestern China from 2000 to 2015." *Biological Conservation* 222: 113–124.

- IUCN. 1997. *A Global Overview of Forest Protected Areas of the World Heritage List*. Gland, Switzerland: Natural Heritage Programme IUCN.

- Iremonger, S., and A. M. Gerrand. 2011. *Global ecological zones map for FAO FRA 2010*. FAO, Rome: Unpublished report.

- Keenan, R. J., G. A. Reams, F. Achard, J. V. de Freitas, A. Grainger, and E. Lindquist. 2015. "Dynamics of global forest area: results from the FAO Global Forest Resources Assessment." *Forest Ecology and Management* 352: 9–20.

- Leblanc, H. A., and R. L. McGraw. 2004. "Evaluation of Inga edulis and I. samanensis for firewood and green-mulch production in an organic maize alley-cropping practice in the humid tropics." *Tropical Agriculture* 91, no. 1: 1–7.

- Leverkus, A. B, D. B. Lindenmayer, S. Thorn, and L. Gustafsson. 2018. "Salvage logging in the world's forests: interactions between natural disturbance and logging need recognition." *Glob Ecol Biogeogr* 27: 1140–1154.

- Lewinsohn, T. M., and P. I. Prado. 2005. "How many species are there in Brazil?" *Conservation Biology* 19, no. 3: 619–624.

- Ludvigsen, M., J. Berg, M. Geoffroy, J. H. Cohen, P. R. De la Torre, S. M. Nornes, H. Singh, A. J. Sørensen, M. Daase, and G. Johnsen. 2018. "Use of an autonomous surface vehicle reveals small-scale diel vertical migrations of zooplankton and susceptibility to light pollution under low solar irradiance." *Science Advances* 4: eaap9887.

- Malvar, M. C., F. C. Silva, S. A. Prats, D. C. S. Vieira, C. O. A. Coelho, and J. J. Keizer. 2017. "Short-term effects of post-fire salvage logging on runoff and soil erosion." *For Ecol Manag* 400: 555–567.

- Marker, L. L., A. J. Dickman, M. G. L. Mills, R. M. Jeo, and D. W. Macdonald. 2008. "Spatial ecology of cheetahs on north-central Namibian farmlands." *Journal of Zoology* 274: 226–238.

- Mayer, A. L., P. E. Kauppi, P. K. Anglestam, Y. Zhang, and P. M. Tikka. 2005. "Importing timber: exporting ecological impact." *Science* 308: 359–360.

- McKinney, M. L. 2002. "Urbanization, biodiversity, and conservation." *BioScience* 52: 883–890.

- McLaughlin, M. E., W. M. Janousek, J. P. McCarty, and L. L. Wolfenbarger. 2014. "Effects of urbanization on site occupancy and density of grassland birds in tallgrass prairie fragments." *J. Field Ornithol* 85, no. 3: 258–273.

- McLaughlin, J., and K. Webster. 2014. "Effects of climate change on peatlands in the far north of Ontario, Canada: a synthesis." *Arctic, Antarctic, and Alpine Research* 46, no. 1: 84–102.

- Munang, R., L. Thiaw, J. Thompson, D. Ganz, E. Girvetz, and M. Rivington. 2011. *Sustaining forests: Investing in Our Common Future: UNEP Policy Series*, Issue 5. Nairobi, Kenya.

- Nepstad, D., C. M. Stickler, and O. T. Almeida. 2006. "Globalization of the Amazon soy and beef industries: opportunities for conservation. *Conservation Biology* 20, no. 6: 1595–1603.

- Nowak, D. J. 2002. *The Effects of Urban Trees on Air Quality*. Syracuse, NY: United States Department of Agriculture Forest Service, Northern Research Station.

- Oliver, C. D., N. T. Nassar, B. R. Lippke, and J. B. McCarter. 2014. "Carbon, fossil fuel, and biodiversity mitigation with wood and forests." *Journal of Sustainable Forestry* 33: 248–275.

- Sabiiti, E. N. 1986. *Fire Effects on Acacia Regeneration*. Ph.D. Thesis. University of New Brunswick.

- Sauer, J. R., J. E. Hines, J. E. Fallon, K. L. Pardieck, D. J. Ziolkowski, W. A. Link. 2011. *The North American breeding bird survey results and analyses 1966–2010*. Version 12.07.2011. USGS Patuxent Wildlife Research Center, Laurel, MD.

- Schmieder, O. 1927. *Alteration*. University of California Publications in Geography II (10).

- Seward, N. W., K. C. Vercauteren, G. W. Witmer, and R. M. Engeman. 2004. "Feral swine impacts on agriculture and the environment." *Sheep and Goat Research Journal* 19: 34–40.

- Silva-Junior, C. H. L., A. C. M. Pessôa, N. S. Carvalho, J. B. C. Resi, L. O. Anderson, and L. E. O. C. Aragão. 2021. "The Brazilian Amazon deforestation rate in 2020 is the greatest of the decade." *Nature Ecology and Evolution* 5: 144–145.

- Smith, H. G., H. G. Smith, P. Hopmans, G. J. Sheridan, P. N. J. Lane, and P. J. Noske. 2012. "Impacts of wildfire and salvage harvesting on water quality and nutrient exports from radiate pine and eucalypt forest catchments in south-eastern Australia." *For Ecol Manag* 263: 160–169.

- Sommer, J. M., M. Restivo, and J. M. Shandra. 2019. "The United States, bilateral debt-for-nature swaps, and forest loss: a cross-national analysis." *The Journal of Development Studies* 56, no. 4: 748–764.

- Soterroni, A. C., F. M. Ramos, A. Mosnier, et al. 2019. "Expanding the soy moratorium to Brazil's Cerrado." *Sci Adv* eaav7336.

- United Nations Environment Programme (UNEP)-WCMC and IUCN. 2018. *Protected Planet Report 2018*. UNEP-WCMC, IUCN and NGS: Cambridge, UK and Gland, Switzerland; and Washington, D.C., USA.

- Van Aarde, R., I. Whyte, and S. Pimm. 1999. "Culling and the dynamics of the Kruger National Park African elephant population." *Animal Conservation* 2, no. 4: 287–294.

- White, R. P., S. Murray, and M. Rohweder. 2000. *Pilot Analysis of Global Ecosystems Grassland Ecosystems*. Washington, DC: World Resources Institute.
- Wilson, C. H., M. S. Strickland, J. A. Hutchings, T. S. Bianchi, and S. L. Flory. 2018. "Grazing enhances belowground carbon allocation, microbial biomass, and soil carbon in a subtropical grassland." *Glob Change Biol* 24: 2997–3009.
- Zhang, L., J. Liu, W. J. Mcshea, Y. Wu, D. Wang, and Z. Lü. 2014. "The impact of fencing on the distribution of Przewalski's gazelle." *The Journal of Wildlife Management* 78, no. 2: 255–263.
- Ziekus, J. G. 1981. "Lignin metabolism and the carbon cycle: polymer biosynthesis, biodegradation, and environmental recalcitrance." *Adv Microb Ecol* 5: 211–243.
- Zon, R., and W. N. Sparhawk. 1923. *Forest Resources of the World, volumes 1 and 2*. New York: McGraw-Hill Book Co., Inc.

CHAPTER 10
Water Resources

Case Study: The Skokomish River

The Skokomish River runs through some breathtaking scenery, starting at the Olympic Mountains of Washington state and eventually emptying into Southern Hood Canal (see Figure 10.1). This natural canal connects to Puget Sound and indirectly to the Pacific Ocean, making it an area with impressive animal and plant diversity. For thousands of years, the Skokomish Tribes' sophisticated society relied on the area's abundant salmon and other natural resources, including several mammal species, such as deer, elk, wolves, and bear (Elmendorf 1960). The Skokomish tribes' ability to harvest and preserve far more of the plentiful salmon than they could consume allowed them to build an expansive trade network based on fish currency that extended across the Cascade Mountains. Each Skokomish tribe managed select fishing areas and would share their catch in large social gatherings of multiple tribal groups, thereby maintaining and even increasing strong social bonds with potential competitors (Lansing et al. 1998).

FIGURE 10.1

The Skokomish River is known for its high water quality and ability to sustain a salmon fishery. A) The river rises in the Olympic Mountains in Washington and runs downslope to Puget Sound. B) A healthy, full-flowing North Fork Skokomish River in Olympic National Park, Washington, north of dams. C) The dammed lower section of the North Fork created Lake Cushman to provide electricity for Tacoma, Washington.

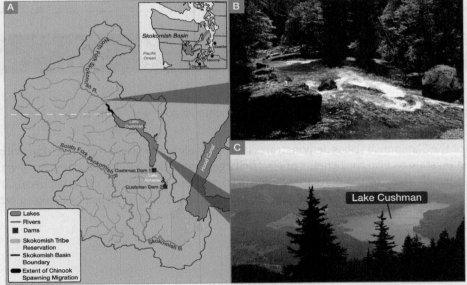

Sources: Map redrawn from Brenkman, Samuel & Sutton, Kathryn & Marshall, Anne. (2017). Life History Observations of Adfluvial Chinook Salmon prior to Reintroduction of Anadromous Salmonids. *North American Journal of Fisheries Management*. 37. 1220-1230. 10.1080/02755947.2017.1353562 and "DRAFT Integrated Feasibility Report and Environmental Impact Statement" (January 2014), US Army Corps of Engineers; © Shutterstock, Inc.; Elwhajeff, Public domain, via Wikimedia Commons; https://commons.wikimedia.org/wiki/File:Mount_Ellinor_Trail_-_Lake_Cushman_View3.jpg.

In 1859, Skokomish tribal society changed abruptly when the Skokomish tribes were forced to move from the larger Hood Canal watershed to a reservation at the mouth of the Skokomish River. Tribal groups that had once traded with one another across great distances were now living in close proximity. Even with this change, the Skokomish River continued to supply abundant fish, and the immediate area surrounding the river supported plentiful game because of lush vegetation. An even more drastic change occurred with the construction of a dam, which diverted the entire North Fork of the Skokomish River to a local utility plant, causing an overall reduction of the Skokomish River's flow by 40 percent (Williams et al. 1985; Jay and Simenstad 1994). The weakened flow diminished the ability of the Skokomish to carry sediments to the river's mouth. Instead, sediments accumulated on the bottom of the Skokomish River, interfering with salmon runs and making the river unnavigable to boats for most of the year. Moreover, the dam created a reservoir that flooded hunting areas and ceremonial sites, and it also caused a precipitous decline in the number of salmon in the North Fork of the Skokomish River. In the end, reduction of a once abundant water resource threatened the Skokomish tribes' way of life.

Consider the value of water as you read through this chapter and ask yourself if our society would be disrupted just like the Skokomish's without the water on which we depend. At a deeper, ethical level, who has the right to use a natural resource in a way that negatively affects others' use? Should the term *ownership* be applied to water? In addition, who is responsible for its management?

This chapter explores water resources and examines society's use of water. We look into the overuse and pollution of water resources, as well as management strategies that can reduce these problems. As you read the chapter, keep the term *sustainability* in your thoughts, because only sustainable use will provide sufficient, and clean, water for future generations.

10.1 Water Resources, an Introduction

Learning Objectives

1. Describe the variety of Earth's water resources.
2. Explain why the distribution of freshwater is not homogeneous across the world.

The story of the Skokomish tribes demonstrates how valuable water is as a resource. Many citizens of Washington state receive the benefits of electricity generated through hydropower; however, the Skokomish people's way of life dramatically changed without the volume of water necessary to support a significant level of salmon fishing. You will find many similar struggles between groups of people across the world when it comes to sharing a limited resource.

Surface Water and Groundwater Are Connected

All of Earth's water resources are linked, which helps to explain how ecosystems far apart can affect each other. Take, for example, the interconnecting water bodies of the Mississippi River watershed (see Figure 10.2), which stretches from small **first-order streams** in Minnesota all the way to New Orleans, Louisiana, where the river empties into the Gulf of Mexico. Thirty-two states and two Canadian provinces contribute to this watershed, making it the world's second largest, second only to that of the Amazon River. Knowledge of this interconnectedness pushes today's river, lake, and even oceanic coastline managers to construct aquatic management plans around the term **watershed (drainage basin)**, which represents the land area where water collects and eventually empties into a body of water.

first-order streams

Headwater streams with no upstream tributaries.

watershed (drainage basin)

The land area where water collects and eventually empties into a body of water.

FIGURE 10.2
(A) The Mississippi River watershed. (B) A view along the Mississippi, looking upriver from Brady's Bluff in Perrot State Park, Wisconsin.

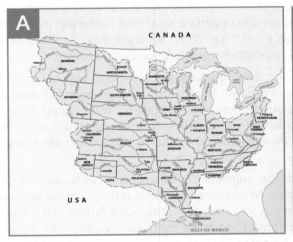

Sources: © Shutterstock, Inc.; Mississippi River from Fire Point in Effigy Mounds National Monument, NPS, https://www.nps.gov/media/photo/gallery-item. htm?pg=3030162&id=60DA8477-155D-4519-3EA2AACB7158D76A&gid=60D8FDB8-155D-4519-3E4DA807907B48E2.

It seems impossible that processes thousands of miles to the north would threaten the Mississippi River Delta and diminish biodiversity levels in the Gulf of Mexico. For thousands of years, the Mississippi River has transported sediments downstream to its mouth, creating the Mississippi Delta—a coastal **wetland** and **estuary** area of about 3 million acres (12,000 km^2). This vibrant productive zone contains 40 percent of the saltwater marshland in the contiguous United States and supports yearly harvests of shrimp, crab, and crayfish. Each of these creatures depends on the wellbeing of all the Mississippi River watershed's first-order streams and the connecting bodies of water between these streams and the Mississippi Delta.

wetland

Land areas where soil is seasonally or permanently saturated with water.

estuary

A transition area between the land and sea where freshwater and saltwater intermix.

Lakes and Oceans

Both natural and artificial lakes can be found along the course of the Mississippi's length. Some natural lakes, such as Lake Pepin, create extremely wide sections of the Mississippi River. Others, such as Lake Winnibigoshish in Minnesota, created by one of the Mississippi River's forty-three dams, widens the river to its maximum width of seven miles. These are but two examples of lakes, larger than many and dwarfed by others. The Laurentian Great Lakes of North America—consisting of lakes Superior, Michigan, Huron, Erie, and Ontario—hold about 21 percent of the world's surface freshwater. Most freshwater lakes are much smaller than any of these great lakes and certainly tiny compared to the oceans.

The Pacific, Atlantic, Indian, Southern, and Arctic oceans collectively contain 97 percent of the world's water. Just like smaller bodies of water, oceans are affected by local activities as well as by those thousands of kilometers away, within the interior of continents or neighboring oceans. See Chapter 5 for an overview of oceans.

Glaciers and Ice Sheets

About 69 percent of Earth's freshwater is stored in glaciers in Antarctica (90 percent), Greenland, Tibet, and other geographical areas, including Washington and Alaska. Glaciers are sources of freshwater, and depending on size and location, they can also influence local weather, climate, and ocean currents. Lambert-Fisher, in Antarctica, is by far the largest glacier, at 400 km long (250 mi), up to 100 km (60 mi) wide, and up to 3.8 km (3 mi) in height.

In Asia, the Tibetan glaciers are a source of headwater for several major rivers that provide freshwater to approximately 2 billion people across nine countries. China, India, Pakistan, Bangladesh, Burma, Laos, Thailand, Vietnam, and Cambodia all depend on these glaciers to sustain their sources of freshwater. Glaciers are also important sources of freshwater in the United States. For example, glaciers in Washington provide 1.8 trillion liters (470 billion gallons) of water every summer, while melted glacial ice in Colorado charges the great Colorado River.

Due to their white color and reflective ability, large glaciers impact weather patterns. Sunlight reflects off the light-colored surface of a glacier, so very little of its energy is absorbed. Instead, the reflected energy disperses into the atmosphere above the glacier, warming up parcels of air and thereby altering pressure and wind patterns. Should these frozen areas melt completely, the darker colored ground surface would become exposed, and it would absorb much more energy and warm readily.

Evidence provided by climatologists suggests Greenland's glaciers, because of their location and size, can alter major ocean currents (Winkelstern et al. 2017). If these glaciers keep melting at an accelerated pace due to global warming, they may disrupt the Gulf Stream and ocean circulation, and consequently the climate of Bermuda and other subtropical areas in the Atlantic. Temperatures in these areas would drop. Northern Europe's climate would be altered too, because Gulf Stream waters currently warm this region.

Groundwater Is a Vital Water Resource

groundwater

Water in the saturated zone of the ground. The water table marks the top of this zone.

In contrast to easily observable surface waters, a much larger fraction of freshwater is hidden below ground. **Groundwater**, which makes up approximately 94 percent of the world's liquid freshwater, resides in pores: spaces between particles of soil, rock, and sand. Its presence supports the network of connected surface freshwaters and provides a vital source of water for households and industry.

As part of the hydrologic cycle, groundwater is replenished by the percolation of liquid water from above through the **zone of aeration** (see Figure 10.3). It does not remain permanently in shallow ground, but moves into the deeper, water-saturated zone also known as the **zone of saturation**. The top of this deeper area is the **water table**, considered the boundary of groundwater. When the downward movement of water reaches clay or another nonporous material, the water accumulates and forms an **aquifer**.

FIGURE 10.3
Precipitation soaks into the ground in a process called infiltration, accumulating as groundwater.

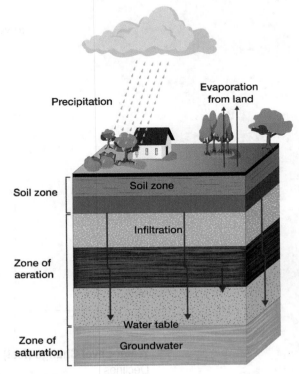

Source: Joseph Shostell; © Shutterstock, Inc.

Aquifers come in various sizes and are located at different depths. We access water in aquifers via wells. The largest one in America—the Ogallala—covers 450,000 km² (174,000 mi²), underlies eight Great Plains states, and provides water for approximately 30 percent of the United States' beef cattle, wheat, and corn, supporting production estimated at \$20–35 billion per year (see Figure 10.4). If we are not careful, unmanaged, nonsustainable withdrawals will empty this once vast resource.

zone of aeration

Relatively shallow area of ground made of soil and air. Water percolates down through this zone before reaching the water table.

zone of saturation

Where groundwater resides, underneath the zone of aeration.

water table

The top of the groundwater in the zone of saturation.

aquifer

An accumulation of water in the ground because the water moving downward through soil comes in contact with clay or another nonporous material.

FIGURE 10.4

The Ogallala is the largest aquifer in the United States As indicated in this 2015 image, the Ogallala's water is being pumped out faster than it can be naturally replenished, with water levels in some areas having dropped by over 45.7 m (150 ft) since the time before the aquifer was first tapped.

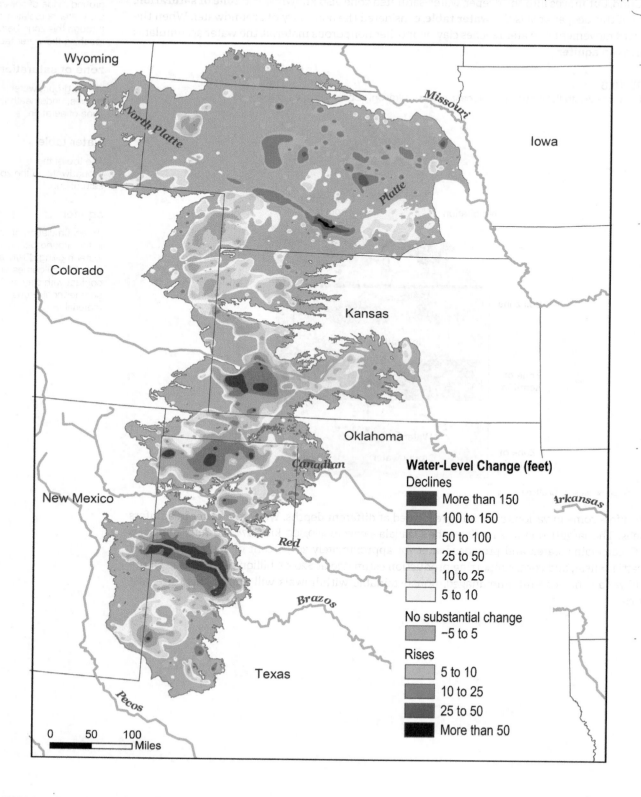

Source: NOAA, https://www.climate.gov/sites/default/files/ogallala_NCA_figure10_3_lrg.png.

Water Scarcity and Abundance

Freshwater resources are unevenly distributed globally, an artifact of regional differences in the incidence of solar radiation, air circulation patterns, and geographical features. The more intense solar radiation over the equator causes air here to warm, expand, and rise. Upon rising, it cools, causing water vapor to condense and form rain, making the equator a region known for heavy precipitation and tropical rain forests (see Figure 10.5). The air parcels, now relatively dry because they have released their moisture, then move considerably northward into the northern hemisphere or southward into the southern hemisphere to the latitudes of 25–35° (see Chapter 11). Here, the air cools and sinks lower, creating the major deserts of the world, such as the Sahara in Northern Africa. On average, deserts usually receive less than 25 cm (10 in) of rain each year.

FIGURE 10.5
Map of annual global precipitation. Dark blue indicates higher precipitation areas; white indicates relatively dry areas. Observe the high precipitation near the equator (red dashed line).

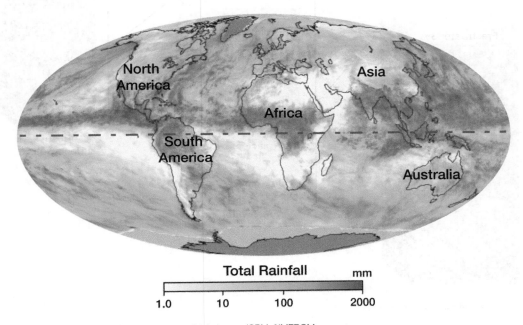

Source: NASA, https://earthobservatory.nasa.gov/global-maps/GPM_3IMERGM.

Unequal distribution of precipitation is also an artifact of geography. Parcels of air blowing over a mountain range become cooler and release precipitation before crossing to the leeward side. The windward side of the mountains receives high precipitation, while the leeward side is dry. This dry area on the leeward side of a mountain range is often referred to as a **rain shadow**. Many deserts are on the leeward side of a mountain range. For example, the Gobi, the fifth largest desert on the planet, is in the rain shadow of the Himalayas. The rain shadow of the Atlas Mountains contributed to the formation of the Sahara.

rain shadow

Dry area on the leeward side of a mountain.

The Limited Freshwater Available to Us

Although there is an abundance of water on the planet, there is a comparative scarcity of freshwater (see Figure 10.6). The vast majority of water (97.5 percent) occurs as saltwater in the oceans. Of the world's freshwater, over 68 percent is locked in glaciers and ice sheets. Another 30 percent is within the ground, leaving less than 1 percent in lakes, rivers, and swamps. Our access to freshwater depends on where we live in the world. Recall that equatorial areas receive great amounts of precipitation, while latitudes north and south of these tropical areas are some of the driest places on

Earth. Kuwait, for example, exists in the Arabian Desert, so it has scarce vegetation and extremely limited freshwater. Access to freshwater also depends on whether the area was covered by glaciers during the world's last glaciation event. For example, receding ice sheets created the Great Lakes of North America. Contrast Kuwait's water-poor land to water abundance in Iceland. This large island, considered part of Europe and home to 340,000 people, has over 13 percent of its land area covered by lakes and glaciers. It also has the largest waterfall in Europe and routinely exports its water internationally.

FIGURE 10.6

The majority of Earth's water exists as saltwater in the oceans. Only approximately 3 percent is freshwater, and of this amount over 68 percent is locked in glaciers and ice sheets. Another 30 percent is within the ground, leaving less than 1 percent accessible as surface water in lakes, rivers, and swamps.

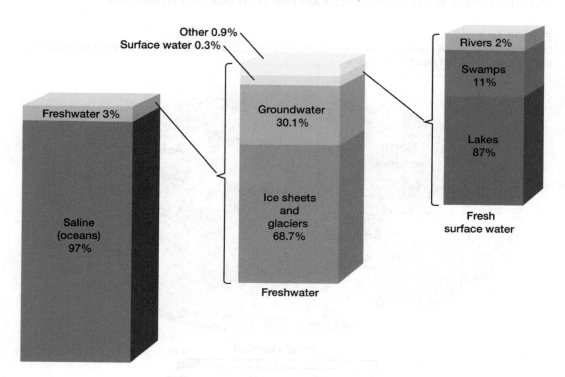

Source: Joseph Shostell; data from USGS.

Key Takeaways

- Surface water and groundwater are connected.
- Examples of the Earth's interconnected water resources are rivers, lakes, oceans, estuaries, wetlands, glaciers, and aquifers.
- Most freshwater is stored in glaciers.
- Groundwater is a vital water resource.
- Freshwater resources are unevenly distributed globally.
- The volume of freshwater accessible to us pales in comparison to the water in Earth's oceans and within ice.

10.2 Important Uses of Water

Learning Objectives

1. Explain why living things depend on water to survive.
2. Identify sources of drinking water.
3. Describe the role of water in the home and in industry.

Animals, plants, fungi, and other taxonomic groups need water to complete their basic metabolic processes (see Chapter 3). Suffice it to say, without water, life as we know it would cease to exist. Water is also one of the main environmental factors in helping to explain a biome's biodiversity (see Chapter 5). Constant high precipitation along with warm temperatures fosters some of the most productive and biodiverse areas of the world.

Critical Thinking Activity: Does Water Scarcity Explain the Abandonment of Mesa Verde?

Human populations need basic resources (food and water) to meet their physiological needs. Throughout history, populations have migrated and settled into new areas; some have been quite successful, whereas others have perished or elected to move elsewhere. When archeologists observe remnants of an ancient civilization, they investigate the settlement area and try to piece together the story of these early people. One case, potentially linked to insufficient water, involves the ancestors of the Pueblo people who settled in Mesa Verde, Colorado, about 1,500 years ago (see Figure 10.7). Their population grew to an estimated 19,200 people by the mid-1200s. About six hundred individuals carved out living areas in the walls of sandstone cliffs. The group thrived for about one hundred years in the cliff dwellings and then mysteriously abandoned the settlement. Why did they move out of their homes? Some suggest the exodus correlates with a twenty-year mega-drought period. A group of archeologists led by Dr. Tim Kohler applied computer simulation software to find answers to these questions (Kohler et al. 2008). Access information about these people through the Mesa Verde National Park's website. Observe the well-constructed cliff dwellings, read Dr. Kohler's paper (see Section 7), and come to your own conclusion as to why these people migrated elsewhere. Dr. Kohler's paper and other peer-reviewed papers about the cliff dwellings of Mesa Verde are available on JSTOR and should be accessible through your school's library or local public library.

FIGURE 10.7
Eight hundred years ago, ancestors of the Pueblo people lived in these now-abandoned cliff dwellings of Mesa Verde in Colorado.

Source: © Shutterstock, Inc.

Major Uses of Water in Society

You drink it, brush your teeth with it, and use it to flush the toilet (see Figure 10.8). Water is important to the individual and to society. On average, a healthy adult takes in approximately 3.2 liters of liquids (≈0.8 gal) per day. Add to this 50–100 liters (13–26 gal) of water-based liquids for personal hygiene, food preparation, and other basic needs (WHO 2012) (see Figure 10.8). Over a year, the average American consumes roughly 6.1 million liters (1.6 mil gal) of water, or about the volume of an Olympic-sized swimming pool. Yet, your water footprint is even greater than this amount, because it does not include virtual (unseen) water use, which is twenty times greater. For instance, manufacturing your favorite pair of jeans required almost 11,000 liters (2,900 gal) of water. Virtual water use accounts for water used in manufacturing, growing food, and all other businesses on which we depend (see Table 10.1).

FIGURE 10.8
Breakdown of typical household water use in the United States.

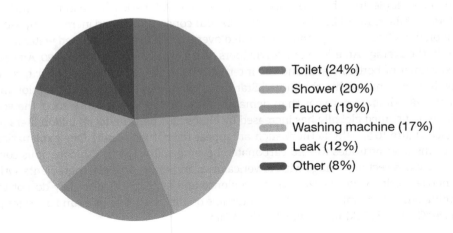

- Toilet (24%)
- Shower (20%)
- Faucet (19%)
- Washing machine (17%)
- Leak (12%)
- Other (8%)

Source: Data from EPA, https://www.epa.gov/watersense/how-we-use-water#:~:text=The average American family uses,in more water-intensive landscapes.

TABLE 10.1 Groundwater Use in the United States

Activity	Percentage
Irrigation	69.5
Public Supply	20.7
Household	4.6
Livestock & Aquaculture	3.9
Industry	3.8
Mining	1.4
Thermoelectric	0.7

Source: Data from EPA.

Drinking Water

Aquifers provide Americans with about half of their drinking water. How does the United States' largest aquifer measure up to those on other continents? It is larger than most, but not all. The Great Artesian Basin in Australia covers an estimated area of 1,700,000 km² (656,374 mi²), or approximately four times that of the Ogallala Aquifer. The Great Artesian Basin underlies one-fifth of Australia and is described as an unsung hero because it provides an invisible but stable source of water for many people living in inland Australia.

Like other continents, Africa has large aquifers, even in some of the driest parts of the continent. In 2012, a team of researchers from the British Geological Survey and University College of London mapped the location and size of African aquifers (MacDonald et al. 2012). They are estimated to hold a far greater quantity of water than lakes and rivers at the surface, and if used sustainably can provide sufficient and clean freshwater for drinking and community irrigation for Africa's future population. Knowledge of the location, volume, and recharging rate of these aquifers is essential to make sure that the removal of their water does not exceed recharging rates (Macdonald 2021). The overall volume of water to be withdrawn from Africa's aquifers is predicted to increase to support rapid population growth and economic development.

Bottled Water—A Fad Dangerous to the Environment

More and more people drink bottled water each year. In 1998, Americans consumed a little over 13.2 billion liters (3.5 billion gal) of bottled water. By 2020, our consumption had increased by 330 percent, to 56.8 billion liters (15 billion gal), and it generated over $14 billion for the bottled water industry. In other words, the average American drank 171.1 liters (45.2 gal) of bottled water in 2020. America is not the top consumer of bottled water, and the international demand for bottled water has increased more rapidly than it has within the United States. For example, per capita consumption in Mexico is 105.6 liters (28 gal) more per year than demand in the United States. Since 2000, the volume of bottled water consumed globally has increased by almost 360 percent, to 391 billion liters (103.3 billion gal) (see Figure 10.9). Why is there such an appeal for bottled water? One explanation is the change in consumer attitudes toward carbonated beverages. Today's health-conscious consumers are more likely to select a beverage with fewer calories and fewer artificial ingredients. Other consumers choose bottled water because of convenience and taste or because they do not trust the water coming out of their taps. Tap water is of terrible quality in a lot of cities and outright polluted in some (see "Critical Thinking Activity: Bottled Water").

FIGURE 10.9
Global bottled water consumption from 2000 to 2020.

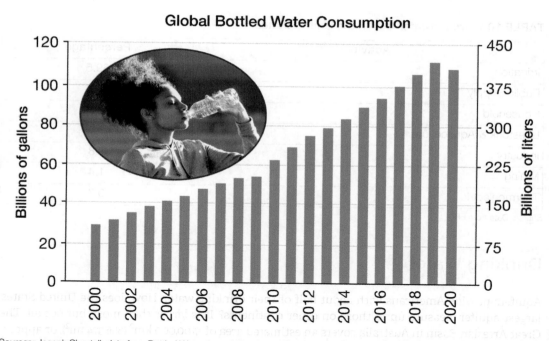

Sources: Joseph Shostell; data from Bottled Water Association, https://bottledwater.org/wp-content/uploads/2021/07/2020BWstats_BMC_pub2021BWR.pdf; © Shutterstock, Inc.

Is our reliance on bottled water sustainable? In 2009, two scientists calculated the energy required to produce bottled water. They considered the manufacturing of plastic, fabrication of plastic into bottles, withdrawing of water, filling bottles, sealing, chilling, and transportation. They said that 2,000 times more energy is used to produce bottled water compared to tap water (Gleick and Cooley 2009). Furthermore, a bottle of water has a water footprint well above the amount of water it contains, in fact, 130 percent more (Niccolucci et al. 2011). The extra water is due to the production of plastic materials. To find out more about where bottled water comes from and whether our bottled water use is sustainable, see "Critical Thinking Activity: Bottled Water".

Critical Thinking Activity: Bottled Water

Almost everyone has at one time or another satisfied their thirst with the convenience of bottled water. What is the source of this water, and is use of bottled water sustainable? Watch the following two videos and consider not just the water itself, but also the materials in the container and the energy used to harvest the water, produce the materials of the bottles, and transport the water. Lastly, consider ethics. Is it ethical to own and sell water?

 Bottling Water

Listen to the Canadian Broadcast Service report on two opposing groups on the issue of bottled water.

View in the online reader

 The Problem with Bottled Water

Listen to this reporter discuss issues with using bottled water.

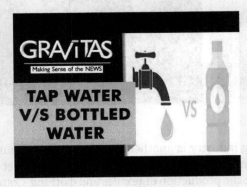

View in the online reader

It's easy to construct a water-use table that reflects water you use around the house. There is not much of a challenge, because you physically have to rotate a knob at a sink or shower to turn the water on or off. However, what about virtual water use, when we do not physically turn a lever to control water? Human society has become quite sophisticated, and our virtual water use has drastically increased, especially in the last few hundred years. The hidden uses—the ones not regularly witnessed by the average citizen—are required by industries to produce the goods and services we use.

Industrial Water Use

All industries utilize water. Here, we consider a few representative examples of industrial water use (see Figure 10.10).

The agricultural industry is heavily reliant on water, but this fact is relatively unknown for those who do not work on farms (see Figure 10.10). Fewer people today are familiar with farming than in any previous generation. Today, most of us obtain fruit, vegetables, and other foods at a supermarket. Because of this, how would most of us know how much water was used to irrigate the fields from which our produce was harvested? Did you know that a dozen ears of corn requires roughly 1,200 liters (322 gal) of water to bring to market?

FIGURE 10.10
Examples of industrial use of water: (A) Irrigation on farm fields, (B) hydroelectric dam, (C) fracking with pressurized water and sand to access natural gas, (D) dyeing of textiles.

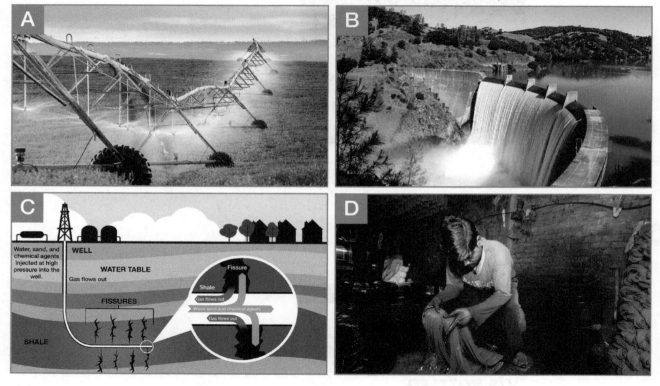

Source: © Shutterstock, Inc.; CRS PHOTO/Shutterstock.com

The textile and clothing industry is another large industrial consumer of water. In 2015, this industry used 79 trillion liters (20.9 trillion gal) of water globally (Seara et al. 2017). Water is required at several stages throughout the production of textiles and clothing. Cotton in blue jeans, for example, began as seeds in an agricultural field. These seeds required water to grow. After harvesting and spinning the cotton, water is used in bleaching, dyeing, and printing. In total, it takes 10,850 liters (2,866 gal) of water to create one pair of cotton jeans (Chapagain et al. 2005). In addition, the textile and clothing industry is one of the biggest polluters of water on the planet. Over 8,000 chemicals, many poisonous, are used in the manufacturing processes of textiles (Kant 2012). This industry is responsible for an estimated 20 percent of Earth's industrial water pollution.

The energy industry relies on water to carry out a variety of processes. Water's high specific heat makes it valuable as a coolant for nuclear reactors. Steam is used to turn turbines that generate electricity in power plants. Drillers pump water at high pressure deep into the ground to fracture shale and extract natural gas (see Chapter 13). Dams are another example of how society utilizes water. Each dam holds back a wall of water for the purpose of flood control, creation of water-recreation areas, or for generating electricity (see B in Figure 10.10).

Let's return to our opening case study about the Skokomish River. Every story has multiple sides, and in this case of the Skokomish River, the sides appear to be the Indigenous peoples and a utility company. Damming the river dramatically changed the Skokomish tribes' lifestyle and culture as the salmon runs dried up and they no longer had their main commodity, fish, to trade. Their entire social structure was based on fishing, and their wealth system was measured by how many fish the tribal community caught and traded. What right did a local utility company have to divert a large percentage of the Skokomish River for the generation of electricity? This issue quickly leads to an ethical debate. If you approach this question from the viewpoint that it is most important to maximize the number of people who benefit, then you would side with the utility company that provides energy for about 10,000 homes in Tacoma, and not with the 800 Skokomish people whose lifestyle was affected by the dam. However, if you consider the "right of first possession," clearly the Native American tribes began using the Skokomish River first and fished it for hundreds of years before the first European explorers even came to North America.

Most environmental problems have no clear yes or no answer, because environmental issues incorporate many dimensions and many subdisciplines. Be careful to not jump too soon onto the bandwagon and pit yourself against the other side. Environmental science is more about trying to find solutions to large-scale issues, such as insufficient water in an arid region, than about taking one of two sides. Remember, there are always multiple sides to every environmental issue.

Bringing It Closer to Home: How Much Water Do I Use?

For a quick calculation of your overall water use, visit this Water Footprint Calculator website. After answering all the questions about water use, analyze your results. One of the most obvious findings may well be the large amounts of unseen (virtual) water you use.

Key Takeaways

- Life would cease without water.
- Water is important to the individual and to society.
- Accounting for virtual water use, our water footprint increases substantially.
- Bottled water use is on the rise and harmful to the environment.
- All industries utilize water to some degree; some industries such as agriculture use it extensively.

10.3 Overuse and Redistribution of Water

Learning Objectives

1. Identify examples of how society overuses freshwater resources.

2. Describe the effects of overusing water resources.
3. Summarize the effects of dams, levees, and canals on natural aquatic ecosystems.

Many human activities overuse or redistribute freshwater resources, negatively affecting aquatic ecosystems. In the opening story, we learned how a dam reduced water in the North Fork of the Skokomish River and severely impacted the Skokomish people. Dam construction, water overuse, and reduction in size of wetlands are three common examples of physical stress on Earth's water resources. For instance, overuse of freshwater leads to shortages. We see examples of overuse in many areas of the world, but most severely in heavily populated cities in arid areas.

Overuse of Water

If a resource is limited, it means that each person will have less of that resource as the total number of people increases. For example, at our current population size of a little over 7.8 billion people, there are approximately 13,342 liters (3,525 gal) of annual precipitation, the ultimate source of freshwater, available per person per day. This calculation is based on a total annual precipitation supply of 37,500 km^3 (9,000 mi^3) that falls on land per year—not counting the water lost through evaporation and transpiration (Wetzel 2001). This is enough water to provide for your current lifestyle needs, as long as the world's human population remains stable.

However, the world's human population is not static at all—rather, it's growing at a fast rate. It was only twenty-five years ago that there were 6 billion people, not 7.8 billion as there are today (see Table 6.1). Such population growth has environmental scientists wondering about the number of people the world can sustain. Let's consider what will happen when the world has 15 billion people, twice as many as today. Under these conditions, it would seem that each person would have exactly half of the water that was available to them relative to today. Each person uses virtual water too. Of course, an accurate calculation of the amount of freshwater available per person considers more than just dividing the amount of freshwater available by the number of people; the calculation must include industrial use of water and geographical location. When not living sustainably, a population can easily overuse freshwater. There are many examples of overuse of water resources, which means society withdraws more water than can be replenished naturally (see Figure 10.11). Some of the egregious examples of water overuse involve the Colorado River Basin, the Ogallala Aquifer, and the Dead and Aral seas (see video link: "Aral Sea Disaster").

Aral Sea Disaster
Listen to the BBC's description of the Aral Sea disaster.

View in the online reader

Las Vegas has an immense thirst for water that has steadily increased since its days as a stopover site for settlers going farther west. Its burgeoning population has doubled since 1990 and continues to grow, which is unusual for a dusty, rocky, dry area like the Mojave Desert. Nevada is one of the driest areas in the United States; some researchers have predicted that in Las Vegas, water will become more costly than oil. Las Vegas survives on a steady stream of tourists. The city was relatively small until 1935, when the Hoover Dam was completed on the Colorado River. The dam created Lake Mead, 48 km (30 miles) away, which supplies Las Vegas with about 90 percent of its water.

Years of drought in the Colorado River Basin, along with global warming and growing water demands on Lake Mead, have overtaxed the reservoir. The water level in the lake is falling, and existing pipes that have been bringing water to Las Vegas are now too shallow. To address this issue, Las Vegas began to plan alternative strategies to acquire water. Deeper pipes were installed, and even more ambitious projects that would bring water in from other areas were considered. The overuse of water in Lake Mead pits Las Vegas directly against Los Angeles, because 750,000 homes in LA are powered by electricity generated from the Hoover Dam.

The ongoing plan, amid contentious debate, is to pump water 525 km (327 mi) from rangelands in northeast Nevada, at an estimated cost of $3–5 billion. Many of the farmers are dead set against this because it would change their rural way of life. Some argue that it's foolish to have lavish demands for water in such an arid area. One question rings loud and clear: Will the continued water demands by Las Vegas overwhelm Nevada's limited water resources? Similar problems are occurring in many other places.

FIGURE 10.11
Global water stress due to withdrawals for domestic, agricultural, and industrial use. Water stress values are based on the ratio of total water withdrawals to available renewable surface and groundwater supplies.

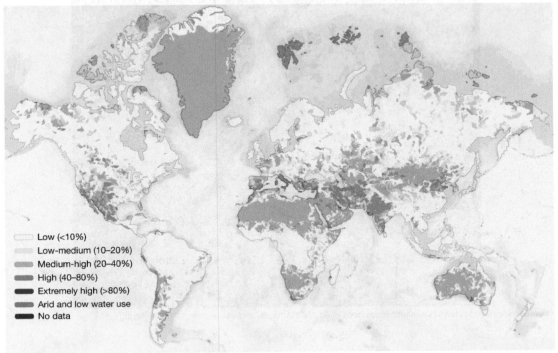

Low (<10%)
Low-medium (10–20%)
Medium-high (20–40%)
High (40–80%)
Extremely high (>80%)
Arid and low water use
No data

Source: World Resources Institute [CC BY-SA 4.0 (https://creativecommons.org/licenses/by-sa/4.0/), https://bit.ly/3hnZw4W.

The Ogallala Aquifer is another example of a stressed water resource within the United States. Farmers across eight states intensively withdraw its water to support the irrigation of farmlands (see Figure 10.4). Described as the "great pump up," this nonsustainable removal of water has taken a toll. Water quantity and quality have diminished considerably, and, for example, about 558 km of streams have already been lost from the area overlying the Ogallala Aquifer (Perkin et al. 2016). By 2017, an estimated 60 percent of the aquifer was depleted. Many wells that have tapped into the Ogallala are now dry, and others are dropping a foot per year. At the current increasing rate of water use for irrigation, the central and southern parts of the Ogallala Aquifer will be dry in the next few decades (Steward and Allen 2016).

Look to the declining water level of Shasta Lake, a reservoir in California, or the Dead Sea, which has dropped 0.9 m (3 ft) per year since Israel, Jordan, and Syria diverted water from its main insource, the Jordan River. The drying up of the Aral Sea in Kazakhstan is considered by some to be the greatest environmental disaster in the world (Figure 10.12). In this case, since the late 1960s, the fourth largest lake in the world has decreased to 10 percent of its original size as a result of water's being diverted for irrigation.

India is by far the greatest consumer of groundwater in the world. It alone accounts for more than 25 percent of global use and consumes more groundwater than China and the United States combined. Groundwater supplies 85 percent of its drinking water and 60 percent of its irrigation water. There is already ample evidence of India overtaxing its aquifers. Consider what management strategy India, a country with a population of 1.38 billion, might follow to use groundwater sustainably as its population continues to grow. By 2027, India's population is expected to be the largest in the world.

FIGURE 10.12
Only a small fraction of the original Aral Sea (freshwater lake) remains after many years of river diversion projects. The Aral Sea in 2018. The drawn line represents the lake's shoreline in 1960.

Lake shoreline in 1960

Source: NASA, https://earthobservatory.nasa.gov/ContentWOC/images/aral/aralsea_tmo_2018233_lrg.jpg

An Example: Israel's Water Dilemma

Israel is a small country of 8.7 million people who reside alongside the Mediterranean Sea. It has struggled throughout its short history to maintain access to freshwater to meet the demands of its growing population. Years of drought, along with population increases and industrialization, have seriously stressed the country's water supply. The Sea of Galilee, on which Israel depends for fresh water, is declining in volume of water and is at an increased risk of salination as the freshwater mass above its saltwater springs is removed.

In 1964, Israel built a system to transport water from the Sea of Galilee to the country's arid region in its south. Soon after construction, Syria, a neighboring country, attempted to redirect the River Jordan, which is the main source of the Sea of Galilee's water. This act was met with firm resistance by Israel and led to the six-day war in 1967. Again, water is precious.

Wetland Size Reductions

Wetlands are land areas in which the soil is saturated with water either seasonally or permanently. They can be freshwater, saltwater, or a combination of both, which is referred to as brackish.

levees

Embankments for preventing flooding.

According to the United States Geological Survey (USGS), Louisiana is losing its wetlands because of dams, **levees**, and shipping canals. Dams on the upper Mississippi River and its tributaries (i.e., Missouri and Ohio rivers) trap land-building sediments, preventing them from reaching Louisiana's wetlands. Levees on the lower Mississippi River prevent the influx of sediments from the surrounding floodplains into the river. In addition, they cause much of the remaining sediments transported by the Mississippi River to bypass the wetlands and become lost to the ocean. Since the construction of these systems of dams and levees, the annual sediment load delivered to the wetlands has been reduced from 400 million metric tons to 170 million metric tons (Meade and Parker 1985; Kesel et al. 1992). The shipping canals along the coast are destructive because they have provided a route for saltwater to travel deep into the wetlands and disrupt wetland functions. Louisiana has lost 25 percent of its wetlands since the turn of the century. Putting this into perspective, this loss is analogous to losing a football field of wetlands every hour. Florida has also lost wetlands—more acreage than any other state, actually—but this problem is not confined to just two states, nor is it a new one. Of the land that would eventually become the lower forty-eight states, an estimated 53 percent of wetland areas disappeared between the late 1800s and the late twentieth century. When we lose wetlands, we also lose the many beneficial ecosystem services they provide, such as protection of water quality, storage of floodwaters, and breeding areas for fish and wildlife.

Physical Stressors, Dams, and Ethics

A dam is another example of a physical stressor that can overtax waters. The Skokomish case study highlighted how dam construction can negatively affect one natural ecosystem while simultaneously forming a new one. Each of the two dams on the Skokomish River created a reservoir ecosystem (see "Case Study: The Skokomish River"). As mentioned earlier, the presence of dams can reduce sedimentation rates in rivers and threaten wetlands.

Engineers have built many large-scale dams, from the Three Gorges Dam recently finished in China, to the Grand Coulee Dam in the state of Washington, completed in 1942. The Three Gorges Dam, built at a cost of $26 billion on the Yangtze River, is 2,335 m (7,661 ft) long, making it the longest dam in the world to date. Hundreds of thousands of Chinese citizens were relocated from the land areas that were eventually covered by a 600 km (370 mi)–long reservoir with a depth of 180 m (600 ft). It is the site of the world's largest power station. The Three Gorges Dam altered the Yangtze River's flow, physical habitat, channel shape, temperature, sediment transport, and other parameters.

Dams affect water resources, but what about their impact on humans? Displacing hundreds of thousands of people for the Three Gorges Dam project, or even a much smaller number of people as in the case of the Skokomish tribes, is no small undertaking. Many needs must be considered. How will people be assisted in their move? Will they be appropriately cared for during the move itself? If their way of life is changed, how will they be encouraged to learn a new lifestyle that may include working in an urban area rather than a rural one? To make this more personal, imagine if tomorrow morning you received a phone call informing you, not asking, that your house must be vacated within six months.

Key Takeaways

- Many human activities overuse or redistribute freshwater resources, negatively affecting aquatic ecosystems.
- Conflicts occur over water use.
- We are losing wetlands due to dams, levees, and shipping canals.
- A dam is an example of a physical stressor that can alter natural aquatic ecosystems and displace people.

10.4 Types and Effects of Water Pollution

Learning Objectives

1. Summarize the differences between point and nonpoint pollution sources.
2. List six different types of water pollutants.
3. Describe the effects of these pollutants on humans, animals, and biodiversity.

water pollution

Any physical, biological, chemical, or radiological change in water that negatively affects the health and survival of humans or other organisms.

In addition to physical stressors, several types of pollution, individually or in combination, reduce the health of water ecosystems. As defined by the EPA, **water pollution** is any human-induced alteration of the chemical, physical, biological, and radiological integrity of water. Water pollution degrades aquatic habitats and negatively affects the health and survival of organisms. The list of pollutants is quite long and includes anything from sewage, garbage, various forms of wastes, and radioactive materials, to heat (see Figure 10.13). These pollutants contaminate our freshwater and saltwater sources, and the connected water compartments of the hydrologic cycle.

Pollution is certainly a global problem, and unlike countries it has no boundaries—moving at the whim of the wind and direction of water flow. And, pollution is not equally concentrated around the world. It tends to be more abundant in more densely populated areas. However, population density only offers a partial explanation for differences in pollution density. Industrialized nations can have more diffuse populations than developing countries, but they generally emit the greatest amount of pollution per capita. Industrialized countries can also more readily afford pollution abatement and to clean up polluted areas, although, unfortunately, many choose not to do so. A common misconception is that the solution to pollution is dilution. Dilution is definitely not the solution to pollution. Water pollution is a serious problem. According to the World Health Organization, at least 2 billion people use polluted drinking water. An estimated nine hundred children under the age of five years old die per day due to a combination of unsafe drinking water, lack of water for good hygiene, and poor access to sanitation. A large percentage of used water is never treated, and an estimated 2 million tons of our wastes are released into Earth's waters daily.

FIGURE 10.13
Common examples of groundwater contamination.

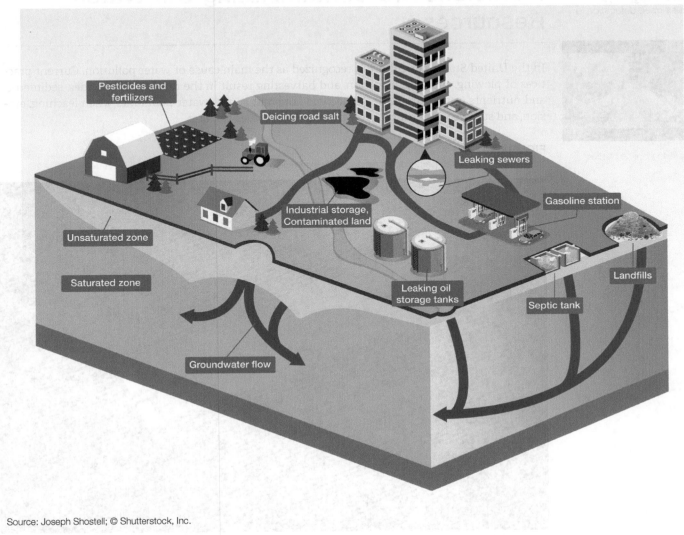

Source: Joseph Shostell; © Shutterstock, Inc.

Open Defecation Is a Problem

Sanitation problems are probably not on your radar. In contrast, a great number of people living in developing countries are faced with poor sanitation on a daily basis, and with this, poor hygiene and waterborne diseases. Over one billion people in the world defecate in the open because they do not have access to plumbing (see video link: "Open Defecation"). Untreated fecal matter that contaminates drinking water spreads disease-causing bacteria, viruses, and parasites. In the East Asia and Pacific region alone, 670 million people lack toilets—leading to high rates of child mortality. Every year in this region, around 750,000 children under the age of five die from diarrheal disease that is a result of poor sanitation and poor water quality. Poor sanitation is dangerous, but it can be corrected.

Pesticides Are Contaminating Our Water Resources

In the United States, agriculture is recognized as the main cause of water pollution. Current practices of plowing, spraying, irrigation, and harvesting result in the release of pesticides, sediments, and nutrients (see Figure 10.14). All become nonpoint source water pollutants when leaching, erosion, and surface water runoff carry them to local bodies of water.

FIGURE 10.14
Crop duster spreading pesticides over potato fields in Ohio.

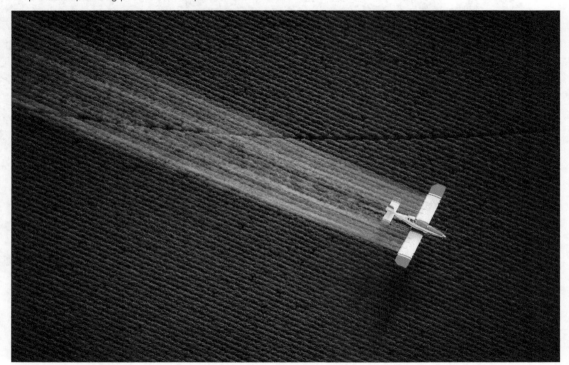

Source: © Shutterstock, Inc.

Pesticides are widely used to increase yields on 330 million acres of agricultural lands, but they are also used in residential areas and businesses. Runoff from either practice carries pesticide residues to nearby bodies of water. Americans use roughly 0.45 billion kg (1 billion lb) of pesticides annually. Some of the applied chemicals reach their intended pest targets, but much of it harms nontarget organisms. For example, pesticide accumulations in aquatic environments are linked to amphibian losses (Brüh et al. 2013; Hayes et al. 2019). The National Water Quality Assessment Program (NAWQA) reported that of the 186 stream sites they sampled, all had detectable levels of pesticides or their breakdown products (Gilliom 2007). They also found pesticides in sampled fish, sediments, and even aquifers.

Excess Nutrients Are to Blame for Enhanced Eutrophication

Conventional farmers apply a lot of fertilizer to their croplands, but most of it is not taken up by the crops. For example, only about one-third of the nitrogen applied in fertilizer ends up in plant parts. Other elements in fertilizer—mainly phosphorus—are absorbed in even lower amounts. Where does the rest end up? Nitrate and other nitrogen compounds and phosphorus compounds in fertilizers are soluble and move wherever water goes—entering rivers and lakes as part of runoff. Phosphorus compounds in fertilizer aren't as soluble and tend to stick to many surfaces, including that of soil. Erosion also delivers these compounds into bodies of water when unprotected soil is washed away.

Agricultural activities and fertilizer use in the Midwest are tied to heavy nitrogen and phosphorus loads in the Gulf of Mexico. Algal growth in aquatic systems is limited by the scarcest resource, which is usually phosphorus or nitrogen. Addition of these nutrients to aquatic ecosystems can cause large **algal blooms**, such as those in the Gulf of Mexico. After blooming, the algal cells die in mass and undergo rapid bacterial decomposition. The bacteria numbers increase and take up much of the oxygen in certain areas of the Gulf of Mexico near the mouth of the Mississippi River. Most aquatic organisms cannot live without oxygen, so these areas become **dead zones** that are devoid of life (Diez and Rosenberg 2008). Watershed managers are concerned with human-induced influxes of nutrients because they trigger algal blooms. A large percentage of the world's waters—including streams, rivers, lakes, estuaries, and coastlines—receive high nutrient loads from agricultural runoff and other anthropogenic activities. The influx of nutrients and accompanying algal growth in these water bodies is known as **cultural eutrophication** (see Figure 10.15). We expect healthy aquatic systems to experience natural eutrophication, but eutrophication due to nutrient influx from human activities and products is problematic (see Chapter 7). Of our many nutrient-containing consumer products, detergents have long been recognized as potent sources of nutrients (Godfrey and Mitchell 1972). Consequently, several companies have partially or wholly removed phosphorus from the detergents they manufacture.

FIGURE 10.15
A scientist collects a sample from nutrient-rich waters.

Source: Joseph Shostell; USGS, https://www.usgs.gov/mission-areas/water-resources/science/nutrients-and-eutrophication?qt-science_center_objects=0#qt-science_center_objects

algal blooms

A rapid population increase of algae, usually due to an over enrichment of nutrients.

dead zones

Aquatic areas with low oxygen concentrations and few organisms; usually caused by bacteria decomposers consuming the majority of oxygen while breaking down masses of dead algal cells.

cultural eutrophication

Eutrophication due to nutrients arising from human activities.

Infectious Agents Threaten Every Nation

Organic wastes from animal farms and cities can have devastating effects on water supplies and can spread deadly diseases. Untreated wastewaters increase incidences of typhoid, cholera, guinea worm disease, intestinal worm infestations, trachoma, and schistosomiasis in human populations. For example, schistosomiasis is caused by a parasitic worm that penetrates the skin. An estimated 200 million people are infected with this parasite. The U.S. Centers for Disease Control and Prevention (CDC) considers fighting this disease a winnable battle, but to do so would mean treating contaminated waters in multiple countries.

A person contracts cholera or typhoid by drinking contaminated water. Cholera, most common in eastern and southern Africa, causes severe vomiting and diarrhea that rapidly dehydrate the body, leading to death if not treated quickly. Typhoid, which can be deadly as well, is caused by a systemic infection of *Salmonella typhii*, a type of bacteria that can cross the intestinal wall to enter the bloodstream. The approximately 3 million cases of cholera and 17–25 million cases of typhoid each year are entirely preventable if drinking water were treated to kill the bacterial pathogens.

It's important to remember that infectious agents are a challenge for all countries, including developed countries such as the United States. The Environmental Protection Agency (EPA), which has the responsibility of enforcing environmental laws and regulations, reports that approximately 3.5 million people in the United States develop an illness by coming into contact with raw sewage. Given the threats of pathogenic bacteria and other infectious agents, the EPA monitors their concentrations near beaches. Approximately 10 percent of coastal waters surveyed near beaches in the United States have bacteria and virus concentrations higher than regulatory benchmarks (Dorfman and Haren 2013; HTB 2020). When people's safety is at risk, advisories are provided or beaches are closed. These closures also affect the economy. For instance, closing down a high-use, large beach in Massachusetts for just one day in 2016 caused the state to lose an estimated $50,000 (Lyon et al. 2018).

Although such instances are rare, in 2018, 210 people became ill across thirty-six states because they consumed romaine lettuce contaminated with *E. coli*. The bacteria originated in an irrigation canal that delivers water to growers in the region.

Organic and Inorganic Pollutants

Every year, billions of dollars go into designing and patenting new synthetic organic compounds that our society uses in plastics, rubbers, and pesticides, among other materials. Accumulated waste from manufacturing, runoff from factories, and compounds that leach from used products contribute to the problem of harmful organic compounds that pollute our water supply. Three common organic pollutants in water are bisphenol A, phthalates, and organic chlorides in pesticides.

bisphenol A (BPA)

Plasticizer in food and beverage plastic containers, and in the epoxy resins of food-containing cans; an organic pollutant and endocrine disruptor.

phthalate

Organic compound used to increase the flexibility of plastics; an endocrine disruptor.

organic chlorides

Organic compounds used in pesticides, Teflon, and PVC pipes.

Bisphenol A contaminates drinking water, lakes, rivers, and oceans. The pollutant enters aquatic environments through municipal and industrial wastewaters, leaching from plastic pollution, and leachate from landfills. It is an endocrine disruptor, which means it may mimic or interfere with the body's hormones. Prenatal exposure to endocrine disruptors can lead to neurological issues (Jiang et al. 2019). Scientists and an informed public placed pressure on the plastics industry to ban bisphenol A from baby bottles. Companies now advertise BPA-free products.

Phthalates contaminate water resources, including bottled water and tap water (Abtahi et al. 2019). Phthalates are found in a wide variety of plastics, including those in toys. Exposure to these chemicals is also correlated to breast cancer rates and DNA damage in sperm (Duty et al. 2003). Public concern about their potential detrimental effects on health led to the Consumer Product Safety Improvement Act in 2009, which banned the use of phthalates in plastic toys.

Organic chlorides are used in the manufacturing of many products, including PVC pipe, Teflon, and pesticides. They are also a by-product of the use of chlorine as a disinfectant. One example, DDT, or dichlorodiphenyltrichloroethane, was widely used as an insecticide nationally and internationally in the 1950s. Its use continued until Rachel Carson's 1962 book, *Silent Spring*, questioned the wisdom of spreading a toxin indiscriminately across expansive areas (see Chapter 1 and Chapter 15). The public became more aware of research data indicating DDT negatively affects fish species, aquatic invertebrates, and birds. In 1972, the United States banned the use of DDT. An international environmental treaty (The Stockholm Convention) was signed in 2004 outlawing the production and use of several organic chlorides, including DDT. India is believed to be the only country still manufacturing it.

Inorganic Pollutants

Inorganic pollutants (heavy metals, salts, and acids) have negative effects on wildlife and, in many cases, human health.

The carcinogen **hexavalent chromium** is used in anti-corrosion coatings, leather tanning, wood preservatives, textile dyes, and stainless steel production. Hexavalent chromium rose to the public's attention in the 2000 movie *Erin Brockovich*, which exposed how wastewater from a compression station contaminated groundwater and caused people in the area of Hinckley, California, to become sick. Unfortunately, this is not an isolated problem. A 2016 drinking-water study from the Environmental Working Group (EWG) documented chromium in drinking water across United States cities. Thirty-one out of the thirty-five cities tested and more than 75 percent of some 60,000 drinking water samples had measurable levels of hexavalent chromium—putting 218 million Americans at risk.

Elevated concentrations of iron, associated trace metals, and acidity degrade water quality and kill aquatic life. The largest sources of iron in many parts of the world are abandoned coal mines. When anoxic, acidic mine drainage carrying dissolved iron comes in contact with oxygenated stream water, the iron precipitates and covers the stream bed and anything in the area for kilometers downstream of the mine discharge (see Figure 10.16). River areas immediately downstream of coal mines have reduced biodiversity.

FIGURE 10.16
Acid mine discharge. The orange-reddish color is due to iron oxide.

Source: © Shutterstock, Inc.

Mercury is a metal used in industry and its concentration is steadily increasing in the global environment. This acute neurotoxin is released from coal-fired power plants as well as from the vinyl chloride industry (570–800 tons per year) and the incineration of wastes. Most of our exposure to mercury comes from food. Wind carries mercury from its source and deposits it in terrestrial and aquatic areas. Bacteria in water take up the inorganic form (Hg) of mercury and convert it into methylmercury, an organic form that is much more toxic. Methylmercury accumulates in increasing concentrations (bioaccumulation) up the food chain and is found in high concentrations within predatory fish such as tuna. Currently thirty-three states have fish advisories warning people of the high mercury levels in fish they catch. Most people get exposed to mercury by eating fish they purchased at grocery stores and restaurants.

One of the largest mercury poisoning events took place in Kumamoto, Japan. Between 1932 and 1968, the Chisso Corporation dumped an estimated 27 tons of mercury-containing compounds into Minamata Bay. Mercury contaminated the fishing waters of the bay, and villagers dependent on the bay for food began to have symptoms of mercury poisoning. Thousands experienced limb numbness, slurred speech, and impaired vision, among other symptoms.

Sodium chloride—table salt—is another inorganic pollutant when it is used along with other salts as a de-icing agent on roadways. Highly soluble in water, the salt dissociates, breaking up into its separate ions of sodium and chloride, and moves with runoff into local waterways (Gardner and Royer 2010). Are these influxes significant enough to harm aquatic life? The Ministry of Water, Land, and Air Protection in British Columbia reports baseline chloride concentrations in the environment to be between 1 and 100 mg/L. In contrast, the average concentration of chloride in roadside snow is about 4,000 mg/L, and can be as high as 19,135 mg/L. Concentrations of chloride in receiving streams have been recorded up to 800 mg/L, which is 200 mg/L higher than what is considered acutely harmful to wildlife. But before we rush to stop applying salt to our roadways, note that its application reduces accidents and injuries, and saves lives. Use of salt on roads also prevents shutdowns due to icy weather that can harm local economies.

One of the reasons for concern about shale-oil drilling is that contaminated water from fracking operations can have elevated concentrations of sodium chloride (see Chapter 13 to read more about fracking).

Groundwater Pollution Has Devastating Effects

We have a vested interest in determining the state of groundwater because it is a source of water for irrigation and drinking. Remember, surface water and groundwater connect through the porous structure of soil (see Figure 10.13), so contamination in one sooner or later spreads to the other. Groundwater and its contaminants (pollutants) tend to move slowly relative to surface water, so groundwater holds on to pollutants longer. Some of the more common pollutants found in well water are nitrates, nitrites, and the herbicide atrazine. Nitrate and nitrite are forms of nitrogen found in fertilizers, sewage, and animal waste. Drinking well water contaminated with high levels of these nutrients can cause methemoglobinemia, or blue baby syndrome. Atrazine is the most common herbicide in the United States; for example, it is used in 75 percent of all cornfields. Ingestion of atrazine, a potent endocrine disruptor, has been linked to irregular menstruation, low estrogen levels in women, low birth weights, and cancer. Atrazine has also caused heart, liver, and kidney damage in nonhuman animals (Jestadi et al. 2014; Lenkowski et al. 2008) and feminization in amphibians (Hayes et al. 2010).

Groundwater pollution is a problem to some extent in every country, but to what degree does it occur in the world's most populous nations, China and India? According to the Chinese Ministry of Water Resources, more than 80 percent of China's groundwater is polluted. The main pollutants are heavy metals and organic compounds. Data from the Central Ground Water Board in India signify the poor quality of groundwater in India. About half of their groundwater is polluted with nitrate, fluoride, and arsenic.

Thermal Pollution

Power plants and industrial manufacturers use water as a coolant. The water absorbs heat and prevents the industrial plant from overheating. Warmed water is then fed back into the environment as **thermal pollution**. An increase in water temperature of even a few degrees can be detrimental to aquatic organisms. Thermal pollution, for example, significantly affects the abundance and community structure of phytoplankton and zooplankton (Lin et al. 2018) and can decrease species richness and diversity of the fish community (Tatiana et al. 2009).

Thermal pollution that warms an aquatic environment can also provide new habitat for organisms, both small and large. Manatees are probably the most popular organism that benefits from these discharges. During winter months, manatees reduce their territory and stay within close range of industrial plants—at times congregating in the hundreds.

thermal pollution

The release of artificially warm water into the environment.

Ocean Pollution

Oceanic pollution is linked to inland pollution caused by human activities. Among the many examples, agricultural activities in the Midwest United States cause nutrient-addition problems in the Gulf of Mexico, and numerous dams have reduced sedimentation rates, affecting Louisiana coastal waters. Furthermore, erosion of small stream banks and **legacy sediments** hundreds of miles away negatively affect Chesapeake Bay on the Atlantic Coast. The problems in the Gulf of Mexico and Chesapeake Bay are signs that even the great size of the oceans is not sufficient to protect them from being harmed by pollutants.

legacy sediments

Sediments or soil structures that are the result of pioneering efforts of early settlers who deforested areas and constructed mill ponds.

FIGURE 10.17
Oil from the Deepwater Horizon spill contaminating Louisiana's coastal marsh.

Source: Elliott Cowand Jr/Shutterstock.com

Our perception of the potential dangers of deep-water oil drilling changed in 2010 when the oil rig *Deepwater Horizon*, located 60 km (40 mi) southeast of Louisiana, exploded and sank, and the oil well began to hemorrhage oil into the Gulf of Mexico. By the time the well was capped, an estimated 4.9 million barrels of crude oil (780 million L [206 million gal]) had been released, contaminating coast-lines in Louisiana, Mississippi, Alabama, and Florida (see Figure 10.17). It became the largest spill in the history of oil drilling and the largest environmental disaster in North America (see Chapter 13). The extent of the damage was deceiving because most of the oil was released in a huge underwater plume in the benthic area. The spill, referred to as the BP oil spill from the name of the oil company British Petroleum (BP), caused extensive damage to marine and wildlife habitats, fishing, and tourism in the Gulf of Mexico and surrounding Gulf States.

Petroleum extraction such as at oil rigs is one of several sources of oil pollution in the oceans. Other significant sources include natural seeps (600,000 metric tons per year), tanker spills, pipeline spills, and oil leaks from vehicles. Natural seepage is by far the largest source of oil released into the environment. Where does this oil go and what does it affect? The answers to these questions are not simple, because oil is a mixture of many different chemicals. What happens to this complex mixture varies depending on the time of year, geographical location, duration of release, and the degree of cleanup. What can be said is that varying amounts will evaporate, dissolve, become buried in sediments, and be consumed by microbes. Natural seeps release oil steadily, over long periods of time, creating environments where communities of microbes have evolved that can effectively utilize the oil as a source of carbon and energy. Oil released into the environment has devastatingly negative effects on other forms of aquatic life (Dyrynda et al. 1997; Peters et al. 1997). All eukaryotic life in oil-contaminated waters are affected, from the smallest algal cell to zooplankton, fish, cetaceans, and birds. A report by the National Oceanic and Atmospheric Administration (NOAA) documented dolphins and whales dying at twice their former rates in the Gulf of Mexico after the BP oil spill.

Pollutants move from continental watersheds to ocean waters through river currents. The existence of gigantic patches of floating garbage in several of the world's oceans is a good example of the tight connection between continents and oceans (see the opening story in Chapter 16).

Natural disasters such as hurricanes and tsunamis pose challenges for nations because they can spread pollutants. In 2017, category 5 hurricane Irma devastated parts of the Caribbean and the Florida Keys. Although terrible, the effects of Irma were small compared to those of tsunamis in 2004 and 2011 that created large-scale environmental disasters. The first tsunami, on December 26, 2004, was the result of a 9.0-magnitude earthquake under the Indian Ocean. Eleven countries, from the African coast to Thailand, were hit by a huge wave of water, with the most serious effects being felt in Indonesia, India, Sri Lanka, and Thailand. About 300,000 people lost their lives, either in the initial wave or in its aftermath. Ocean waters flooded valuable agricultural land, depositing salt that will hinder any future plant growth. Saltwater moving over land spread sewage into freshwater supplies, and this contamination greatly increased the risk of disease outbreaks such as cholera, typhoid, and dysentery.

Then, in 2011, a similar-sized earthquake occurred off the Pacific Coast of Japan. Its physical force triggered a tsunami that traveled an estimated 10 km (6 mi) inland, killing approximately 20,000 people. To make matters worse, the tsunami damaged the Fukushima Daiichi Nuclear Power Plant, initiating a reactor meltdown. Plant workers were able to eventually stabilize the reactor temperatures by pumping in cooler sea water, but not before an undisclosed amount of radionuclides were released (see Chapter 13). Later, Japan's government approved the discharge of the radioactive coolant waters into the Pacific Ocean. The many potentially harmful effects of this radiation on marine communities have yet to be completely documented.

Key Takeaways

- Water pollution is any human-induced alteration of the chemical, physical, biological, and radiological integrity of water. It is a global problem.
- Sources of water pollution can be divided into two categories: point and nonpoint sources.
- Open defecation, pesticides, excess nutrients, infectious waste, and toxic substances all pollute water resources.
- Groundwater pollution has devastating effects.
- Thermal pollution harms biodiversity.
- Much of ocean pollution originates as inland pollution caused by human activities.
- Natural disasters can spread pollutants.

10.5 Water Management

Learning Objectives

1. Identify and understand ways people and corporations can decrease water use.
2. Recognize challenges that watershed groups encounter when undergoing remediation work.
3. Summarize the process of sewage treatment.
4. Explain the significance of the Clean Water Act.
5. Identify key methods of controlling water pollution.

Water management is the management of water resources. Our aim in water management is to harness the benefits of water while protecting water resources against pollution and overuse. In the opening story, we asked, "Who is responsible for managing water?" Individuals, industries, and governments all depend on water, and they all have a shared responsibility for its management. Sound conservation management of any aquatic body—a creek, large river, lake, estuary, or even an ocean—begins with developing a management plan that focuses on human activities in watersheds. Earlier we defined a watershed as the area of land where water collects and eventually empties into a body of water. All of the world's large watersheds, even the Amazon in South America, consist of a series of smaller, interconnected watersheds. Therefore, environmental groups interested in managing Chesapeake Bay, the Gulf of Mexico, or the Sea of Japan take the strategy of including even the smallest streams in the larger watershed.

Watershed Groups and Funding

In 2000, a group of citizens in southwestern Pennsylvania got together with a mission to clean up Redstone Creek, which was polluted with mine drainage from an abandoned coal mine. They called their group the Greater Redstone Clearwater Initiative. Over the years, they have worked with the Fayette County Watershed Coordinator, a county employee, who facilitates watershed funding events and other activities. Their work is challenging, fulfilling, and at times frustrating when they encounter difficulties in their remediation work. Ever since the mine closed and filled up with water, high quantities of iron have been getting discharged into the stream. The GRCI's plan is to treat the mine discharge and restore the stream to its pre-mine state.

However, the difficulty of remediation is not the main obstacle for most watershed groups. Funding is. Limited funding from the state and federal governments in the form of grants means that watershed groups are competing with each other for the same pot of money. So much aquatic remediation work needs to be accomplished that there are never sufficient funds to support all watershed groups that want to help. Another challenge is not having the background in environmental science to understand how to proceed through the steps of remediation, which can even include litigation issues.

Conserve and Decrease the Use of Water

The easiest and cheapest method to help reduce the strain on our water resources is to conserve and therefore use less water. People living in all areas, but especially in naturally arid regions, such as the American Southwest, Kuwait, Israel, and Algeria, are encouraged to develop conservation strategies.

For example, water-poor Algeria is reevaluating a return to a traditional foggara irrigation system, which consists of an underground channel connected to a network of vertical shafts buried in a sloping plateau (UNDESA 2005). This mostly underground system reduces evaporation loss and, because of its position downslope from an aquifer, uses only gravity instead of pumps to move the water. Like the Skokomish sharing fishing weirs, Algerians can find it beneficial to share foggara, because without water, land has little or no value.

Graywater
Listen to Richard Trethewey explaining the use of graywater in toilet tanks.

View in the online reader

There are many ways to conserve water in your home (see Table 10.2). Do you have float bottles in toilet tanks? Have you insulated your water pipes or planted drought-resistant plants in your yard? Why not install a low-flow showerhead that can reduce water use from 37.9 liters (10 gal) to less than 9.5 liters (2.5 gal) per minute? You could take shorter showers or turn off the water while brushing your teeth. A highly efficient washing machine can reduce water and energy use by up to 50 percent. Washing dirty dishes with an efficient, water-conserving dishwasher instead of by hand can reduce water use by 19,000 liters (≈5,000 gal) per year. Another option is to use graywater (used faucet water) to flush the toilet (see video link: "Graywater").

TABLE 10.2 Water Conservation Methods at Home

Do You Follow These Methods to Conserve Water at Home?
Collect rainwater
If living in a dry area, replace lawn with drought-tolerant plants
Reuse graywater from shower and wash basin to flush toilet
Turn off water while brushing teeth
Install low-flow shower heads and faucets
Take short showers
Install water-saving dual flush buttons on your toilet
Find and fix any leaks

At the industry level, we can also focus on ways to improve water efficiency. Much of the water in agriculture is wasted because the majority of farms in the world rely on flood irrigation, a cheap, low-technology method. Most of the water that floods a field is not taken up by the crop plants and ends up as runoff. Less wasteful methods are low-pressure spray and drip irrigation (see Figure 10.18). Compared to flood irrigation, drip irrigation reduces evaporation and lowers water use by 25 percent.

Creating New Freshwater: Desalination

Some regions with limited natural freshwater resources can create freshwater from saltwater. It may surprise you to know that there are over 19,000 **desalination** plants at work in the world today (see video link: "Desalination"). Desalination plants remove salt and other impurities from saltwater to create freshwater. Remember, saltwater is much more plentiful than freshwater. The largest such plant in the United States is near San Diego, California, and it provides 189 million liters (50 million gal) of freshwater daily even during increasingly frequent dry seasons.

FIGURE 10.18
A drip irrigation method as shown here with this eggplant saves water and reduces runoff compared to flood irrigation.

Source: Joseph Shostell; © Shutterstock, Inc.

desalination

Creating freshwater from saltwater.

 Desalination

Hear more about United Arab Emirates' solution for obtaining freshwater.

View in the online reader

Wastewater Treatment

To protect drinking water, fish, and wildlife, we treat sewage coming from residences, businesses, and industries. Because sewage is mostly water (99.94 percent), with the remaining fraction composed of dissolved and suspended solids, it makes sense to treat and recycle this water.

Sewage treatment is a multistep process that starts with pretreatment, or screening out large debris, followed by primary, secondary, and tertiary treatments (see Figure 10.19). Suspended solids and grease are removed in the primary phase and then treated separately. Bacteria added and aerated during secondary treatment colonize and break down dissolved organic matter. In tertiary treatment, chlorine or ultraviolet light kills any infectious agents, including the bacteria added earlier.

FIGURE 10.19

Management of sewage begins where it first forms (for example, in bathrooms) and continues at the wastewater treatment plant. At the end, treated water returns to the environment. Numbers represent steps of sewage management.

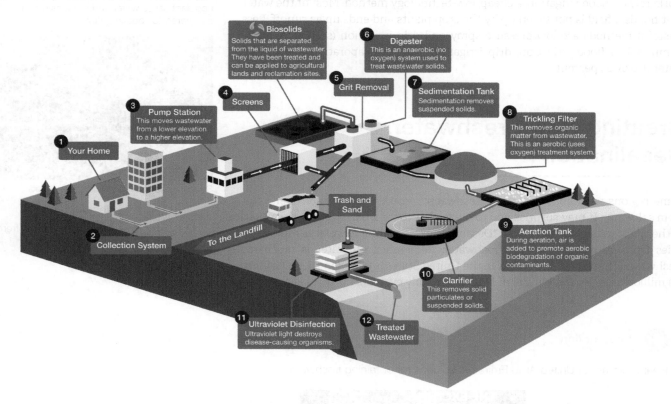

Source: Joseph Shostell; © Shutterstock, Inc.

Pollution Control and Legislation

The Environmental Protection Agency (EPA) divides sources of water pollution into two categories: **point sources**, which are stationary, discrete sources of pollution, and **nonpoint sources**, which are more diffuse.

Chimneys, pipes, wastewater treatment plants, factories, coal mines, and oil wells are all examples of point sources because they are clearly identifiable sources of pollution. Atmospheric pollutants from chimneys and other sources settle on lakes, rivers, and oceans. Pipes from urban areas carry wastewater, which is used water containing soaps, oils, nutrients, human wastes, and chemicals, among other things that originate in households and industries. Even high-temperature water discharge can be considered wastewater if the heat disrupts the natural environment. Not all businesses release the same type or quantity of pollutants, and not all pollutants are equally harmful. Hazardous materials can also be used by companies only to eventually end up as part of wastewater. Many toxic compounds used in homes and industries end up in wastewater. **Volatile organic compounds (VOC)** found in paints and oils are one example. A particularly nasty VOC is trichloroethylene (TCE), a component of many household cleaning products that is also used to degrease metal parts in industry. At one time, TCE was used to remove caffeine from coffee beans, but it was banned in food products once scientists realized that it causes cancer. TCE breaks down in soil, but this process can take years (Holton 1999). Mother Nature can naturally sequester small amounts of pollutants, but she can quickly be overwhelmed by the large volume of pollutants released by cities.

Point sources of pollution are only part of the water pollution problem. Most water pollution comes from nonpoint sources, such as stormwater runoff from urban areas, and pesticide and nutrient runoff from farmlands. These pollutants are more difficult to identify and control because there is no single place from which they are emitted. For example, stormwater runoff collects and transports pollutants from human-created impervious areas, including rooftops, highways, and parking lots. Soils and plants can absorb and detoxify some pollutants (Kömives et al. 2005). Impervious surfaces such as rooftops not only collect pollutants, but also prevent this natural process of detoxification, so water that accumulates on them runs right into nearby bodies of water. At higher latitudes, where pollutants accumulate in snow that persists for the winter, warmer temperatures in the spring result in a rapid influx of water and pollutants it carries.

Identifying the source of pollution is key to stopping it. This applies to point sources and nonpoint sources alike. The challenge for water managers is to locate the source or sources. Being able to detect the presence of a pollutant is also crucial, especially because regulatory limits may be in the parts per million or even the parts per billion level, both undetectable without special equipment. For example, scientists studying South Florida's coastal waters were interested in finding out whether human-derived pollutants were present in waters close to heavily populated areas. They detected cholesterol, estrone (an estrogen), DEET (an insect repellent), and even caffeine (Singh et al. 2010). Researchers from the U.S.G.S. Water Science Center detected five pharmaceutical drugs such as acetaminophen in groundwater used for public drinking water (Fram and Belitz 2011). These drugs are not removed by wastewater treatment, so mitigation is a priority. Interestingly, heavy consumption of caffeine products and the ability of scientists to detect and measure its concentrations in water make caffeine a useful tool for identifying leaky septic systems (Peter et al. 2006). Being able to locate leaking systems is critical in much of southern Florida and its Keys, which rely on septic systems rather than on modern sewage treatment plants.

State and Federal Water Legislation

When a preponderance of evidence indicates a pollutant can cause serious harm to the environment and living things, the quickest way to reduce the pollutant is to cut it off at its source. Legislation to remove the use of specific toxins can quickly eliminate the source. The Clean Water Act (CWA) of 1972 is a powerful federal law designed to protect and maintain the chemical, physical, and biological integrity of our nation's waters. It's enforced by the EPA, which implements the **National Pollutant Discharge Elimination System**. Under the CWA, as well as the Clean Air Act, the EPA has established regulatory control of many pollutant emissions, including inorganic pollutants like mercury.

National Pollutant Discharge Elimination System

A system controlled by the Environmental Protection Agency and used to regulate and prevent pollution discharge into navigable waters.

Mercury is a potent neurological poison that contaminates inland waters, oceans, and groundwater. Because most mercury pollution in water originates from emissions of mercury into the atmosphere, limiting these emissions is key to reducing mercury pollution. In 2011, under the authority given to it by the Clean Air Act, the EPA issued the Mercury and Air Toxic Standards (MATS) rule. MATS limits mercury emissions from coal- and oil-fired power plants. As a result of this rule, by 2017 there was about an 82 percent drop in mercury emissions from power plants. In 2003, the EPA began to limit the emissions of mercury from chlorine production plants. Chlorine is commonly used in the production of vinyl products such as pipes and flooring. The EPA estimates that mercury emissions from chlorine-producing plants have been reduced by 88 percent relative to pre-2003 levels. In addition, the EPA now limits mercury emissions from public and medical waste incinerators. Mercury-containing batteries were cited as another significant source of mercury pollution. Prior to 1996, mercury was commonly used in batteries. After they were thrown away, the batteries were either incinerated or left in landfills. To phase out the use of mercury in batteries, Congress passed the Mercury Containing and Rechargeable Battery Management Act of 1996. Mercury is now banned from most batteries. This is an example of reducing a pollutant at its source. The EPA also acted to reduce the availability of elemental mercury in domestic and international markets. The Mercury Export Ban Act, created because of the existence of the CWA and signed into law on October 14, 2008, prohibits elemental mercury exports from the United States, with the goal of reducing the commercial use of mercury globally. This law went into effect in 2013.

Critical Thinking Activity: Is Plastic in Your Toothpaste?

Trillions of plastic microbeads (<5 mm in size) make their way from personal care products to streams, lakes, and oceans every day (see Figure 10.20). These nonbiodegradable beads begin as ingredients in our toothpastes, shower gels, anti-aging creams, and facial scrubs. To provide a sense of the magnitude, a single bottle of gel may contain a few hundred thousand microbeads. Normally, a wastewater treatment plant is effective at removing pollution and other debris from household wastewater, but in this case, it is not. The microbeads are too small to be removed, and unfortunately they are eventually released into the environment. Fish mistake the microbeads as a food source and ingest them. In recognition of this pollution source and large presence of plastics in our oceans and national waters, President Barack Obama signed the Microbead-Free Waters Act in 2015. Based on this law, a phaseout of microbeads in products began in 2017. In observance of this law, Proctor and Gamble, the manufacturer of Crest toothpaste, removed plastic microbeads from its toothpastes. Similarly, Johnson and Johnson removed microbeads from Neutrogena and their other products in 2017.

Did you know about the plastic in these products? Many research studies indicate that plastic microbeads have negative effects on wildlife and fish and pose a health risk to humans (Barboza et al. 2020, Danopoulos et al. 2021). Plastic microbeads contaminate food webs and are found in bivalves (Zhao et al. 2018), crustaceans (Zhang et al. 2019), fish, and mammals (Nelms et al. 2018) including humans. Although they are now banned in the United States and Canada, you could still encounter products with microbeads by purchasing from international suppliers or when traveling overseas. To protect yourself and the environment, confirm the absence of microbeads from a product prior to purchase.

Instead of microbeads, some companies have turned to non-toxic ingredients such as corn kernel meal, ground peach seeds, or ground walnut shells.

FIGURE 10.20
Did you know...until recently, trillions of plastic microbeads in personal hygiene products entered and contaminated water resources? They were in (A) toothpastes, (B) shower gels, anti-aging creams, and other facial and body scrubs.

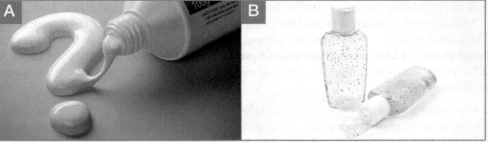

Sources: © Shutterstock, Inc.

International Laws and Controlling Ocean Pollution

One country may have a sound management strategy, but without the collective force of the international community, effective management cannot occur. In other words, there are few controls when it comes to pollution in the oceans. Creating and enforcing international laws are some of the largest problems with tackling pollution in international ocean waters. However daunting it might be, numerous international groups have formed with specific environmental goals in mind. One of the many success stories concerns dolphins (see Figure 10.21). After years of high dolphin mortality through bycatch (capture of nontargeted animals by commercial tuna-fishing operations), the Agreement of the International Dolphin Conservation Program (AIDCP) was ratified. This is a binding agreement among twelve countries for dolphin conservation and ecosystem management of the eastern tropical Pacific Ocean. Working with the tuna industry, this group is helping to significantly reduce dolphin mortality. Check out other international groups like the International Union for Conservation of Nature (IUCN) or Conservation International to see how they are protecting and managing waters around the world.

FIGURE 10.21
Mortality of dolphins in bycatch.

Source: Manuel Ruiz-Garcia

Individual countries don't have to form an international partnership to help prevent and reduce oceanic pollution. In 2006, Congress passed the Marine Debris Research, Prevention, and Reduction Act to establish a Marine Debris Program (NOAA MDP). The program focuses on the identification, reduction, and prevention of scattered pieces of waste (debris) in marine areas. For example, the program sponsors community-based projects to remove marine debris such as derelict fishing nets. Unilateral action can help even if it's not the entire solution to the problem.

Sustainable Use of Water

In context of water management, sustainability implies that water use should not negatively affect water quality or quantity. Furthermore, sustainability also means that a body of water shouldn't be overtaxed or compromised chemically, physically, or biologically. Can our water resources be sustained? Yes, although we are currently having great difficulty with this task. Observe the evidence around the world and come to your own conclusion.

Key Takeaways

- Funding is a main obstacle for watershed groups.
- Conserving water by decreasing our water use helps to reduce the strain on water resources.
- We can create new freshwater by desalination.
- We treat wastewater to protect drinking water, fish, and wildlife.
- There are two categories of water pollution: point sources and nonpoint sources.
- Legislation that prohibits the use of a pollutant can quickly eliminate its source.
- International groups form to achieve common environmental goals.

10.6 A Look to the Future: An Update on the Skokomish River

Learning Objective

1. Explain how the Skokomish River story is applicable to management of other water resources.

What does the future hold for our water resources? Will we practice sustainable methods and preserve water resources for future generations?

Water Ethics

Water is limited in some places now, and eventually will be limited everywhere if the population keeps growing and we keep using water unsustainably. When water is a limited resource, we all have to cut back. In instances in which some people will not get to use the amount of water they want, who makes the decisions about water allocation? For example, at the time of writing this book, the State of California has imposed mandatory restrictions of water use. Those who do not comply are faced with a $500 fine. Is this the "right" decision? Who should get the water? That's a difficult question to answer and really depends on your perspective. Think back to the Skokomish example. Did the utility company have the right to redirect water of the North Fork of the Skokomish River to generate electricity? Remember, the utility redirected not just some of the water, but all of the water. Certainly, we can understand that the tribal peoples suffered. This becomes an ethical discussion, for we are trying to decide what is wrong and what is right, a discussion that will tap into your own experiences and cultural upbringing. Again, be careful to not take sides, for that is the easy way out. Rather, most solutions to conflicts about the environment come with compromises in which everyone wins something, but no one wins everything.

FIGURE 10.22
Salmon numbers are on the rise in the Skokomish! A Skokomish First Nation member netting migrating salmon.

Source: The Old Major/Shutterstock.com

After a lengthy protest, the Skokomish Tribal Nation reached a $5.8 billion settlement with the City of Tacoma, the Washington state government, and the federal government over access to water. As a result, water is now released into the North Fork of the Skokomish River, and to improve salmon numbers, safe fish passages were added through the dam area, two fish hatcheries were constructed, and salmon habitat was improved (see Figure 10.22). In addition, the Skokomish Tribal Nation is now included in the evaluation of water flow. All of these changes are having a positive impact on the salmon population.

One significant concept about water is that it cycles (see Chapter 3). The water we drink and use to grow food moves through our bodies and then ends up back in the ground, air, and oceans. It is yours today and then someone else's tomorrow, and vice versa. Water is an ecosystem good, which belongs to everyone and all living things.

Key Takeaways

- Most environmental science solutions come with compromises.
- Water is part of a cycle.

FIGURE 10.23 Visual Overview: Sustainable Use of Water Resources
Summarizing figure: Sustainable use of water resources depends on understanding Earth's water resources (10.1), a recognition of the importance of these resources (10.2), care to not overuse water resources (10.3), diligence to prevent pollution (10.4), steadfast adherence to sustainable management strategies (10.5), and management practices that protect water resources for future generations (10.6).

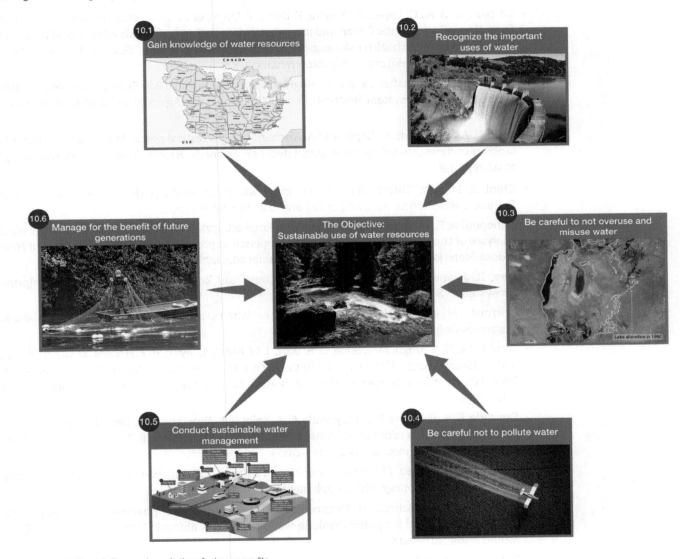

Sources: Joseph Shostell; See previous citations for image credits.

10.7 References

- Abtahi, M., S. Dobaradaran, M. Torabbeigi, S. Jorfi, R. Gholaminia, et al. 2019. "Health risk of phthalates in water environment: occurrence in water resources, bottled water, and tap water, and burden of disease from exposure through drinking water in Tehran, Iran." *Environ Res* 173: 469–479.

- Barboza, L. G. A., C. Lopes, P. Oliveira, F. Bessa, V. Otero, et al. 2020. "Microplastics in wild fish from North East Atlantic Ocean and its potential for causing neurotoxic effects, lipid oxidative damage, and human health risks associated with ingestion exposure." *Science of the Total Environment* 717. https://doi.org/1016/j.scitotenv.2019.134625.

- Boesch, D., R. B. Brinsfield, and R. E. Magnien. 2001. "Chesapeake Bay Eutrophication: Scientific Understanding, Ecosystem Restoration, and Challenges for Agriculture." *J. of Environmental Quality* 30: 303–320.

- Brüh, C. A., T. Schmidt, S. Pieper, and A. Alscher. 2013. "Terrestrial pesticide exposure of amphibians: an underestimated cause of global decline?" *Scientific Reports* 3, no. 1135. https://doi.org/1038/srep01135.

- Chini, C. M. 2017. "Direct and indirect urban water footprints of the United States." *Water Resources Research* 53, no. 1. https://doi.org/10.1002/2016WR019473.

- Danopoulos, E., M. Twiddy, R. West, and J. M. Rotchell. 2021. "A rapid review and meta-regression analyses of the toxicological impacts of microplastic exposure in human cells." *Journal of Hazardous Materials.* https://doi.org/10.1016/j.jhazmat.2021.127861.

- Diez, R. J., and R. Rosenberg. 2008. "Spreading Dead Zones and Consequences for Marine Ecosystems." *Science* 321: 926–929.

- Dorfman, M., and A. Haren. 2014. *Testing the Waters,* 24th ed. San Francisco, CA: Natural Resources Defense Council.

- Duty, S. M., N. P. Singh, M. J. Silva, D. B. Barr, J. W. Brock, L. Ryan, R. F. Herrick, D. C. Christiani, and R. Hauser. 2003. "The relationship between environmental exposures to phthalates and DNA damage in human sperm using the neutral comet assay." *Environ Health Perspect* 111, no. 9: 1164–1169.

- Dyrynda, E. A., R. J. Law, P. E. J. Dyrynda, C. A. Kelly, R. K. Pipe, and N. A. Ratcliffe. 1997. "Changes in immune parameters of natural mussel *Mytilus edulis* populations following a major oil spill." *Marine Ecology Progress Series* 206: 155–170.

- Elmendorf, W. W. 1960. *The Structure of Twana culture.* Pullman: Washington State University ResearchStudies Monographic Supplement.

- Fram, M. S., and K. Belitz. 2011. "Occurrence and concentrations of pharmaceutical compounds in groundwater used for public drinking-water supply in California." *Science of the Total Environment* 409: 3409–3417.

- Gardner, K. M., and T. V. Royer. 2010. "Effect of road salt application on seasonal chloride concentrations and toxicity in South-Central Indiana streams." *Journal of Environmental Quality* 39: 1036–1042.

- Gilliom, R. J., et al. 2007. *The Quality of Our Nation's Water. Pesticides in the Nation's Streams and Ground Water, 1992–2001.* USGS.

- Gleick, P. H., H. S. Cooley. 2009. "Energy implications of bottled water." *Environmental Research Letters* 4. https://doi.org//10.1088/1748-9326/4/1/014009.

- Godfrey, G., and D. Mitchell. 1972. "Eutrophication and Phosphate Detergents." *Science* 177: 816–817.

- Gvirtzman, H., G. Garven, and G. Gvirtzman. 1997. "Hydrogeological modeling of the saline hot springs at the Sea of Galilee, Israel." *Water Resources Research* 33, no. 5: 913–926.

- Hayes, T. B., P. Case, S. Chui, D. Chung, C. Haeffele, et al. 2019. "Pesticide mixtures, endocrine disruption, and amphibian declines: are we understanding the impact?" *Environmental Health Perspectives* 114: 40–50.

- Hayes, B. H., V. Hjoury, A. Narayan, M. Nazir, A. Park, et al. 2010. "Atrazine induces complete feminization and chemical castration in male African clawed frogs (*Xenopus laevis*)." *PNAS* 107, no. 10: 1612–1617.

- Heal The Bay (HTB). 2020. " 2019–2020 Beach Report Card." Santa Monica, California: Heal The Bay.

- Holton, W. C. 1999. "TCE treatment pasta-bilities." *Environ Health Perspect* 107, no. 9: A462–A464.

- Jay, D., C. A. Simenstad. 1994. "Downstream effects of water withdrawal in a small, high-gradient basin: erosion and deposition on the Skokomish River delta." *Estuaries* 17: 702–715.

- Jestadi, D. B., A. Phaniendra, U. Babji, T. Srinu, S. Bhavatharini, and L. Periyasamy. 2014. "Effects of short term exposure of atrazine on the liver and kidney of normal and diabetic rats." *Journal of Toxicology* 214: 1–7.

- Jiang, Y., J. Li, S. Xu, and Y, Zhou. 2019. "Prenatal exposure to bisphenol a and its alternatives and child neurodevelopment at 2 years." *Journal of Hazardous Materials* 388: 121774.

- Kömives, T., G. Gullner, and Z. Kiràly. 2005. "Phytoremediation of soils polluted with chloroacetanilide herbicides." *Cereal Research Communications* 33, no. 1: 393–397.

- Lansing, J. S., P. S. Lansing, and J. S. Erazo. 1998. "The Value of a River." *Journal of Political Ecology* 5: 1–20.

- Lenkowski, J. R., M. Reed, L. Deininger, and K. A. McLaughlin. 2008. "Perturbation of organogenesis by the herbicide atrazine in the amphibian *Xenopus laevis*." *Environmental Health Perspectives* 116, no. 2: 223–230.

- Lin, J., X. Q. Zou, F. M. Huang. 2018. "Effects of the thermal discharge from an offshore power plant on plankton and macrobenthic communities in subtropical China." *Mar Pollut Bull* 131: 106–114.

- Lyon, S. F., N. H. Merrill, K. K. Mulvaney, and M. J. Mazzotta. 2018. "Valuing coastal beaches and closures using benefit transfer: an application to Barnstable, Massachusetts." *Journal of Ocean and Coastal Economics* 5, no. 1. https://doi.org/10.15351/2373-8456.1086.

- MacDonald, A. M., H. C. Bonsor, B. E. O. Dochartaigh, and R. G. Taylor. 2012. "Quantitative maps of groundwater resources in Africa." *Environmental Research Letters* 7, no. 2. https://doi.org/10.1088/1748-9326/7/2/024009.

- Nelms S. E, T. S. Galloway, B. J. Godley, D. S. Jarvis, P. K. Lindeque. 2018. "Investigating microplastic trophic transfer in marine top predators." *Environ Pollut* 238: 999–1007.

- Niccolucci, V., S. Botto, B. Rugani, B., and Nicolardi V. 2011. "The real water consumption behind drinking water: The case of Italy." *Journal of Environmental Management* 92, no. 10: 2611–2618.

- Peter, K. A., S. P. Opsahl, and J. P. Chanton. 2006. "Tracking anthropogenic inputs using caffeine, indicator bacteria, and nutrients in rural freshwater and urban marine systems." *Environmental Science and Technology* 40, no. 24: 7616–7622.

- Peters, E. C., N. J. Gassman, J. C. Firman, R. H. Richmond, and E. A. Power. 1997. "Ecotoxicology of tropical marine ecosystems." *Environmental Toxicology and Chemistry* 16, no. 1: 12–40.

- Perkin, J.S., K. B. Gido, J. A. Falke, K. D. Fausch, H. Crockett, E. R. Johnson, and J. Sanderson. 2016. "Groundwater declines are linked to changes in Great Plains stream fish assemblages." *Proceedings of the National Academy of Sciences* 114, no. 28: 7373–7378.

- Singh, S. P., A. Azua, A. Chaudhary, S. Khan, K. L. Willett, and P. R. Gardinali. 2010. "Occurrence and distribution of steroids, hormones, and selected pharmaceuticals in South Florida coastal environments." *Ecotoxicology* 19: 338–350.

- Skoumal, R. J., M. R. Brudzinski, and B. S. Currie. 2015. "Earthquake induced by hydraulic fracturing in Poland Township, Ohio." *Bulletin of the Seismological Society of America* 105, no. 1. https://doi.org/10.1785/0120140168.
- Soeder, D.J., and W. M. Kappel. 2009. Water resources and natural gas production from the Marcellus Shale: U.S. Geological Survey Fact Sheet 2009–3032, 6 p.
- Steward, D. R., and A. J. Allen. 1916. "Peak groundwater depletion in the High Plains Aquifer, projects from 1930 to 2110." *Agricultural Water Management* 170: 36–48.
- Syers, J. K., A. E. Johnston, and D. Curtin. 2008. "Efficiency of soil and fertilizer phosphorus use. Reconciling changing concepts of soil phosphorus behavior with agronomic information." *FAO Fertilizer and Plant Nutrition Bulletin* no. 18. Rome, Italy: FAO.
- Tatiana, T. P., L. M. Neves, and F. G. Araujo. 2008. "Effects of a nuclear power plant thermal discharge on habitat complexity and fish community structure in IIha Grande Bay Brazil." *Marine Environmental Research* 68, no. 4: 188–195.
- United Nations Department of Economic and Social Affairs (UNDESA). 2005. Good Practices in Agricultural Water Management Case Studies From Farmers Worldwide. Thirteen Session, April 11–22, New York.
- United States House of Representatives Committee on Energy and Commerce (USHR-CEC) Minority Staff. 2011. "Chemicals Used in Hydraulic Fracturing." USH-CEC, Washington, DC.
- Vallentyne, J. R. 1972. "Freshwater supplies and pollution: Effects of the demophoric explosion on water and man." In: *The Environmental Future* (Ed.: Polumin, N.). London: Macmillan Press Ltd., 181–211.
- Walker, L., and S. Wu. 2017. "Pollinators and pesticides." In: *International Farm Animal, Wildlife and Food Safety Law* (Eds.: Steier, G., and K. Patel). https://doi.org/10.1007/978-3-319-18002-1_17.
- Walter, R. C., and D. J. Merritts. "Natural Streams and the Legacy of Water-Powered Mills." *Science* 319, no. 5861: 299–304.
- Wetzel, R. G. 2001. *Limnology Lake and River Ecosystems Third Edition*. San Diego, CA: Academic Press, 3.
- Williams, J. R., H. E. Pearson, J. D. Wilson. 1985. *Streamflow Statistics and Drainage-Basin Characteristics for the Puget Sound Region, Washington, Vol. I: Western and Southern Puget Sound*. Open File Rep. 84-144-A, U.S. Geological Survey, Tacoma, Washington.
- World Health Organization (WHO). 2012. *The Human Right to Water and Sanitation*. UN-Water Decade Programme on Advocacy and Communication and Water Supply and Sanitation Collaborative Council, Zaragoza, Spain.
- Winkelstern, I. Z., M. P. Rowe, K. C. Lohmann, W. F. Defliese, S. V. Petersen, and A. W. Brewer. 2017. "Meltwater pulse recorded in last interglacial mollusk shells from Bermuda." *Paleoceanography and Paleoclimatology*. https://doi.org/10.1002/2016PA003014.
- Zhang F., X. Wang, J. Xu, L. Zhu, G. Peng, P. Xu, et al. 2019. "Food-web transfer of micro-plastics between wild caught fish and crustaceans in East China Sea." *Mar Pollut Bull* 146: 173–182.
- Zhao J., W. Ran, J. Teng, Y. Liu, H. Liu, X. Yin, et al. 2018. "Microplastic pollution in sediments from the Bohai Sea and the Yellow Sea, China." *Sci Total Environ* 640–641: 637–645.

CHAPTER 11
Air Quality, Climate Change, and Air Pollution

polar amplification

A much higher increase in the Arctic's surface temperature compared to other global areas.

aerosols

Tiny solid and liquid particles in the atmosphere of either natural or anthropogenic origin.

Case Study: Drowning of Polar Bears and Melting of Arctic Ice

On August 23, 2008, a team of scientists located and captured an adult female polar bear (*Ursus maritimus*) and her yearling cub in northern Alaska and then freed them and tracked their movements over the next two months (Durner et al. 2011). Before release, they surgically implanted a temperature logger near the base of the mother's tail and fitted her with a collar containing a global positioning system unit and satellite uplink. Inside of the collar, they attached an accelerometer to detect and record activity. On an hourly basis, the bear's location was uploaded via satellite, and the researchers noted her activity. Late in October, the mother, labelled 20741, embarked on a continuous swim for nine days, covering a distance of 687 km (427 mi) (see Figure 11.1). Polar bears are avid swimmers, and there is anecdotal evidence of bears' being sighted in open water several kilometers offshore or from the nearest ice floe, but George Durner's study documented something new. Not until now did a research project validate and shed light on the long-distance swimming ability of polar bears. Durner's project also detailed the great cost of such a long excursion through chilly waters—between 2 and 6°C (35.6–42.8°F). By the end of the trip, the mother's weight had dropped by 22 percent, and in addition, she lost reproductive fitness. When the researchers captured her a second time, she was no longer lactating and her yearling cub was absent, most likely drowned during the long passage.

FIGURE 11.1
Arctic ice is a critical part of habitat that polar bears use to hunt seals. Under the current and rapid climate change and increased global temperatures, Arctic ice mass is dwindling, and as a result polar bears swim longer distances in search of food.

Source: © Shutterstock, Inc.

Polar bears are apex predators, with an overall population between 23,000 and 26,000 individuals scattered across the relatively uninhabited Arctic (Hamilton and Derocher 2018; Wiig et al. 2015). They have an incredibly high demand for energy, and their diet consists almost exclusively of seals (Pagano 2018). Their ambush predatory behavior of hunting seals on ice made for a successful evolutionary strategy. Polar bears are stealthy predators who use their keen sense of smell to locate a seal's breathing hole, where they then wait patiently for the seal to resurface. When it does, the bear swipes at it with large claws and then bites into the seal's neck. A healthy bear may eat only the energy-rich fat of the seal and leave the rest of the carcass. "Healthy" may not be the most appropriate term, because much of the Arctic food chain is contaminated with DDT and other toxic substances carried by circulating parcels of air from lower latitudes (Hung et al. 2016). These toxic substances biomagnify, and the polar bear is at the top rung of the food chain in the Arctic. Thus, polar bears are one of the most contaminated mammals on the planet (see Chapter 1).

Polar bear hunting strategy is now in jeopardy because of rising temperatures. The Arcfic's ice mass has been shrinking by 14 percent yearly, and its ice sheets are also breaking up earlier and forming later in the season each year. Furthermore, the Arctic's temperature is increasing more rapidly (**polar amplification**) than that of anywhere else on the planet. This unprecedented change is driven by an increase in the atmospheric concentration of greenhouse gases (GHG) (Weatherly and Zhang 2001), **aerosols**—tiny solid and liquid particles (Shindell 2009), and reduction in the Arctic's ability to reflect solar radiation (Dai 2021).

If conditions don't reverse, polar bears are predicted to lose roughly two-thirds of their population by 2050. Loss of Arctic ice and high levels of air pollution may well exterminate several polar bear subpopulations, including the one in the Beaufort Sea area where bear 20741 lives (Amstrup et al. 2010; Dietz et al 2019).

In this chapter, we discuss how air quality, climate change, and global air pollution relate to many environmental issues, including those affecting the Arctic and polar bears.

11.1 Climate and Atmosphere Overview

Learning Objectives

1. Identify the layers of the atmosphere and discuss their significance to life on Earth.
2. Explain the location and function of greenhouse gases in providing a stable atmospheric temperature.
3. Explain the difference between weather and climate.
4. Describe the formation of convection cells in the atmosphere.

Earth's atmosphere helps to redistribute water, moderate air temperature, generate weather, and shield us from harmful x-rays and ultraviolet radiation. In this first section, we explore the components of the atmosphere, including its layers, gases, and the natural greenhouse effect.

The Atmosphere Has Layers

The atmosphere has five component layers stacked on top of each other that differ in density, temperature, altitude, and gas composition (see Figure 11.2). The layers are the troposphere, which we live in, stratosphere, mesosphere, thermosphere, and exosphere. To gain some perspective on relative size, if the world were an apple, the first four layers would be comparable to the thickness of the peel, or roughly one-hundredth of the Earth's diameter. The exosphere extends much farther outward and by itself is close in thickness to the Earth's diameter.

FIGURE 11.2
Earth's atmosphere has five general layers: the troposphere closest to Earth's land surface, the stratosphere with essential ozone, the mesosphere, the thermosphere, and the exosphere. (A) Note the temperatures, events, and structures within each layer. (B) A view of Earth's atmosphere from space.

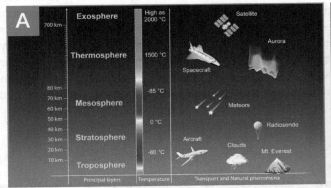 

Source: © Shutterstock, Inc.

Animals, plants, and other living things exchange air with the **troposphere**—the layer closest to the ground (see Figure 11.2). Its thickness varies from approximately 17 km (10.6 mi) at the equator—its thickest point—to about 7 km (4.3 mi) at the poles. The troposphere is the densest layer, making up about 75 percent of the entire atmosphere's mass. This layer primarily contains nitrogen (78 percent) and oxygen (21 percent), with smaller amounts of water vapor and other gases, and it is the site of most weather formation. Ninety-nine percent of the atmosphere's water vapor is here, and temperature decreases as altitude increases. Air in the troposphere mixes well vertically and contains most of society's **air pollutants**, which can become chemically altered and then return to the ground via wet and dry deposition, and be even carried long distances, such as to the Arctic (opening story).

Immediately above the troposphere lies the **stratosphere**, which extends to a height of around 50 km (31 mi). It contains an **ozone** layer—extremely important to us because it absorbs an estimated 95 percent of incoming ultraviolet radiation that can damage living tissues. The stratosphere's temperature rises with increasing altitude, an outcome of this absorbed UV radiation. Pollution does occur in this layer, but most of it originates from supersonic transports, aerosol sprays, and nuclear weapons. Some pollutants, including nitrogen oxides and free chlorine, react with and destroy the protective ozone (Hammond and Maugh 1974; Portmann et al. 2012). Another notable pollutant—particle-bound mercury—becomes oxidized and falls back to Earth, contaminating the Arctic and other ecosystems (Lyman and Jaffe 2011).

troposphere

Atmospheric layer closest to the ground.

air pollutants

Environmental contaminants of air.

stratosphere

Atmospheric layer immediately above the troposphere extending to a height of around 50 km (31 mi).

ozone

A gas (O_3) located within the troposphere and stratosphere. It contributes to smog in the troposphere and absorbs 95 percent of ultraviolet radiation coming into the stratosphere.

mesosphere

A cold atmospheric layer immediately above the stratosphere. It extends to about 85 km (53 mi) above the Earth's surface.

thermosphere

Atmospheric layer between the mesosphere and exosphere.

exosphere

Outermost layer of the atmosphere.

The **mesosphere**, immediately above the stratosphere, is a cold layer in which the temperature drops with increasing altitude. Extending from the stratosphere to a height of about 85 km (53 mi), this layer plays an important role as a protection zone against incoming small meteors. Next is the **thermosphere**, named for its heat—rising to temperatures that exceed 1,000°C (1,832°F). Importantly, the thermosphere absorbs both X-rays and UV radiation from the sun. It extends from the mesosphere to more than 640 km (400 mi) from Earth's surface, contains the ionosphere, is home to the international space station, and abuts the last layer, the **exosphere**. Collectively, these atmospheric layers insulate and protect life on Earth's surface.

The Atmosphere Stabilizes Temperature

Without an atmosphere, Earth would have extreme temperature swings between day and night, similar to what occurs on the moon and well outside the tolerance range for most living things and certainly for humans. Therefore, one important function of the atmosphere is to provide a moderate and stable temperature conducive to life. Naturally formed greenhouse gases—carbon dioxide (CO_2), nitrous oxide (N_2O), methane (CH_4), water (H_2O), and ozone (O_3)—maintain the atmosphere's temperature and prevent large temperature swings (see Figure 11.3). Greenhouse gases generally get a bad rap because of anthropogenic emissions that are causing climate change. However, naturally formed greenhouse gases serve a vital purpose. We want their presence—in natural concentrations—to continue, because without them, the average temperature on Earth would drop considerably, some suggest to as low as –18°C (–0.4°F).

FIGURE 11.3
The greenhouse effect, in which the atmosphere traps the sun's energy and keeps Earth warm. The effect is similar to the way a greenhouse keeps its interior warmer than the outside.

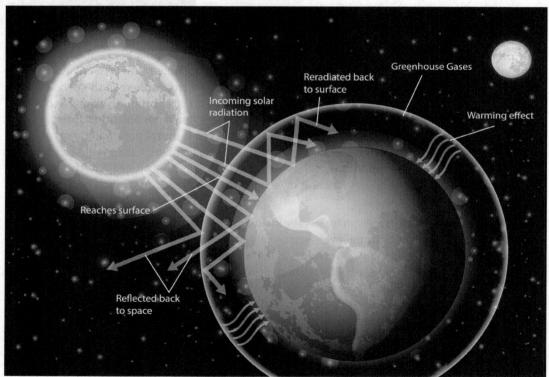

Source: © Shutterstock, Inc.

Temperature at Earth's surface is also dependent on the reflective nature of the ground itself, or **albedo** (see Figure 11.4). Albedo can range from 0 to 1, with dark surfaces having very little reflective power, instead absorbing more energy. Tar roads and other black-colored land features have no reflective power. On the other hand, snow- and ice-covered areas have a high albedo and reflect a large fraction of the incoming solar radiation. As the polar regions thaw and transform from snow and ice to water, the albedo of these regions decreases, and Earth's surface absorbs more energy and becomes warmer (opening story). This is why the Arctic is warming faster than other parts of the planet.

albedo

Reflectivity of a surface on a scale of 0 to 1. The higher the albedo score, the greater the reflectivity.

FIGURE 11.4
A world albedo map. Albedo, a measurement of reflectiveness, varies across location and is highest in snow, ice, and desert areas. This map only represents terrestrial areas.

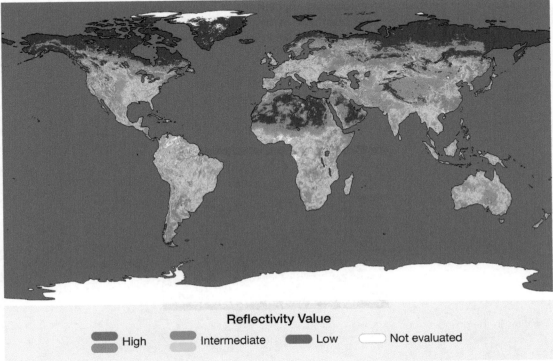

Reflectivity Value

High   Intermediate   Low   Not evaluated

Source: Image courtesy Crystal Schaaf, School for the Environment, University of Massachusetts Boston, based upon data processed by the MODIS Land Science Team.

Weather, Climate, and Air Circulation Patterns

Weather, climate, and air circulation patterns pertain to the troposphere. Earth's weather patterns are the indirect result of the unequal distribution of solar radiation on Earth, the rotation of Earth on its axis, and the physics of gases. Gases tend to move toward areas where the pressure is lower, and heat makes gases less dense so it lowers gas pressure (see Chapter 5 and Chapter 10). Those who study **weather** work in the field of **meteorology** and are interested in the daily changes in air temperature, wind, air pressure, and precipitation. Long-term patterns in weather are referred to as **climate**, a topic studied by scientists called climatologists.

weather

The daily changes in air temperature, wind, air pressure, and precipitation.

meteorology

The scientific study of the atmosphere.

climate

Long-term patterns in weather.

lower pressure area

An area of the atmosphere
that has a lower pressure
relative to the region
surrounding it.

Hadley cells

Large convection cells in
the atmosphere that exist
between the equator and
30°N and 30°S latitudes.

Ferrel cells

Large convection cells in
the atmosphere located
between 30°N and 60°S
latitudes.

polar cells

Large convection cells in
the atmosphere between
60° and the pole.

Coriolis effect

Movement of the air in
large convection cells is
deflected due to the force
of the Earth's spinning
from west to east.

trade winds

Air moving toward the
equator.

Solar radiation is most intense at the equator—resulting in greater warming of the troposphere here relative to other areas. As parcels of air warm, become less dense, and rise, they create a **lower pressure area**. Cooler air in the lower troposphere moves toward the equator to replace the ascended air, which has risen into the upper troposphere and moved northward in the northern hemisphere and southward in the southern hemisphere. As air moves upward and toward the poles, it becomes cool and, less dense, and begins to descend back to Earth's surface. These circular movements of air—large convection cells called **Hadley cells**—exist between the equator and 30°N and 30°S latitudes. Additional cells are located between 30°N and 60°S latitudes—called **Ferrel cells**—and between 60° and the poles—called **polar cells**—for a total of six convection cells (see Figure 11.5). The movement of the air in these cells is also deflected due to the force of the Earth's spinning from west to east, referred to as the **Coriolis effect**. Winds of the world such as the **trade winds** that move west and the westerlies that move east transport heat, moisture, and pollutants. For example, the westerlies carry pollution originating in China eastward across the Pacific Ocean to the United States. As a result, atmospheric concentrations of sulfate, ozone, and carbon monoxide are unnaturally higher in the Western United States.

 Convection Cells

Watch, listen, and learn about global air circulation patterns.

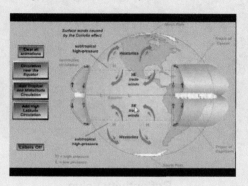

View in the online reader

As air moves from the equator poleward and cools, the water it holds begins to condense, leading to precipitation. After precipitation falls, the cool, now-dry air continues to move. The descent of this air near the 60° latitudes helps to explain the location of some of the world's deserts. In addition to the trade winds already discussed, there are also jet streams influencing weather patterns—literally rivers of air in the higher altitudes of the troposphere that move eastward at speeds in excess of 480 km per hour (300 mph) (see Figure 11.5). The jet streams affect weather patterns by pushing weather systems.

FIGURE 11.5
Earth's main air circulation patterns in the troposphere are primarily a result of air that is more intensely warmed at the equator, in combination with Earth's rotation. (A) The patterns include three pairs of large, moving parcels of air (convection cells: Polar, Ferrel, & Hadley), trade winds, westerlies, and polar easterlies. Warm and cool air are marked by red and blue arrows, respectively. (B) A cross-sectional view of the convection cells and the relative locations of polar and subtropical jet streams.

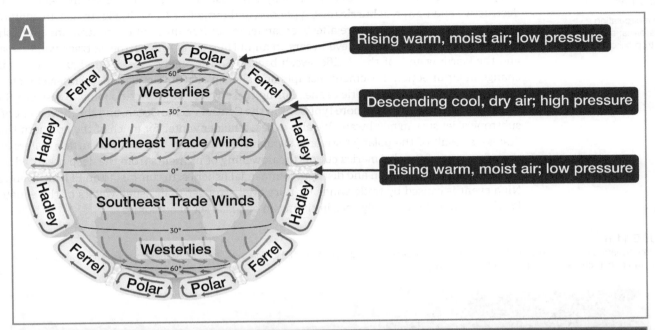

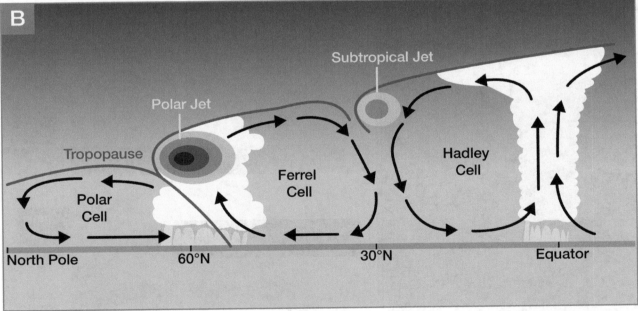

Sources: © Shutterstock, Inc.; National Weather Service JetStream, NOAA, https://commons.wikimedia.org/wiki/File:Jetcrosssection.jpg.

Storms and El Niño

hurricanes

Violent circulating windstorms; also known as a tropical cyclones.

At times, the development of some weather systems leads to the creation of storm events and even destructive and powerful **hurricanes**, typhoons, and tornadoes (see A in Figure 11.6). In addition to creating storms, the atmosphere affects ocean temperatures, nutrient concentrations, and fishing. Approximately every three to seven years, in an El Niño event, the northeast trade winds weaken and the warm waters of the Pacific swash back to South America (see C in Figure 11.6). A single change in air direction movement disrupts and alters global air circulation, weather, climate, and the distribution of tropospheric ozone. During these years, we expect flooding in western South America, the propagation of more typhoons in the Central Pacific Ocean, and the movement of the subtropical jet stream northward. We also expect a milder winter for much of the northern United States—a result of the polar jet stream's swinging farther east. The warmer surface waters along the west coast of South America cut off the upwelling of nutrients from the deep ocean, which in turn lowers fish production and disrupts commercial fisheries. In contrast to an El Niño event, a La Niña event is caused by trade winds that are even stronger than usual. Waters of the equatorial Pacific become unseasonably cold, initiating an opposite set of outcomes.

FIGURE 11.6
The atmosphere can produce violent storms and affect ocean currents. (A) In 2018, Hurricane Michael totally destroyed Mexico Beach, Florida. (B) Winds and ocean currents in normal and (C) El Niño years.

- The atmosphere has five major layers that differ in density, temperature, altitude, and gas composition.
- The troposphere is the lowest and densest of the atmospheric layers and is the location of most weather.
- The stratosphere contains beneficial ozone that absorbs ultraviolet radiation.
- Natural concentrations of greenhouse gases (water vapor, carbon dioxide, methane, nitrous oxide, and ozone) are beneficial to life because they absorb solar radiation. The trapped heat warms the lower atmosphere.
- Long-term patterns in weather are referred to as climate.
- Large, circular movements of air (convection cells) in the troposphere are due to the more intense solar radiation at Earth's Equator, air moving to lower pressure areas, and Earth's rotation.

11.2 Global Climate Change

Learning Objectives

1. Compare and contrast natural climate change and human-induced climate change.
2. Identify the causes of climate change.
3. Summarize the effects of climate change.
4. Examine why people doubt climate change.

With the current trend of rising global temperatures, it is very likely that you will have the opportunity to narrate a story about a time of cooler temperatures to your grandchildren. Our climate is changing—a conclusion based on a plethora of scientific data. In this section, we discuss climate change, its causes, and its effects.

Evidence of Climate Change

In their quest to comprehend long-term climate patterns, climatologists rely on weather balloons, radar, satellites, aircraft, oceanic buoys, and even ice cores for data on multiple variables. Additionally, measurements of tree rings, glacier size, pollen remains, and ocean sediments have proved helpful in building the climate history of Earth (see Figure 11.7). The collected data to date are compelling and provide strong evidence of Earth's changing climate (Thompson 2010; Hamza et al. 2020; TRS and NAS 2020).

FIGURE 11.7

Paleoclimatologists (climatologists studying past climate) determine historical climate conditions by analyzing cores from (A) ice, (B) coral reefs, and (C) trees.

Source: Courtesy of Mark Twickler and NOAA.

Milankovitch cycles

Periodic wobbling of the Earth and a change in its axis tilt, in predictable incidences every 41,000 or 100,000 years.

Rest assured, climate variation does occur naturally, but as we will soon discuss, it can be (and is) affected by anthropogenic activities. Variations in the sun's release of energy and in the Earth's orbit are linked to long-term and predictable climate change. For example, periodic wobbling of the Earth and predictable changes in its axis tilt every 41,000 or 100,000 years—**Milankovitch cycles**—correlate with past climate change (Milankovitch 1941; Hays 1976). Yet these cycles do not account for the rapid climate change (i.e., increased temperatures) that has been occurring since the end of the pre-industrial period (around 1850). A surge in carbon dioxide emissions from human activities during this same time frame explains the difference.

All greenhouse gases, either naturally or unnaturally formed, absorb both incoming and outgoing heat, so they trap it in the atmosphere and keep it from escaping into space. Anthropogenic emissions of GHGs surpass natural emissions and magnify this warming effect. It is also a positive feedback cycle, so, like a ball rolling down the hill, it accelerates on its own accord. In a domino effect, the increased surface temperature melts Arctic ice (opening story), which reduces surface reflectivity, which increases the surface's absorption of solar radiation, which, as a final step, increases average air temperatures. One question for climatologists is, "How can we stop this positive feedback cycle?" Were you aware that the current rapid trend of increased warming is in the opposite direction of the natural cycle (Marsicek et al. 2018)?

Within the last one hundred years, the surface temperature of Earth has risen 0.77°C (1.4°F), and it is projected to increase another 1.1–6.4°C (2–11.5°F) in the next one hundred years. This may not seem like a great change, until we place this into a historical context and consider that only a 5°C difference sets us apart from the last ice age. In the interest of preventing or slowing further temperature increases, we focus on the GHGs we can control: those released by society. These are carbon dioxide, methane, nitrous oxide, and fluorinated gases. Of the four, carbon dioxide is both the most prevalent in the atmosphere and the one we release in the greatest quantity. More than 75 percent of human-released GHGs are carbon dioxide. These emissions (≈35 billion tons per year) have skyrocketed since the mid-twentieth century (see Figure 11.8) (Quéré et al. 2018) and are more than 374,230 percent higher relative to 1750. Methane and nitrous oxide emissions have similar trends. The fourth main group—fluorinated gases—is the most potent and fastest growing of all the GHGs. See "Critical Thinking Activity: Interpreting Graphs".

FIGURE 11.8
Atmospheric concentrations of individual GHGs over time. Take note: Three of the four graphs display increasing trends.

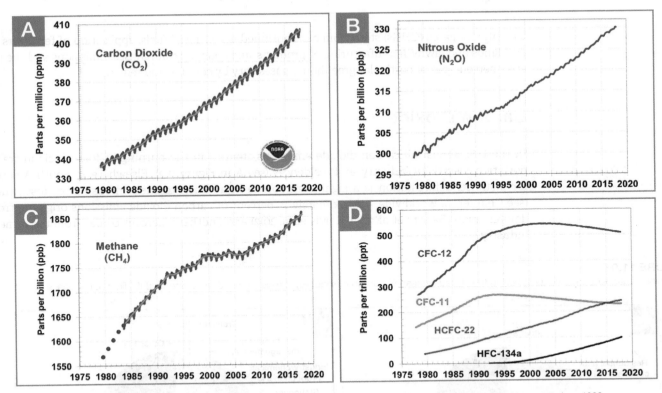

Source: NOAA Research News, https://research.noaa.gov/article/ArtMID/587/ArticleID/2359/NOAAâs-greenhouse-gas-index-up-41-percent-since-1990.

Critical Thinking Activity: Interpreting Graphs

Observe Figure 11.8. A cursory look might lead you to mistakenly conclude that carbon dioxide, methane, and nitrous oxide (graphs, A, B, and C) have stronger increasing trends than, for example, HCFC-22 (green line in graph D). A closer inspection of the Y-axis scales reveals another story. The Y-axes of the graphs for carbon dioxide, methane, and nitrous oxide are all truncated. They do not start at zero, a clear distinction from the fluorinated gas graph. If the HCFC-22 were graphed on a scale that ranged from 40 ppt to 240 ppt, it would appear quite different. Now it would display a much steeper incline. Another common mistake in graph interpretation is the assumption that the scale of units (in this case, atmospheric concentration of the pollutant) is the same across graphs. This is not always true! A comparison of the Y-axis titles indicates three different magnitudes. The most concentrated, carbon dioxide, is in parts per million, whereas methane and nitrous oxide are in parts per billion, and fluorinated gases are in parts per trillion. Therefore, to avoid these common mistakes, and before reaching any conclusions, first observe and understand the graph's axis scales and units. Then, take a look at the displayed data and compare between graphs.

A third driver of climate change is the emissions of aerosols (opening story). Data presented by NASA suggests aerosols are responsible for as much as 45 percent of Arctic warming (Shindell and Faluvegi 2009). Next, we look into the origin of GHGs and aerosols.

Origins of GHGs and Aerosols

Greenhouse gases (GHGs) stem from our continued use of fossil fuels, application of fertilizers on croplands and lawns, manufacturing of products, and consumer purchases. Emissions and the relative percentages of particular greenhouse gases vary by country and region.

Carbon Dioxide

In the U.S., almost all carbon dioxide emissions stem from the burning of fossil fuels in transportation, electricity, industry, and residences (see A in Figure 11.9). Elsewhere, in South America for instance, deforestation is a significant source in addition to the combustion of fossil fuels (see Chapter 9). Worldwide, approximately 15 percent of carbon dioxide emissions originate from deforestation (Baccini et al. 2012, Harris et al. 2012) and another 5 percent comes from the cement industry.

FIGURE 11.9

Emission sources of greenhouse gases in the United States: (A) carbon dioxide, (B) nitrous oxide, (C) methane, and (D) fluorinated gases.

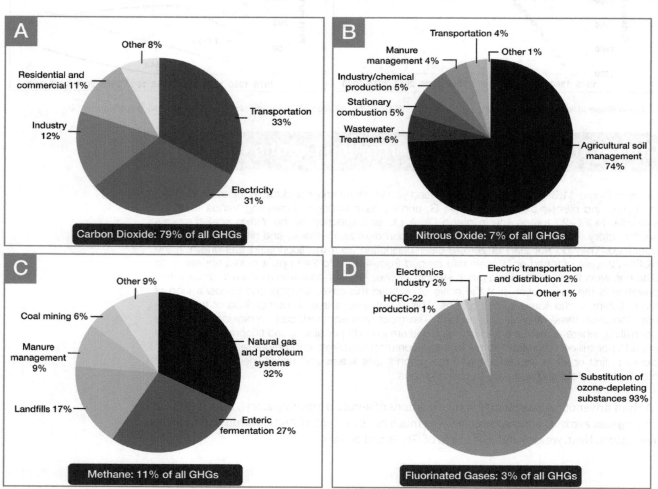

Source: Data from Overview of Greenhouse Gases, EPA, https://www.epa.gov/ghgemissions/overview-greenhouse-gases.

Of the various forms of fossil fuels, coal combustion has the largest carbon footprint—releasing about twice as much carbon dioxide as burning methane. The world's coal plants help generate approximately 40 percent of society's electricity.

Methane Sources

Compared to carbon dioxide, other greenhouse gases—methane, nitrous oxide, and fluorinated gases—are far less abundant. However, molecule to molecule, the other three main greenhouse gases have a much greater wallop on **global warming**. With thirty times the warming potential of carbon dioxide, methane makes up 11 percent of all anthropogenic greenhouse gas emissions, making it the second most common greenhouse gas. Methane originates from multiple sources, including landfills, agriculture such as rice cultivation, livestock, and the natural gas industry (see Figure 11.9).

Nitrous Oxide Is a Potent Greenhouse Gas

Nitrous oxide (N_2O) is a greenhouse gas mostly recognized by the public as laughing gas. It is colorless, nonflammable, and sweet smelling. Even though N_2O is a thousand times less abundant in the atmosphere than carbon dioxide, it has three hundred times the warming potential. Nitrous oxide composes about 7 percent of society's GHG emissions. The majority of anthropogenic nitrous oxide emissions comes from the agricultural sector (see Figure 11.9). Synthetic and organic fertilizers, livestock manure, and burning crop residues are all sources. Significant emissions of nitrous oxide also come from the combustion of fossil fuels and the industrial production of nitric acid (used in fertilizers) and adipic acid (to create nylon). Despite recycling and recovery, nylon production still accounts for the yearly release of at least 400,000 metric tons of nitrous oxide (Sato et al. 1998). Society's emissions of nitrous oxide continue to increase each year, primarily due to increasing fertilizer use.

Fluorinated Gases Are Potent but Least Abundant

Flourinated gases are the most potent of the greenhouse gases. For instance, one hydrofluorocarbon (HFC) molecule has the same warming effect as 1,300 carbon dioxide molecules. We use HFCs as refrigerants in several types of products and appliances, including air conditioners and refrigerators. HFCs were developed as replacements for hydrochlorofluorocarbons (HCFCs), another group of refrigerants that were discovered to deplete beneficial ozone in the stratosphere. Once we understood the connection between HCFCs and ozone, the EPA enacted a policy that called for the cessation of production of these gases by 2020. Emissions of HCFCs and HFCs occur mainly in developed and semi-developed countries, where people have the financial resources to purchase air-cooling equipment. Our demand for refrigerants has caused emissions of fluorinated gases to increase faster than emissions of other greenhouse gases.

Aerosols

Aerosols are tiny solid and liquid particles in the atmosphere of either natural or anthropogenic origin. Two types of aerosols—sulfates and black carbon (soot)—have a particularly strong effect on climate change. These aerosols originate from the burning of carbon-containing fuels (Novakov and Rosen 2012) and can have opposite effects on temperature. For instance, sulfate aerosols have a reflecting ability and therefore help to offset some of the global warming effects caused by greenhouse gases. In contrast, black carbon aerosols absorb solar radiation and contribute to global

global warming

Increase of the Earth's average atmospheric temperature.

warming. Substantial changes in air-quality regulation in the 1970s reduced sulfate aerosols and in doing so benefited human health and improved air quality, but simultaneously reduced the reflective nature of the atmosphere. Therefore, reduced emissions of sulfate aerosols and continued emissions of black carbon aerosols promote global warming. Dr. Drew Shindell's research (2009) and that of many other climate scientists indicates that aerosols help to explain the rapid warming trend in the Arctic (opening story). Aerosol emissions drift northward from nearby and highly industrialized Europe and North America into the Arctic. This explains why, for example, the Arctic's temperature is rising more rapidly than Antarctica's.

Effects of Climate Change

Climate change comes with a number of consequences. For a creative analogy, imagine yourself as the Earth. More or less, you are the same, except your head is replaced with Earth's sphere. At this point in time, you are at the doctor's office and hear her say, "It looks like you have a case of excess greenhouse gases. You have a hot temperature, your glaciers are melting, and there is drought on your left cheek." In this section, we look into the cascading effects of elevated GHGs.

Melting Ice, Flooding, and Changes in Ocean Currents

Earth periodically goes through ice ages when temperatures drop, snow accumulates, and ice sheets advance. During the most recent one, about 18,000 years ago, roughly one-third of Earth's land was covered by ice and every continent had mountainous glaciers. Remnants of this past ice age still linger with us today, in large ice sheets in Antarctica and Greenland, and in glaciers in other geographic areas. Currently, less than 10 percent of Earth's land remains covered by ice, and due to global warming, we are quickly losing this as well (see Figure 11.10) (Konrad et al. 2018). Melting land ice causes the sea level to rise because it adds volume to the oceans. How much of the remaining ice on land will melt, and how high will the oceans rise as a result? In contrast, melting of icebergs and frozen sea water do not contribute much to sea-level rise because they are already in the water.

FIGURE 11.10
The effects of global warming are all around us. Here are two photographs of the same glaciated area in Alaska, one (A) taken in 1941 and the second (B) sixty-three years later, in 2004.

Sources: USGS, https://www.usgs.gov/media/images/muir-and-riggs-glaciers-muir-inlet-alaska-1941; USGS, https://www.usgs.gov/media/images/muir-and-riggs-glaciers-muir-inlet-alaska.

thermal expansion

The expansion of volume due to warming; a significant cause of rising sea levels.

Since 1900, sea levels have increased 23 cm (9 in). Not all rising sea levels are due to additional water from melted ice on land. A second significant source of increased sea levels is **thermal expansion**. As much as 90 percent of solar energy trapped by greenhouse gases is absorbed as heat by the oceans. When water warms, it expands and takes up a greater volume. Earth's oceans have an enormous capacity to absorb heat; an estimated 50 percent of sea-level rise is a result of thermal expansion.

The current rate of sea-level rise is about 3.5 mm (0.14 in) per year. These small yearly changes have resulted in a significant increase in sea level over the last 150 years (see Figure 11.11). Rising sea levels are being felt by the 2.3 billion people who inhabit coastal areas, because their homes are at greater risk from flooding with every passing year (Wadey et al. 2017). Loss of all Earth's 24 million cubic kilometers (5.7 million mi^3) of ice combined with thermal expansion would raise sea levels by another 60 m (197 ft) or more. At the current rate of ice loss it would take a few thousand years to melt all of Earth's land ice. On a shorter timeline—and fast approaching reality—is the rising of sea level by just one meter (3 ft) by 2100. People living in low-lying areas will be particularly vulnerable to even small changes in sea level. For example, the Republic of the Marshall Islands (RMI) is an atoll nation that has a mean elevation of two meters above sea level. RMI and other island nations—including Kiribati, Tuvalu, and the Maldives—are the countries most threatened by climate change. They are expressing concern over their very survival, but is the rest of the world listening?

FIGURE 11.11

Rising sea levels (A) threaten low-lying areas such as (B) the archipelagic nation Maldives, which sits an average of about one meter (3.3 ft) above sea level, and (C) U.S. coastal cities, where the average number of flood days per year has increased since the 1950s.

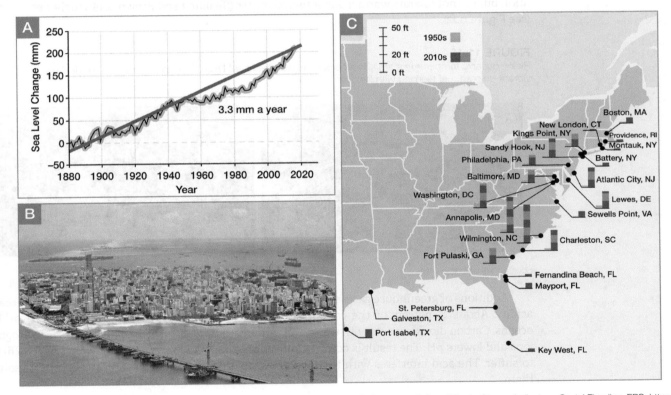

Sources: Joseph Shostell; Data from NASA, https://climate.nasa.gov/vital-signs/sea-level/; © Shutterstock, Inc.; Climate Change Indicators: Coastal Flooding, EPS, https://www.epa.gov/climate-indicators/climate-change-indicators-coastal-flooding.

A release of large volumes of freshwater from glacial ice does more than increase sea level; it also disrupts the density of ocean water and has the potential to alter ocean currents and regional climates. In the world as we know it, the Gulf Stream carries warm water from the Gulf of Mexico and the tropical Bahamas and West Indies across the North Atlantic to Northern Europe. The movement of warm water to Northern Europe means this region enjoys a much milder winter climate than other regions at the same latitude. But there are warning signs of the Gulf Stream's collapse. If it does, Northern Europe would experience an average temperature drop of about 5–10°C (9–18°F).

Changes in Species Distributions, Droughts, and Food Security

Biomes (see Chapter 5) are the result of temperature and precipitation conditions, and the species within them are adapted to those conditions. Global climate change driven by human influence presents a major challenge to species, especially the ones with a narrow tolerance for change and limited dispersal ability. Organisms capable of dispersing, such as birds and some large mammals (including polar bears) that can travel great distances have a much greater chance of surviving, but only if they can move to areas not already colonized by humans. For most organisms, plants included, there will be a general poleward shift in distribution, to land areas that historically have been too cold.

Aquatic ecosystems will also experience profound alterations as tropospheric temperatures increase and ice sheets melt. Lakes will decrease in size, depth, and number. Larger, warmer, and deeper oceans will offer new habitats for those species able to adapt. For some groups of organisms and even communities, the prognosis is rather poor, in part because they need access to solar radiation but cannot tolerate warmer water temperatures (Spalding and Brown 2015; Hughes et al. 2018) (see Figure 11.12).

FIGURE 11.12
Rising oceanic temperatures are killing coral reefs worldwide. (A) Dead, bleached coral reef. (B) Healthy, vibrant-colored reef teeming with life.

Source: © Shutterstock, Inc.

Additions of greenhouse gases to the atmosphere have another consequence for aquatic areas: acidity. About 26 percent of the carbon dioxide released by society is absorbed by the world's oceans. Carbon dioxide reacts with water and forms carbonic acid, which in turn releases hydrogen ions and lowers pH. The result is ocean acidification. Shell-building species and corals are the first to suffer. The acid interferes with the organisms' ability to build shells and can actually dissolve them.

Agricultural systems are affected too. As temperatures rise, farmers may have difficulty growing traditional crops and may need to switch to plant species acclimated to warmer environments. Intense heat waves are becoming more frequent, and lengthy droughts damage crops and therefore threaten food security (Li et al. 2019). The data are not all doom and gloom though. A warmer climate opens up new growing areas, ones that had been too cold for particular crops. Then again, rearrangement of species distributions is not always considered beneficial from a human perspective, such as the projected movement of southern pests northward.

Extreme Weather Events

Over the last few decades, we have observed an uptick in heat waves, droughts, downpours, and a change in hurricanes. "Are hurricanes and other inclement weather events changing as a consequence of increased greenhouse gases in the atmosphere?" Today's hurricanes are 10 percent slower than those of the late 1940s and 1950s (Kossin 2018). Hurricane speed, which is inversely proportional to rainfall, is a good predictor of rainfall and possible flooding. Thus, slower-paced hurricanes drop greater volumes of rain and increase the likelihood of flooding. For example, in 2019, Hurricane Dorian slowed to a crawl of 2 kph (1 mph) in the Bahamas and then remained stationary—creating devastating flooding and destruction. Simulation data from the National Science Foundation suggests hurricanes of the future will, on average, be even slower, stronger, and 24 percent wetter than they are today (NSF 2018).

Urban Heat Island Effect

Are you one of the 80 percent of Americans who live in a city? If so, you are experiencing hotter temperatures than your fellow Americans. In a time of warming air and heat waves, cities can be like hot islands in the middle of cooler rural areas (see Figure 11.13). This is the **urban heat island effect**. Temperatures average 1.3°C (2.4°F) higher inside cities relative to rural farm areas, and some cities have daily maximum values as much as 15°C (27°F) degrees higher (Climate Central 2014). Why are urban areas so much hotter? Most cities have little to no green space. There are no significant clusters of trees and other plants to provide shade. Vegetation also cools the air by releasing water vapor. Another reason has to do with construction materials. Concrete and asphalt—common in city landscapes—absorb heat during the daylight period and then radiate heat in the evening. Unlike urban areas, rural areas have few roads, buildings, roofs, and parking lots.

> **urban heat island effect**
>
> Air temperatures are higher in cities relative to surrounding rural areas.

FIGURE 11.13
Urban areas can have hotter temperatures than surrounding rural areas. Differences between temperatures in cities and rural areas average 1.3°C (2.4°F), but can be much greater.

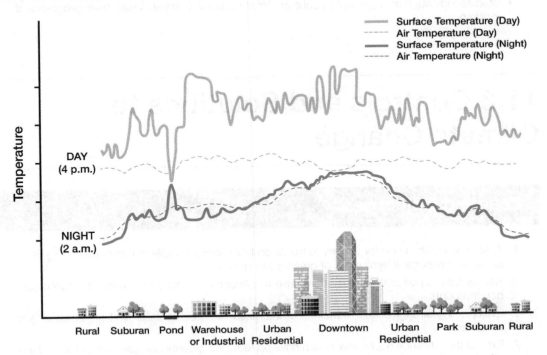

Sources: Joseph Shostell; © Shutterstock, Inc.; data from Urban Heat Islands, USGS, https://www.usgs.gov/media/images/urban-heat-islands.

Scientific Consensus, So Why the Doubt?

There is strong agreement among climatologists and other scientists about climate change. Ten out of ten climatologists will tell you, "The climate of the Earth is changing." Most (97 percent) climatologists will also state that humans are the cause of Earth's rapid climate change (Cook et al. 2016). Given this consensus among scientific experts, why does the public still have doubt about global warming? Although a growing number of Americans think global warming is real, one in eight Americans still think global warming is not happening (Leiserowitz et al. 2021). According to Dr. Peter Howe of Utah State University, a person's degree of doubt correlates with where they live (Kaufmann et al. 2016). Those less likely to doubt live in places receiving record warm temperatures. Doubters often live in colder areas where freezing temperatures still prevail.

Key Takeaways

- Findings from a large number of scientific studies provide strong evidence of Earth's rapidly changing climate.
- GHGs trap heat in the lower atmosphere. As a result, air temperatures increase.
- The main source of GHGs is the combustion of fossil fuels. Other sources of GHGs include use of refrigerants containing HCFCs or HFCs, landfills, livestock, and fertilizers.
- Climate-change effects include global warming, ocean acidification, melting of ice sheets, flooding, changing of ocean currents, increase of storm events, heat waves, longer droughts, and more precipitation. These changes affect species distributions and croplands and threaten food production.
- Studies indicate that a person's doubt of climate change correlates with their geographical location.

11.3 Controls and Solutions to Climate Change

Learning Objectives

1. Acknowledge the need for society to transition from nonrenewable to renewable energies to lessen anthropogenic emissions of greenhouse gases.
2. Recognize the power that consumers have to influence company decisions and lessen carbon footprints.
3. Evaluate the strengths and limitations of international agreements to limit greenhouse gas emissions.
4. Explain the influence governments can have on reducing greenhouse gas emissions, and the effect of rolling back helpful policies.
5. Summarize how a wedge approach and carbon capture are helpful in reducing the rate of climate change.

Are the predicted short-term or long-term effects of climate change sufficient to call us to action? There is a much greater sense of immediacy for some people than others, however. If you extrapolate the consequences out to 50, 100, or 5,000 years, more and more people might feel obligated to respond. In this section, we explore solutions to climate change.

Individuals Make a Difference

Dig a little into climate change issues and Greta Thunberg's name likely comes up. She was the sixteen-year-old who travelled on a solar-powered sailboat from Sweden to the United States back in 2019 to support the environmental movement in America (see Figure 11.14). Her voice, then and today, carries a message from the next generation: Address climate change and address it now! Listen to her speak at the U.N.'s climate Action Summit in the "Greta Thunberg" video that follows. Ms. Thunberg's message came at the same time as waves of youth protested around the world. The second message she carries is that the actions of individuals matter. Your actions make a difference. Support the use of renewable energies and lessen your carbon footprint.

FIGURE 11.14
Climate activism. (A) Sixteen-year-old climate activist Greta Thunberg arrives in New York after crossing the Atlantic in a sailboat. Her voice echoes the strong sentiment of youth around the world. (B) In Montreal, Canada, hundreds of thousands march with Ms. Thunberg to protest the lack of action to curb climate change.

Sources: lev radin/Shutterstock.com; Maria Merlos/Shutterstock.com

Greta Thunberg
Listen to sixteen-year-old Greta Thunberg addressing the United Nations about climate change.

View in the online reader

Transition to Renewable Sources of Energy

Renewable energies are viable alternatives for society to maintain energy use without generating greenhouse gases, but there is a lot of room for improvement. Currently, only about 7 percent of the electricity in the United States comes from solar (1 percent) and wind (6 percent). However, we do have the capacity to transition. Just look to Florida Power and Light Company's completion of four new solar power plants as part of their 30 by 30 initiative. They plan to install 30 million solar panels by 2030. Wind energy projects are on the rise as well. The United States has over twice the wind power capacity compared to ten years ago, enough to provide electricity to 25 million homes. Leading environmental states such as California have ambitious and profoundly needed renewable energy plans. By 2030, 50 percent of California's electricity will come from renewable energy, and by 2045, it will increase to 100 percent. In the transportation network, we are beginning to see the conversion from gasoline-powered cars and trucks to a fleet of electric vehicles. Gas stations may well be a distant memory in the not-so-distant future, replaced by renewable charging stations linked to hydroelectric dams, windmills, solar panels, or geothermal facilities.

International Agreements

Agreements to protect the environment develop from peoples' awareness of the environment, each other, and the connection between human activities and the environment's health. Here we mention three impactful international agreements related to climate change: the United Nations Framework Convention on Climate Change, the Kyoto Protocol, and the Paris Agreement. On May 9, 1992, member states of the United Nations met in Bonn, Germany, because they recognized the significance of international laws, the value of environmental legislation, and the need to protect the global climate for current and future generations. They were also fully aware of the prodigious volume of environmental data collected by many nations that revealed changing climate conditions and the effects these conditions had on society and the environment. The group adopted the international environmental treaty titled United Nations Framework Convention on Climate Change (UNFCCC), which came into force in 1994. The treaty's objective is the "stabilization of greenhouse gas concentrations in the atmosphere at a level that would prevent dangerous anthropogenic interference with the climate system." While this treaty was an important milestone in recognizing anthropogenic greenhouse gases and had wide-sweeping support, it was not legally binding—meaning it had no teeth. It did however provide a framework for future agreements and prompted the membership parties to continue to meet routinely.

Kyoto Protocol

A binding agreement (reached in 1997) for thirty-seven developed nations plus the European community to reduce greenhouse gas emissions to 5 percent below 1990 levels by 2012.

Encouragement changed to commitment with the adoption of the **Kyoto Protocol**. Adopted in 1997 and enforced in 2005, this binding agreement called for thirty-seven developed nations plus the European community to reduce greenhouse gas emissions to 5 percent less than 1990 levels by 2012. Another step forward, yes, but the Protocol only included 18 percent of global greenhouse gas emissions and the two largest emitters—the United States and China—were not included. President George W. Bush and the U.S. Senate spoke out against the Protocol because reducing emissions would place an economic burden on the United States and because developing nations did not have to reduce emissions. For example, China—the largest GHG emitter—was excluded. Together, the two countries made up roughly 40 percent of GHG emissions. In 2012, the membership parties reconvened in Doha, Qatar, to amend the Kyoto Protocol. The amendment extended the Kyoto agreement to 2020, and called for nations to reduce GHG emissions to 82 percent of 1990 levels.

Building on the Convention and Kyoto Protocol, the international community met again in 2015, where they adopted the Paris Agreement. This time, the United States and China signed and committed to reduce carbon dioxide emissions (see Figure 11.15).

The Paris Agreement has shortcomings, but it has set the global community on a more environmentally sustainable path. One form of assessment of a global goal of zero anthropogenic carbon dioxide emissions comes from the Intergovernmental Panel on Climate Change (IPCC). Their most recent reports evaluate whether we are on track to keep global warming at a maximum of 1.5°C above pre-industrial levels, and the ramifications if we fail to reach this target (IPCC 2019). Joint international efforts such as the Kyoto Protocol and Paris Agreement along with full implementation of national and international measures will help to move us toward this goal. To do this requires a rapid, thorough, and far-reaching response involving all sectors of society. The global community would need to drop greenhouse gas emissions 45 percent by 2030 and arrive at net zero by 2050. Should we miss these benchmarks, and the temperature rises to 2.0°C, sea level will rise 10 cm (4 in) higher than it is now, and the Arctic Ocean will open (become ice-free) once per decade rather than once per century (see "Case Study: Drowning of Polar Bears and Melting of Arctic Ice").

FIGURE 11.15
On April 22, 2016, Secretary of State John Kerry signs the Paris Agreement on behalf of the United States.

Source: State Department photo/ Public Domain

Government Interventions

Government leadership can have a strong positive or negative effect on greenhouse gas (GHG) emissions and the rate of climate change. The United States government has had a relatively short history of intentionally addressing sources of carbon dioxide emissions, and this influence is not always consistent—it varies over time and with each administration. In 2007, the Supreme Court ruled (*Massachusetts v. EPA*) that GHGs were air pollutants and therefore subject to the **Clean Air Act**. The EPA was then required to determine if GHGs endangered the public, and therefore were in need of regulation. After review of scientific data, the EPA concluded on December 15, 2009, that GHGs do endanger the public's health and their welfare. GHGs now fall under the Clean Air Act's Prevention of Significant Deterioration (PSD) program (which targets new stationary sources) and Title V, the EPA's operating permit system. Title V requires organizations that are sources of identified air pollutants to obtain an operating permit. Permittees provide reports to the EPA at least on a yearly basis.

> **Clean Air Act**
>
> The primary federal law within the United States that addresses air pollution.

Back in the 1970s, the United States wasn't intentionally focusing on carbon dioxide, yet the creation of the Energy Policy and Conservation Act in 1975 affected carbon dioxide emissions. The Act established fuel-economy benchmarks for passenger cars and set the standard at 27.5 miles per gallon (11.7 km/L) by 1985. These are the **Corporate Fuel Economy (CAFE) standards** set and enforced by the National Highway Traffic and Safety Administration (NHTSA). The first benchmark was more than double the fuel economy of average passenger cars manufactured in 1974. Through innovation, research, and design improvements, automakers met these standards, and continue to do so as the standards become stricter. Because of these standards, vehicle emissions have dropped by roughly 3 percent per year. Ford's Ecoboost and Toyota's Synergy Drive are two examples of technologies that automakers have implemented in their efforts to meet the new benchmarks.

> **Corporate Fuel Economy (CAFE) standards**
>
> Set benchmarks for automakers of how far automobiles must travel on a gallon of gas.

The Energy Independence and Security Act (EISA) of 2007, signed by President George W. Bush, also helped move the United States toward more efficient vehicles, in addition to supporting the capture of greenhouse gases and promoting the use of renewable fuels. The Act amended the CAFE standards from 27.5 to at least 35 mpg, applicable to all passenger and nonpassenger automobiles manufactured in 2020. Furthermore, the Act gave power to the secretary of transportation to establish a credit-trading program to incentivize automakers to exceed the fuel-efficiency standards. Automakers that exceed the standard can profit by selling credits to automakers that failed to meet the standards.

Under the direction of President Barack Obama in 2010, the NHTSA (which sets CAFE standards) and the EPA (which sets GHG standards) began to work jointly to develop rules for fuel economy and GHG emissions related to passenger cars and light trucks beginning in 2017. By 2025, new cars were to have an average fuel efficiency of 55 mpg (FR 2012). An auto advocacy group challenged the rule, and the Trump administration rolled back these advances, proposing in their place the SAFE Vehicles Rule. The SAFE Rule froze efficiency standards to 40 mpg by 2026, and prohibited individual states from establishing their own fuel efficiency standards separate from those of the federal government. Instead of saving fuel, the bold rule erased incentives for automakers to design more fuel-efficient models, and dismantled decades of hard-fought environmentally friendly legislation in California and other states. An analysis of the new rule by Dr. Dan Sperling of University of California, Davis concluded the United States would end up releasing 870 million tons more carbon dioxide compared to Obama's phase two plan, and consumers would have to pay an additional $130 billion in fuel costs. President Joseph Biden's administration plans to review the SAFE Vehicles Rule.

What about government intervention outside the United States? The Chinese government is developing a massive trading system for their power sector, which is the source of about half of the country's GHG emissions. China's commitment to regulating GHGs goes a long way toward controlling global emissions, because it burns more coal and produces more GHGs than any other nation. Their solution includes a massive credit-trading system for power plants and continued rapid adoption of renewable energy sources such as wind and solar. Right now, China is the undisputed global leader in the development and adoption of renewable sources of energy. China is also heavily investing in a large public transportation system of high-speed trains and subways, and attempting to expand consumer adoption of electric cars. In early 2019, Tesla—a leading producer of electric cars—reached an agreement to become China's first completely foreign-owned automobile factory. In this special agreement with the Chinese government, tariffs will not apply to the estimated 500,000 electric cars produced annually in the new $2 billion car plant.

Wedge Approach

wedge approach

A combination of mini-solutions (wedges) that collectively flatten the GHG emissions curve.

No single environmental action can resolve the carbon dioxide emissions problem. A **wedge approach** acknowledges this, and instead offers a combination of mini-solutions that collectively flatten the emissions curve. Each solution appears as a slice, or a wedge, of the stabilization triangle. There is no specific number of wedges, but in the case of greenhouse gases, there are probably more than twelve. Efficiency, wind energy, solar energy, switching of fuel sources, carbon capture, biomass fuels, nuclear energy, and ending deforestation are all included, and these can be further divided into smaller wedges (see Figure 11.16).

FIGURE 11.16
We can solve some environmental problems by using a wedge approach. To help flatten the trend of anthropogenic GHG emissions, we combine a number of smaller solutions. Each solution appears as a slice (a wedge) of the stabilization triangle.

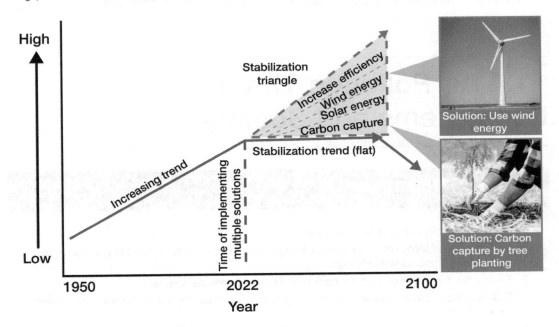

Sources: Joseph Shostell; © Shutterstock, Inc.

Carbon Capture

There are also methods to remove carbon dioxide molecules from the atmosphere. Reforestation offers one nontechnical solution. Planting 500 billion trees—a 25 percent increase in forested area—could store 200 gigatonnes of carbon and remove 25 percent of atmospheric carbon dioxide (Bastin et al. 2019). We have already developed technology to capture carbon dioxide emitted from coal- and gas-fired power plants, and from the industry sector. One technology is based on removing carbon dioxide molecules from smokestack emissions. The captured carbon dioxide is pressurized into a liquid and injected deep underground for permanent storage. This method, called **carbon dioxide capture and sequestration**, can reduce carbon dioxide emissions from large stationary sources by as much as 80–90 percent.

carbon dioxide capture and sequestration

A technological method to capture carbon dioxide emitted from power plants and other large stationary sources of carbon dioxide.

Key Takeaways

- Individuals make a difference in reducing the speed of climate change.
- Fossil fuels contain carbon that is released by combustion in the form of CO_2. Therefore, reducing their use lessens CO_2 emissions.
- Renewable energies are viable alternatives for society to maintain energy use without generating greenhouse gases.
- The Kyoto Protocol and Paris Agreement are international agreements to help control greenhouse gas emissions.
- Government leadership can have a strong positive or negative effect on greenhouse gas emissions. The Clean Air Act, Corporate Fuel Economy Standards, and Energy Independence and Security Act have helped to lessen GHG emissions in the United States.
- A wedge approach offers a combination of solutions to flatten the GHG emissions curve.

- There are methods of removing carbon dioxide molecules from the atmosphere. An example is reforestation.
- Carbon dioxide capture and sequestration reduces carbon dioxide emissions.

11.4 Air Pollution Threatens Ecosystems and Society

Learning Objectives

1. Identify the main atmospheric pollutants.
2. Recognize that some greenhouse gases negatively affect the environment in addition to playing a role in global climate change.
3. Explain the formation of acid deposition and how it threatens species.
4. Examine the mixture of pollutants in smog and asses their impact on human and environmental health.
5. Compare and contrast the severity of indoor and outdoor pollution.

The very idea of air pollution in an uninhabited place seems counterintuitive, doesn't it? Yet our observations and analyses of PCBs and mercury in polar bear tissues and of haze in the Arctic's atmosphere—far from metropolitan areas—inform us of the ability of air pollutants to travel across large geographical distances. Anthropogenic greenhouse gases and aerosols populate the Arctic's atmosphere, as do a host of other air pollutants. Back in the mid-twentieth century when scientists first observed Arctic haze, they sampled and tested it to determine its consistency and origin. Their studies revealed high concentrations of vanadium, which is a metal byproduct of burning oil. They also analyzed fine-grained soot and detected high concentrations of nickel, manganese, iron, titanium, and chromium—all associated with the combustion of coal. These and other air pollutants are ubiquitous environmental contaminants in air that threaten ecosystems and society.

Poor air quality diminishes respiratory and cardiovascular function and increases risk of disease and premature death. According to the World Health Organization (WHO), nine out of ten people breathe highly polluted air and an estimated 7 million people die from air pollution annually. In this section, we discuss the types, sources, and effects of common air pollutants (see Table 11.1).

TABLE 11.1
Major air pollutants, their sources, and health effects.

Pollutant	Major Anthropogenic Sources	Health Effects
Carbon monoxide	Transportation (cars, trucks, vans, SUVs, buses, and planes)	Acute exposure: headache, dizziness, decreased physical performance, death
Sulfur oxides	Stationary combustion sources such as coal-fired power plants, industry	Acute exposure: inflammation of respiratory tract, aggravation of asthma
Nitrogen oxides	Transportation, stationary combustion sources such as coal-fired power plants	Acute exposure: emphysema, bronchitis
Particulate matter	Stationary combustion sources such as coal-fired power plants, industry	Irritation of respiratory system, cancer

Pollutant	Major Anthropogenic Sources	Health Effects
Ground-level ozone	Created from chemical reactions of nitrogen oxides and volatile organic compounds in the atmosphere	Asthma, coughing, shortness of breath, increased cancer risk (Kim et al. 2018)
Hydrocarbons	Transportation (cars, trucks, vans, SUVs, buses, and planes)	Many, including pulmonary toxicity, cancer, abdominal pain, hepatoxicity, central nervous system (CNS) effects, and death

Natural Pollution

Not all pollutants in the atmosphere are anthropogenic in origin; some arise from natural sources. Natural sources of pollutants include volcanoes, forest fires, the ground (i.e., radon seeping through soil), ozone, sea spray, and dust storms. Here we highlight passive degassing and eruptions of volcanoes in more detail, bringing up wind circulation patterns.

Do natural pollutants overwhelm and alter ecosystems? Any effective answer to this question depends on the type of pollutant, the relative amounts of natural and unnatural pollutants, and the consistency of emission—consistently low or sporadically large. For example, Dr. Helen Amos, of Harvard University, tailored the question to just mercury. She asked, "When you go out and measure mercury in the environment today, how much of that mercury occurs naturally and how much is the result of anthropogenic releases?" Currently, human activities account for about 30 percent of atmospheric emissions, with the remaining a combination of legacy mercury (which is mercury released to the environment in the past), and a significant amount of natural mercury from volcanoes (Amos et al. 2013). What about carbon dioxide and sulfur dioxide, which are linked to climate change and acid rain, respectively? The approximately 450 subaerial (open to the air) volcanoes on Earth inject about 0.54 Gt of carbon dioxide into the atmosphere yearly, which is a factor of ten lower than the 35.9 to 38.2 Gt emitted by society (Burton et al. 2013, Le Quéré, et al. 2015). A gigaton (Gt) is equal to one billion tons. Volcanoes also emit about 23.0 Tg (Carn et al. 2017) of sulfur dioxide per year, far less than the 100–150 Tg released each year through combustion of fossil fuels, and a much smaller fraction than biomass burning (Granier et al. 2011). One teragram (Tg) is equal to one trillion grams. Overall, volcanic sources of carbon dioxide and sulfur dioxide pale in comparison to emission from society.

Acid Rain

Acid rain degrades terrestrial and aquatic ecosystems. The vast majority of acid rain originates from the release of sulfur dioxide (SO_2) and nitrogen oxides (NO_x) into the atmosphere upon combustion of fossil fuels. In the presence of sunlight, these molecules undergo chemical reactions with oxygen and water to form sulfuric acid (H_2SO_4) and nitric acid (HNO_3), which eventually fall back to Earth (see Figure 11.17). Acid rain doesn't necessarily kill organisms directly, but instead increases their susceptibility to a variety of stressors, such as disease, insects, and temperature swings. Up to 17 percent of Earth's natural terrestrial ecosystems already receive acid rain in amounts above their critical threshold (Bouwman et al. 2002) (see Chapter 9). In addition, our oceans, from which many people obtain their food, are acidifying (see Chapter 10).

FIGURE 11.17

Formation of acid rain. Sulfur dioxide (SO₂) and nitrous oxide (NO₂) in emissions undergo chemical reactions with water and oxygen in the atmosphere, forming sulfuric acid (H₂SO₄) and nitric acid (HNO₃). These acids fall in precipitation—acid rain—that causes environmental degradation.

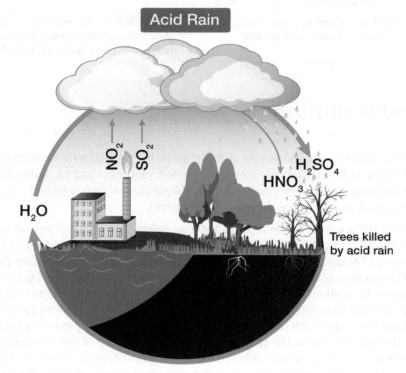

Source: © Shutterstock, Inc.

Loss of Protective Ozone

Ozone (O_3) can be beneficial or harmful, depending on altitude. Beneficial ozone forms naturally in the stratosphere, whereas bad ozone is at ground level in the troposphere and mostly forms from anthropogenic activities. Stratospheric ozone filters out harmful ultraviolet radiation in sunlight, so it protects life on Earth's surface. Without this ozone layer, skin cancer and cataracts would be very common. In 1983, British scientists discovered a hole in the protective ozone above Antarctica, and later a smaller one was located over the Arctic (Farman et al. 1985) (see Figure 11.18). These ozone holes were the result of chlorofluorocarbons (CFCs) released from refrigerators, air conditioners, solvents, aerosol spray cans, and Styrofoam puffing agents. Winds move CFCs into the stratosphere, where ultraviolet light strips the CFCs of chlorine atoms. Each freed chlorine atom has the capacity to bind to and destroy over 100,000 ozone molecules before it moves out of the stratosphere. The next section about smog discusses ground-level ozone.

FIGURE 11.18

Ozone hole. (A) A 2019 image of the stratosphere's exceptionally depleted ozone ("ozone hole") over Antarctica (source: NASA). The darker the color, the less ozone (measured in Dobson units). (B) Tropospheric ozone originates from a reaction of nitrogen oxides with volatile organic compounds. Heat and sunlight accelerate this reaction.

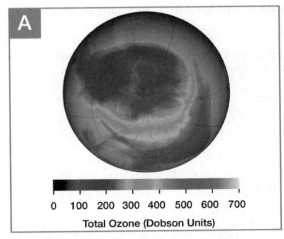

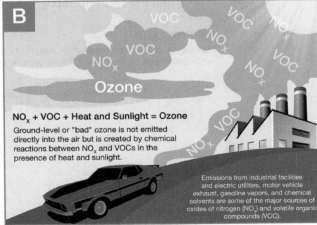

Sources: NASA, https://ozonewatch.gsfc.nasa.gov/Scripts/big_image.php?date=2019-09-08&hem=S&section=HOME; EPA, https://www.epa.gov/ground-level-ozone-pollution/ground-level-ozone-basics.

Persistent Organic Pollutants and Heavy Metals

Persistent organic pollutants (POPs) and heavy metals (i.e., mercury and lead) are particularly problematic pollutants. Both have the ability to persist in the environment and continually threaten ecosystems long after they are produced. PCBs and other POPs, as well as mercury, travel great distances by air and deposit in the Arctic, where they contaminate the food web and consequently exist in high concentrations in polar bear tissues (see "Case Study: Grasshopper Effect") (Letcher et al. 2009; Sonne et al. 2017). Chapter 1 and Chapter 15 further detail these and other air pollutants.

Smog

Smog is a mixture of pollutants in the lower atmosphere, most often in urban settings. When first coined, the word represented smoke from burning coal combined with fog, which adequately represented London's 1952 killer smog. Today, we usually refer to smog as a mixture of nitrogen oxides (NO_x), sulfur dioxide (SO_2), carbon monoxide, volatile organic compounds, particulate matter, and ozone. Volatile organic compounds are a particularly reactive group of molecules released from cleaning solvents, many paints, and gasoline. All but ozone are primary pollutants in vehicular and industrial emissions released directly into the atmosphere (see B in Figure 11.18). Ozone as well as some particulate matter are secondary smog pollutants because they form from primary pollutants that are already in the atmosphere. Smog is a pressing environmental problem that puts nearly 40 percent of Americans at risk of disease and premature death (see "Bringing It Closer to Home: Identifying Your Risk of Exposure to Tropospheric Ozone") (Di et al. 2017). Two of smog's components—particles (particulate matter) equal to or less than 2.5 μm in size (PM2.5) and ozone—are key factors in measuring the quality of the air we breathe.

smog

A mixture of air pollutants including ozone due to fossil fuel combustion; originally considered as a combination of smoke and fog.

air inversion

A layer of cold air near the ground becomes trapped by a layer of warmer air above.

The Los Angeles basin and Boise Valley both suffer from prolonged periods of smog due to the synergistic effect of air inversion and pollution emissions (see Figure 11.19). During an **air inversion**, a layer of trapped cold air near the ground becomes insulated by a layer of warmer air above and sets up strong vertical stability. If there are no strong winds to disrupt the inversion over a city, it will continue to trap anthropogenic pollutants—progressively worsening air quality.

FIGURE 11.19
Temperature inversions are when a warm layer of air overlays cooler air. (A) During an inversion, air pollution is redirected back downward. (B) An inversion keeping smog over Los Angeles.

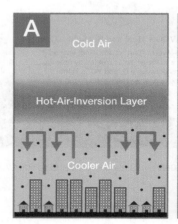

Source: © Shutterstock, Inc.; Andrius Kaziliunas/Shutterstock.com

Bringing It Closer to Home: Identifying Your Risk of Exposure to Tropospheric Ozone

Exposure to moderate or high levels of ozone decreases lung function and can cause inflammation of the airways, throat irritation, chest pains, wheezing, shortness of breath, asthma attacks, and, in extreme cases, death. Are you aware of the tropospheric ozone concentration in your area? Also, given your particular lifestyle and home location, what is your risk of exposure to ozone? Here you will address both of these questions, beginning with ozone concentration. Go to the Environmental Protection Agency's ozone website here. Enter your home's zip code, or city name, in the search box to see the current ozone value. The numerical value is on a scale of 0 to 500, with good air quality having an ozone value of less than 51. Next, compare the ozone value at your home to the range of values at other U.S. cities listed. A few cities have ozone values slightly higher than 50, meaning the air quality is acceptable, but people who are more sensitive to air pollutants may still experience health issues. Type "Visalia, California" in the search box. In summer 2022, the ozone value was 67. Because the value was above 50, there was a health message that said, "Unusually sensitive people should consider reducing prolonged or heavy exertion outdoors." The site also forecasts tomorrow's air quality, and therefore you can use it to plan ahead, for example, to decide whether to run outside. If you live in an area with a low ozone value, and if there are no sources of ozone in your residence and/or buildings you frequent, then in answer to the second question, your risk of ozone exposure is low. Finally, be aware that when you travel or live abroad, you can encounter air quality much poorer than that in the United States. For example, in Gurugram, a suburb of New Delhi, India, the air quality can at times exceed 200! To check international cities, click on "International" at the top of the screen. However, air quality is worsening in the United States because of smoke from large wildfires. More people in the Western United States are likely to experience this regularly in the states than ever before (Kalashnikov et al. 2022).

Indoor Air Quality

Being indoors does not necessarily offer you protection from air pollutants. Yes, in cases of high concentrations of fine particulate matter and ozone on hot days, there are likely fewer health risks inside an air-conditioned house than outside, but indoor air pollution exists and can be deadly. Concentrations of air pollutants can be two to five times higher and sometimes greater than one hundred times higher inside a home than outside. To make matters worse, the average American spends roughly 90 percent of their time indoors. Reasonable takeaways from these facts are to determine and reduce the sources of indoor air pollutants in your home, school, or work setting. Just what are these indoor air pollutants (see Figure 11.20)?

FIGURE 11.20
Indoor air pollution has many sources.

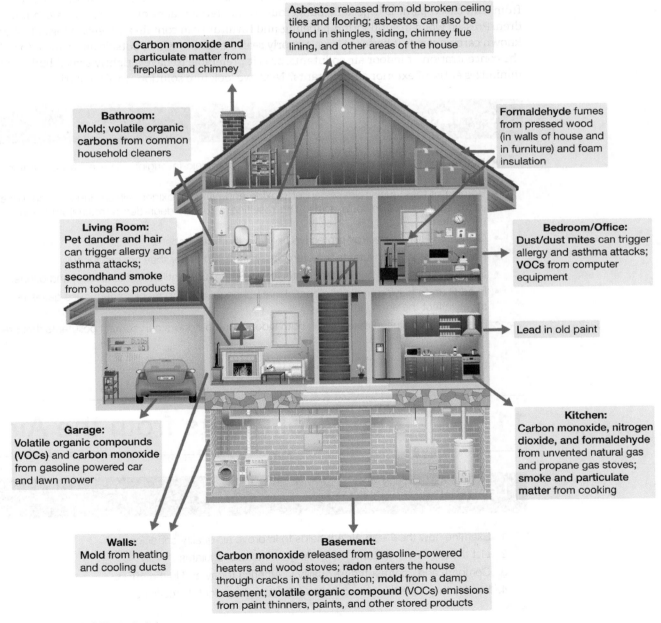

Carbon monoxide and particulate matter from fireplace and chimney

Asbestos released from old broken ceiling tiles and flooring; asbestos can also be found in shingles, siding, chimney flue lining, and other areas of the house

Bathroom:
Mold; volatile organic carbons from common household cleaners

Formaldehyde fumes from pressed wood (in walls of house and in furniture) and foam insulation

Living Room:
Pet dander and hair can trigger allergy and asthma attacks; secondhand smoke from tobacco products

Bedroom/Office:
Dust/dust mites can trigger allergy and asthma attacks; **VOCs** from computer equipment

Lead in old paint

Garage:
Volatile organic compounds (VOCs) and carbon monoxide from gasoline powered car and lawn mower

Kitchen:
Carbon monoxide, nitrogen dioxide, and formaldehyde from unvented natural gas and propane gas stoves; smoke and particulate matter from cooking

Walls:
Mold from heating and cooling ducts

Basement:
Carbon monoxide released from gasoline-powered heaters and wood stoves; radon enters the house through cracks in the foundation; mold from a damp basement; volatile organic compound (VOCs) emissions from paint thinners, paints, and other stored products

Source: Joseph Shostell; © Shutterstock, Inc.

radon gas

An indoor toxin emanating from the natural breakdown of uranium in soil and bedrock. It enters buildings through drains and through cracks in foundations.

There is a lengthy list, but some of the most prevalent ones are radon, asbestos, smoke, lead, and biological agents. **Radon gas** emanating from the natural breakdown of uranium in soil and bedrock enters buildings through drains and cracks in floors and walls and becomes trapped inside. According to the EPA, an estimated 21,000 Americans die from radon-induced lung cancer every year. Asbestos, a pollutant most common in older homes, can be wrapped around pipes, in floor and ceiling tiles, and in some types of shingles. Dangers of long-term exposure to asbestos are well documented. Asbestos fibers move into the lungs and can cause asbestosis—a lung disease that makes breathing difficult—and lung cancer.

Indoor smoke has a number of possible sources, including burning solid fuels and smoking. Globally, three billion people are exposed to smoke when they burn solid fuels (such as wood or coal) for cooking or heating in improperly vented areas (Thompson 2019). Smoke from using tobacco, which is entirely preventable, contains many known carcinogens and is a strong irritant of the lungs (Hecht 2011). Incidences of pneumonia and bronchitis increase in people exposed to secondhand smoke, or what is now referred to as passive smoking (see Chapter 15). Commonly used building materials can also be sources of indoor air pollutants. For instance, in older homes, dust from lead-based paint is especially dangerous to the development of the nervous system in children. Pressed wood in subflooring, paneling, and furniture can contain and release formaldehyde, a known carcinogen. Is it better to have a poorly sealed house in which outside air wafts in to reduce the concentration of indoor air pollutants, or is it preferable to have a tightly sealed building that minimizes entry of exterior air pollutants? Next, we look into solutions to air pollution.

Key Takeaways

- Not all pollutants in the atmosphere are anthropogenic in origin; some arise from natural sources.
- Burning of fossil fuels releases sulfur dioxide and nitrogen oxides, which undergo reactions in the atmosphere to form acids. The resulting acid rain degrades terrestrial and aquatic ecosystems.
- CFCs and HCFCs destroy protective ozone in the stratosphere.
- Persistent organic pollutants threaten ecosystems long after they are produced.
- Smog is a mixture of particulate matter, NO_x, SO_2, CO, volatile organic matter, and ozone.
- In addition to playing a role in global climate change, anthropogenic greenhouse gases negatively affect the environment.
- Based on air pollution data, the air both indoors and outdoors can contain pollutants that are harmful to living things.

11.5 Cleaning Pollutants from the Air

Learning Objectives

1. Examine how the Clean Air Act helps to improve air-quality conditions.
2. List the six main pollutants the EPA monitors and regulates.
3. Compare and contrast the air quality in America today and in the 1950s.
4. Identify the steps the United States took to reduce acid deposition.

5. Describe the regulation of fluorinated gases to protect stratospheric ozone.
6. Provide methods to reduce indoor concentrations of air pollutants.

"America the Beautiful," the incredibly popular patriotic song, did not adequately describe parts of the United States during the late forties, fifties, and much (if not all) of the sixties. Air pollution in large U.S. cities during those periods was much worse than today. At the time, residents of Los Angeles endured notoriously bad air quality laden with a combination of nitrogen oxides, volatile organic carbons, ozone, and particulate matter. Smoke and fumes billowed out from steel and chemical plants, oil refineries, backyard trash incinerators, and vehicle tailpipes. On particularly smoggy days, parents kept their kids out of school, athletes trained indoors, and those who braved the outdoors developed throbbing headaches and had difficulty breathing. In this section, we discuss methods of reducing air pollution. We begin with the single most important federal law, the Clean Air Act.

Clean Air Act and the EPA

Killer Smog in Donora, Pennsylvania, in 1948 and in London in 1952 were strong indicators that air quality was dismally poor and needed to be improved in the United States and abroad (see video link: "Killer Smog"). The Air Pollution Control Act of 1955 was the first major federal legislation involving air pollution in the United States. It preceded other important air pollution legislative acts and provided critical funding for air pollution research. In contrast to its name, it did not empower the federal government to control air pollution. Federal control of air pollution came later, with the Clean Air Act of 1963, and further expanded with the Air Quality Act of 1967 and Clean Air Acts (CAAs) of 1970 and 1990. In addition, the federal government created the Environmental Protection Agency (EPA) in 1970 to develop standards and enforce the CAA. For example, the EPA set limits on atmospheric concentrations of six important outdoor air pollutants to protect human health, referred to as the National Ambient Air Quality Standards. These six primary pollutants, which the EPA calls criteria pollutants, are carbon monoxide, lead, nitrogen oxides, particulate matter, ozone, and sulfur dioxide. Because of the CAA, concentrations of criteria pollutants have declined as an aggregate by 78 percent since 1970 (see Figure 11.21). Additionally, the EPA regulates 187 less abundant but toxic air pollutants suspected to cause cancer or other debilitating health problems. Formaldehyde—a known carcinogen found in pressed wood—and asbestos are two examples. States play a role in pollution mitigation as well. The CAA requires each state to develop an implementation plan that describes how it plans to control air pollution. The EPA updates its standards for the common pollutants and toxic pollutants as additional peer-reviewed research comes forward.

Killer Smog

View archived footage of the 1952 killer smog of London.

THE GREAT SMOG OF LONDON: WHEN
POLLUTION KILLED 12,000 OVER A WEEKEND

View in the online reader

FIGURE 11.21

The effectiveness of the Clean Air Act, enforced by the EPA, can be visualized by comparing the United States trend of decreasing emissions of six principal air pollutants (as an aggregate) to positive population growth and several other statistics (data are presented as percentage change relative to 1970).

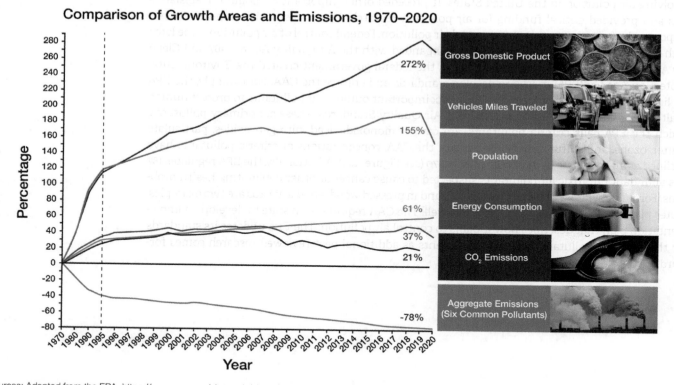

Comparison of Growth Areas and Emissions, 1970–2020

Gross Domestic Product — 272%

Vehicles Miles Traveled — 155%

Population — 61%

Energy Consumption — 37%

CO_2 Emissions — 21%

Aggregate Emissions (Six Common Pollutants) — -78%

Sources: Adapted from the EPA, https://www.epa.gov/air-trends/air-quality-national-summary; © Shutterstock, Inc.

Reducing Acid Deposition and Smog

The CAA amendments of 1990 addressed the issue of acid deposition by focusing on reducing sulfur dioxide emissions. A break from previous legislation, it set an overall cap for the aggregate total emissions from the nation's power plants, rather than stipulating an emissions cap for individual power plants. Such action allowed for an innovative cap-and-trade market approach (see Chapter 18). The cap was set at 8.95 million tons, which was a 50 percent reduction compared to 1980. Owners of power plants had the option to reduce emissions by a number of different methods, such as installing pollution-control devices, or they could purchase allowances from another power plant that had opted to reduce emissions. Each allowance in this market approach was equal to one ton of sulfur dioxide. Owners were financially incentivized; if their power plant reduced emissions, they could sell the saved allowances to another owner. By 2007, the United States reached the targeted cap, and by 2010 emissions had dropped even lower, to 5.1 million tons. Today, we are at 1.3 million tons, a 96 percent drop relative to 1970.

The 1990 CAA amendments also targeted nitrogen oxides, a major source of acid rain and smog. However, in this case, the federal government opted for a traditional, rate-based regulatory system. Every power plant in the United States is required to continuously monitor their emissions of sulfur dioxide and nitrogen oxides, and then report those emissions at least four times each year to the EPA. Power plants attempt to stay within their approved allowances in order to avoid stiff penalties. Thanks to these regulations, emissions of nitrogen oxides have plummeted by over 96 percent since 1970.

In Los Angeles and across America, smog has significantly declined. Through the power given to it by the CAA of 1970, the Environmental Protection Agency monitors and regulates not just sulfur dioxide and nitrogen oxides—two components of smog—but all six common primary pollutants that compose smog. In addition to the reductions in sulfur dioxide and nitrogen oxide levels, we have also witnessed decreases in the concentration of ozone (in troposphere), particulate matter, carbon monoxide, and lead. Clearly, the CAA has made and continues to make a significant impact on the quality of air we breathe. Any governmental action to diminish the EPA's power to enforce this Act threatens the health of humans and the environment. After an air pollutant is detected and labelled a concern, the next logical course of action is to either eliminate or mitigate the pollutant. As an example, the EPA set national standards to reduce pollutants from coal-fired power plants. To meet emission standards, coal-fired electric power plants can install air pollution control devices called scrubbers in their smokestacks to capture and remove sulfur compounds, nitrogen oxides, and mercury before they are released into the atmosphere.

Sometimes, as in the case of lead, a pollutant is eliminated from a product—taking care of the pollution source. Compliments of amendments to the CAA in 1990, lead has been banned from gasoline since 1996, and as a result, levels of lead in American children dropped by over 80 percent and their IQs increased (Grosse et al. 2002). Other methods of reducing lead in air involve building cleaner, more efficient engines and refineries, thus producing cleaner fuels. Inspection and maintenance programs are important too, to ensure the continued functioning of pollution detection and collection equipment in automobiles. Did your CHECK ENGINE message ever light up in your car? This is an effect of the 1990 CAA, which requires automobiles to include a diagnostic system intended to inform the driver of the existence of a malfunctioning pollution-control device. One way to positively contribute to reducing emissions is to properly maintain your car's engine.

Regulation of Fluorinated Gases

In an exceedingly rare moment in human history, there was universal agreement among the world's nations to address the issue of ozone loss in the stratosphere. The discovery of holes in the protective ozone layer in 1985 and the realization of what was at stake prompted a special meeting of the United Nations in Montreal, Canada. They developed and adopted an agreement known as the **Montreal Protocol** to phase out chlorofluorocarbons (CFCs) and other ozone-damaging compounds, which were used mostly for cooling and refrigeration. Since its inception in 1987, there have been four amendments to the Montreal Protocol, the latest one in 2016 calling for the phasing down of the production and consumption of hydrofluorocarbons (HFCs) (see Figure 11.22). Nations had begun to use HFCs as an alternative to CFCs, and while HFCs do not harm stratospheric ozone, they are a powerful greenhouse gas. Although the world effectively worked together to solve the problem of declining stratospheric ozone, the hole over Antarctica and smaller holes elsewhere have not fully recovered. CFCs are stable molecules that can last up to 100 years, and therefore it will take many more years before the layer fully repairs. Nonetheless, these measures have prevented an estimated 280 million cases of skin cancer and 45 million cataracts in the United States alone.

FIGURE 11.22
This graph demonstrates the potential benefits of international collaboration to reduce CFC emissions. Observe the estimated atmospheric concentrations of chlorine (which depletes ozone) under different scenarios of international collaborations.

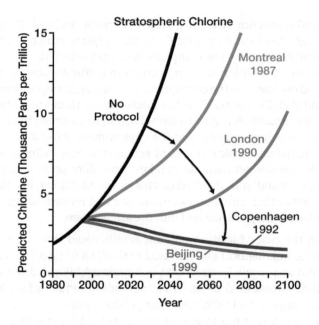

Source: Data from NOAA, https://csl.noaa.gov/assessments/ozone/2014/twentyquestions2014update.pdf.

Maintain Regulations

Thousands of research projects and peer-reviewed publications reveal the negative effects of mercury on human health and the environment. We know this metal is a potent neurotoxin that accumulates in tissues and magnifies in concentration up the food chain. We also know coal-burning power plants are the main source of mercury as a pollutant. These pieces of information drove the decisions leading up to the development of regulatory standards for mercury and other toxins emanating from power plants. As a result of these standards, an estimated 17,000 American lives are saved each year. They also prevented the spread of toxins across millions of acres of lakes, countless streams, and other environmental areas. Regardless of these benefits, the Environmental Protection Agency, through pressure from the president's office, can attempt to weaken these protective regulatory standards. For example, under President Donald Trump, the EPA argued that it was too costly for power plants to accommodate enacted standards. Their calculation did not include the saving of billions of dollars in health care as President Obama did a few years earlier, or President Biden did later.

Controlling Indoor Air Pollutants

What is the best method to mitigate indoor smoke, radon, asbestos, lead, and biological agents? To reduce particulate matter originating from smoke, eliminate the use of tobacco and refrain from using any wood-burning device. To protect against radon diffusing from the rock and soil beneath your home, seal and caulk any cracks in the foundation of your house. Another strategy is to install a ventilation pipe extending from the house's foundation to the outside.

Eliminating formaldehyde is a challenge because it is a common component in, for example, pressed wood, carpet, drapery, paint, and foam insulation. Take note of the World Health Organization's recommendation to make sure the air in your house has a formaldehyde concentration of less than 80 parts per billion (ppb). Formaldehyde test kits are available to check if the concentration of formaldehyde in the air in your home is at a safe level. The way to reduce formaldehyde in the air is to replace any formaldehyde-based products and to continuously vent your home. Some companies have found their niche in providing formaldehyde-free wood and thus helping to promote sustainability. One such company, Columbia Forest, produces formaldehyde-free hardwood plywood that has great versatility in use for cabinets, furniture, and even toys. They use a soy-based adhesive in their product as an alternative to formaldehyde.

When it comes to asbestos contamination, contact a local professional before you attempt to remove it yourself or conduct any remodeling work. Just as with radon, before purchasing a home, smart buyers have ceiling tiles and other potential areas that might contain asbestos sampled and tested. The danger with asbestos removal is the tendency for small asbestos fibers to become airborne, because the most common way for asbestos fibers to enter the body is through breathing. Professional asbestos removers wear respirators and vented eye protection and seal off their work area to isolate any potential contamination. Importantly, they spray a liquid detergent on any asbestos-containing material, thereby preventing asbestos from becoming airborne during removal.

It is also possible to protect yourself and your family from lead poisoning. Regulation of lead-containing products has changed considerably over the last several decades. Lead in nonfood consumer goods such as toys is covered in the Federal Hazardous Substances Act (FHSA). The Act authorizes the Consumer Product Safety Commission (CPSC) to ban certain products if they may cause substantial personal injury or illness from customary use. In 1978, the CPSC banned the sale of lead-based paint intended for households, furniture, and toys. Ten years later, in 1988, changes in the Safe Drinking Water Act restricted the use of lead in pipes and solder, and then in 1995 the Food and Drug Administration (FDA) banned the use of lead solder in food cans. If your home was constructed prior to 1978, then it is probably prudent to have a lead inspection done by a certified inspector. She or he can inform you whether there is lead-based paint in your home, and if there is lead, advise you on the safest method of abatement. These Acts in addition to the banning of leaded gasoline have significantly reduced lead in households.

Biological agents such as bacteria, viruses, fungi, and insects can be kept at manageable levels by routinely following a few basic routines. First, maintain any cooling and heating equipment inside your home. That means changing all the air filters in a timely manner. Keep the house well vented, clean, and at a relative humidity between 30 percent and 60 percent. Next, we return to the opening story and predict the future of polar bears.

11.6 A Look to the Future: The Fate of Polar Bears

Learning Objective

1. To review the opening case story, weigh the evidence of climate change and air pollution, and hypothesize about the success of polar bears in the future.

Now at the end of the climate change and air pollution chapter, let us revisit the opening story and hypothesize what the future holds for polar bears. The positive feedback cycle of global warming, increased aerosol and greenhouse gas emissions, and growing human population paint a dire future for polar bears, without even considering heavy metals, PCBs, and other pollutants. In essence, polar bears are losing in an evolutionary race of adaptation in a rapidly changing environment. We hypothesize a loss of 66 percent of polar bears by 2050 if Arctic ice mass continues to decline at the current rate. Will society's actions offer the solution polar bears need? A perpetual optimist will say "yes," but only time will tell. In the Arctic, we predict we will see a substantial increase in shipping traffic as ships take advantage of ice-free summer waters (Dalsen et al. 2012). Polar bears in the already fragile Arctic ecosystem will need to contend with the air pollution and trash coming from these ships in addition to trying to adapt to ice loss.

Key Takeaway

- Arctic ice is melting at an unprecedented rate and polar bears are struggling to adapt to an increasingly open-water habitat.

FIGURE 11.23 Visual Overview: Air Quality, Climate Change, and Air Pollution
Summarizing figure: Earth's atmosphere (11.1) consists of several layers and provides many services essential for life. Society's emissions of greenhouse gases are causing climate change (11.2), but there are solutions (11.3). Similarly, anthropogenic air pollutants negatively affect ecosystems (11.4), yet we have the capability to reduce or eliminate these emissions (11.5). Reducing GHG emissions and improving air quality gives all life, including polar bears (11.6), a brighter future.

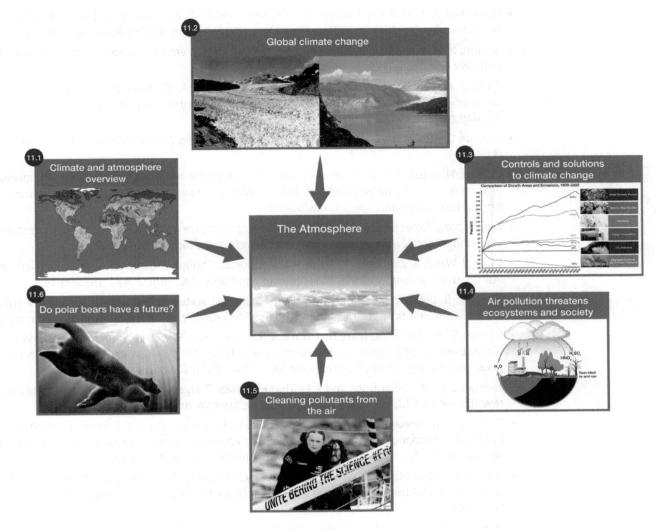

Sources: Joseph Shostell; See previous citations for image credits.

11.7 References

- Amos, H. M., D. J. Jacob, E. M. Streets, and E. M. Sunderland. 2013. "Legacy impacts of all-time anthropogenic emissions on the global mercury cycle." *Global Biogeochem. Cycles* 27, no. 410. https://doi.org/10.1002/gbc.20040.

- Amstrup, S. C., E. T. DeWeavver, D. C. Douglas, B. G. Marcot, G. M. Dumer, C. M. Bitz, and D. A. Bailey. 2010. "Greenhouse gas mitigation can reduce sea-ice loss and increase polar bear persistence." *Nature* 468: 955–960.

- Aulinger, A., V. Matthias, M. Zeretzke, J. Bieser, M. Quante, and A. Backes. 2016. "The impact of shipping emissions on air pollution in the greater North Sea region—Part 1: Current emissions and concentrations." *Atmos. Chem. Phys.* 16: 7390758.

- Baccini, A., S. J. Goetz, W. S. Walker, et al. 2012. "Estimated carbon dioxide emissions from tropical deforestation improved by carbon-density maps." *Nature Climate Change* 2: 182–185.

- Bastin, J., Y. Finegold, C. Garcia, D. Mollicone, M. Rexende, et al. 2019. "The global tree restoration potential." *Science* 365, no. 6448: 76–79.

- Bouwman, A. F., D. P. van Vuuren, R. J. Derwent, and M. Posch. 2002. "A global analysis of acidification and eutrophication of terrestrial ecosystems." *Water Air Soil Pollut.* 141: 349–382.

- Burton, M., G. Sawyer, and D. Granieri. 2013. "Deep carbon emissions from volcanoes." *Rev. Mineral Geochem.* 75: 323–354.

- Carn, S. A., V. E. Fioletov, C. A. McLinden, C. Li, and N. A. Krotkov. 2017. "A decade of global volcanic SO2 emissions measured from space." *Scientific Reports.* https://doi.org/10.1038/srep44095.

- Climate Central. 2014. *Summer in the City: Hot and Getting Hotter.* Climate Central, Princeton, NJ.

- Cook, J., N. Oreskes, P. T. Doran, et al. 2016. "Consensus on consensus: a synthesis of consensus estimates on human-caused global warming." *Environmental Research Letters* 11. https://doi.org/10.1088/1748-9326/11/4/048002.

- Dai, H. 2021. "Roles of surface albedo, surface temperature and carbon dioxide in the seasonal variation of Arctic amplification." https://doi.org/10.1029/2020GL090301.

- Di, Q., Y. Wang, A. Zanobetti, Y. Wang, P. Koutrakis, C. Choirat, F. Dominici, and J. Schwartz. 2017. "Air pollution and mortality in the Medicare population." *N. Engl. J. Med.* 376: 2513–2522.

- Dietz, R., R. Letcher, J. Desforges, et al. 2019. "Current state of knowledge on biological effects from contaminants on Arctic wildlife and fish." *Science of the Total Environment* 696: 133792.

- Durner, G. M., J. P. Whiteman, H. J. Harlow, S. C. Amstrup, E. V. Regehr, and M. Ben-David. 2011. "Consequences of long-distance swimming and travel over deep-water pack ice for a female polar bear during a year of extreme sea ice retreat." *Polar Biology* 34, no. 7: 975–984.

- Farman, J. C., B. G. Gardiner, and J. D. Shanklin. 1985. "Large losses of total ozone in Antarctica reveal seasonal CLOx/NOx interaction." *Nature,* 315: 207–210.

- Granier, C., B. Bessagnet, T. Bond, A. D'Angiola, H. D. Van der Gon, G. F. Frost, et al. 2011. "Evolution of anthropogenic and biomass burning emissions of air pollutants at the global and regional scales during the 1980–2010 period." *Climate Change* 109: 163–190.

- Grosse, S. D., T. D. Matte, J. Schwartz, and R. J. Jackson. 2002. "Economic gains resulting from the reduction in children's exposure to lead in the United States." *Environ Health Perspect* 110, no. 6: 563–569.

- Hamilton, S. G., and A. E. Derocher. 2018. "Assessment of global polar bear abundance and vulnerability." *Anim Conserv* 22: 83–95.

- Hammond, A. L., and T. H. Maugh, II. 1974. "Stratospheric pollution: multiple threats to Earth's ozone." *Science* 186, no. 4161: 335–338.

- Hamza, Y. G., S. K. Ameta, A. Tukur, and A. Usman. 2020. "Overview on evidence and reality of climate change." *IOSR Journal of Environmental Science, Toxicology and Food Technology* 14, no. 7: 17–26.

- Harris, N. L., S. Brown, S. C. Hagen, et al. 2012. "Baseline map of carbon emissions from deforestation in tropical regions." *Science* 336, no. 6088: 1573–1576.

- Hecht, S. S. "Tobacco Smoke Carcinogens and Lung Cancer." In: *Chemical Carcinogenesis, Current Cancer Research* (Ed: Penning, T. M.). Springer Science+Business Media, LLC, Berlin, Germany.

- Hughes, T. P., J. T. Kerry, and T. Simpson. 2018. "Large-scale bleaching of corals on the Great Barrier Reef." *Ecology* 99, no. 2: 501.

- Hung, H., A. A. Katsoyiannis, E. Brorström-Lundén, K. Olafsdottir, W. Aas, et al. 2016. "Temporal trends of persistent organic pollutants (POPs) in arctic air: 20 years of monitoring under the Arctic Monitoring and Assessment Program (AMAP)." *Environmental Pollution* 217: 52–61.

- Kalashnikov, D. A., J. Schnell, J. T. Abatzoglou, D. L. Swain, and D. Singh. 2022. "Increasing co-occurrence of fine particulate matter and ground-level ozone extremes in the western United States." *Science Advances* 8: eabi9386.

- Kaufmann, R., Mann, M. L., Global, S., Liederman, J. A., Howe, P. D. et al. 2016. "Spatial heterogeneity of climate change as an experiential basis for skepticism." *Proceedings of the National Academy of Sciences of the United States of America* 114 (1): 67–71.

- Kim, K. J., J. Shin, and J. Choi. 2018. "Cancer risk from exposure to particulate matter and ozone according to obesity and health-related behaviors: a nationwide population-based cross-sectional study." *Cancer Epidemiology, Biomarkers and Prevention.* https://doi.org/10.1158/1055-9965.EPI-18-0508.

- Konrad, H., A. Shepherd, L. Gilbert, A. E. Hogg, M. McMillan, A. Muir, and T. Slater. 2018. "Net retreat of Antarctic glacier grounding lines." *Nature Geosciences* 11: 258–262.

- Kossin, J. P. 2018. "A global slowdown of tropical-cyclone translation speed." *Nature* 558: 104–107.

- Le Quéré, C., R. Morearty, R. M. Andrew, et al. 2015. "Global carbon budget." *Earth Syst. Sci. Data* 7: 349–396.

- Leiserowitz, A., E. W. Maibach, C. Roser-Renouf, G. Feinberg, and P. Howe. 2019. *Climate change in the American mind.* Yale Program on Climate Change Communication and George Mason University Center for Climate Change Communication.

- Letcher, R. J., J. O. Bustnes, et al. 2009. "Exposure and effects assessment of persistent organohalogen contaminants in Arctic wildlife and fish." *Sci Total Environ* 408, no. 15: 2995–3043.

- Lyman, S. N., and D. Jaffe. 2011. "Formation and fate of oxidized mercury in the upper troposphere and lower stratosphere." *Nature Geoscience* 5, no. 2: 114–117.

- Marsicek, J., B. Shuman, P. J. Bartlein, S. L. Shafer, and S. Brewer. 2018. "Reconciling divergent trends and millennial variations in Holocene temperatures." *Nature* 554: 92–96.

- Matthias, V., A. Aulinger, A. Backes, J. Bieser, B. Geyer, M. Quante, and M. Zeretzke. 2016. "The impact of shipping emissions on air pollution in the greater North Sea region—Part 2: scenarios for 2030." *Atmos. Chem. Phys.* 16: 759–776.

- Milankovitch, M. 1941. *Kanon der Erdbestrahlung und seine Anwendung auf das Eiszeitenproblem.* Belgrade, Mihaila Curcica.

- National Science Foundation (NSF). 2018. "Hurricanes: stronger, slower, wetter in the future?" *News Release* 18-034.

- Novakov T., and H. Rosen. 2013. "The black carbon story: early history and new perspectives." *Ambio* 42, no. 7: 840–851.

- Portmann, R. W., J. S. Daniel, and A. R. Ravishankara. 2012. "Stratospheric ozone depletion due to nitrous oxide: influences of the other gases." *Phil. Trans. R. Soc. B* 367: 1256–1264.

- Quéré, C. L., R. M. Andrew, P. Friedlingstein, et al. 2018. "Global carbon budget 2017." *Earth System. Sci. Data* 10: 405–448.

- Sato, K., M. Aoki, and R. Noyori. 1998. "A 'green' route to adipic acid: direct oxidation of cyclohexenes with 30 percent hydrogen peroxide." *Science* 281: 1646–1647.

- Shindell, D., and G. Galubegi. 2009. "Climate response to regional radiative forcing during the twentieth century." *Nat Geosci* 2: 294–300.

- Sonne, C., R. J. Letcher, B. M. Jenssen, J. Desforges, I. Eulaers, E. Andersen-Ranberg, K. Gustavson, B. Styrishave, and R. Dietz. 2017. "A veterinary perspective on One Health in the Arctic." *Acta Vet Scand* 59: 84. https://doi.org/10.1186/s13028-017-0353-5.

- Spalding, M. D., and B. E. Brown. 2015. "Warm-water coral reefs and climate change." *Science* 350, no. 6262: 769–771.

- The Royal Society (TRS) and National Academy of Sciences (NAS). 2020. *Climate Change Evidence and Causes Update 2020.* The Royal Society and the U.S. National Academy of Sciences.

- Thompson, L. M. 2019. "Household air pollution from cooking fires is a global problem." *Environments and Health* 119, no. 11: 65–68.
- Wadey, M., S. Brown, R. J. Nicholls, and I. Haigh. 2017. "Coastal flooding in the Maldives: and assessment of historic events and their implications." *Natural Hazards*. https://doi.org/10.1007/s11069-017-2957-5.
- Weatherly, J. W., and Y. Zhang. 2001. "The response of the polar regions to increased CO2 in a global climate model with elastic-viscous-plastic sea ice." *J Clim* 14: 268–283.
- Wiig, Ø., S. Amstrup, T. Atwood, et al. 2015. *Ursus maritimus. The IUCN Red List of Threatened Species 2015*: e. T22823A14871490.

CHAPTER 12
Geology and Mineral Resources

Case Study: Mining in Arkansas Diamond Park

Crater of Diamonds State Park in Arkansas is the only diamond-producing place in the world open to the public where you can profitably make use of the old saying, "finders, keepers." Since it transferred from private to public land and became a state park in 1972, more than 33,100 diamonds have been discovered by park visitors, some of them quite valuable (see Figure 12.1). For a nominal fee of $8 for adults or $5 for children, you can spend all day mining and looking for diamonds and an assortment of more than forty other rocks and minerals on the eroded surface of a volcanic crater field. You have the option to bring your own mining supplies, or to rent shovels, buckets, screens, and an assortment of other items.

FIGURE 12.1
Finders keepers. (A) Ms. Bobbie Oskarson holds up an 8.5 carat diamond she unearthed in Crater of Diamonds State Park. The park's policy is finders keepers, and thus Ms. Oskarson took the $1 million gemstone with her when she exited the park. (B) Other park visitors in search of diamonds. (C) The entrance to Crater of Diamonds State Park.

Sources: Associated Press; Kimberly Boyles/Shutterstock.com

Before becoming a park, the land was privately owned, first as a farm, and then by a mining company. It was during this earlier period, in 1924, when the largest diamond discovered in the United States—Uncle Sam—was unearthed. If you were to visit the land today, where would you search and dig? One auspicious place might be a lower part of the old farm field, because the diamonds, with the help of gravity, would have settled there. Some park visitors prefer to dig holes and search in the location where the old mining company discarded the mining waste referred to as **tailings**, in hopes that the waste contains some mistakenly discarded gemstones. It is still possible to find valuable diamonds in Crater of Diamonds State Park today, as attested by the ever-growing list of diamonds found each month. An average of two are found every day (see video link: "Finding Diamonds"). Will you be one of the next visitors to this one-of-a-kind site? Gemstone diamonds such as Ms. Oskarson's and the more recently discovered 3.72 carat Caro Avenger in 2019 make up only about 20 percent of the approximately 150 million carats of diamonds mined each year worldwide, or in the case of Crater of Diamonds State Park, found by tourists. The remaining 80 percent are considered industrial diamonds and are used in cutting materials, drilling for minerals, computer chip production, and other industrial activities. In both cases and representative of many geological resources (i.e., metals), a great quantity of Earth materials must be extracted and processed to produce a small amount of a needed geologic resource.

Finding Diamonds

Listen to Park Interpreter Margi Jenks discussing finding diamonds at Crater of Diamonds State Park.

View in the online reader

12.1 Earth's Dynamic Geologic Resources

Learning Objectives

1. Identify Earth's internal geologic layers.
2. Explain how today's geologic structures are the result of past geologic processes.
3. Describe the theory of plate tectonics.
4. Compare and contrast physical, chemical, and biological weathering events.
5. Identify the three main types of rocks and explain how they form.

geology

Scientific study of the Earth's physical structure.

geologists

Scientists who study geology.

geologic

Relating to the geology of the Earth.

Why can diamonds be found in Crater of Diamonds State Park (opening story), but not in other places? In this chapter, we pursue the answers to this and other questions related to **geology**—the study of Earth's physical structure and the processes acting on it. Scientists who study geology are **geologists**. Geology helps us to understand Earth's dynamic **geologic** resources and the origin of valuable minerals in countless products we use on a daily basis. Geology is an important part of environmental science because of the many steps in bringing geologic resources to market that can have wide-ranging negative effects on the environment. In this chapter we discuss these effects in addition to methods of extracting geologic resources sustainably. We begin with a description of Earth's geologic structure.

The Earth Has Layers

Jules Verne's 1864 classic *Journey to the Center of the Earth* provides a thrilling story of the interior of the Earth, but however much we might wish such a story were true, collected indirect data cause us to shelve Verne's tale in the fantasy section of the local bookstore (Verne 1864). We have been unable to travel deep enough into the Earth to take direct measurements, but we still have enough indirect evidence to allow us to separate fact from fiction. Why haven't we traveled deeper into Earth's interior to take direct measurements? It just gets too hot, the pressure is too great, and we don't have the technology to do so—yet.

Geologists collect data about the Earth's interior by studying the transmission of seismic waves caused by **earthquakes**, volcanic eruptions, and other sudden movements of materials within the Earth. Seismic waves are similar to the waves created when a pebble is tossed into a pond—with the waves traveling outward from a point of origin (see Figure 12.2 and Table 12.1). We also obtain information about Earth' interior through studying meteorites, because they may be composed of similar elements and are of similar density to Earth's deeper interior. Evidence is also collected from the study of geothermal energy. *Geo* means "Earth," and *thermal* means "heat." Heat continuously rises up from Earth's interior and is released at Earth's surface, signifying that Earth's interior is warmer relative to where we live at the surface. Finally, the presence of Earth's magnetic field implies that there must be moving magnetic material inside the Earth.

earthquakes

Shaking of the ground usually due to a release of energy from the interaction of two adjacent tectonic plates.

FIGURE 12.2
Earth's interior structure, as revealed by seismographic data. Seismographs detect seismic waves generated by earthquakes; by studying how these waves change as they travel through the interior of the Earth, seismologists can infer information about composition and density at different depths. For example, P waves (white arrows) can travel through liquid rock, but other types of seismic waves (red arrows) cannot. P waves also bend when they travel from one medium (such as solid rock) to a different medium (such as liquid rock).

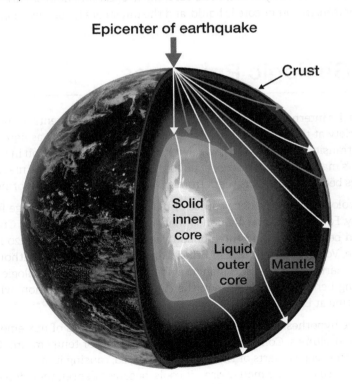

Source: Joseph Shostell; © Shutterstock, Inc.

TABLE 12.1

Layer	Temp (up to)	Thickness
Crust	1,000°C (1,800°F)	5–60 km (3.1–37.3 mi)
Mantle	3,700°C (6,692°F)	2,900 km (1,800 mi)
Outer core	5,000°C (9,032°F)	2,300 km (1,400 mi)
Inner core	6,000°C (10,800°F)	Radius: 1,221 km (759 mi)

Sources: NASA, https://solarsystem.nasa.gov/planets/earth/in-depth/#:~:text=There the temperature is as,the mantle, the thickest layer; Anzellini, S., Dewaele, A., Mexouar, M., Loubeyre, P., and Morard, G. 2013. Melting of iron at Earth's inner core boundary based on fast x-ray diffraction. Science 340: 464-466; National Geographic: https://www.nationalgeographic.org/encyclopedia/core/#:~:text=The outer core, about 2,200, and 9,932 Fahrenheit); National Geographic: https://www.nationalgeographic.org/encyclopedia/mantle/#:~:text=The temperature of the mantle,a measurement of this increase; Licence Earle, S. (2015). Physical Geology. Victoria, B. C.: BCcampus. Retrieved from https://opentextbc.ca/geology/.

The Earth consists of four main layers of different thicknesses. They are, from inside to outside: inner core, outer core, mantle, and crust (see Figure 12.2). As a reference for relative size, the core is about 70 percent of the size of our moon. In relation to the rest of the planet, the core would be analogous to the pit of a nectarine relative to the rest of the fruit.

We live at the outermost layer of the world, the crust, and therefore know more about this layer than any other (see Figure 12.2). Almost like oil on water, the lighter crust pieces, both oceanic and continental, overlies the deeper and denser mantle. It is the combination of the crust plus the uppermost section of the **mantle** that forms the **lithosphere**, which is broken into about twelve large sections called **tectonic plates**. These plates "float" on top of the next layer, the **asthenosphere**, in the mantle. See "Bringing It Closer to Home: Exploring My Tectonic Plate".

Earth's mantle and the rest of Earth's interior increase in temperature and pressure with depth. At hotter temperatures, the rocks within the mantle soften to the consistency of Play-Doh, and at greater depths, they are partially molten. The **core**, the deepest and hottest part of Earth's interior, consists mainly of iron; the outer core is liquid, and the inner core is solid (see Figure 12.2).

Internal Geologic Processes

Knowledge of Earth's internal structure has relevance to us because events in the core and mantle affect life and society at the surface. The inner core expands very slowly as liquid iron transforms in to a solid. This transition releases heat, which in turn drives the convection in the outer core that gives rise to Earth's magnetic field (Waszek et al. 2011). Although invisible, the magnetic field is helpful to living things because it protects them from space radiation and solar storms.

Long-term geologic events over the course of billions of years set the stage for geologic structures we see today. For example, the diamonds that people are now finding in Crater of Diamonds State Park formed between one and three billion years ago, 140–190 km (87–120 mi) underground, within the mantle. Volcanic eruptions can bring diamonds to the surface, although this is a relatively rare event. Earth is a dynamic planet, evidenced by its many geologic processes, some internal—occurring beneath the crust, as in the case of diamond formation, whereas others are external—originating at Earth's surface.

Scientists have hypothesized that there are two general patterns of movement in the mantle: convection cells and plumes. Convection cells form as a result of temperature differences in the mantle. Matter in the deepest parts of the mantle is warmed, causing it to become less dense, so it ascends toward the crust. As the matter rises, it cools, becomes denser, then descends and repeats the process in a large circular pattern (see Figure 12.3). The cells act as conveyor belts for the tectonic plates above, causing them to move (**plate tectonics**) (see "Plate Tectonics").

mantle

The layer of the Earth between the outer core and the crust.

lithosphere

Earth's crust and the uppermost portion of the mantle.

tectonic plates

Continental and ocean-sized sections of the lithosphere that move on top of the mantle.

asthenosphere

Immediate layer of mantle underneath tectonic plates.

core

The deepest part of the interior of the Earth.

plate tectonics

The movement of the tectonic plates.

FIGURE 12.3
Convection in Earth's mantle. (A) Large, slow-moving convection cells in the mantle constantly move warm, less-dense matter toward the crust, where it cools and then descends to be warmed again. These cells drive the movement of tectonic plates in the crust (B). Arrows indicate the direction of plate movement.

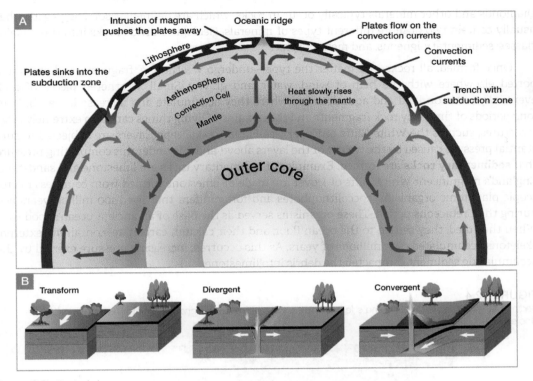

Source: © Shutterstock, Inc.

Plate Tectonics
Listen to an explanation of plate tectonics to understand how the Earth's crust moves.

WHAT ARE
TECTONIC PLATES?

View in the online reader

    The second pattern of movement in the mantle is a **mantle plume**—a narrow upwelling of hot rock. Plumes originate at the outer core–mantle boundary and extend upward to the surface. Approximately 45–50 mantle plumes have been detected around the world, and these help to explain the formation of Hawaii and Iceland, for example, that are in the middle of tectonic plates. Some scientists have theorized that mantle plumes may help to cool the Earth's core.

mantle plume

Narrow upwellings of hot rock originating at the boundary of the outer core and mantle, and extending to Earth's surface.

External Geologic Processes

External geologic forces originate above the ground (see Chapter 8 and Chapter 11). Water and wind, for example, cause **erosion**: the movement of weathered materials to a new location. Water is the most common force behind erosion because of its abundance and power. Rivers carve through rock, and oceanic waves crash down relentlessly on beaches, eroding them. The force generated by the movement of water can take on other forms, such as glaciers scraping underlying bedrock (physical or mechanical **weathering**) and carrying the debris elsewhere. Wind is also a powerful force of erosion, for example as it sweeps soil up into the atmosphere (see Chapter 8). Even the tallest mountains formed by converging plate boundaries will eventually succumb to weathering and erosion processes—decreasing in size until one day they will cease to exist at all. Actions of plant roots, lichens, burrowing animals, and microscopic organisms in and on rocks are all forms of biological weathering, but these are also examples of physical weathering. Chemical weathering is a third type of weathering caused by chemical reactions that break the bonds of molecules found in rocks. An example is acid rain dissolving limestone rock (see Chapter 11).

erosion

Movement of weathered materials to a new location.

weathering

The process of wearing away rocks physically, biologically, or chemically.

Rocks and the Rock Cycle

Diamonds and other minerals typically occur in rocks, which are defined as solid aggregates that usually contain two or more different types of minerals. Geologists divide rocks into three major classes: sedimentary, igneous, and metamorphic.

Once formed, all rocks—no matter the type—undergo weathering, fragment, and are transported elsewhere with the help of wind, water, and gravity. Small, weathered pieces of rock eventually settle on land and aquatic areas, where they accumulate and increase in depth. Over long periods of time, tiny rock fragments and the remains of living things can form extremely large structures, such as the White Cliffs of Dover (see Figure 12.4). Deeper layers are subjected to substantial pressure caused by the weight of the layers above, and it is under this compacting pressure that **sedimentary rocks** are formed. Examples of sedimentary rocks are limestone and sandstone. England's magnificent White Cliffs of Dover are made of limestone formed from countless microscopic planktonic organisms: coccolithophores and foraminifera that lived 100 million years ago during the Cretaceous period. These organisms served as the base of an ancient ocean's food web. When they died, they settled to the ocean floor, and their calcium carbonate–containing external skeletons accumulated over millions of years. As this occurred, increasing pressure exerted by the accumulating sediment compacted the debris into limestone.

sedimentary rock

Rock formed by an accumulation of many small pieces—of eroded rock, organic debris, or a combination of both—that are subjected to high pressure from overlying layers.

FIGURE 12.4
Sedimentary rock makes up England's famous White Cliffs of Dover. (B) Igneous rock forms as lava cools. (C) Cooled igneous rock in hand.

152 m (500 ft) tall

Source: Joseph Shostell; © Shutterstock, Inc.

igneous rock

Rock formed when magma cools and solidifies.

Igneous rocks form when molten material cools and solidifies. There are two types of igneous rocks: intrusive igneous rocks, which form underground from cooling magma, and extrusive igneous rocks, which form above ground from cooling lava. Magma that reaches the surface is called lava. During Earth's early history, most rocks were igneous. Today, there are still many examples of igneous rocks. Common types are granite and basalt. Granite is a major component in continental plates, and we fabricate it into countertops, tombstones, and other durable structures. Basalt makes up the bedrock of volcanic islands such as Hawaii.

Metamorphic rocks form when heat and pressure transform preexisting rocks. All three types of rocks—sedimentary, igneous, and metamorphic—can undergo this process at subduction zones. During the transformation, the original rocks can take up new minerals, so their composition changes. Slate and marble are two examples of metamorphic rocks. Slate, used for roofing and floor tiles, formed from shale, a sedimentary rock made of compacted clay, silt, and mud. Marble, used to fabricate statues and flooring, formed from limestone.

Because sedimentary, igneous, and metamorphic rocks may be transformed into other types of rock, they are components of the **rock cycle** (see Figure 12.5). The rock cycle serves as a reminder that matter cycles, and in this case, the Earth is recycling its rocks. Rocks form, break down, and then reform again, countless times. In the next section, we look into the economics of rocks as geologic resources.

> **metamorphic rock**
>
> A preexisting rock transformed when subjected to heat and pressure.

> **rock cycle**
>
> The geologic process by which igneous, sedimentary, and metamorphic rocks are created and transformed to each other.

FIGURE 12.5
The rock cycle explains how rocks are formed and degraded, as well as the interconnections among the three types of rocks.

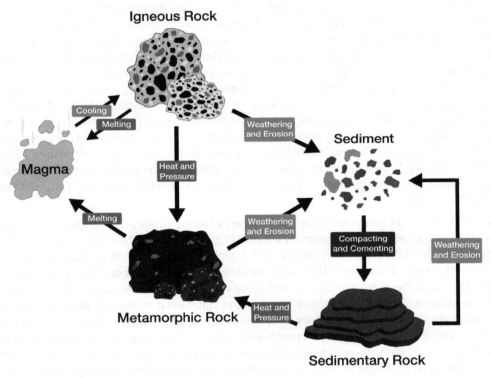

Source: Joseph Shostell; © Shutterstock, Inc.

Key Takeaways

- The Earth has layers.
- Earth's internal geologic structure and processes affect life at the surface.
- The external geologic forces of water and wind cause erosion.
- There are three main classes of rocks: sedimentary, igneous, and metamorphic.
- The different types of rocks are parts of an interconnecting cycle.

12.2 The Economics of Minerals and Other Geologic Resources

Learning Objectives

1. Provide examples of how minerals are valuable to society. Consider both metal and non-metal minerals.
2. Explain the difference between a reserve and a resource.

mineral

A naturally formed and solid inorganic substance with a particular crystalline structure.

The products we depend on, from the wedding ring with its diamond, to the pencil you use for taking notes, to your cell phone and car, all contain substances that formed by geologic processes (see Figure 12.6). By strict definition, some of these substances are minerals. **Minerals** are inorganic, naturally occurring substances that are also solid and have a specific chemical and crystal structure. An inorganic substance (see Chapter 2) does not derive from nor consist of living material. In other words, a naturally formed diamond is a mineral, but wood and pearls are not. Artificial, the opposite of natural, implies that something is manmade, and there are many examples of these, even diamonds. However, human-manufactured diamonds do not meet the definition of a mineral because they are artificial. A "specific chemical and crystal structure" means that a mineral has an expected repeating arrangement of atoms no matter where it is found in the world. Based on this definition, ice is a mineral, unless we are talking about ice cubes formed in your freezer (because these are artificial). What about metals, are they minerals? Yes and no. The majority of metals occur naturally in mineral ores combined with other elements, and we extract the metals from these ores. Although rarer, there are abundant examples of metals in mineral form. A pure gold nugget is a perfect example. But beware, not every geologic resource that looks like gold, is gold (see "Critical Thinking Activity: Fool's Gold").

resource

The total amount of a mineral or other geologic substance in the Earth.

reserve

The part of a resource that is considered economically viable to extract, given current technology.

commodity

A natural good or material that is bought and sold.

We often apply the terms *resources* and *reserves* when discussing diamonds and other mined materials. Geologic resources and reserves are related, but they are different, and it is important to distinguish them. The total amount of any useful geologic material (such as diamonds or gold) in the crust—the part of the Earth that we have access to—is a **resource**. Only a portion of this amount is extractable, given the current technological capabilities and market. This smaller part, called the **reserve**, will fluctuate in size over time, at times even increasing, although this might seem counterintuitive given that we are constantly extracting geologic materials. However, as we extract a material from the ground, we may become aware of its rate of depletion, review what we consider as reserve, and then reclassify some more of the resource as reserve. Reclassification can also occur when an increased value of a mineral due to demand and limited supply makes a portion of a mineral resource cost-effective to extract. A mineral is also an example of a **commodity** because it is bought and sold. There are different types of commodities. Mined minerals are called hard commodities, whereas agricultural products such as wheat are soft commodities. Hard commodities serve as raw materials used for manufacturing products we purchase, from a diamond ring to a new laptop computer.

Geological materials are further classified by how they are used by society; for example, as a fuel or nonfuel. Our dependence on minerals and other geologic materials as fuel resources and raw materials for manufacturing means that their supply can affect national economies. As discussed later, mining, processing, and using geologic materials also affect the environment.

FIGURE 12.6
We depend on many geologic substances daily throughout our lives. Here are examples of the average amounts of minerals and other materials each American uses during their lifetime.

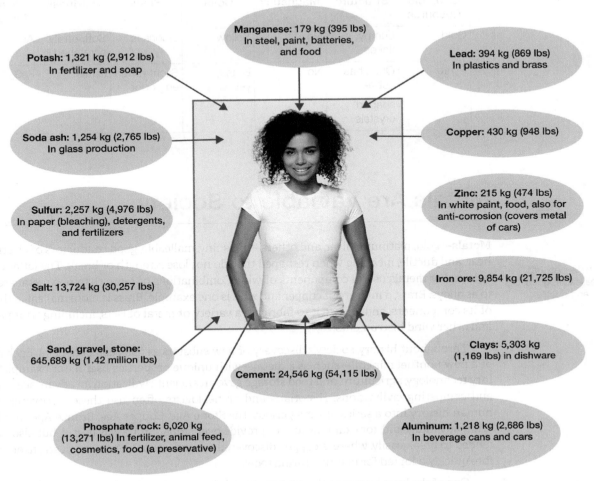

Sources: Joseph Shostell; © Shutterstock, Inc.; data from USGS, https://pubs.usgs.gov/periodicals/mcs2021/mcs2021-potash.pdf; https://pubs.usgs.gov/periodicals/mcs2020/mcs2020-sulfur.pdf; https://www.usgs.gov/faqs/how-large-lifetime-supply-minerals-average-person.

Critical Thinking Activity: Fool's Gold

mineralogist

Person who studies minerals.

Throughout history, people have mistakenly identified minerals, with occasionally depressing and serious consequences. For example, the untrained eye can easily mistake pyrite for gold, which is why this mineral is called fool's gold. One of the best examples of being fooled occurred in the 1600s, when early colonists in New England sent a shipload of "gold" to England, only to be informed that it was worthless fool's gold. There are also many examples of miners out west during the 1800s mistakenly thinking they had discovered gold, and therefore were about to become rich. Other, more knowledgeable miners tested the geologic material to make sure that they had indeed discovered gold.

What characteristics of minerals do **mineralogists** use to identify and classify them? Minerals, including pyrite (fool's gold), are identified by color, hardness, and presence or absence of crystals. Other ways to determine the identity of a mineral is by taste (think table salt), by its ability to fluoresce, or by determining if it's magnetic, radioactive, or dissolvable in acid.

By using these methods, one comes to realize that a rock can consist of one mineral or several (which is usually the case). Study the list of physical properties in Table 12.2 for both pyrite and gold and then suggest how the colonists could have prevented their calamity.

TABLE 12.2 Physical Properties of Gold and Pyrite

Geologic Resource	Structure	Magnetic?	Color	Smell	Hardness	Chemical Structure
Gold	Lumpy, flakes	No	Yellow	Odorless	Soft, easily scratched	Au
Pyrite	Often has cube-shaped crystals	No	Brassy yellow	Slight rotten egg odor	Brittle	FeS$_2$

Metals Are Valuable to Society

metals

Geologic substances that are shiny, malleable, good conductors, and ductile.

Metals—gold, platinum, silver, and others—are shiny, malleable, good conductors of electricity and heat, and ductile, meaning when reshaped they do not lose strength or break. The latter characteristic makes metals useful components of wire. Combinations of more than one metal are referred to as alloys. Brass, a mixture of copper and zinc, is one example. Brass is more malleable than either of its components, and we use it to fabricate a variety of metal objects, including trumpets, tubas, and other wind instruments.

Throughout history, society's discovery of new substances has been beneficial. Each discovery of a new nonfuel mineral—such as a metal—with unique properties useful (for example) for military technology, agriculture, and food storage gave an ancient civilization an advantage over nature and competing civilizations. Historians and archeologists often use these discoveries to divide human history into a series of time periods: the Stone Age, Copper Age, Bronze Age, and Iron Age. What advantage did, for example, copper provide over stone? Stone was useful, but also brittle and tended to break easily, whereas copper, discovered around 4,200 BC, was much stronger and therefore quickly adopted for manufacturing tools.

One of the least known and most used metals in current society is tantalum. There are approximately 40 milligrams of tantalum in the average cell phone, and if you are similar to most people, you carry at least that much with you—more if you carry around other electronic gadgetry. Tantalum has unique properties that are quite useful in electronics. For example, this metal maintains its functions under a range of temperatures, and it can withstand corrosion by most acids. About half of the tantalum mined today becomes part of capacitors found in almost all electronic products, including our beloved cell phones. On the global-market level, tantalum is worth billions of dollars; therefore, it is mined wherever it is accessible in Earth's crust—currently, in Australia, Brazil, Canada, Mozambique, Thailand, Portugal, Nigeria, and the Democratic Republic of Congo (D.R.C., formerly Zaire). We remove it from the Earth as a raw ore called coltan, a combination of columbite and tantalite that is worth up to $100 per pound. A mining or trading company sells the ore to a processing company, which in turn sells purified tantalum to a company that manufactures capacitors. In a healthy supply chain, there is a clear understanding of where a geological material comes from, and whether ethical guidelines were followed (see "Critical Thinking Activity: What Is in a Cell Phone?").

Critical Thinking Activity: What Is in a Cell Phone?

Unfortunately, starting in around 1998, rebels from Rwanda and Uganda, two neighboring countries of D.R.C., began to exploit the people of the D.R.C. to extract coltan with the goal of raising capital to fund their militias (Jackson 2002). From 1997 to 1999, Uganda's coltan exports increased significantly—2,700 percent (2.5 tons to 70 tons)—and children were exploited to work in the mines (Lopez et al. 2017).

Consumers (you and I) may have no idea whether a purchase—a cell phone, for example—has helped to fuel a conflict in Africa. How would we know? There probably wasn't any special label on our phones stating where the tantalum came from. Cell phone companies and other companies that use tantalum in their products can have supply chains that extend from the ore mine to the manufacturing site, and finally to the store shelf. Would it be advisable to have labels on the end products stating whether, for example, a product contains tantalum from Africa? Stephen Jackson states (Jackson 2002) that we should be careful not to penalize local people who desire to make an honest living of mining. Again, what do you recommend? Finally, there is evidence that the mining of coltan has disrupted the natural environment and killed endangered gorillas, even when they were in national parks. Is there a safe way to remove coltan from the D.R.C. without exploiting people and without harming wildlife? Read the final reports provided by the United Nations (UN 2003) and ENACT (2022) and come to your own conclusion.

Metals have economic value. For instance, we commonly use copper in electrical wiring, aluminum in soda cans, and gold in computer circuitry, jewelry, coins, and dentistry. Upon consideration of the many commodities we make with metal, one quickly comprehends the economic significance of metal production. In 2019, metal production in the United States had an estimated value of $28.1 billion (USGS 2020). One-third of this total is gold ($9.0 billion), 28 percent is copper ($7.9 billion), 19 percent is iron ore ($5.3 billion), 7 percent is zinc ($2.0 billion), and the remainder is an assortment of other metals. Given their usefulness to society, the U.S. government identifies and monitors thirty-five critical minerals linked to the economy and national security. Check out Figure 12.7 for examples of geological material production by state.

Nonmetal Geologic Substances Are Valuable to Society

Nonmetal, nonfuel mineral production in the United States is valued at over $58 billion, more than twice the value of metals (see Figure 12.7). These industrial ores and minerals make up a more diverse group, including, for example, limestone, clays, sand, gravel, gypsum, crushed rock, and diamonds, among others. Many are critical ingredients of buildings and roads, and all are useful in commercial and industrial activities. Ceramics, paints, construction materials, glass, detergents, electronics, and paper production all depend on nonmetal, nonfuel minerals. Gravel, for example, is used in roads, and limestone mixed with gypsum makes concrete. Diamonds (see "Case Study: Mining in Arkansas Diamond Park"), another non-metal mineral, are the hardest substance on Earth, so in addition to becoming jewelry they have value in grinding, drilling, cutting, and polishing. Just how valuable is a diamond mine? The DeBeer's Victor Diamond mine in Canada had an estimated $6.7 billion impact on Ontario during the eleven years it was open, between 2008 and 2019.

FIGURE 12.7
Nonfuel geologic materials produced in the United States from mining were valued at over $86 billion in 2019. Examples are highlighted, but all states are sources of multiple geologic materials.

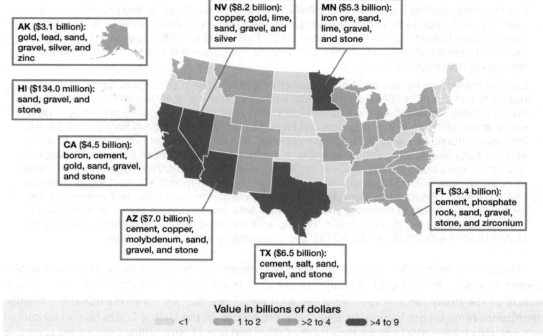

AK ($3.1 billion): gold, lead, sand, gravel, silver, and zinc

HI ($134.0 million): sand, gravel, and stone

CA ($4.5 billion): boron, cement, gold, sand, gravel, and stone

NV ($8.2 billion): copper, gold, lime, sand, gravel, and silver

MN ($5.3 billion): iron ore, sand, lime, gravel, and stone

FL ($3.4 billion): cement, phosphate rock, sand, gravel, stone, and zirconium

AZ ($7.0 billion): cement, copper, molybdenum, sand, gravel, and stone

TX ($6.5 billion): cement, salt, sand, gravel, and stone

Value in billions of dollars
<1   1 to 2   >2 to 4   >4 to 9

Source: USGS. 2020. Mineral Commodity Summaries 2020; https://pubs.usgs.gov/periodicals/mcs2020/mcs2020.pdf.

Geologic Fuels: Coal and Uranium

Some geologic resources such as coal are neither minerals nor metals. Coal consists of the remains of ancient plants that lived 200–375 million years ago. After the plants died, their decaying mass became buried, and millions of years of geologic heat and pressure transformed the mass into coal. Society's extraction and use of coal and other geologic fuels are the sources of many current environmental problems (see Chapter 13). Acid rain, increasing concentrations of greenhouse gases in the atmosphere, and smog are just a few of the environmental issues associated with using coal and other carbon-based geologic fuels. The United States receives approximately one-third of its electricity from the combustion of coal, and another 20 percent from nuclear energy (uranium). As discussed in Chapter 14, wind power, geothermal, hydropower, and solar power offer more sustainable methods of meeting our energy needs because they are renewable sources of energy.

Companies Invest in the Exploration of Geologic Resources

Mineral exploration is an important and integral part of the mineral business, and companies that intend to be around long term may spend millions of dollars each year on this single segment. Identifying new mineral resources helps to ensure that mining companies adequately prepare for their future while simultaneously protecting investor capital. Exploration can also lead to expansion and diversification. Some megacorporations that mine minerals operate across dozens of countries and have a total revenue in the hundreds of billions of dollars. These companies may invest hundreds of millions of dollars in research exploration in a single year.

Glencore, a mining and trading conglomerate, is one of the world's top producers of copper, nickel, cobalt, alloys, and other geologic-derived commodities. Their 146,000 employees and rising market value attest to the value of minerals and other geologic resources, and that it is worth investing in the exploration of their deposits. Geologic commodities from Glencore and other mining companies are passed to downstream industries that inject an estimated $3 trillion into the U.S. economy per year. In the next section, we assess the effects mining activities have on the environment.

Key Takeaways

- Many of the products we use—from our cell phones to construction materials to jewelry—contain geologic substances.
- Minerals are inorganic, naturally occurring substances that are also solid and have a specific chemical and crystal structure.
- Only a portion (the reserve) of a geologic resource is extractable given the current technological capabilities and market.
- Metal and nonmetal geologic substances are valuable to society.

12.3 The Effects of Mining Nonfuel Geologic Resources

Learning Objectives

1. Identify the main types of mining.
2. Explain how the mining and processing of geologic resources generates wastes and degrades the environment.
3. Summarize the environmental issues of mining waste storage sites.

We buy a lot of products that contain minerals and other geologic resources, but the true costs of most of these products do not match their sales prices. True cost is much higher than sales price because it includes hidden costs—environmental damage caused through exploration, mining, processing, and manufacturing, in addition to potential negative effects on humans and the expense of caring for those harmed (see Chapter 2). Even the price of expensive diamond products such as wedding rings does not include all hidden costs. For example, the Udachnaya diamond mine in Russia, near the Arctic Circle, has disturbed the surface ecosystem with a hole 2 km (1.2 mi) wide and 640 m (2,100 ft) deep. However, the negative effects of this mine are comparatively less than those of some of the diamond mines in Africa that exploit workers and have been used to fund civil war conflicts. The diamonds from these African mines are referred to as blood or conflict diamonds.

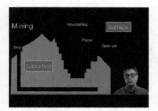
In this section, we discuss the environmental impact of society's reliance on nonenergy geologic materials, focusing on mining, processing of mineral ores, and the manufacturing of products that contain them (see video link: " Mining "). Coal, oil, and gas are covered in detail with other energy sources in Chapter 13.

Mining and Drilling

Mining is a time-consuming, dirty, and exhausting activity. With advances in technology at least at the industrial level, it has developed into a very sophisticated process heavily dependent on specialized and large-scale machinery. A constant challenge for mining operations is to be able to access and extract the sought-after mineral deposits as efficiently as possible. But even in the best-case scenarios, a large part of mining is devoted to the removal of non-ore material. For example, up to 2.8 tons of earth must be extracted and processed to acquire enough gold for a single standard gold ring. Therefore, mining gold and other extremely profitable materials involves machinery that will process large volumes of rock quickly (see "Bringing It Closer to Home: How Much Earth Was Extracted for My Gold Jewelry?").

Bringing It Closer to Home: How Much Earth Was Extracted for My Gold Jewelry?

Are you wearing a gold ring? What about a gold necklace? Gold earrings? The gold in rings, earrings, bracelets, and necklaces was a geologic resource in the ground until a mining company extracted and processed it. How much earth did the miners have to extract for your gold jewelry? For a rough estimate, fill in Table 12.3 adding in the type and number of gold jewelry items you possess. For instance, if you own two gold rings, insert "2" in the "Number I Own" column (column three). Then, for the fourth column, multiply columns two (Equivalent to standard size ring) and three (Number I own). Last, total all the values in the fourth column and multiply this number by 2.8 tons, which is an estimate of how much earth is extracted for every standard gold ring. Is this number more or less than what you expected?

TABLE 12.3 Calculation of Earth Removed

Jewelry	Equivalent to Standard Size Ring	Number I Own	Total (Multiply Columns Two and Three)
Ring	1		
Earrings	1		
Thin bracelet	1		
Thick bracelet	3		
Nose ring	1		
Thin necklace	2		
Thick necklace	4		
Small pendant	0.5		
Large pendant	1		
Other	?		
		Total:	
		Total multiplied by 2.8 tons:	

There are two types of mines: **surface mines** that access metallic and nonmetallic ore deposits at or relatively close to the surface, and **subsurface mines** that reach geologic deposits deeper in the ground (see Figure 12.8). Of the two, surface mines are much more common, making up 97 percent of the total number of mines (Hartmann and Mutmansky 2007). How do mining strategies differ between the two types of mines? One notable difference is in equipment size. Larger equipment is used in surface mining to bulldoze trees, soil, and the top layers (the **overburden**) of earth in order to expose the ore.

surface mine

A mine close to the surface; examples are strip mines and open-pit mines.

subsurface mine

A mine that extracts geologic materials from underground.

overburden

The layer of earth above a targeted ore.

FIGURE 12.8

Mining is divided into two general categories: surface mining and underground mining. (A) Aerial view of a surface mine, an abandoned copper mine outside the city of Butte, Montana. Note the size of the pit and tailings pond. (B) Two trucks transport gold ore from an open-pit surface mine in Australia. (C) Silhouette of underground miner with jackhammer drill.

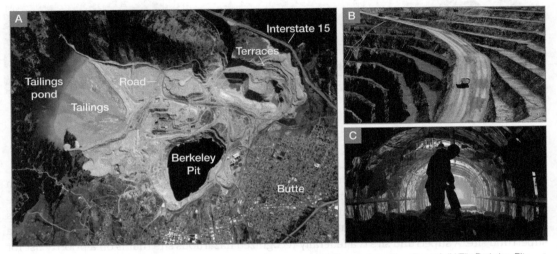

Sources: Joseph Shostell; NASA, Public domain, via Wikimedia Commons, https://commons.wikimedia.org/wiki/File:Berkeley_Pit_Butte,_Montana.jpg; © Shutterstock, Inc.

Surface-mining equipment can be mammoth in size, sometimes dwarfing even the largest non-mining vehicles (see Figure 12.9). The largest is the bucket-wheel excavator, a custom-built machine that can be 95 m (311 ft) in height and 215 m (705 ft) long. To put this into perspective, this one vehicle is more than a football field in height and two football fields long. Its massive size allows it to move about 240,000 cubic meters of earth each day, or a rectangular prism the length and width of a football field that is 175 feet deep. Just as large as its size is its price, the largest ones costing up to $100 million, further proof that large-scale mining is expensive.

Surface Mining (Strip Mining) and Mountaintop Removal Mining

Strip mining, open-pit mining, and placer mining are three different types of surface mining.

Strip Mining

Strip mining is a type of surface mining used when the targeted ore is near the surface and the overburden is removed in strips, creating a long ditch. When the mining operators begin the second strip of overburden, they discard it in the previously created ditch. **Mountaintop removal mining** is a severely destructive type of strip mining that decimates a mountain layer by layer (see Figure 12.9).

FIGURE 12.9
The grand scale of mining machines used in surface mining makes it possible to change landscapes quickly and drastically. (A) Dump truck. (B) Bucket-wheel excavators. (C) Such machines allow removal of entire mountaintops.

Source: © Shutterstock, Inc.

Open-Pit Mining

Open-pit mining is the most common type of surface mining. Those such as the Berkeley Pit, an abandoned copper mine in Butte, Montana, are quite deep and broad—literally a huge conical hole in the ground (see A in Figure 12.8). This one mine is almost 545 m (1,800 ft) deep, and it now contains a contaminated lake that is part of a massive hazardous area listed by the federal government as a superfund site. A superfund site is a federally recognized hazardous site that is on a priority list for further investigation and possible remediation. The pit and nearby tailings area and pond are laced with arsenic, cadmium, and lead—metals that are detrimental to wildlife and ecosystem services. Thousands of soil samples taken from the Butte area indicate average concentrations of arsenic of 214 ppm, with some samples having a much higher amount—as high as 11,900 ppm (Barry 2012). For reference, the Montana Department of Environmental Quality reported 11.5 ppm as the average background (natural) concentration of arsenic in soil across Montana (MDEQ 2013). An estimated 3,000 migrating geese died in 2016 when they landed in the poisonous water. Well-planned excavation efforts in open-pit mines create a series of vertical platforms called benches used by mining trucks to transport ore out of the mine. Open-pit mines that produce building supplies in the form of sand, stone, clay, and the like are called quarries. Surface mines do produce needed materials for societies, but most people think they are not aesthetically pleasing—a blight in a landscape.

Placer Mining

Placer mining is another form of surface mining used to find and remove precious metals (such as gold) and gemstones from loose deposits of sand and other materials. The objective in placer mining is to access a placer deposit, which forms when dense minerals and metals wash downslope to a stream or other low-lying area. Stream placer deposits are by far the most common, and miners have had success in panning for gold and diamonds in these areas.

Solution Mining (at Surface or Underground)

Solution mining is a method of mining water-soluble minerals such as salt and potash (see Figure 12.10). Freshwater is pumped into underground deposits of minerals, causing water-soluble minerals to dissolve. The water containing the dissolved minerals is then pumped to the surface, where the mineral is concentrated and recovered. Copper and other metals are also harvested through solution mining (Briggs 2015). In these cases, a dilute acidic solution is used. About 90 percent of uranium within the United States is obtained through solution mining.

FIGURE 12.10

In solution mining, a water-based solution is injected into the ground through a well to dissolve and leach out a geologic resource. For example, solution mining is used to extract potash—an ore that contains potassium. (A) At the Bonneville Salt Flats in Utah, a solution of potash is brought to the surface and routed into a canal, (B) then directed through pipes to solar evaporation ponds (C). After the water evaporates in these ponds, the dried ore is harvested and transported.

Sources: Joseph Shostell; Potash—A Vital Agricultural Nutrient Sourced from Geologic Deposits, USGS, https://pubs.usgs.gov/of/2016/1167/ofr20161167.pdf.

Subsurface Mining

Subsurface mining occurs beneath the surface to access deeper deposits of minerals. In these scenarios, the overburden is too thick, and thus too expensive to remove. Instead, tunnels are created to reach the deposits. Underground mines are less noticeable, but they can have serious impacts on the environment (see Figure 12.11). For example, the Retsof Salt Mine, in Genesee Valley, New York, collapsed in 1994, with several negative effects. Water from the principal aquifer system in the Genesee Valley flowed into the mine. By January 1996, water levels in local wells had dropped by 107 m (350 ft) (USGS 1998). Underground potable water was affected as far as 10 miles away, becoming unavailable for many people or becoming chemically altered with higher salinity. Two large sinkholes developed, one 183 m (600 ft) and the other 244 m (800 ft) in diameter. Both caused structural damage to residential and business areas. In addition, air quality was reduced in the area because methane and hydrogen sulfide gases were released when the mine collapsed. Analysis of the area around the mine indicated that the ground will probably continue to sink for the next 100 to 200 years (Van Sambeek 1994).

Bringing It Closer to Home: How Close Do You Live to a Superfund Site?

Check out the Environmental Protection Agency's website devoted to superfund sites to determine the one closest to your home. Our frontier mentality has resulted in the number of superfund sites increasing each decade.

FIGURE 12.11

Subsidence—sinking of the ground—is an extremely worrisome effect of subsurface mining. Photos show sink holes in (A) Tampa, Florida, and (B) Rigal, Latvia.

Sources: Courtesy of Florida Geological Survey; Radowitz/Shutterstock.com

Processing of Geologic Materials Generates Waste

Concentrations of minerals and metals in extracted ore are too low for use in product development. For instance, the concentration of copper in copper oxide ore is less than 1 percent. Ores like this undergo a process in which the geologic resource (copper, in this case) is isolated and concentrated. The exact processing method used depends on the geologic resource and the ore's chemistry. There are two general processing methods in the production of copper and other metals: hydrometallurgy (using a water solution) and pyrometallurgy (using heat). Copper oxide ore must be crushed in preparation for either type of processing.

Low-grade copper oxide ore is processed with hydrometallurgy that begins with the addition of a dilute sulfuric acid, which dissolves the copper and leaches it from the ore. At this stage, the copper concentration has increased to 60–70 percent and there is a slurry of copper compounds and radioactive materials. In the next steps, solvent extraction and electroextraction (electrowinning), copper is separated out and removed from the slurry. The concentration of copper in this last part of processing reaches 99.99 percent. This stage also generates a liquid waste that contains radioactive materials.

mine tailings

Ore waste from mines.

smelting

The addition of heat to a metal ore to extract the desired metal.

Copper ores that contain sulfur (copper sulfide ores) are usually processed with pyrometallurgy. The process takes three general steps: roasting, smelting, and electrolysis. First, during the roasting stage, the ore is heated to remove sulfur and moisture. Silica and limestone are then mixed with the roasted ore and heated in a furnace. Two layers form, one with the desired resource (matte copper), and the second with waste (or slag), later discarded as **mine tailings**. In the second step, called **smelting**, matte copper is heated in a series of smelting furnaces and copper concentrations increase to 99 percent. In the third and final step, electrolysis, sheets of the concentrated copper are exposed to a liquid containing copper sulfate and acid. An electric current drives positively charged copper ions to negatively charged copper plates (cathodes), and boosts the copper content to 99.99 percent. Increasing the concentration of copper improves its electrical conductivity, a property useful in wiring applications.

Acid mine drainage, heavy metal contamination, and radioactive materials produced by both types of processing present serious problems to the local terrestrial ecosystem and connecting aquatic ecosystems (see Chapter 13). Heating sulfide ores is also a chief source of sulfur dioxide and, indirectly, acid rain formation; according to the EPA, approximately 23.4 million tons of sulfur dioxide and nitrogen oxides are released from metal smelting operations in the United States alone every year. Thus, processing metal ores pollutes the lithosphere, hydrosphere, and atmosphere.

Smelting is also a significant source of carbon dioxide emissions. Aluminum production alone accounts for approximately 1 percent of these emissions globally. Of this, about half is due to combustion of fossil fuels used to generate the large amounts of electricity required for smelting and electrolysis during purification (Gautam et al. 2018, Tyabji and Nelson 2010). An additional 17 percent comes directly from electrolysis, when oxygen atoms in aluminum oxide—an impure form of aluminum in bauxite (aluminum ore)—chemically react with carbon and form carbon dioxide. All tallied up, approximately 1.5 kg (3.3 lb) of carbon dioxide is released during the production of one kilogram (2.2 lb) of aluminum.

> **acid mine drainage**
>
> Acidic solution draining from a mine; often contains heavy metals.

Improperly Stored Mine Wastes

Mining facilities generate large volumes of waste. The specific wastes (tailings) vary depending on location, type of ore, and method of processing, and are often an accumulation of solid waste and acidic liquid laden with heavy metals. A mining company typically secures the tailings in place with a dam. How secure the wastes are depends on the design and quality of the dam. For instance, a dam composed of the very material it is supposed to hold—the tailings—is economical and quickly constructed, but not very stable. Tailings dams are often envisioned as perpetual holding areas, and yet there are many examples of their failure (see Figure 12.12). In reality, dams are subjected to earthquakes and other forms of geologic activity as well as heavy precipitation and flooding, now enhanced in many areas by climate change. In time, these dams, and there are 3,500 worldwide, will fail (Martin and Davies 2000). One of the worst tailings dam failures occurred in Southern Spain.

The Los Frailes Tailings Dam Failure

On April 25, 1998, a tailings dam containing lead and zinc mining waste failed in Aznolcóllar, near Seville in southern Spain. Once released, the toxic slurry and sludge moved as a wave into Río Agrio, a feeder stream to the larger Guadiamar. The wave created a path of destruction, radically changing the environment and killing both flora and fauna. In total, an estimated 1.3 million cubic meters of tailings entered the Guadiamar River Basin, reducing the river's pH to 3—too low for fish and other aquatic organisms to survive (López-Pamo et al. 1999). Oxygen levels in the river plummeted, and toxins contaminated the water and surrounding terrestrial areas in the wave's path. Thirty-seven tons of dead fish were collected from the Guadiamar River, and the acidic waters even reached the famed Guadalquivir River that flows through Seville and Doñana National Park (García et al 2003). Until the dam was sealed in 1999, as much as 84,400 liters of toxic waste continued to move into the river every day. A decade after the breach, environmental scientists noted that concentrations of toxins had decreased, but were still higher in than the surrounding environment (Olias et al. 2012). Now, there are concerns about the contamination of groundwater and aquifers (see "Critical Thinking Activity: Who Should Cover Restoration Costs?"). These and other negative effects of mine wastes are clear incentives for us to sustainably manage geologic resources (discussed next).

FIGURE 12.12

Example of a tailings dam failure. On January 25, 2019, an iron ore tailings dam ruptured near Brumadinho, Minas Gerais, Brazil, sending a sea of mud and mine wastes through the mining community and local town, and killing 248 people. (A) After the dam failed, mine waste mixed with mud was strewn across a large area. (B) The mine waste reached and contaminated the region's main river, the Paraopeba.

Source: © Shutterstock, Inc.

Los Frailes Tailings Dam

Site of one of Spain's largest environmental disasters and one of the world's worst tailings dam failures.

Critical Thinking Activity: Who Should Cover Restoration Costs?

The **Los Frailes Tailings Dam** failure is arguably Spain's worst environmental disaster. The cost for restoration, which is not yet fully complete, is in the hundreds of millions of dollars, paid by the Andalusian government and the Spanish Environmental Ministry. Part of this story includes the litigations that followed the failed dam. For example, the Andalusian government sued Boliden, the company that owned the mine, in the amount of $89.8 million to cover restoration efforts. In turn, Boliden sued the Spanish construction company Dragados, which they contracted to build the tailings dam, for 107 million Euros.

Who is responsible for the restoration work involved? Is it the people of Andalusia? Is it Boliden? Is it the Spanish government? Boliden is a huge international corporation and certainly has the finances to cover clean-up costs, even back in 1999 when it reported a revenue of more than $1 billion. They have grown considerably since that time, and now have an annual revenue in excess of $52.5 billion. Boliden has a series of investors, each of whom paid to own part of the company. Are they responsible? Do not forget, Boliden produces a commodity eventually incorporated into products people purchase, even those in Southern Spain closest to the environmentally damaged area. Are these local consumers to blame too? Which entity—corporation, government, or individual people—is responsible for environmental restoration costs incurred by the Los Frailes Tailings Dam's failure?

Maybe the old saying "actions speak louder than words" is applicable here, because in 2013 the regional Spanish government announced it intended to reopen the Aznalcóllar mine and invited proposals from mining corporations. Based on this decision, the government and mining companies acknowledge the potential for future habitat degradation as an acceptable consequence of conducting business. What do you think?

Key Takeaways

- Mining produces large volumes of waste because only a small fraction of mined materials contain the ore of interest.
- There are two types of mines: surface mines and subsurface mines.
- Examples of surface mining include strip mining, open-pit mining, and placer mining.
- Underground mines are less noticeable, but they can have serious impacts on the environment.

- Processing of ore often produces acid waste (acid mine drainage) laden with heavy metals.
- Tailings dams are thought of as perpetual storage sites but there are many examples of their failure due to poor design, nonideal composition, and natural geologic events.

12.4 Sustainable Use of Geologic Resources

Learning Objectives

1. Discuss how the building of smaller consumer products can support the sustainable use of geologic resources.
2. Recognize and explain the value of renewable energy use to power mining activities.
3. Discuss the benefits and limitations of recycling geologic resources.
4. Apply the concept of substitution to society's sustainable use of geologic resources.
5. Examine and summarize the influence of key federal laws on society's path toward the sustainable use of geologic resources.

When asked to describe mining activities, people often begin their answers with words such as *dirty*, *filthy*, and *pollution*. Their remarks are not far from the truth, and are supported by a slew of environmental studies. However, a newer business strategy is taking hold in the mining sector based on sustainable development. In 1998, in response to wide criticism of their notoriously poor environmental and social track records, nine of the world's largest mining companies convened to discuss sustainability. The group agreed to commission the International Institute for Environment and Development (IIED) to conduct a two-year study of the mining sector's role in transitioning to sustainable development. This study became known as the Mining, Minerals and Sustainable Development (MMSD) project. MMSD established a framework of guiding principles of sustainable development (IIED 2002). Ten years later, IIED conducted a review to assess the mining sector's progress toward sustainable and responsible mining. It listed achievements, ongoing challenges, and new issues. One of the achievements of MMSD was the creation and implementation of best practices for sustainable development of minerals. Translating these practices through the strata of large-scale corporations is still a challenge, and successes predominantly occur in the large-scale mining sector rather than in small mining operations. A major outcome of the study is the adoption of the study's best practices by the International Council on Mining and Metals (ICMM). ICMM also has agreed not to conduct mining on World Heritage Sites.

In this section, we apply sustainability and ethics to how we extract, process, and use geologic resources. Specific topics include reduction, abatement of pollution emissions, substitution, recycling, and restoration.

Reducing Use of Geologic Resources: Building Smaller and Differently

Mines are unable to disgorge diamonds, metals, and other useful geologic materials forever. While we might wish for an endless abundance of minerals, there is a finite amount, and we extract them from the ground faster than their natural rate of geologic replenishment. In other words, mineral resources are nonrenewable. The best way to conserve diamonds and other geologic resources is to use less of them. Scaling down the size of a product is one obvious option. For example, on average, smaller cars take less geologic materials to make than do larger cars. Consumers who choose to purchase smaller cars reduce their use of geologic resources. Of course, there are other ecofriendly benefits of owning a small car, such as better fuel economy. Building smaller and differently also applies to a product's packaging, which can contain petroleum-based plastic. Petroleum is a geologic resource. Today's sustainable-minded consumers consider information about a product's natural resources, including those in a product's packaging, when they make a purchasing decision.

Pollution Abatement: A Goal of Zero Carbon Mining

FIGURE 12.13
Floating solar panels on tailings ponds help to power mining activities and reduce air pollution emissions.

Source: © Shutterstock, Inc

Are the negative impacts of mining inevitable? The answer to this question is debatable, but based on a typical mine's accumulated waste and pollution emissions, there is plenty of room for mining operations to become more environmentally sustainable. A good place to start is by taking an input-output systems approach to quantify the amount of matter and energy entering (the input) a mining project, and the amount of pollution produced and released (the output). This approach accounts for the large energy inputs required to power heavy machinery and to conduct daily activities. Mines are often in remote, off-grid areas that require diesel fuel to be trucked across long distances to supply onsite generators. The fossil fuel combusted in transportation to reach the mining site, and at the mining site, releases greenhouse gases and other pollutants into the atmosphere. Progressive mining companies see this as wasteful and instead are turning to renewable energy to power their activities (see Figure 12.13). A sign of the movement toward more sustainable mining, in 2017 B2Gold constructed a 7 megawatt solar plant to power mining activities at Namibia's largest gold mine. Other mining companies, including Glencore, adopted a renewable strategy as well. Glencore's 3 megawatt wind turbine generator delivers energy to their nickel and copper mine (Raglan Mine) in northern Quebec, Canada. Their move to renewable energy prevents the release of almost 5,000 tons of greenhouse gases per year!

Mining companies are also capable of applying sustainability improvements to the smelting process. Apple and the Canadian government are investing in a new collaboration between aluminum producer Alcoa and the mining company Rio Tinto to manufacture more environmentally friendly aluminum. The venture's new $50 million smelting technology research and development center, which opened in 2020, will commercialize the use of inert anodes (negatively charged plates) for electrolysis during aluminum production. Using inert anodes, oxygen forms rather than carbon dioxide (see Section 3). Alcoa patented this technology, and since 2009 has repeatedly tested it by manufacturing aluminum on a research scale. The company now plans to scale the production commercially, and anticipates that aluminum produced through inert anode technology will enter the global market by 2024.

Wastewater: Tailings Ponds, Recycling, and Treatment

Limited freshwater resources, the integral role water plays in mining operations, and the value of water to society make the sustainable management of water resources imperative. There are several strategies to offset polluted wastewater originating from active and abandoned mines. Secondary processing (recycling) is at the top of the list of best sustainable practices. Recycling of mine tailings and wastewater boosts efficiency and minimizes waste generation. Vale's copper mine in Para Brazil recycles almost all of its water from a tailings pond, and this allows it to avoid withdrawing 900,000 cubic meters of water per year from clean water sources (Toledano and Roorda 2014).

Despite recycling wastewater, a mining facility adhering to sustainable practices still generates at least a nominal amount of wastewater. In some cases, there may even be voluminous quantities of wastewater due to inflows from geologic water and precipitation. All of these waters, and water used in mining activities, are tested for toxins, monitored, and treated if necessary. Lime additions raise the pH of acidic effluent, and when sufficient space is available, a series of settling ponds help to remove dissolved solids. Membrane-based filtration (Adiga 2000), electrodialysis, and chemical and biological treatments all have merit and are implemented based on the type of wastewater and the mine. If the goal is storage, our lessons in tailings pond accidents inform us to localize and stabilize tailings with durable, well-designed dams. Good sustainability practices also affect mine closure and have effects on the site long after closure. Discussions about ethical and environmentally sustainable closure start early in the life of a mine, and they involve the local community to formulate a clear idea of postclosure land use. Mining company Teck Cominco began to strategize with Indigenous peoples and the local community thirty years before they closed the Sullivan mine near Kimberley, Canada, in 2001. For almost a century, the production of zinc, lead, silver, and tin supported the local economy and employed about half of Kimberley's population. The site now has a solar power plant and is an extension of the local ski resort.

Substitutes

Are we not essentially diners at the periodic table—choosing what we want and (because it is a buffet) how much as well? Such an analogy works because a buffet continues as long as each tray remains stocked with food. However, our demand for more products is straining Mother Nature's finite natural resources buffet. Circuit boards, for example, have evolved from normally having eleven elements in the 1980s to sixty in the 2000s, and society has substantially ramped up the extraction of copper, zinc, gold, and other metals during the same time interval (Johnson et al. 2007). When a natural resource such as a metal is in high demand, but is naturally rare, or has become rare because of human use, we try to substitute. Economic importance, regional conflict and stability, and environmental impact are also drivers of substitution.

We are constantly in search of good substitutes for metals. Glass is gaining a great reputation as a superior material to copper in the telecommunication industry. Human-hair-diameter glass fibers—optical fibers—are assembled into cables that last longer, are more reliable, use less energy, and have a thousand times greater bandwidth than copper wire (see Figure 12.14). In fiber-optic communications, information is encoded in light that can travel through these cables much more quickly than electrical signals travel through copper wire. According to the International Telecommunications Union, the telecommunications industry is investing hundreds of billions of dollars in fiber-optic network infrastructure. Optical fiber cables are also not as susceptible to water damage. After flood damage to its copper-based wire centers in New York City, Verizon began to convert to fiber-optics. Verizon and other companies understand the advantage of replacing their old copper networks. Most important, fiber-optic cables rely on less energy and release less heat relative to copper cables.

FIGURE 12.14
Substituting copper cables with glass fiber cables (fiber-optics) substantially increases bandwidth and reduces energy needs, so it is more ecofriendly. (A) Cut optical fiber cable. (B) Optical fiber cables connected to a data center.

Source: © Shutterstock, Inc.

Recycling Metals and Minerals

It is far more energy efficient to conduct urban mining than it is to mine new geologic resources to replace these materials. Urban mining is the recycling of materials cast aside during the development of products or from the deconstruction of current products when they reach the end of their designed usefulness. Recycling is an important sustainability strategy, especially for metals and select minerals that are expensive to mine and process, and because mining and processing cause substantial environmental damage. Recycling reduces waste, saves energy, and helps to meet the world's demand for metals and minerals. Approximately one-third of a mine's operating costs go to covering energy requirements needed to excavate and process massive volumes of earth.

Automobiles, beverage cans, and appliances are examples of products with geologically derived components and short useful lifespans. Eighty-five percent of all used automobiles are recycled, primarily for their steel and iron. Each year the United States recycles over 64 million metric tons of metals valued at about $40 billion, clearly a very profitable business (see Chapter 16).

There are limits to recycling due to lag times, challenge of recovery, and cost. Lag time refers to the time a recyclable substance is tied up in a consumer product. For example, the lag time of metals in a car is twelve to fifteen years (the lifetime of the average car). Contrast this with the lag time of steel that makes up a beverage can—weeks. Valuable metals in other consumer products are extremely difficult and costly to recycle, and therefore are lost at the end of the products' lifespans. An example is titanium added as a whitener to paint and toothpaste. In both cases, it is easier and cheaper to obtain replacement titanium from its primary source (conventional mining) than from recycling used paint and used toothpaste. In general, metals are highly sought after in recycling, but many nonmetals, including stone, salt, clay, and silica materials, are not.

Companies such as Glencore carry out mineral exploration, mining, and processing, but they have also developed methods to recycle circuit boards, integrated circuits, and mobile phones (see Figure 12.15). Their Horne Smelter in Quebec, Canada, is the world's largest processor of electronic scrap. This smelter can process 840,000 tons of recyclables each year, preventing (for example) precious metals locked up in obsolete products from being discarded in landfills. Cell phones in use now number about 5 billion in the world, and that number is projected to surpass the number of people on the planet. Recycling them is smart business because it's both profitable and good for the environment (see video link: "From Garbage to Gold, Recycling Electronic Waste").

FIGURE 12.15
Talk is cheap, but minerals in cell phones are worth plenty. Glencore "mines" cell phones, recycling the precious metals inside. Cell phones usually become obsolete in 1.5 years, and with over 5 billion cell phone plan subscribers today, the value of this recycling market is nothing less than phenomenal. Rectangles contain weight and value of metals in an average cell phone. The red values represent the value of precious metals in 3 billion cell phones, about the number retired each year.

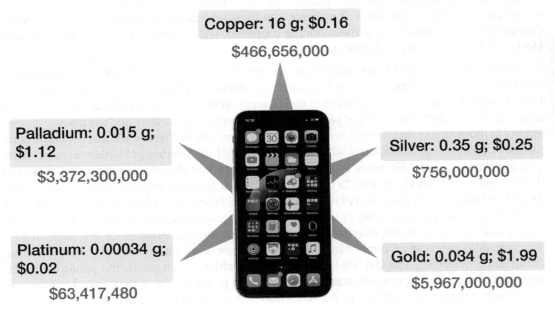

Copper: 16 g; $0.16
$466,656,000

Palladium: 0.015 g; $1.12
$3,372,300,000

Silver: 0.35 g; $0.25
$756,000,000

Platinum: 0.00034 g; $0.02
$63,417,480

Gold: 0.034 g; $1.99
$5,967,000,000

Sources: Joseph Shostell; Cincila/Shutterstock.com; data from U.S. Geological Survey Fact Sheet 2006-3097 (usgs.gov) and https://www.dailymetalprice.com/metalprices.php.

Environmental Protection Laws and Restoration

Enactment of strong environmental protection laws are an effective way to support sustainable mining practices. The **Resource Conservation and Recovery Act (RCRA)** of 1976 is the primary act of legislation overseeing sustainable methods to treat, store, transport, and dispose of hazardous solid wastes generated from industrial, commercial, domestic, and other activities, including mining. Created in 1976 as an amendment to the Solid Waste Disposal Act of 1965, RCRA came as a response to the increasing accumulation of municipal and industrial waste and the desire to protect public health and the environment from the mishandling and disposal of wastes. The law and its amendments direct the Environmental Protection Agency (EPA) to identify and list hazardous wastes, and authorize it to develop and enforce guidelines (regulations) for management of these wastes. Under the RCRA, a person or company must apply for and secure a permit to treat, store, or dispose of hazardous solid waste. Noncompliance of stipulations in a permit, or management of hazardous waste without a permit, has consequences. The EPA notifies the offender, who has thirteen days to meet compliance, after which the EPA may commence civil action in a U.S. District Court. Failing to take corrective action may result in fines of up to $25,000 per day and/or imprisonment for one year.

Resource Conservation and Recovery Act (RCRA)

Legislative act overseeing sustainable methods to treat, store, transport, and dispose of hazardous solid wastes generated from industrial, commercial, domestic, and other activities, including mining.

Comprehensive, Environmental Response Compensation and Liability Act (CERCLA)

A federal law that gives authority to the EPA to investigate and clean up uncontrolled and abandoned hazardous waste areas as well as emergency releases of waste. CERCLA also created a tax on the chemical and petroleum industries to fund restoration efforts.

The enactment of the **Comprehensive, Environmental Response Compensation and Liability Act (CERCLA)**, known as Superfund, in 1980 has also helped to fund restoration efforts of hazardous waste areas (see Chapter 15). Then, in 1986, President Ronald Reagan signed the Superfund Amendments and Reauthorization Act (SARA) that allowed for the continuation of CERCLA with some amendments. Only sites identified by the Environmental Protection Agency on the National Priorities List (NPL) qualify for cleanup under SARA. A number of abandoned nonenergy mineral mines are included in this list. For example, the long-abandoned Ely copper mine in Vershire Orange County, Vermont, was actively mining copper from 1821 through 1920, and since then, its 1,800 acres have been waiting for restoration.

When it comes to legislative support for sustainable practices, it is not just the enactment of new laws, but also amendments to and removal of outdated laws that matter. The General Mining Law of 1872 is a perfect example of an outdated mining law in need of reform. This law was created as an incentive to settle the untamed west. Here we are some 150 years later, and the law still defines mining as more important than other uses of publicly owned land. The law allows people and companies to prospect on public land with the possibility of discovering gold, diamonds, or other geologic deposits. Upon discovery, a person stakes a claim, and the government sells the land to them for no more than $5 per acre. To be sure, not all public lands are open to mining claims. Presidential and congressional authority and the Federal Land Policy and Management Act (FLPMA) of 1976 have removed vast quantities of land from mineral prospecting and mining, but the outdated mining law still needs reform. There are three main issues. One, it gives too much discretion to mining companies over use of public lands. Second, this law does not contain any environmental protection provisions. Third, the law fails to address royalties, which means the public loses vital resources without proper compensation. As long as these issues continue, the General Mining Law will remain controversial and an obstacle to strong environmental protection.

A mining company's environmental responsibilities continue even after a mine closes. Ethical mining companies restore mined lands—as much as possible—to their former, natural condition (see Figure 12.16). Part of the process includes trying to reestablish the original contours of the land, as well as restoring native plant communities. Common restoration techniques involve leveling and topsoil replacement followed by planting of vegetation. Length of recovery for ecosystems depends on the extent of initial degradation, geographic location, and climate (Naeth and Wilkinson 2014).

FIGURE 12.16

Restoration of mining lands post-closure. Mine restoration often includes (A) laying down new topsoil and (B) plantings that help the ecosystem recover. (C) Many thousands of abandoned mines like this one litter the U.S. landscape, and many times this amount exist across the world. The majority are sites of environmental pollution and in need of remediation.

Source: © Shutterstock, Inc.

Key Takeaways

- The use of geologic resources can be reduced by building smaller and differently designed products.
- Mining operations can use renewable energies rather than fossil fuels to power their activities.

- Several strategies, including recycling and lime treatments, can mitigate pollution in wastewater originating from active and abandoned mines.
- When possible, we find substitutes for specific geologic resources in our products because they are scarce, expensive, or have a pronounced negative effect on the environment.
- Recycling is an important sustainability strategy, especially for metals and select minerals.
- Enactment of strong environmental protection laws are an effective way to support sustainable mining practices.

12.5 Geological Hazards

Learning Objectives

1. Identify examples of hazardous geologic processes.
2. Explain the connection of earthquakes to tectonic plate boundaries.

Active geologic processes continually mold Earth's internal and external physical structure, from small mineral-laden rocks to mountain ranges extending across a continent. They are also capable of manifesting in violent events (earthquakes, tsunamis, volcanic eruptions, and landslides) that are dangerous to life.

Earthquakes

The vast majority of earthquakes occur near the boundaries of tectonic plates. Here, we discuss earthquakes in more detail, bringing up their frequency, average magnitude, and associated loss of life with them. Tectonic plates are constantly moving, but their edges get stuck on neighboring plates due to friction (see "Bringing It Closer to Home: Exploring My Tectonic Plate"). Any location where neighboring plates meet is called a fault line. Over time, energy builds up at the fault until it overcomes the friction, and the plates move suddenly, releasing a large amount of stored energy in the process. The energy released through the rock is an earthquake.

Bringing It Closer to Home: Exploring My Tectonic Plate

Click here to view the United States Geological Survey's map of tectonic plates to ascertain the name of the plate you live on. Next, click here to go to National Geographic's interactive tectonic plate boundaries website. Click on "SHOW" to highlight tectonic plate boundaries. Determine the types of plate boundaries for your plate. Finally, click here to explore an interactive map that combines tectonic plate, earthquake, and volcanic data from the USGS, NASA, and the Smithsonian. On the left side of the screen, click on "Earthquakes, Volcanoes, and Tectonic Plate Boundaries." Note the connection between boundary type, boundary location, and presence of earthquakes and volcanoes.

Just how frequent are earthquakes and how often should we expect large ones such as Japan's historic 9.03 magnitude earthquake in 2011 (see Figure 12.17)? The United States Geological Survey (USGS) estimates that millions of earthquakes occur each year, but most go unnoticed, a result of their occurring in remote areas or not being powerful enough to be detected with our current seismographs. Globally, we detect about fifty earthquakes every day, which equates to more than 18,000 per year. Most of these are small and really are not of much concern to us, unless they are leading up to a larger, damaging earthquake. Scientists can offer a general statement that stress is building up at a particular fault line, but have yet to accurately predict the occurrence of an earthquake. In other words, we cannot forecast earthquakes on a timeline shorter than a few decades.

FIGURE 12.17

Earthquakes can be dangerous. (A) The number of large-magnitude earthquakes across the world is quite small each year; nonetheless the number of deaths from earthquakes can reach hundreds of thousands (Data source: USGS). The photo shows a rescue team searching for survivors after an earthquake in Van, Turkey, in 2011. (B) An earthquake can trigger a tsunami.

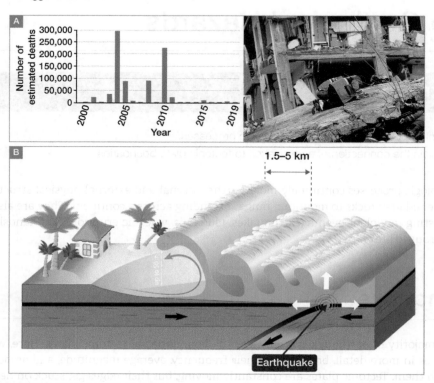

Sources: Joseph Shostell; data from USGS, https://www.usgs.gov/natural-hazards/earthquake-hazards/lists-maps-and-statistics; Prometheus72/Shutterstock.com; © Shutterstock, Inc.

Earthquakes and Environmental Pollution
Watch, listen, and learn about the effects of a major earthquake in Japan.

View in the online reader

The strength (or energy) of an earthquake is measured on a logarithmic scale. There is a great difference in strength between (for example) 6.1 and 7.1 magnitude quakes. For every whole number difference, the ground shakes ten times more, and the energy released is thirty-two times greater. To put this into perspective, one quake with a magnitude of 8.7 releases as much energy as 23,000 quakes of magnitude 5.8. Living at the surface of a planet with an active interior, we can easily be disrupted by the release of this much energy because it is enough to destroy buildings, roads, and other structures (see Figure 12.17). For example, a quake offshore of Japan in 2011 partially or wholly destroyed over one million buildings and unfortunately killed almost 19,000 people. The quake shifted the seafloor and caused tsunamis—large waves—to form in the overlying water. Waves of water of up to ten meters high hit Japan's coastline. Many of the deaths were due to the tsunamis (see Chapter 10). Earthquakes of up to a magnitude of 4.0 can also be induced by humans during hydraulic fracturing (Ellsworth 2013, Koslowska et al. 2018).

Volcanoes

Our knowledge and understanding of volcanoes have changed considerably since the time of the ancient Romans, who believed that volcanoes were chimneys for Vulcan's (the god of fire) workshops located deep within the ground. Today, we have an evidence-based explanation of why volcanoes form and the processes within them, thanks to scientists called volcanologists who study volcanology—the scientific study of volcanoes.

Volcanoes are vents in the ground from which lava, rocks, and ash are sometimes spewed great distances. They are also sources of carbon dioxide, mercury, and sulfur dioxide, and can significantly affect ecosystems and climate (see Chapter 15). The cone structure of a volcano is an effect of molten magma's welling up from Earth's outer core to its surface. Lava that spills from the vent cools into rock. Over time, this rock builds up, layer upon layer, after each eruption (see A in Figure 12.18). Thus, a conical volcano was shaped by its past eruptions. Volcanoes can be destructive, but they have many benefits such as forming new land areas and bringing up minerals from deep under Earth's crust. Do you remember the diamonds from the opening story? The crater in Crater of Diamonds State Park is a unique type of volcano called a maar that exploded violently in the distant past. Pressure from magma and superheated water overcame the weight of the overlying rock, sending it skyward. Much of the rock filled the crater when it landed. Usually, we expect a rim to be present with a crater, but in this case, most of it has been eroded away by wind and water over the course of millions of years. At the base of the volcano's crater, there is a narrow tube that extends into the mantle where the diamonds originally formed. During the eruption, some diamonds within the mantle were lifted to the surface, and later discovered by gem-seeking tourists. Geologists suggest that locating similar maar volcanoes may help us to find new sources of diamonds. Of course, volcanologists also share useful information about the activity of volcanoes, warning us of pending dangers such as induced landslides, discussed next.

volcanoes

Vents in Earth's crust that can spew hot gases and molten rock.

FIGURE 12.18
Volcanic eruptions and landslides are examples of geological hazards. (A) View of Mount Mayon, an active Volcano on the Island of Luzon in the Philippines. (B) A landslide in Giampilieri, Italy, sends debris down streets, covering cars, damaging buildings, and killing people.

Sources: © Shutterstock, Inc.; Lucky Team Studio/Shutterstock.com

Landslides

A landslide is the mass movement of rock, organic matter, and soil down a slope. It arises from a triggering event and continues because of gravity (see B in Figure 12.18). Volcanic eruptions, earthquakes, forest fires, precipitation, and human activities can all act as triggers. Each year, landslides cause thousands of deaths and billions of dollars in property damage. They are becoming a greater threat to society because people are increasingly settling on less desirable, unstable slope areas. Added to this are the increased heavy precipitation events related to climate change.

Key Takeaways

- Earth's active geologic processes are capable of creating violent events such as earthquakes, tsunamis, volcanic eruptions, and landslides.
- Most earthquakes occur near the boundaries of adjoining tectonic plates. They can also be induced by mining.
- Volcanoes can be destructive, but they have many benefits, such as furnishing minerals.
- A landslide (the mass movement of rock, organic matter, and soil down a slope) can be triggered by an earthquake.

12.6 A Look to the Future: Revisiting Crater of Diamonds State Park

Learning Objective

1. Examine the opening case story about diamonds and the threads of this story throughout the chapter and recommend a logical pathway for the diamond industry toward sustainability.

Is mining in Crater of Diamonds State Park representative of the mining industry? What does the future of mining diamonds look like? Crater of Diamonds State Park is an anomaly for two reasons: it is a source of diamonds, and people may keep what they find. A lucky tourist need not expend much energy or time to extract a diamond, unlike at the Victor Mine in Northern Ontario. The Canadian mine is a $1 billion construction investment and requires a continuous sink of energy to maintain normal operations. Similar to other mining operations, the Victor Mine facility relies on energy to power massive machines that excavate and haul ore, and pumps to remove water (100,000 cubic meters per day) and prevent flooding.

As we learned from Section 5, the application of renewable energy technologies helps reduce air pollution, but this is a substantial financial investment incurred by the mining company. Therefore, sustainable mining of diamonds requires both a large source of energy and a huge financial investment. The company must also have the capacity to effectively and sustainably manage massive quantities of waste.

To obtain a single one-carat diamond, an average of 1,750 tons of earth must be extracted. From an ethical perspective—beyond our desire for a product—are the environmental, economic, and social costs of mining diamonds adequately justified? Are mined diamonds essential to present-day society? Diamonds are, but mined diamonds are not. Tracy Hall's production of the world's first synthetic diamond in 1954 changed the future of diamonds forever (Hall et al. 1955). Synthetic diamonds are commonly used in industry and make up the majority of the industrial diamond market. The same cannot be said for the gemstone industry. Over the last few decades, synthetic diamonds have grown in prominence and acceptance by society for jewelry too, but they make up only 2–3 percent of the diamond gemstone market. Looking to the future, millennials' and Generation Z's heightened environmental awareness and desire to save money will likely encourage retailers to sell more synthetic diamonds.

Does a shift to synthetic diamond production strike a win for Mother Nature? The diamond industry's 2019 report suggests that the production of lab-grown diamonds releases three times more greenhouse gases relative to mined diamonds (Trucost 2019). A full comparison would of course need to include habitat destruction, landscape scars, and generated waste. However, if the main negative feature of synthetic mining is carbon dioxide emissions, then increased reliance on renewable energies would point to synthetic diamonds as the more sustainable way of obtaining diamonds in the future. While you contemplate the ethics of whether to purchase a mined or synthetic diamond, why not plan a visit to Crater of Diamonds State Park? You may just walk away with a quality diamond of your own and have a memorable story to tell.

Key Takeaways

- Diamonds are useful to industries.
- If a diamond-mining company is to be environmentally sustainable, it must adopt sustainability practices, including the use of renewable energies.
- Increased acceptance by consumers of synthetic diamonds in jewelry will lessen demand of mined diamonds. It will be useful to examine the efficiency and best practices used in the manufacturing of synthetic diamonds to see how they consider and protect the environment.

FIGURE 12.19 Visual Overview: Geology and Mineral Resources
Summarizing figure: We live on a geologically active world (12.1) that furnishes useful and economically valuable substances (12.2). Obtaining these resources by mining have, unfortunately, created many environmental problems (12.3). Knowledge of the negative effects of mining encourages us to move toward sustainability (12.4), although we still have a long way to go. Earth's geologic processes can also be hazardous to human life (12.5). The future holds many promises and challenges for the mining industry, even for the diamond industry (12.6).

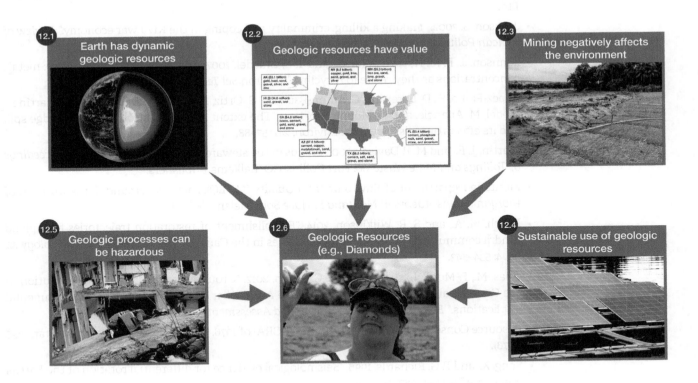

Sources: Joseph Shostell; See previous citations for image credits.

12.7 References

- Adiga, M. R. 2000. *Plating Waste Water Treatment and Metals Recovery System*. United States Patent.
- Barry, S. L. 2012. *Coming to the Surface: the Environment, Health, and Culture in Butte, Montana*. Doctoral dissertation. The University of Montana, Missoula, MT.
- Briggs, D. F. 2015. *Recovery of copper by solution mining methods. Arizona Geological Survey Contributed Report* CR-115-A.
- Ellsworth, W. L. 2013. "Injection-induced earthquakes." *Science* 341, no. 6142: 142.
- Enhancing Africa's Response to Transnational Organised Crime (ENACT). 2022. *Mining and illicit trading of coltan in the Democratic Republic of Congo*. Note, "organised" is the European form of "organized".
- Gautam, M., B. Pandey, and M. Agrawal. 2018. "Carbon footprint of aluminum production: emissions and mitigation." In: *Environmental Carbon Footprints Industrial Case Studies* (Ed.: Muthu, S. S.). Elsevier Inc., New York, NY.
- Hartmann, H. L., and J. M. Mutmansky. 2007. *Introductory Mining Engineering, Second Edition*. John Wiley and Sons, Inc. Hoboken, NJ.
- International Institute for Environment and Development. 2002. *Breaking New Ground Mining, Minerals, and Sustainable Development*. London and Sterling, VA: Earthscan Publications Ltd.
- Jackson, S. 2002. "Making a killing: criminality and coping in the Kivu war economy." *Review of African Political Economy* 29, no. 93–94: 517–536.
- Johnson, J., E. M. Harper, R. Lifset, and T. E. Graedel. 2007. "Dining at the periodic table: metals concentrations as they relate to recycling." *Environ Sci Technol* 41: 1759–1765.
- López-Pamo, E., D. Barettino, C. Antón-Pacheco, G. Ortiz, J. C. Arránz, J. C. Gumiel, B. Martínez-Pledel, M. Aparicio, and O. Mountouto. 1999. "The extent of the Aznalcóllar pyritic sludge spill and its effects on soils." *Sci. Total Environ.* 242: 57–88.
- Martin, T. E., and M. P. Davies. 2000. "Trends in the stewardship of tailings dam." In: *Proceedings of Tailings and Mine Waste '00*. Fort Collins, CO: Balkema Publishers.
- Montana Department of Environmental Quality (MDEQ). 2013. *Background Concentrations of Inorganic Constituents in Montana Surface Soils*. Helena, MT.
- Naeth, M. A., and S. R. Wilkinson. 2014. "Establishment of restoration trajectories for upland tundra communities on diamond mine wastes in the Canadian Arctic." *Restoration Ecology* 22, no. 4: 534–543.
- Olias, M., F. Moral, L. Galván, and J. C. Cerón. 2012. "Groundwater contamination evolution in the Guadiamar and Agrio aquifers after the Aznalcóllar spill: assessment and environmental implications." *Environmental Monitoring and Assessment* 184: 3629–3641.
- Resource Conservation and Recovery Act (RCRA) of 1976. Pub. L. No. 94–580, §2150, 90 Stat. 2795 (1976).
- Song, X., and P. G. Richards. 1996. "Seismological evidence for differential rotation of the Earth's inner core." *Nature* 382: 221–224.
- Toledano, P., and C. Roorda. 2014. *Leveraging Mining Investments in Water Infrastructure for Broad Economic Development: Models, Opportunities and Challenges*. Columbia Center on Sustainable Investment, Columbia University.
- Trucost. 2019. *The Socioeconomic and Environmental Impact of Large-Scale Diamond Mining*. Trucost ESG Analysis S&P Global.

- Tyabji, N., and W. Nelson. 2010. *Mitigating emissions from aluminum.* Columbia Climate Center Earth Institute, Columbia University.

- United Nations (UN) 2003. S/2003/1027.

- United States Geological Survey (USGS). 1998. *Effects of the 1994 Retsof Salt Mine collapse in the Genesee Valley.* New York: USGS.

- United States Geological Survey (USGS). 2020. *Mineral Commodity Summaries 2020.* United States Geological Survey. https://doi.org/10.3133/mcs2020.

- Van Sambeek, L. L. 1996. "Dissolution induced mine subsidence at the Retsof Salt Mine in solution mining." Research Institute Meeting Papers: Cleveland, Ohio, October 20–23, 1996. Pf 289–309.

- Verne, J. 1864. *Voyage au Centre de la Terre.* Paris, France: Pierre-Jules Hetzel.

- Waszek, L., J. Irving, and A. Deuss. 2011. "Reconciling the hemispherical structure of Earth's inner core with its super-rotation." *Nature Geoscience* 4: 264–267.

CHAPTER 13
Nonrenewable Energy Sources

Case Study: Deepwater Horizon

Petroleum (crude oil), a thick, unrefined liquid of **hydrocarbons** and other compounds, is the base material for manufacturing more than 6,000 products we use every day. Transportation fuels, tar, fertilizers, cosmetics, insecticides, soaps, and vitamin capsules all have humble beginnings as crude oil obtained from the ground. Contemporary society's economy relies, at least in part, on using, buying, and selling these petroleum products, which in turn drives our continual search for new sources of crude oil. Most certainly, we benefit from having a dependable source of fuel. Regrettably, not all news is positive when it comes to oil and other forms of fossil fuels. Sometimes the negative consequences accrue over years, decades, and centuries, whereas in other cases a catastrophe may occur in an instant.

Within a single year, the world experienced four large-scale oil-spill catastrophes in different regions of the world—off the coasts of Australia, the United States, Nigeria, and China. The largest and most memorable of these events, the *Deepwater Horizon* incident off the coast of Louisiana, was the world's worst marine environmental disaster regarding oil, second only to the intentional oil spill that occurred during the Gulf War in 1991, in the Persian Gulf (Atlas and Hazen 2011). On April 20, 2010, the semi-submersible oil rig *Deepwater Horizon*, owned by Transocean and leased by British Petroleum (BP), suffered an explosion. A failed blowout prevention system (BOP) allowed an influx of methane gas to reach the drilling rig, where it ignited (see Figure 13.1). In the initial explosion, 11 of the 126 people on the rig were tragically killed and another 17 injured. Once ignited, the methane gas continued to burn for thirty-six hours, while several emergency support vessels attempted to control the firestorm and the Coast Guard searched for survivors. During the second day, the drilling rig, already partially collapsed, sank and eventually settled on the ocean floor 1,500 m (≈ 4,900 ft) below the surface.

FIGURE 13.1

The *Deepwater Horizon* (DH) incident reminds us of the potential scale of oil disasters. (A) Emergency crews douse flames on the burning DH oil rig. (B) Location of DH in the Gulf of Mexico and extent of oil spill.

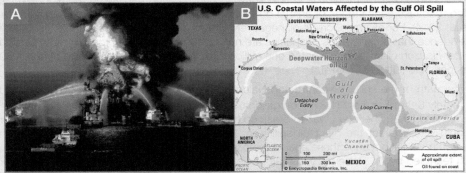

Source: U.S. Coast Guard; https://www.britannica.com/event/Deepwater-Horizon-oil-spill.

It was at this great depth that another problem was just beginning: the release of 7.9–11.1 million liters (2.1–2.9 million gallons) per day of crude oil into the Gulf of Mexico (McNutt et al. 2012). BP and its partner company Halliburton attempted to contain the leak by sealing the well, but they were unsuccessful for five months. By that time, an estimated 780 million liters (206 million gallons) of crude oil had been released (Spier et al. 2013). During the entire time, the oil dispersed through deep-sea currents, blanketed benthic (bottom) areas, floated to the surface, and contaminated large sections of the southern U.S. coastline. As the oil spread more widely,

---

petroleum (crude oil)

A thick, unrefined liquid of long-chain hydrocarbons and other compounds; a fossil fuel.

hydrocarbons

Molecules that consist of chains or rings of carbon atoms, with hydrogen atoms attached to the carbons.

it threatened an ever-increasing number of ecosystems and habitats, and eventually covered at least 112,110 km^2 of open ocean. Unfortunately, oil reached over 1,000 km (621 mi) of sensitive coastal wetlands within the Mississippi River Delta, where one-third of the nation's fish production occurs (Mendelssohn et al. 2012). These wetland areas are still attempting to recover to this day, over a decade after the accident. Oiling degrades soil quality, and it directly kills foundational marsh grass species such as *Spartina alterniflora*, and indirectly, the invertebrate fauna they support (see A in Figure 13.2). Akin to the trees of a forest, marsh grasses maintain a number of services for the broader community and ecosystem, and their presence is essential for a great number of species. They slow the flow of water, which helps to increase sediment settling. Marsh grass species also provide shelter and offer a source of food. We expect healthy marsh areas to teem with *Manayunkia aestarina*, a polychaete worm, but the taxon is scarce in oiled areas where grasses have died. Without basal prey species, the predatory community of crabs, shrimp, and fish crashes and biodiversity plummets. Oiling also disrupts community structure and biodiversity by covering and killing benthic microalgae—the main food and source of energy for many invertebrate species, including *M. aestuarina* (Fleeger et al. 2019, Galván et al. 2011). Fish are also adversely affected when oil emulsions stick to their gills, reducing their capacity to obtain essential oxygen.

FIGURE 13.2
The wide-ranging effects of the *Deepwater Horizon* oil spill. (A) BP consultants and the National Oceanic and Atmospheric Administration's (NOAA) Natural Resources Damage Assessment Team check for oil in marsh sediments. (B) An oiled and critically endangered Kemp's ridley sea turtle (*Lepidochelys kempii*) is prepared for cleaning. (C) A C-130 aircraft drops an oil-dispersing chemical in the Gulf of Mexico.

Sources: NOAA; U.S. Air Force photo/Tech. Sgt. Adrian Cadiz

Long-term and even short-term exposure to crude oil is harmful to almost all species. Beyond crude oil's sticky consistency and tendency to adhere to wings, membranes, and other body structures, it contains carcinogenic volatile organic compounds (VOCs) and polycyclic aromatic hydrocarbons (PAHs) (see B in Figure 13.2). Not only is the environment contaminated by these chemicals, but so too are cleanup crews, who experience nausea, difficulty breathing, headaches, and dizziness (Suárez 2005). A chief concern after the *Deepwater Horizon* accident was the exposure of fish embryos in critical spawning and rearing habitats in the Northern Gulf of Mexico, because early stages of animal development are extremely sensitive to toxins (Incardona et al. 2014). For example, crude oil negatively affects the developing hearts of fish. There is strong evidence that other groups of species are negatively affected by oil too. In the case of the *Deepwater Horizon* oil spill, an estimated one million birds (Haney et al. 2014a, 2014b) and 1,000 dolphins perished (Litz et al. 2014).

In the aftermath of the spill, BP contracted Nalco Holding Company to synthesize and provide approximately 6.8 million liters (1.8 million gallons) of Corexit oil dispersants (9527A® and 9500®) (see C in Figure 13.2). The intent was to break up the oil into droplets for more rapid degradation, and hopefully to prevent the giant oil spill from washing ashore. However, use of oil dispersants is controversial because these agents expose already suffering aquatic life to new toxins. A research team led by Dr. Roberto Rico-Martínez of Avenida Universidad demonstrated that toxicity to aquatic life can increase fifty-two-fold when Corexit 9500 mixes with oil (Rico-Martínez et al. 2012). Other toxicology laboratories, including Dr. Sylvain De Guise's at the University of Connecticut, provided critical and informative data about the negative effects of Corexit on aquatic life. Dr. De Guise's research group tested the toxicity of the dispersant on oyster reefs, and found the chemical to be more detrimental to oysters than oil (Jasperse et al. 2018).

Cleanup costs for this large-scale catastrophe are exorbitant, with BP taking on the brunt of the expenses, from cleanup costs to fines. Legal fees alone within the United States are estimated at $680 million. To date, the ultimate cost to BP is almost $145 billion (Lee et al. 2018), which does not include ongoing litigation in Mexico. Companies Halliburton and Transocean each reached settlements of slightly over $1 billion. Never before, nor since, has the United States faced such an enormous threat from an oil spill. The *Deepwater Horizon* incident called for a monumental response of 47,000 people, 120 aircraft, and over 6,400 vessels. It is the only spill to qualify as a Spill of National Significance (USCG 2010).

The *Deepwater Horizon* incident provides an example of the potential negative effects that our choices regarding energy—including source, method of extraction, and use—can have on the environment. In this chapter, we assess the world's nonrenewable energy sources, considering their distribution, use, and environmental effects. As you proceed through the material, consider your own energy use, where you receive this energy, and the positives and negatives of relying on different nonrenewable energy sources to meet your (and the world's) energy demands.

13.1 Overview of Nonrenewable Energy Resources

Learning Objectives

1. Identify and describe the primary nonrenewable energy resources society depends upon.
2. Comprehend how we measure energy.
3. Assess the value of calculating an Energy Return on Investment (EROI).
4. Summarize society's energy consumption.

Among all living things, humans stand apart in our addiction to energy—well beyond what our individual bodies require. Although we are intelligent and understand our need to access free ecosystem services such as clean air, clean water, and healthy soil, we seem oblivious to the environmental destruction our choices regarding energy use have caused. Many of the environmental issues we discuss in this book, including acid rain (see Chapter 11), rapid climate change (see Chapter 11), eutrophication (see Chapter 10), and acid mine drainage (see Chapter 12), are the result of our energy consumption and reliance on fossil fuels in the form of oil, natural gas, and coal. However, do not be misguided into thinking that **fossil fuels**—organic fuels derived from prehistoric plants and animals that died millions of years ago—are the only energy sources that cause environmental problems. For example, nuclear energy has great potential, but its associated mining activities leave behind barren landscapes, and its use creates radioactive waste that has to be safely contained for tens of thousands of years.

fossil fuels

Nonrenewable organic fuels (i.e., coal, petroleum, and natural gas) derived from plants and animals that died millions of years ago and were gradually buried by layers of rock.

In order to meet the increasing demands for energy by a growing population (see Chapter 6), we have, in the opinion of many environmental scientists, become careless. Look no further than our opening story of the *Deepwater Horizon* incident, which caused the environmental degradation of a large section of the Gulf of Mexico. The event had serious ramifications for the fishing industry and other industries, as well as on the economies of states such as Louisiana that had crude oil splash up on their coastlines. Sad but true, energy-related accidents are becoming the norm, albeit most are on a smaller scale, at least individually, than the *Deepwater Horizon* tragedy.

Just as some choices might lead to environmental disasters and destruction of ecosystem services—clear signs of nonsustainability—other choices can lead to sustainability. As you contemplate the issues of our nonrenewable energy use, consider that there are pros and cons to every energy source. In this first section, we review sources of energy, how to measure energy, and energy consumption. Later sections discuss specific nonrenewable energies in detail.

What Are the Sources of Society's Energy?

Globally, current society's greatest sources of energy are oil, coal, and natural gas, together totaling 80 percent (see A in Figure 13.3). The remainder consists of biofuels and waste (trash-to-energy) (9.5 percent), nuclear (5 percent), and renewables.

FIGURE 13.3
A breakdown of global society's sources of energy (A). (B) We divide energy sources into two broad categories: nonrenewable and renewable.

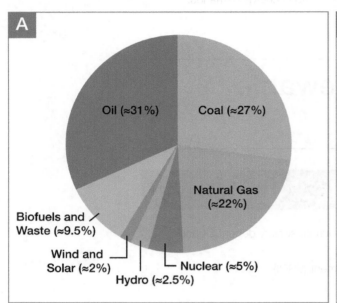

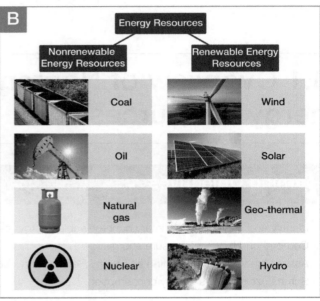

Sources: Joseph Shostell; Data from IEA World Energy Balances 2019, https://iea.blob.core.windows.net/assets/fffa1b7d-b0c5-4e64-86aa-5c9421832d73/WORLDBAL_ Documentation.pdf; © Shutterstock, Inc.

nonrenewable energies

Energy fuels (coal, petroleum, natural gas, uranium) society uses faster than their natural replenishing rate.

renewable energies

Energy fuels replenished naturally faster than we utilize them.

Based on replenishing rates relative to societal use, we classify energy sources into two categories: nonrenewable and renewable (see B in Figure 13.3). **Nonrenewable energies** are utilized faster than their natural replenishing rate and include the fossil fuels—oil, coal, natural gas, as well as nuclear energy, a nonfossil fuel. On the other hand, **renewable energies** are replenished naturally, faster than we utilize them. Wind, solar, hydroelectric, and geothermal all fall into this second category (see Chapter 14). They too can negatively affect ecosystems and wildlife, although on a smaller and different scale than nonrenewables.

Nonrenewable energy reserves are unevenly distributed globally. Like nonenergy geologic reserves (see Chapter 12), they originate in the ground and are extracted through various methods of mining. Scan Figure 13.4 and note the location of major deposits of oil, coal, natural gas, and uranium. We seek out and extract these primary resources from the ground because of their potential energy (see Chapter 2) and our ability to transform them into a useable form of energy such as electricity. In the following section, we discuss these energy transformations and energy units.

FIGURE 13.4
Coal, oil, natural gas, and uranium are distributed unevenly across the world. A small number of countries have the vast majority of reserves. Symbols on the world map indicate those geographical areas with the greatest reserves. Values are relative percentages of total world reserves for a given resource.

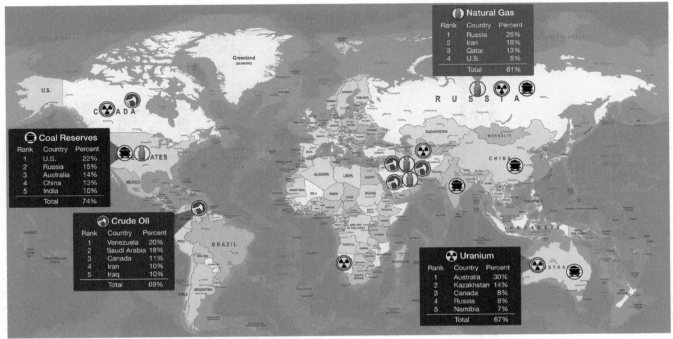

Sources: © Shutterstock, Inc.; data from EIA, https://bit.ly/3eHvxXO.

How Do We Measure Energy?

According to the U.S. Energy Information Administration, American families pay an average of $115 per month on electricity, and individually we spend roughly $3.40 per gallon of gasoline—more in some states and less in others. To be sure, energy use comes with a price tag, and the more we use, the more we pay. For convenience and fairness, we have developed a system of energy units meaningful to the consumer, seller, and the energy industry. Regrettably, at the time of purchase, consumers only receive a small fraction of the potential energy originally found within a mined resource. As we discuss here—following a recap of energy units—a large portion of energy is lost from a system before reaching the consumer (see Chapter 3).

Energy Units

Units of measurement help us to effectively and accurately describe things that we use. There are two commonly used energy units, the joule and the British thermal unit. These units are useful when we want to describe how much energy is stored in an ore, how much energy is lost during transformation, or how much energy individuals use on a monthly basis (see Figure 13.5).

FIGURE 13.5

We describe energy usage with units of energy such as the joule and British thermal unit (Btu). For example, a 60-watt light bulb uses 60 joules per second. If left on all day (24 hours), this bulb would consume 5.2 million joules (5.2 megajoules).

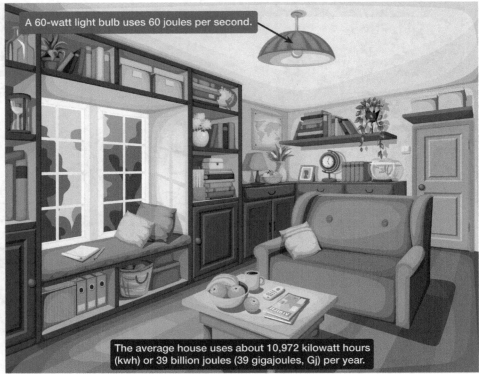

A 60-watt light bulb uses 60 joules per second.

The average house uses about 10,972 kilowatt hours (kwh) or 39 billion joules (39 gigajoules, Gj) per year.

Sources: Joseph Shostell; © Shutterstock, Inc.; data from EIA, https://www.acmeelectricalservices.com/blog/electrical-repairs-tampa-fl#:~:text=According to the U.S. Energy,it until you need repairs.

British thermal unit

Equal to approximately 1,055 joules; originally defined as the amount of energy needed to warm one pound of water by one degree Fahrenheit.

uranium

A radioactive chemical element that is used to power nuclear reactors; it has an atomic number of 92.

Having standards of measurement that are accepted and used by all companies and countries is very useful, especially today, a time of heavy international trade. Originally, standard units such as the meter, gram, liter, and joule were developed so that people knew what they were buying. It also provided a way for consumers to confirm they were being treated fairly. By using standard units and converting each form of energy into the same unit (British thermal unit or joule), we can compare the energy content of different energy sources. In doing so, we can then decide, for example, whether it is more economical to use natural gas or coal as our source of energy. One **British thermal unit** (Btu) is equal to approximately 1,055 joules and was originally defined as the amount of energy needed to warm one pound of water by one degree Fahrenheit. What is quickly discernable is the great energy richness of **uranium** compared to other commonly used forms of energy (see Figure 13.6). Of course, decisions about energy use should be based on more than just energy density. Accessibility of an energy source, transport, economics, potential pollution, and remediation costs are also considered.

FIGURE 13.6

Uranium has a higher energy density than other nonrenewable sources of energy. One uranium fuel pellet (about the size of a thimble) can yield about the same amount of energy as one ton of coal, 481 cubic meters (629 cubic yd) of natural gas, or 564 liters (149 gal) of crude oil.

One uranium fuel pellet (about the size of your finger tip) = 481 m³ (17,000 ft³) of natural gas = One ton of coal = 564 L (149 gal) of crude oil

Sources: Joseph Shostell; © Shutterstock, Inc.; data from https://www.nei.org/fundamentals/nuclear-fuel#:~:text=Uranium.

Energy Transformations

The electrical energy used to power the lights and electric machines in our homes was not always electrical energy. We obtain natural sources of energy—primary sources of energy—such as coal and petroleum from the environment and then transform them into electrical energy and other forms of energy we need. A large percentage of the potential energy within nonrenewable primary energy sources is lost to the surrounding environment as heat and never delivered to the end user—the consumer (see Figure 13.7). The loss is due to the inefficiency of power plants that generate the electricity and the inefficiencies of transmission lines (power lines) that transport and distribute electricity from the power plants to our homes. An estimated 62–74 percent of the potential energy contained in coal, natural gas, or nuclear fuel is lost in the generation, transportation, and distribution of electricity before a person even switches a light on in their house (see "Bringing It Closer to Home: Which Light Bulb Best Conserves Energy?"). Additionally, a significant fraction of the electrical energy (electricity) that arrives at your house—for example, to be able to turn your lights on—is not converted into light, and instead is lost, again as heat. Because energy is lost with each energy transformation, one way to reduce energy loss is to reduce the total number of transformations between a primary energy source and the form of energy the consumer uses (see Chapter 3).

Bringing It Closer to Home: Which Light Bulb Best Conserves Energy?

One of the quickest and easiest ways to conserve energy and reduce an energy bill is to switch from incandescent and compact fluorescent bulbs (CFBs) to light-emitting diode (LED) bulbs. **Incandescent light bulbs** (ILBs) lose approximately 95 percent of their energy as heat because they are based on an outdated technology created by Thomas Edison back in 1879 that relies on a filament of metal's becoming hot enough to glow (Gayral 2016). On the other hand, the 75 percent more energy-efficient **fluorescent light bulbs** use a different technology that uses argon and mercury gases. When energized, these gases cause a substance called phosphor that lines the bulb to glow. Slightly more expensive, **light-emitting diodes** (LED) require even less energy (90 percent less) than an incandescent bulb, contain no hazardous mercury, and last up to twenty-five times longer. The U.S. Department of Energy compared the life cycles of the three types of lamps and found the LED to be the least environmentally harmful (USDOE 2012). Their analysis included manufacturing, use, and disposal. Based on their findings, LED lightbulbs are the most environmentally friendly choice. What type of light bulbs are in your residence? Incandescent? CFB? LED? No matter whether you have opted for LEDs, all of us will make the change to LED bulbs eventually. Under the Energy Independence and Security Act (EISA) of 2007, it is now illegal to sell most incandescent bulbs. The change went into effect January 1, 2020. When Americans fully adopt an energy efficient electricity policy, which includes using their stockpiles of bulbs and exchanging their incandescent light bulbs for LED bulbs, we will have significantly reduced our annual energy use. All we have to do is swap out our light bulbs.

incandescent light bulbs

These inefficient bulbs lose approximately 95 percent of their energy as heat because they are based on an outdated technology.

fluorescent light bulbs

A bulb that uses fluorescence to produce visible light.

light-emitting diodes

Energy-efficient light bulb; requires 90 percent less energy input than an incandescent bulb.

FIGURE 13.7

Very little of the energy stored in coal, oil, natural gas, and uranium reaches consumers. Much is lost in the generation, transport, and distribution of electricity before a consumer even turns a light on in their house. More is lost by the light bulb during the conversion of electricity to light, with efficiency depending on the type of light bulb used.

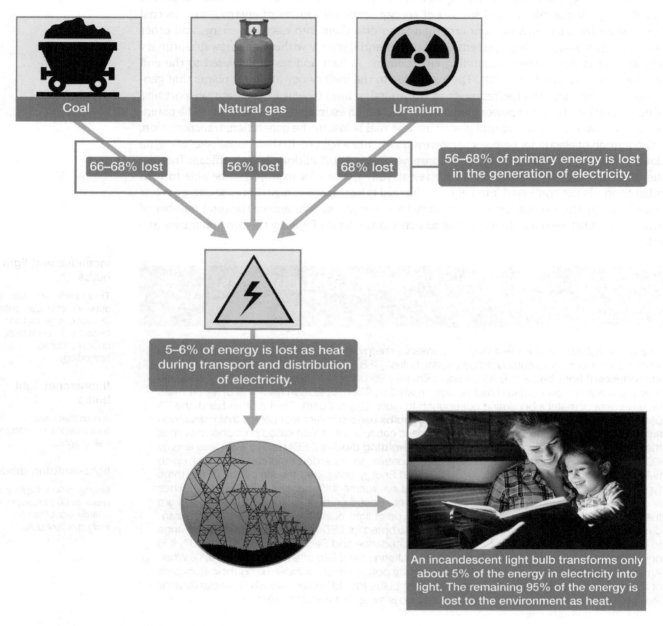

Coal

Natural gas

Uranium

66–68% lost   56% lost   68% lost

56–68% of primary energy is lost in the generation of electricity.

5–6% of energy is lost as heat during transport and distribution of electricity.

An incandescent light bulb transforms only about 5% of the energy in electricity into light. The remaining 95% of the energy is lost to the environment as heat.

Sources: Joseph Shostell; © Shutterstock, Inc.; data from EIA, https://www.eia.gov/tools/faqs/faq.php?id=105&t=3.

Unlike coal, natural gas, and uranium, most crude oil (about 70 percent of it) is used for transportation. Oil supports the nation's 255 million cars and light trucks that Americans use to drive three trillion plus miles each year. Crude oil is transported to a refinery where it is heated and separated into gasoline and other products via fractional distillation. About 45–48 percent of the crude oil is converted to gasoline. How much of the potential energy in gasoline translates into usable energy for the driver who wishes their car to move? As with other sources of energy, transformations between forms of energy results in the loss of large percentages of energy. In the end, only a small fraction of the energy (12–30 percent) of gasoline is transformed into mechanical energy that moves the car forward (see Figure 13.8). The greatest losses are due to the low efficiency rate (28–32 percent) of the internal combustion engine.

FIGURE 13.8

Today's gasoline-powered cars are more efficient than ever, but a large percentage of fuel energy is still lost—not transformed into mechanical energy that moves a car forward. Depending on car type, model, and age, 70–88 percent of the energy is lost in various forms, but the engine is always the greatest source of loss.

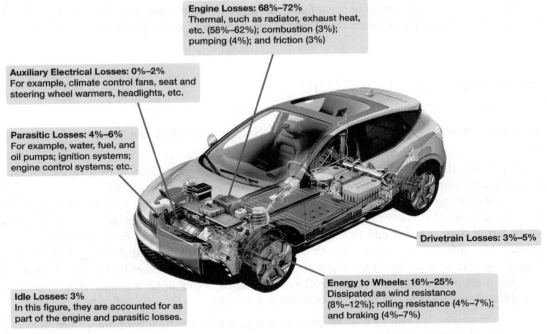

Engine Losses: 68%–72%
Thermal, such as radiator, exhaust heat, etc. (58%–62%); combustion (3%); pumping (4%); and friction (3%)

Auxiliary Electrical Losses: 0%–2%
For example, climate control fans, seat and steering wheel warmers, headlights, etc.

Parasitic Losses: 4%–6%
For example, water, fuel, and oil pumps; ignition systems; engine control systems; etc.

Drivetrain Losses: 3%–5%

Idle Losses: 3%
In this figure, they are accounted for as part of the engine and parasitic losses.

Energy to Wheels: 16%–25%
Dissipated as wind resistance (8%–12%); rolling resistance (4%–7%); and braking (4%–7%)

Sources: Based on data from the U.S. Department of Energy, https://www.fueleconomy.gov/feg/atv.shtml; © Shutterstock, Inc.

Net Energy

It takes energy to explore, extract, transport, and process an energy source. **Net energy** takes these energy investments into account. Net energy is the amount of energy generated from an energy source minus the energy investments to generate that energy. The comparison of energy return to energy invested is often expressed as the **Energy Return on Investment** (EROI), which is a ratio of the amount of energy generated divided by the amount of energy invested to produce the energy. For example, if it takes six units of energy to produce ten units of energy, then the ratio would be ten divided by six or 1.67:1. The higher the ratio, the larger the net energy; when the ratio is less than 1, there is a net energy loss. Once an EROI of a fuel is calculated, it can be compared with EROIs of other fuels. This is valuable information because it helps companies to determine the fuel type that provides them with the best return for their investment.

The EROI values of fuels are not only different from each other, but they can also change over time. For example, the EROI for coal was much higher in the past, when deposits were more plentiful, of higher quality, and easier to access (Hall and Cleveland 1981; Cleveland 1992). In the United States, the EROI values for coal have dropped from above 100:1 in the early 1900s, to 70:1 in the mid-1980s, to roughly 30:1 today, and will continue to decline as deposits become more scarce and the quality of the deposits diminish. Coal is an example of a finite resource that we have already begun to exhaust. Similar to coal, the EROIs for oil and gas have also decreased over time. These EROIs have declined from 100:1 in the 1930s, to 30:1 in the 1990s, to less than 20:1 today—in some cases less than 10:1 in areas where deposits are almost exhausted (Cleveland 2005, Murphy and Hall 2011). Calculated values of EROI for nuclear are higher than for coal, oil, or gas, although not all studies agree with this assessment (Weißbach et al. 2013). A nation's, state's, or company's decision about whether to opt for a particular energy source considers factors beyond initial energy investments and EROI. Factors that may affect choice of nuclear energy over other fuels, for example, include plant longevity, decommissioning, long-term storage of radioactive materials, and accidents such as what transpired at Fukushima, Japan, in 2011.

net energy

The energy available to the consumer after accounting for energy lost due to exploration, extraction, transportation, and processing.

Energy Return on Investment

A ratio of the quantity of energy supplied to the quantity of energy invested to exploit the energy resource.

EROIs drop when they adequately represent the environmental impacts of mining, refining, and other facets of energy production (Salehi et al. 2020). There are also the environmental costs of using the energy on the consumer end. Inclusion of environmental costs and remediation of polluted areas further reduce EROIs of nonrenewable sources of energy. For example, the energy, resources, and finances needed to solve fossil fuel-driven climate change is incalculably large. By 2100, flooding from rising waters will cost $14 trillion worldwide annually. Who will cover this cost?

Energy Consumption

Every year, our energy consumption increases. Globally, we consumed over 600 quadrillion Btus in 2019.

Obviously, the demand for energy must be great because countries and companies continue to invest large sums of money to explore, extract, process, and transport energy sources. For example, in the opening story, British Petroleum paid up to $1 million per day to lease the *Deepwater Horizon*, and invested many millions of dollars in associated drilling and personnel costs before a single barrel of oil was brought to the surface. Furthermore, the demand for primary energy—in this case fossil fuels—is great enough that we continue to access the same energy sources even though we continue to have tragic environmental disasters. Do not forget that British Petroleum has also spent billions of dollars in mitigation costs related to this single accident. Why do we seek out these energy sources and place the environment at risk?

Countries seek out energy sources because energy is linked to quality of life, government stability, and military power. Without a constant supply of energy, our society would revert to a state similar to that of our ancient ancestors. Imagine a life with no self-propelled cars and no electricity to support refrigerators, cell phones, and the countless other electrical gadgets we find useful in our lives. A high standard of living—a condition that most inhabitants in the United States and other industrialized countries enjoy—depends on having enough energy to power it: to light and heat our homes, power our cars, treat wastewater, produce agricultural products, and so on.

Up to this point, we have identified the four main nonrenewable energy sources, energy units, transformations—some of which are very inefficient—and reasons why society uses energy. Next, we cover the pros and cons of each of these nonrenewable energies.

Key Takeaways

- We classify energy sources into two categories: nonrenewable and renewable.
- Coal, oil, natural gas, and uranium are examples of nonrenewable energy resources because we use them faster than they are naturally replenished.
- Standardization and comparisons are the main goals of having units of measurement. For energy, we rely on units such as the joule and British thermal unit (Btu).
- Much of the potential energy in primary energy sources such as coal is lost as heat in the generation, transportation, and distribution of electricity.
- The Energy Return on Investment (EROI) is the amount of useful energy divided by the amount of energy invested to generate this useful energy. We use EROI to rank fuel types.
- The EROIs of energy are different from each other and change over time (i.e., the EROI for coal is lower today than it was thirty years ago).

13.2 Coal, the Pros and Cons

Learning Objectives

1. Identify the pros and cons of using coal as a source of energy.
2. Describe the distribution of coal and the conditions in which it forms.
3. Discuss and comprehend the value of coal to industries, residential homes, and the economy.
4. Explore and acknowledge the negative effects of coal use on the environment.
5. Identify methods we have used to lessen the negative effects of coal.

How should we summarize our 3,000-year history with coal? Should we say it gave us warmth and therefore sheltered us from the cold, or was it a source of our environmental grief, or something else? In this section, we look into the formation and distribution of coal, its benefits and drawbacks as a fuel source, and strategies to lessen coal's environmental impacts (see "The History and Future of Coal").

 The History and Future of Coal

Watch this documentary about the history and future of coal use.

View in the online reader

What Is Coal?

Coal is a combustible, carbon-rich, black to brownish-black sedimentary rock. Chemically, it consists of mostly carbon, smaller concentrations of nitrogen, hydrogen, oxygen, and sulfur, and a number of trace elements, including mercury and fourteen other hazardous substances. The quality of coal as an energy resource improves with higher carbon content. The jet-black coal called anthracite is the highest grade, with a carbon content of 85–98 percent. Coal is also a relic of the past, and is all that remains of swampy forests that lived hundreds of millions of years ago.

coal

A combustible, carbon-rich, black to brownish-black sedimentary rock; an example of a fossil fuel.

peat

A precursor to coal; spongy material consisting of layers of partially decomposed plants. Forms in acidic, low-oxygen wetlands.

The remains of these plants accumulated faster than they decomposed, forming many layers of partially decayed plant material referred to as **peat**. Under the right geologic conditions, peats are buried and then subjected to high temperature and pressure over millions of years. The peats are compacted, hardened, chemically altered, and metamorphosed into coal (see Figure 13.9).

FIGURE 13.9

Coal formation. Dead vegetation accumulates and is covered by layers of sediments. Over millions of years, high temperature and pressure transform the dead plant matter into coal.

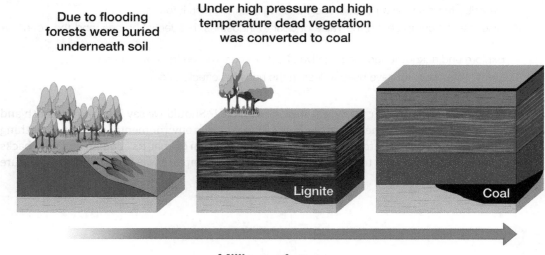

Source: © Shutterstock, Inc.

Distribution of Coal Reserves

Coal is located on every continent, but is neither distributed evenly, nor mined and produced equally across nations (see A in Figure 13.10). Approximately 95 percent of all coal reserves are located in three regions of the world—North America, Europe/Eurasia, and the Asia-Pacific. This means that a large part of the world, including South America, Central America, the Middle East, and Africa, only has a combined total of around 5 percent. Countries in these coal-scarce regions cannot depend on coal as a significant source of energy unless they import it. The United States has the largest reserves of coal of any country in the world, holding approximately 22 percent of the world's total deposits.

FIGURE 13.10
Use of coal. (A) Global production of coal by nation (histogram) and percentage of coal production in United States by state (pie graph). Coal use has benefits and drawbacks. (B) On the positive side, energy in coal can be transformed into needed electricity; however, acid drainage from coal mines (C) degrades the environment, so it diminishes ecosystem goods and services.

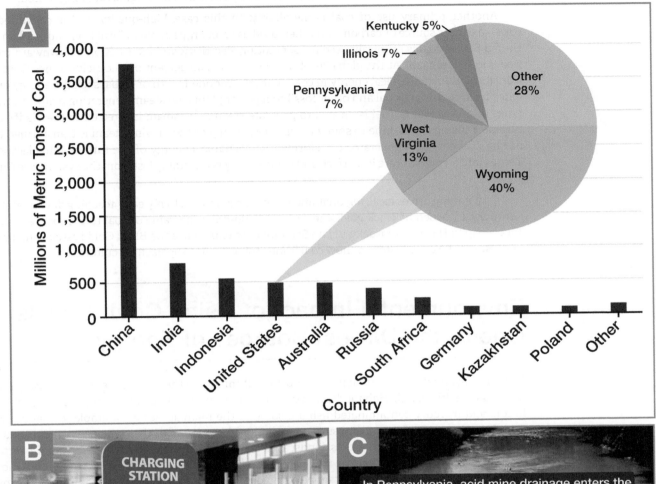

Sources: Joseph Shostell; data from Enerdata, https://yearbook.enerdata.net/coal-lignite/coal-production-data.html and WIA, https://www.eia.gov/tools/faqs/faq.php?id=69&t=2; © Shutterstock, Inc.; EPA, https://19january2017snapshot.epa.gov/sites/production/files/styles/large/public/2016-09/pa_conemaugh_before_and_after_0.jpg.

Benefits of Using Coal

Humans have long recognized the value of coal as a reliable and useful form of energy, initially just as a source of heat to warm themselves, their dwellings, and their food. Reminiscent of these first coal users, poor rural areas of the world (over 400 million people) still use coal today as their primary source of energy for cooking and heating (UNDP and WHO 2009). Not until the late 1600s and Thomas Savery's steam engine did people recognize the even greater versatility of coal. By the early 1800s, coal-fueled steamships were typical on the seas and engineers had developed the first steam locomotives for transport on land. Today, most coal-powered steam engines are long retired.

Another primary use of coal is metallurgy. In this case, high-quality coal is converted to coke—a denser source of carbon—and then used as an energy source to form iron and steel. In the United States, coal is primarily used for generating electricity, and its use is on a downward trend (see B in Figure 13.10). At the global level, a little less than 40 percent of electricity comes from the transformation of chemical energy in coal. In total, over one-fourth of global society's energy originates from coal. Many coal and other fossil fuel power plants are steam-generating plants. In these types of power plants, fuel is burned to generate steam. The steam is directed to the blades of a turbine, causing the turbine to spin. At this stage, energy of the moving steam is transformed into mechanical energy. A generator transforms the mechanical energy of the turbine into electricity. These transformations are imperfect, and some energy is inevitably lost from the system (see Chapter 2).

Coal mining drives local, regional, and national economies. In my early teaching days in eastern Kentucky, I learned of black gold, a term used to describe the value of coal to the local economy. Take a trip to Hazard, Kentucky, in late September to experience the Black Gold Festival and better understand the deep history of how coal is intertwined with Appalachian culture.

Environmental Impact of Using Coal: Coal Is One of the Dirtiest Sources of Energy

Coal mining and coal combustion pose substantial threats to the environment, and consequently to human health as well. Habitat degradation, acid mine drainage, climate change, acid rain, air pollution, and mercury-contaminated fish are some of the many issues attributable to coal use (see C in Figure 13.10). Surface and subsurface coal mines have many of the same negative impacts. At the more visible surface-mine sites, landscapes are scarred by deforestation, removal of overburden, and strip mining (see Chapter 12). The extremely destructive process of mountaintop removal has obliterated hundreds of mountain peaks across Appalachia. Discarded wastes have buried over 3,200 km (2,000 mi) of the once pristine and biodiverse headwater streams of the Mississippi River (EPA 2010). These were some of the most biodiverse streams in the entire United States.

Coal production and use have significant impacts on the quantity and quality of freshwater. Every kilogram (2.2 lbs) of coal consumed to meet our energy needs requires the use of about 77 liters (20 gal) of water (Pimental et al. 1982). Water is used to extract and wash coal, at times to transport coal, and to cool thermoelectric plants, 30 percent of which are coal. Water is also used to manage coal dust and to cool cutting equipment used in mines. In addition to lowering water quantity, coal mining also affects water quality. Effluent from active and abandoned coal mines is typically highly acidic and rich in toxic heavy metals (Hyman and Watzlaf 1997). Water from these mines drains into adjoining streams and rivers, where it can kill aquatic life and devastate biodiversity. High concentrations of dissolved iron in effluent from subsurface mines present a double threat to species. It is lethal to aquatic life in dissolved form (at high concentrations), and also lethal when exposed to oxygen and chemically converted to a precipitate. The yellow-orange precipitate blankets the bottom of streams and suffocates aquatic life for tens of kilometers downstream of a coal mine (see Figure 10.16).

Coal use is a significant source of greenhouse gases. Burning coal accounts for one-fourth of energy-related carbon dioxide emissions in the United States, and is a driving factor of climate change (see Chapter 11) (see Figure 13.11).

FIGURE 13.11

In 2019 and 2020, an unprecedented number of large bushfires burned for months across Australia. Drier conditions and more severe fires are indirect—but expected—effects of the increasing concentrations of greenhouse gases in the atmosphere that are driving rapid climate change. (A) Distribution of massive bushfires in Australia that billowed smoke to New Zealand. (B) Unlike the billion mammals and birds that perished in these fires, this lucky koala bear was saved.

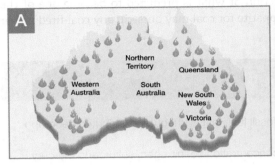

Source: © Shutterstock, Inc.

Coal combustion leads to acid rain formation (see Chapter 11). Sulfur dioxide (SO_2) and nitrogen oxides (NO_x) released into the atmosphere chemically react with water vapor to form sulfuric acid and nitric acid, respectively. They lower the pH of the water vapor, which ends up precipitating as acid rain onto terrestrial and aquatic ecosystems, where it can harm forest and fish communities (see Figure 11.17).

Burning coal to generate electricity creates dry ash waste, very similar to a charcoal grill. In the case of the grill, there are a couple of scoops of coal ash, far less than the 100 million tons produced every year in the United States alone. Half of this coal ash is recycled into concrete, wallboard, bricks, and roofing materials, but the remainder ends up in landfills, ponds, lakes, and other sites. Our coal use is also a source of toxic heavy metals. More than half of all anthropogenic emissions of mercury comes from society's use of coal. Mercury now contaminates food webs of our oceans and freshwater systems.

How Can We Make Coal Use More Environmentally Friendly?

Well-managed, law-abiding coal-mining companies and coal-fired power plants tightly adhere to current environmental legislative laws. Dust and water runoff must be controlled, and the site restored to its original habitat or returned to another beneficial end use. The Clean Air Act (CAA) Amendments of 1970 set the stage for air-quality control in the United States. It gives authority to the Environmental Protection Agency (EPA) to set, review, and revise national ambient air-quality standards for six criteria pollutants, including sulfur dioxide and nitrogen oxides, and to regulate 187 hazardous air pollutants, including mercury (see Chapter 11).

Air quality has significantly improved since the 1970s. Newer power plants and older retrofitted power plants have flue gas desulfurization equipment—"scrubbers"—that remove sulfur before it leaves a smokestack. Scrubbers can also capture mercury, particulate matter, and nitrogen oxides, further reducing the negative effects of coal combustion. Clearly, we have made progress in making coal more environmentally friendly, but coal is still a significant source of air and water pollutants. Why? Smokestack scrubbers are not 100 percent effective, and not all coal-fired power plants have scrubbers. In addition, coal power plants continue to be one of the largest sources of carbon dioxide emissions. Carbon capture and sequestration (CCS) is minimally available now, but not widely tested nor incorporated nationwide or globally.

The best way to reduce pollution from coal use is to burn less coal, and to remediate thousands of abandoned mines scattered across the United States. At the international level, Spain and England are examples of countries phasing out coal mining completely as a means to reduce carbon dioxide emissions and limit global temperature increase. In contrast, in defiance of the Paris Agreement, China is scheduled to open hundreds of new coal-fired power plants, and the Australian government has recently approved the construction of what is predicted to become one of the world's largest coal mines. At this rate, China's appetite for coal may outstrip any coal-fired power plant closures elsewhere in the world.

Key Takeaways

- Coal is a nonrenewable source of energy (a fossil fuel) that is unequally distributed geographically.
- Coal is carbon rich but also contains small concentrations of nitrogen, sulfur, and mercury.
- Humans have long recognized the value of coal as a reliable and useful form of energy. Today, the coal industry supports tens of thousands of jobs in the United States alone and boosts regional, state, and national economies.
- Coal mining and coal combustion pose substantial threats to the environment, and consequently to human health. Acid mine drainage and air pollution are examples of some of the many issues attributed to coal use.
- To lessen pollution from coal we should abide by environmental legislative laws and carefully manage dust and water runoff from active coal mines, burn less coal, and remediate abandoned mines.

13.3 Oil, the Pros and Cons

Learning Objectives

1. Compare and contrast the pros and cons of oil use.
2. Describe the process of oil formation.
3. Give an accounting of Earth's oil reserves: where they exist and the types.
4. Analyze an average person's (you) dependence on petroleum-based products and provide multiple examples.
5. Identify the negative effects of oil use on the environment.
6. Be aware of current strategies to make oil use more environmentally friendly.

The *Deepwater Horizon* accident (opening story) affected many types of oceanic species. Dolphins, fish, turtles, and sea birds struggling in oil gave us all pause to consider their plight and the seriousness of the incident. A number of research studies since the incident occurred also point out the long-term effects of oil on the Mississippi River Delta and Gulf of Mexico ecosystems (Lichtveld et al. 2016, Rohal et al. 2020).

What Is Oil?

Oil forms from accumulated and subsequently covered organic matter in the oceans. Upon death, algae, bacteria, and other aquatic creatures are either taken up into the food web or settle to the ocean bottom. The molecules that compose these organic remains consist mainly of carbon and hydrogen. In time, the remains are covered by many layers of organic debris coming from the water column above. Over tens to hundreds of millions of years, high pressure and heat convert the organic matter into oil. Contrary to common thought, oil does not exist in vast underground lakes or pools. The oil itself is unobservable with the naked eye, because it exists as tiny droplets in pore spaces of sedimentary rocks. Once a well is drilled, underground pressure drives the oil up the well to the surface. To maintain this pressure, water, gas, or steam is often injected into the "reservoir" of oil. Just where are the world's oil reserves?

Deposits of crude oil are unevenly distributed globally. The Middle East contains nearly 50 percent of Earth's oil reserves. Venezuela, the country with the largest oil reserves (20 percent of the total), along with Middle Eastern countries, parts of Africa (Libya, Algeria, Angola, and Nigeria), and Ecuador make up the **Organization of the Petroleum Exporting Countries** (OPEC). OPEC countries help to provide a regular supply of oil to other countries that utilize oil but do not have sufficient reserves to meet their consumption rates. Close to 80 percent of all oil reserves are in OPEC countries. Similar to coal and natural gas, the size of a country's oil reserve does not necessarily match its contribution to global production. For example, the United States and Russia are first and third in the world for oil production, yet neither country ranks in the top five in oil reserves. Within the United States, five states, led by Texas, produce close to 70 percent of U.S. oil.

Organization of the Petroleum Exporting Countries

An organization of countries with a majority control of the global oil market. They help to provide a regular supply of oil to other countries.

Deepwater Sources of Oil

With advances in technology, we are accessing more oil and gas deposits underneath our oceans. The infamous Macondo well (opening story) extended 1,524 meters (5,000 ft) below the *Deepwater Horizon* to the bottom of the ocean, and an additional 4,054 m (13,300 ft) into the ocean floor (Wassel 2012). Advances in drilling and production make it possible to drill at twice this depth with great expense—hundreds of millions of dollars. Decisions about investments into rigid platforms mounted on the seafloor or floating rigs are based on exhaustive exploration. Ten years may pass between initial seismic exploration, test drilling, and extraction of the first barrel of oil. Total offshore U.S. oil production exceeds 600 million barrels per year (AGI 2018). Offshore production of oil accounts for roughly 29 percent of total oil global production.

Tar Sands

A general outcry for additional oil to meet energy demand has encouraged mining of low-quality sources called tar sands or oil sands. **Tar sand oil** is a mixture of sand, clay, bitumen, and water. The target resource is the bitumen, a thick, black, sticky mix of hydrocarbons. It is dirtier and more expensive to mine than conventional oil. There are two general methods to extract tar sand: strip mining for deposits close to the surface, and injection of high-pressure steam for deeper deposits. In the latter method, steam loosens the target hydrocarbons—the bitumen—and they flow up the well to the surface. Mining and processing of bitumen is controversial because of its large carbon and water footprints relative to conventional oil. Currently about 5 percent of the oil used in the United States is imported through the Keystone Pipeline from tar sands in Alberta, Canada, the world's largest known reserve of this oil source.

tar sand oil

A low-quality source of oil consisting of a mixture of sand, clay, bitumen, and water.

There Are Benefits of Using Oil, but They Are Hard to Justify

Oil does provide many benefits to society, the most obvious being a source of fuel for transportation. One barrel of crude oil yields approximately 72 L (19 gal) of gasoline (see Figure 13.12). Once extracted from the ground, crude oil is sent to a refinery where it is cleaned and separated into a variety of fuel and chemical products. Heating oil, diesel fuel, and jet fuel are some examples. In addition, chemical substances (petrochemicals) from petroleum are used to make a host of products, including plastics, pesticides, rubber, dishwashing liquids, ammonia, deodorant, and crayons.

FIGURE 13.12

In 2020, the United States consumed 6.6 billion barrels of oil (EIA, 2021). One barrel is 159 liters, or 42 gallons. (A) Before use, the oil is extracted from the ground, refined by distillation, and the finished products are transported to consumers. (B) Most of the oil used in the United States is produced domestically, but 11 percent is imported, mainly from Canada. (C) Products made from crude oil (EIA).

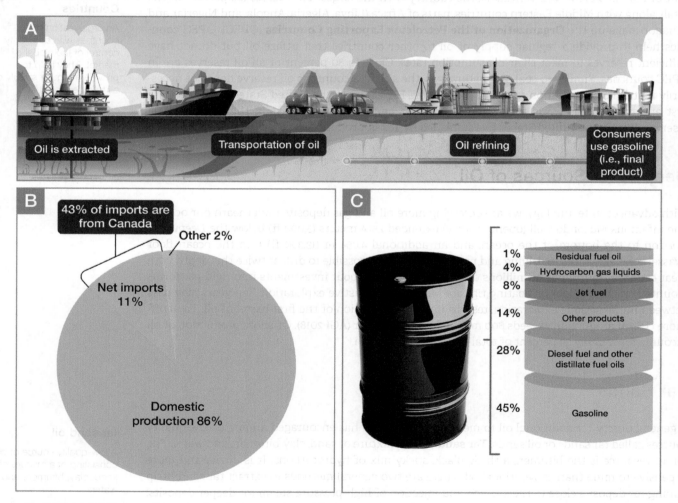

Sources: Joseph Shostell; © Shutterstock, Inc.; data from EIA, https://www.eia.gov/energyexplained/oil-and-petroleum-products/where-our-oil-comes-from.php and EIA, https://www.eia.gov/energyexplained/oil-and-petroleum-products/imports-and-exports.php; data from EIA, https://www.eia.gov/energyexplained/oil-and-petroleum-products/.

Petroleum's broad usefulness as a source of fuel and chemicals for a great number of industries means that oil-producing nations have great economic power. Just in the United States, the oil and natural gas industries support over ten million jobs and infuse more than $1.3 trillion into the economy. The oil industry is so well integrated with downstream industries and linked to products available on shelves that just about every person in modern society benefits from the existence of petroleum. Most assuredly, the pertinent question isn't if you benefit, but whether the benefit comes with a price of environmental degradation? Suppress the urge to ask the seemingly similar but meaningless question, "Is the benefit greater than the environmental damage?" (See video link: "ANWR".)

🎥 **ANWR**

Listen to reporter Tegan Hanlon of Alaska Public Media discussing the controversy of drilling for oil in the Alaska National Wildlife Refuge.

View in the online reader

Environmental Impact of Using Oil

Oil use has many of the same environmental issues as coal use: carbon dioxide emissions linked to rapid climate change, nitrogen oxides and sulfur dioxide linked to acid rain, and water pollution, in addition to other ones. Maybe the most obvious additional one is that oil is a liquid, and oil-mining companies sometimes have trouble preventing it from spilling into the environment. In the *Deepwater Horizon* incident (opening story), 780 million liters (206 million gal) of crude oil leaked from a broken well into the Gulf of Mexico, killing an untold number fish, dolphins, birds, zooplankton, and algae. Over a decade later, the Gulf of Mexico ecosystem has still not fully recovered. This was the largest accidental oil spill in the history of the oil industry, and brought the issue to the public's attention, but oil spills are routine.

After extraction (see Figure 13.13), crude oil is transported to a refinery for cleaning and separation into a series of useful products. All stages of transport such as carrying oil on tanker ships and moving oil through pipelines have the potential for failure, with the consequence of oil spillage. I tend to agree with my colleague who said, "Oil and an 800-pound gorilla have something in common: Neither of them can be contained indefinitely, and when they get out, they go wherever they want."

FIGURE 13.13

After extraction, crude oil is sent to a refinery for cleaning and separation by distillation. Note the distillation tower and the petroleum products coming from the tower.

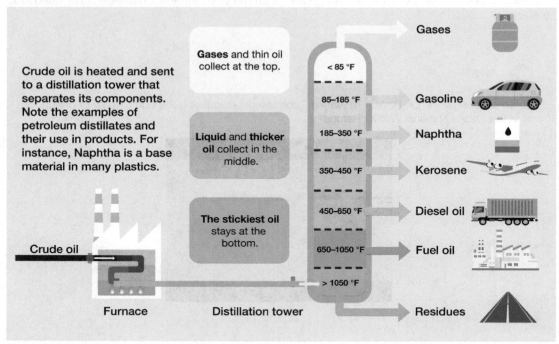

Source: © Shutterstock, Inc.

The extraction and refining of oil depend on a supply of water. Common methods of oil mining call for injecting high-pressure steam or liquid water underground into an oil reservoir. These injections help to maintain the underground pressure needed to drive the oil to the well and up to the surface. Any water that flows back to the surface from the oil well contains a mixture of arsenic, mercury, and many other hazardous substances (Wollin et al. 2020). One of the key challenges of using large volumes of water to obtain oil is managing the wastewaters so that they do not contaminate natural water resources. Much of the controversy over mining tar sands in Alberta, Canada, centers on the construction of large tailings ponds to contain the contaminated wastewater (Tenenbaum 2009). Extraction and refining of tar sands requires three times more water than conventional oil, and by law the contaminated water may not be released into the environment. On average, two to four barrels of water are required to process every barrel of oil (Foote 2012). Try as they might to contain these wastewaters, Canada's Environmental Defence reports that tar sands' tailings ponds leak an estimated 11 million liters (2.9 million gal) of contaminated water into surrounding groundwater every day (ED 2008). This agency's upper estimate, given continued development of tar sands, is over 72 million liters (19 million gal) of wastewater lost per day.

Now return to the hundreds of petroleum-based products: countless plastic toys, plastic bottles, basketballs, golf balls, bicycle tires, nail polish, nylon clothes, trash bags, etc. All these have a short "cradle to grave" life. They end up in landfills and in the broader environment where they degrade aquatic and terrestrial ecosystems. Plastics, especially microplastics, are ingested by fish and wildlife and become parts of food webs. Toxic petrochemicals leach out of the plastics and move into the organisms that ingest them, disrupting the organism's physiology and increasing their morbidity. Any perceived benefits of using conventional plastic products up front are later recognized for what they are: short sighted and wasteful.

Critical Thinking Activity: To Drill or Not to Drill in the Arctic National Wildlife Refuge

About 60 percent of the oil the United States consumes is imported. In a time of political instability and pending oil shortage, some suggest it is time to drill for oil in a 1.5 million-acre section of Alaska's Arctic National Wildlife Refuge (ANWR). Why should the United States finance other countries when we have untapped "pools" of oil here? These are some of the opinions American proponents of drilling express about ANWR's oil. Opponents of the drilling explain how ANWR's position in the northeast corner of Alaska represents one of the last pristine ecosystems of the United States, and the small volume of oil there wouldn't sustain the United States very long anyway. Are either of these points of view valid? Take a closer look into ANWR and the oil market and come to your own conclusion.

How Can We Make Oil Use More Environmentally Friendly?

Oil is a finite, dirty source of energy that we depend on. These realities encourage countries to steadily wean themselves off of oil and replace it with cleaner sources of energy. Large oil companies, including BP and Royal Dutch Shell, are now preparing for this future and investing in natural gas, a much lower-carbon energy source. Natural gas burns more cleanly than oil, so it releases less carbon dioxide. Still other companies, such as the French energy giant Total, are widely investing in renewables (see Chapter 14).

Short of a complete transition to an alternate fuel type, what immediate steps can be taken to make oil use more environmentally friendly? One obvious way is to enact methods that reduce the chance of spills and pipeline leaks. In reviewing the actions that led to the *Exxon Valdez* oil spill off the coast of Alaska in 1989, investigators determined that the ship's radar system wasn't functional—and hadn't been for more than a year. Apparently, the *Exxon Valdez* departed from port without a thorough Coast Guard inspection. One year after the spill and consequent loss of 40 percent of the sea otter population in Prince William Sound, Congress passed the Oil Pollution Act of 1990 to enable the EPA to prevent and respond to catastrophic oils spills. New legislation also followed the *Deepwater Horizon* explosion. President Obama's administration implemented tighter regulations to prevent similar tragedies in the future.

There are also ways to lessen the contribution of oil to carbon dioxide emissions and smog production. For example, driving less often, using smaller cars, and improving mass transportation systems all reduce overall oil-related emissions of carbon dioxide, nitric oxides, and sulfur dioxide.

Oil companies can choose to protect natural water resources by improving the efficiency of water recycling, which reduces overall need for water withdrawn from local rivers. In tar sand operations, tailings ponds are usually considered essential sources of water, but tailings ponds come with risks. After mine closure, these tailings ponds need to be reclaimed. In 2010, the tar sands industry in Canada completed reclamation of its first tailings pond. Reclamation of a tailings pond involves setting up a drainage system, replacing soil, revegetation, and establishing a long-term monitoring program.

What about the many nonfuel cradle-to-grave products developed from petroleum? Most, but not all, of these hundreds of products have nonpetroleum alternatives. It takes time for companies to conduct research to determine viable solutions. For example, Albus Golf, Ltd., based in Barcelona, Spain, recently developed the first biodegradable golf ball: the EcoBioBall, which does not contain petroleum plastic and completely degrades in water within forty-eight hours. Plastic from fermented plant starch is now available too, to replace petroleum plastic plates, cups, and utensils.

Key Takeaways

- Oil is a nonrenewable fuel (a fossil fuel). It is unevenly distributed globally.
- Oil does provide many benefits, the most obvious being a source of fuel for transportation. Moreover, petroleum is used as a raw ingredient in the formation of a host of commonly used products.
- Oil use is the origin of many environmental issues: oil spills, carbon dioxide emissions linked to climate change, nitrous oxide and sulfur dioxide linked to acid rain, water pollution, water withdrawals, and accumulation of cradle-to-grave products in the environment.
- We can make oil use more environmentally friendly with technologies aimed at reducing oil spills and pipeline leaks, and by enacting and enforcing environmental protection laws. The best way to prevent oil pollution is to switch to an alternative, renewable source of energy and stop using oil.

13.4 Natural Gas, the Pros and Cons

Learning Objectives

1. Understand the structure of natural gas, how it forms, and the distribution of natural gas fields.
2. Appreciate the value of natural gas as a source of energy.
3. Contemplate and understand the limitations of natural gas as a source of energy.
4. Recognize how natural gas production and use cause the release of chemicals harmful to humans and the environment.
5. Identify measures including available green technologies to help protect the environment from natural gas production and use.

Charlie Clark of Pennsylvania considers himself a lucky man. As a dairy farmer and family man, he was always financially strapped, that is until Chief Oil and Gas approached him about drilling a natural gas well on his property. Today the Clarks earn royalties in the amount of $10,000 per month, and they recently built a new barn without borrowing a cent from the bank.

What Is Natural Gas?

natural gas

A plentiful fuel source consisting of a mixture of short-chain flammable gases, but predominantly methane.

Natural gas is a plentiful fuel source consisting of a mixture of small-sized flammable gases. Methane (CH_4) is the most abundant and smallest hydrocarbon molecule in this mixture. Methane's molecular structure hints at the pros and cons of relying on natural gas as a source of energy. On the one hand, the higher the hydrogen-to-carbon ratio, the higher the energy efficiency of a fuel. Methane has a higher hydrogen-to-carbon ratio (four hydrogens to one carbon) relative to other fuels and therefore has a higher energy efficiency and fewer carbon dioxide emissions when it is combusted. In other words, burning one kilogram of methane produces more energy than burning one kilogram of octane. Less of it is necessary to produce the same amount of energy, so less carbon is released. On the other hand, carbon is part of methane, and therefore burning methane releases carbon dioxide into the atmosphere.

Natural gas and oil are formed under somewhat similar conditions and therefore are frequently found together. We can trace the formation of natural gas back millions to hundreds of millions of years ago to vibrant marine plant and animal communities, now long since perished. The remains of these organisms, covered with sediments and subjected to higher temperatures and pressures, changed chemically and physically over time.

About 80 percent of the natural gas fields economically feasible for mining are located in just ten countries. The largest one is a 3,626 km² (1,400 mi²) deposit underneath the coastal waters of Iran. By country, Russia has the largest reserves because it possesses multiple large gas fields. Within the United States, Texas has the greatest natural gas reserves, followed by Pennsylvania (where the Clarkes live), Oklahoma, Louisiana, and Ohio. Observe the national network of pipes in the natural gas distribution system displayed in Figure 13.14. There are clear hot-spot areas like Texas where there is dense blue.

FIGURE 13.14
Natural gas use is becoming increasingly common. (A) A bus fuels up at a natural gas fueling station. (B) Looking a little different from the more common gasoline nozzle, a natural gas line is connected to a car. (C) The natural gas distribution system in the contiguous states.

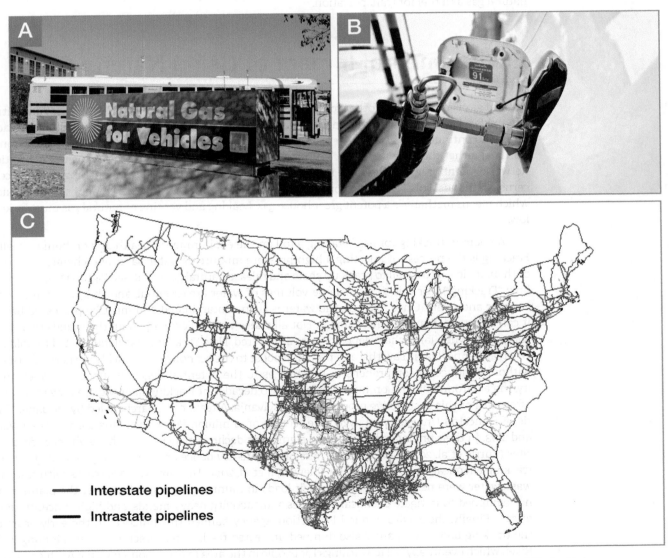

— Interstate pipelines

— Intrastate pipelines

Sources: Michael Vi/Shutterstock.com; © Shutterstock, Inc.; U.S. Department of Energy, https://afdc.energy.gov/fuels/natural_gas_distribution.html.

Benefits of Using Natural Gas: It Is Cleaner than Either Coal or Oil

Natural gas is the cleanest fossil fuel, cleaner than coal and petroleum. Natural gas produces about 43 percent less carbon dioxide compared to coal and 30 percent less than oil (Casper 2010). Fewer impurities exist in natural gas too. It produces a tiny fraction (<0.1 percent) of the sulfur dioxide and only about 20 percent of the nitrogen oxides. Natural gas emits an inconsequential amount of mercury and a tiny fraction of particulate matter (<0.3 percent) compared to coal.

These advantages, plus a plentiful supply, present natural gas as a desirable source of energy. The natural gas industry continues to grow each year. About 32 percent of our energy in the United States comes from natural gas, and worldwide, about 24 percent. We transform it into electricity (about 33 percent of our electricity), use it to heat stoves and outdoor grills, and, similar to oil, use natural gas as a raw material for a variety of products. Less known and less frequently, we also use natural gas as a fuel for transportation.

Environmental Impact of Using Natural Gas

Natural gas is greener than other fossil fuels, but it is still a source of greenhouse gases and nitrogen oxides. Even if we substitute natural gas for every other fossil fuel, global warming and acid rain will continue, just at a slower rate. Because of this, natural gas is seen as more of a transition fuel rather than the final step. Unintentional leaks from pipes in the methane transportation network, intentional venting from storage tanks, and losses from wells are ongoing and real concerns. Methane's global warming potential is about thirty times greater than that of carbon dioxide, which means methane is a potent greenhouse gas. Leaking and venting of natural gas must be kept low.

A boom in fracking for gas is taking a toll on the environment's health and on human health. Fracking is the process of injecting a high-pressure mixture of water, sand, and chemicals—many of them toxic—into a well to break up shale and release natural gas or oil (see Figure 13.15) (see video link: "Fracking"). For this to work, large volumes of water are essential, and this is taxing to local streams and rivers. Once injected, the water is then contaminated and must be processed before it can be returned to the environment. Not all states were quick to open up their lands to drilling companies when large shale deposits were discovered. New York and Maryland elected to hold off, whereas Pennsylvania saw this as a potential boost to the economy and quickly authorized drilling without conducting comprehensive research as to the potential negative effects on water quality, the environment, and on human health. Two decades of fracking later, we are now seeing the aftermath of this destructive process in Pennsylvania. A team of researchers led by Dr. Janet Currie of Princeton University analyzed the records of 1.1 million Pennsylvanians born between 2004 and 2013. In their findings, they reported significant declines in average birth weight near fracking sites (Currie et al. 2017). Other researchers highlighted evidence of poor drilling-well integrity and fracking chemicals in drinking water (Llewellyn et al. 2014). Up through 2016, trucks with fracking wastewater were permitted to empty their loads in municipal sewage plants, yet the plants were not equipped to mitigate chemical additives, radioactivity, heavy metals, and high concentrations of salt. Finally, the Environmental Protection Agency banned this practice. In the early years of the fracking boom, companies also dumped untreated frack water directly into the Monongahela River, which eventually led to warnings for people in the area to drink bottled water. As this practice became unlawful, some fracking companies resorted to dumping untreated wastewater at night to save costs. The burden of the harmful effects of fracking wastewater will fall on local communities, the health-care industry, and the environment for years to come. Fracking is also responsible for earthquakes up to a magnitude of 4.0, which can cause property damage and endanger lives.

FIGURE 13.15

In fracking, toxic chemicals, water, and sand are injected thousands of meters into the ground to obtain natural gas. (A) Water acquisition for the mining and (B) wastewater from the mining threaten water resources.

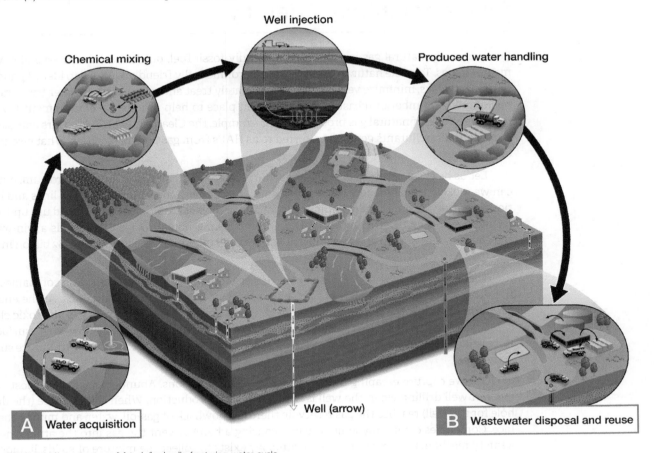

Well injection

Chemical mixing

Produced water handling

Well (arrow)

| A | Water acquisition |

| B | Wastewater disposal and reuse |

Source: EPA, https://www.epa.gov/hfstudy/hydraulic-fracturing-water-cycle.

Fracking

What is fracking?

HOW DOES FRACKING WORK?

View in the online reader

How Can We Make Natural Gas Use More Environmentally Friendly?

Comparatively, natural gas is the most ecofriendly fossil fuel, but its use causes several environmental issues. To make natural gas use more environmentally friendly, we need to identify and stop natural gas leaks, minimize venting, and appropriately treat and manage wastewater from fracking operations. A number of measures are already in place to help protect the environment from the negative effects of natural gas production. For example, the Clean Air Act (CAA) covers emissions of hazardous air pollutants generally referred to as HAPs from gas and oil facilities. What else can we do?

Let us be clear, natural gas is a cleaner source of energy than either coal or petroleum, but how can we make it even greener? For starters, emissions of methane from leaks in gas lines and intentional venting must be kept to a minimum. At almost no net cost, the industry could use up-to-date technology to significantly (by 40–80 percent) reduce methane leakage. Doing so is a win-win for the environment and for the gas industry, which could potentially recoup another $2 billion in profits.

There are new innovative methods to detect methane leaks from pipes. Gas companies now use drones, planes, and satellites to detect gas leaks in large distribution systems. At the end of a gas or oil well's life, the site undergoes remediation to prevent future leaks of gas and toxic chemicals to the surface. Cement is pumped into the well, effectively blocking any flow to the surface. In terrestrial areas, the wellhead is severed below the surface so as to not interfere with future surface activities.

Can we capture escaping methane? Yes, in some situations. Abundant methane is lost at the stage of well drilling when the well is nearly ready for production. When the wellbore (the drilled hole for the well) reaches the gas reservoir, there is a flowback of gas, oil, water, and mud to the surface. Companies commonly ignite the gas (causing a flare) or vent the gas into the atmosphere as a safety mechanism. However, green technology exists to collect the mixture of solids, liquids, and gases and then separate out the gas and send it to a sales pipeline for consumer consumption. The equipment for this is portable because this particular way to capture methane only occurs at the beginning of the life of a gas or oil well. As of January 1, 2015, the EPA required all natural gas fracking operators to capture emissions coming directly from wells. The change in legislation potentially prevents the release of 1.9 billion cubic meters (68 Bcf) of methane each year.

There are other sources of methane besides the natural gas industry. Landfills and sewage plants are two of these sources. We can capture methane released from landfills and water sewage plants by adding methane recovery systems. At landfill sites, suction pipes are inserted into holes drilled through the layers of refuse to the bottom. Vacuum suction directs the gas to a central location for processing. Landfill operators partner with power stations to transform the methane into electricity. In Vancouver, landfills have used this strategy to reduce greenhouse gas emissions by 33 percent compared to 1990 levels.

Some of the greatest challenges to making natural gas more environmentally friendly have to do with water. A vast amount of freshwater is needed in hydraulic fracturing, and large amounts of wastewater are produced. Therefore, the strategy is to use water efficiently. One recommended practice is to recycle wastewater and use the wastewater as a source of fracking water. Any produced wastewaters that are not recycled are often injected into the ground for long-term storage or appropriately treated and managed at the surface. Storing wastewater deep underground or managing wastewater on the surface are problematic and can still harm ecosystems. The best option to reduce the negative effects of using natural gas as a source of fuel is to switch to a renewable source of energy.

Key Takeaways

- Natural gas is unevenly distributed globally and is mostly methane.
- Natural gas is plentiful, and it is cleaner than other fossil fuels.
- Natural gas use releases greenhouse gases and nitrogen oxides—pollutants linked to climate change and acid rain. Natural gas mining (fracking) needs large volumes of water and produces large amounts of wastewater.
- Examples of measures to help protect the environment from the negative effects of society's natural gas use include detecting and stopping methane leaks, green technology to collect vented methane at natural gas wells, and the Clean Air Act that covers emissions of hazardous air pollutants from gas facilities.

13.5 Nuclear Energy, the Pros and Cons

Learning Objectives

1. Compare and contrast the value of nuclear energy with that of fossil fuels.
2. Demonstrate an understanding of the distribution of uranium deposits and society's dependence on nuclear energy.
3. Explain how nuclear reactors work.
4. Reflect on the benefits of nuclear energy to society.
5. Identify the risks of mining uranium and conducting fission reactions.
6. Provide solutions to the negative environmental effects of nuclear energy use.

For the last six decades, uranium has been a reliable but controversial source of energy. We give it high marks as a high-energy-density fuel with practically no carbon emissions when used in a nuclear reactor to generate electricity. At the same time, we cannot forget disturbing images of Russians fleeing from the Chernobyl disaster in 1986, which resulted in the immediate evacuation of over 100,000 people and eventual relocation of 340,000 (Elbaradei 2008). Nor can we erase the image of a tsunami slamming into Fukushima, Japan, in 2011, or dismiss the resulting loss of power that caused the nuclear reactor to melt down. In this section, we compare the pros and cons of using nuclear energy.

What Is Uranium?

Uranium ore is the raw source of nuclear energy. It is an abundant and natural resource with an unequal geographical distribution and broad range of concentrations across deposits. Some twenty countries operate uranium mines, but a small collective of four countries produces most of the world's uranium (see Figure 13.16). Australia is the clear leader, with 30 percent of the total, followed distantly by Canada (8 percent), Russia (8 percent), and Namibia (7 percent). The United States, with 1 percent, is twentieth. Ironically, the top holder of uranium reserves (Australia) doesn't have a single nuclear power plant. All of Australia's uranium is exported to the United States, India, Europe,

Japan, South Korea, and China, save for a small amount used for nuclear medicine. The United States has the largest number of nuclear reactors in the world, a total of 98 out of about 450 worldwide.

About one in five homes in the United States receives electrical power from nuclear power plants. Your home city may be near one of the sixty locations of commercially operating power plants scattered across thirty U.S. states (see "Bringing It Closer to Home: Is There a Nuclear Power Plant Near My Home?"). Comparatively, France's current energy policy strongly supports nuclear energy. About three out of every four residences in France receives electricity from a nuclear power plant.

Bringing It Closer to Home: Is There a Nuclear Power Plant Near My Home?

There are five dozen commercial nuclear power plants in the United States. Is one located in the city where you live? If so, how close is it to your home? Some U.S. states have several nuclear reactors, and others have none. Go to the United States Nuclear Regulatory Commission's nuclear facility locator here. The web address directs you to an interactive map of the United States that identifies each nuclear power plant. Hover your cursor over or click on any of the icons to find out more information. As you can tell, almost all of the nuclear power plants are located in the eastern half of the United States.

How Do Nuclear Reactors Work?

Nuclear power plants are not so different from fossil fuel power plants. Rather than combusting coal or natural gas, a nuclear power plant uses a fission reaction to heat water. The fission reaction begins when uranium atoms are bombarded with neutrons. When the nucleus of a uranium atom absorbs a neutron, it becomes unstable and splits immediately, releasing heat and radiation in the process (see Figure 13.16). Products of uranium decay go on to split more uranium atoms in a chain reaction. This is why control is necessary and why reactors can melt down.

The fission reaction occurs in a containment vessel lined with several feet of concrete and metal to prevent the release of radiation outside the fission area. Workers at the nuclear power plant control the fission reaction, and indirectly the heat of a reactor's core, by inserting control rods to absorb neutrons, and by the existence of a cooling system.

FIGURE 13.16
Nuclear energy. (A) Nuclear chain reactions (fissions) generate heat. (B) In a nuclear power plant, heat released by controlled nuclear fission reactions is used to produce steam, which, in turn, drives an electricity-generating turbine.

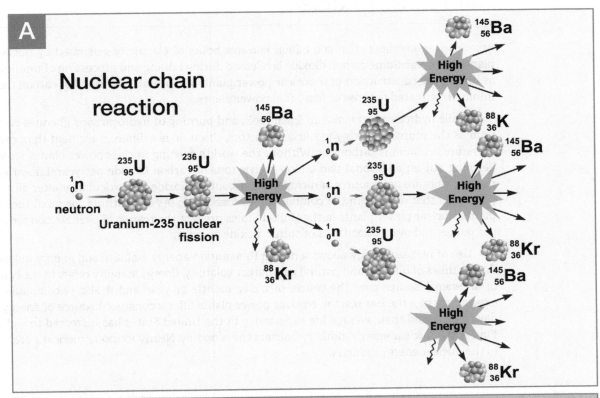

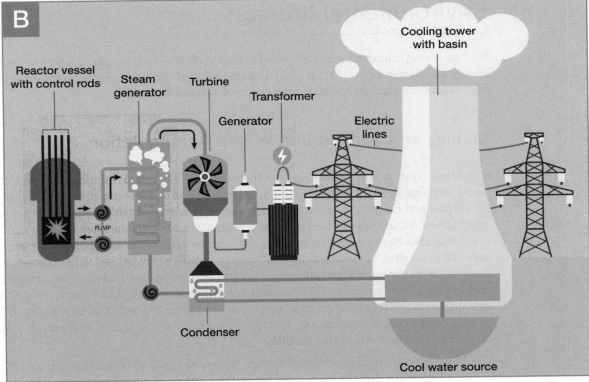

Benefits of Using Nuclear Energy: Cleaner than Fossil Fuels

Americans enjoy more than 800 billion kilowatt hours of electricity generated by nuclear power plants each year. Some carbon dioxide is released during mining and processing of uranium as well as during the construction of a nuclear power plant, but, overall, emissions of carbon dioxide are minimal compared to those of fossil fuel power plants.

While hydrocarbons make up fossil fuels, and burning of hydrocarbons liberates carbon, uranium is the source of energy in nuclear reactors. Uranium is a different element than carbon and therefore uranium is carbonless. Without the world's existing nuclear power plants, we would be belching out an additional two billion metric tons of carbon dioxide per year. Likewise, nuclear power plants are not a source of nitrogen oxides, sulfur dioxide, or particulate matter, all significant pollutants that arise from the combustion of fossil fuels. As a substitute for fossil fuel–powered plants, nuclear power plants in the United States prevent the release of over 286,000 tons of nitrogen oxides and over 346,000 tons of sulfur dioxide per year.

Use of nuclear energy allows a nation to maintain energy stability and energy independence during times of oil, coal, and natural gas market volatility. Energy stability refers to the consistency of an energy source over the course of a day, month, or year; and it also encompasses the life expectancy of a nuclear reactor. Nuclear power plants offer a consistent source of energy 24-7, 365 days a year, and their average life expectancy in the United States has increased to eighty years. Finally, the nuclear energy industry bolsters the economy. Nearly 100,000 Americans are employed in the nuclear energy industry.

Environmental Impact

Nuclear energy comes with its own set of pollution risks. A decision about whether to use nuclear energy should come after there is a full understanding of the negative effects of mining, processing, and transporting uranium, fission reactions, and radioactive waste.

Mining for Uranium and Waste Accumulation

half-life

The amount of time it takes for half of a radioactive sample to decay.

All nuclear reactors require uranium as a fuel source. The hundreds of nuclear reactors around the world consume about 67,000 tons of uranium per year, and this is obtained from conventional open-pit surface and deep mines as well as leach mines. Low-grade uranium mines are very similar to other mines in that they produce hazardous wastes typical of all mines (see Chapter 12). High-grade uranium mines have a higher concentration of uranium in the ore and are a greater source of radiation. At these sites, dust suppression and remote handling may be used to help protect the miners from radiation exposure. Uranium itself is only weakly radioactive, making it relatively safe to work with. Most of the radioactivity originates from uranium's radioactive decay products such as radium and radon that have accumulated in the ore since it formed. It takes about 4.5 billion years for half of a sample of uranium 238, the most common form of uranium (>99 percent) to decay. This amount of time is uranium 238's **half-life**.

The uranium ore is ground and treated with acid to separate out the uranium by leaching. Whatever does not dissolve becomes tailings. Next, the uranium solution is purified and dried to form a concentrated uranium powder called yellowcake. The uranium ore is then chemically converted to uranium hexafluoride (UF6) gas and placed in a centrifuge cylinder and rotated at a high speed. Centrifugal force causes heavier molecules (those that contain uranium-238) to move to the sides of the cylinder. Lighter molecules (those that contain uranium-235) stay closer to the center of the cylinder. The gas in the middle of the cylinder is collected and moved to another centrifuge cylinder, and the process is repeated. By this centrifugation process, the concentration of uranium-235 is then increased (enriched) from its natural concentration in ore of 0.7 percent to between 3 percent and 5 percent.

Finally, uranium fuel rods are created for use in a nuclear reactor. The enriched uranium is converted to a powder and pressed into fuel pellets. These pellets are inserted into hollow tubes to form the fuel rods. The rods last for about 1.5 years; when spent, they are stored in a circulating water system on the reactor site. The term "spent" is a misnomer because the rods will remain dangerously radioactive for thousands of years. Opponents of nuclear energy state that it is unethical and unreasonable to hand off radioactive wastes generated today to generations in the distant future. Over the course of nuclear energy use, the United States has accumulated over 88,000 tons of nuclear waste, which is now stored at eighty sites in thirty-five states (see Figure 13.17). Where is the safest place to store radioactive waste? To date, Americans cannot agree on a long-term repository site for accumulated radioactive waste.

FIGURE 13.17
Nuclear energy is seen as a clean source of energy, but it presents serious environmental and health issues as well. Here are the storage sites of spent and highly radioactive uranium fuel rods.

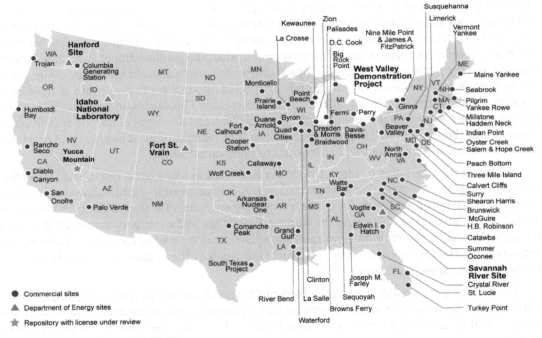

Source: Department of Energy, GAO-17-174.

Radioactive wastes from a mine are usually contained in a tailings dam and covered with water. These dams are closely monitored to prevent the release of polluted water and radiation. Uranium mines are well vented to reduce the exposure of miners to radiation, and both uranium miners and workers in nuclear power facilities wear dosimeter badges that measure cumulative radiation exposure. Of course, the long half-life of uranium means the dangers of radiation continue long after mine closure. However, the radioactivity of an isotope is a measure of its rate of decay. The shorter the half-life, the greater the radioactivity. Uranium-235 and uranium-234 as well as the decay products of uranium-238, such as radon-222, have shorter half-lives compared to uranium-238's and are more radioactive.

To protect the public and the environment from radiation exposure after a mine is closed, the mining company often covers the tailings pond with a thick layer of clay and soil. The layer reduces gamma radiation and radon emissions. Covering the tailings also prevents wind from transporting particulate matter from the tailings. Mine tailings can also be stored in the mines.

In the United States, the Uranium Mill Tailings Radiation Control Act (UMTRCA) covers the remediation of uranium tailings. The Act gives power to the EPA to set standards for handling and disposal of tailings. Each mine site is evaluated to determine the type of remediation needed. In cases where tailings are close to a residential population or surface waters, such as the Atlas Uranium Mill tailings pile in Moab, Utah, the tailings are relocated. In that case, uranium tailings were about 225 meters (738 ft) from the Colorado River. Under UMTRCA, the Department of Energy is responsible for remediation of former mining sites. The goal in remediation is to isolate the radioactive and contaminated materials and prevent them from harming ecosystems and humans. Subsurface barriers may be added to isolate the tailings waste from groundwater.

The World's Worst Nuclear Reactor Accident: Chernobyl

Of the three known nuclear reactor accidents, Chernobyl stands out as the nuclear energy industry's greatest black eye. Loss of radiation at the Fukushima Daiichi Nuclear Power Plant in Japan was the result of a tsunami, but the melting of the core of a reactor at the Chernobyl Nuclear Power Plant in the former U.S.S.R. (now in Ukraine) was the result of a flawed reactor design, a weak security backup system, and mistakes made by plant operators. Considered the world's worst nuclear accident, a reactor meltdown occurred during a safety test of the power plant's fourth reactor. Prior to the test, the operators shut down the reactor's vital control systems, including an automatic shutdown mechanism. A power surge occurred when the graphite-tipped control rods were inserted into the nuclear fuel. Graphite-tipped control rods are considered one of the design flaws of Chernobyl's reactor system. When graphite is inserted into nuclear fuel, the rate of the fission reaction initially increases rather than immediately decreases. This caused an uncontrollable chain reaction in the reactor core that culminated in an explosion and discharge of 50 tons of radioactive material into the atmosphere. Exposure to high levels of radiation causes sickness and mortality across a range of species. Mammals in particular respond rather poorly.

Following the Chernobyl incident, the closest 600 hectares (ha) (1,483 acres) of local pine trees perished (Geras'kin et al 2008). The next 3,800 ha (9,390 acres) of forest in the radius away from Chernobyl did not produce any seeds for the first five to seven years after the accident. The radiation spread across large areas of Ukraine, the Russian Federation, and Belarus, contaminating 800,000 ha (2,000,000 acres) of agricultural land and 700,000 ha (1,730,000 acres) of harvestable timberlands. Ten days after the Chernobyl incident, extremely low levels of the radiation reached the western United States (Beiriger et al. 1986).

Cancer biologists predict the worst effects of Chernobyl are still to come. Epidemiologist Dr. Elisabeth Cardis predicts we will see upward of 40,000 cases of cancer in the Belarus, Russian Federation, and Ukraine communities exposed to radiation fallout from the Chernobyl accident (Cardis et al. 2006).

The nuclear reactor incidents at Chernobyl and Fukushima, along with issues with the long-term storage of radioactive waste, have inhibited the growth of the nuclear energy industry in the United States. California, for instance, is on the verge of closing its remaining nuclear power plants and replacing them with renewable sources of energy. Other countries have already exited the nuclear power field entirely. For example, one year after the Chernobyl incident, Italy began to shut down all four of its nuclear power plants. In contrast, China and to some extent India are scaling up nuclear power production. The International Energy Agency predicts a 46 percent increase in nuclear power production by 2040, almost all from India and China.

Chernobyl
Watch and listen to journalist Richard Carleton explore Chernobyl.

View in the online reader

Building and Dismantling of Nuclear Power Plants Is Expensive

Nuclear power plants are expensive to construct and decommission. Cost estimates for a new nuclear reactor range from a few billion dollars to $10 billion, leading some economists to say nuclear power is too expensive to finance. Costs are also exorbitant at the end of a nuclear reactor's lifespan.

How Can We Make Nuclear Energy Use More Environmentally Friendly?

Accumulating radioactive waste, maintaining containment of spent fuel rods, and controlling fission reactions are problems only germane to nuclear power use. What can we do to improve in these areas and better protect the environment and humans? Nuclear reactors today demonstrate improved designs developed out of experience and failures such as the Chernobyl meltdown. International cooperation has dramatically improved in the years since then. Sharing of nuclear reactor design structures would have revealed disparities and design flaws at Chernobyl and would likely have prevented the fourth reactor's meltdown. Since Chernobyl, global collaboration and discourse over nuclear energy procedures is the rule. The International Atomic Energy Agency (IAEA) is the generally accepted body to offer assistance in the form of advice, services, and training for membership nations. One of the popular slogans of the IAEA is, "An accident anywhere is an accident everywhere."

Is there a safer way to store nuclear waste? The U.S. Nuclear Waste Policy Act (NWPA) of 1982 initiated the search for a long-term repository site. Four years later, three sites were recommended: Yucca Mountain in Nevada, Hanford in Washington, and Deaf Smith County in Texas. Amendments to the NWPA in 1986 designated Yucca Mountain as the sole site for consideration. Residents of Nevada and the backrooms of Congress referred to this law as the "screw Nevada bill." Strong opposition built up in Nevada, and by 2008 the Democratic Party took a stance to defend Nevada. Then Senator Barack Obama wrote, "After spending billions of dollars on the Yucca Mountain project, there are still significant questions about whether nuclear waste can be safely stored there." The conclusion by the majority of environmental scientists was that there are no guarantees that radiation can be contained by sealing radioactive waste in human-engineered containers and interring them deep underground for hundreds of thousands of years. Even a site at the base of a mountain may be affected by seismic activity, volcanic activity, and water percolation. In 2011, President Obama suspended funding of the Yucca Mountain repository site. Eight years later, President Donald Trump reinitiated the idea, but quickly reversed his decision due to political pushback and outcries of protest from residents of Nevada. In 2021, the newly appointed Department of Energy Secretary Jennifer Granholm stated that the Biden administration opposes the use of Yucca Mountain as a site to store nuclear waste. A radioactive waste disposal site in Yucca Mountain fits the profile of many environmental issues in which local communities are not included in the decision process (Thorne 2012), nor do they benefit. The Western Shoshone tribes are staunchly opposed to a radioactive dumpsite in Yucca Mountain, which is within their historical lands. Until countries identify secure storage sites, radiation waste will remain a problem. One step in the right direction is to reduce the generation of radioactive waste through reprocessing.

There is also an alternative: a different type of nuclear reactor called a thorium molten salt reactor. Back in the 1950s and 1960s, the United States experimented with thorium as a nuclear fuel. Thorium ore is more abundant in the environment and less dangerous than uranium ore. Being a nonfissile isotope, thorium-232 cannot initiate a nuclear chain reaction by itself. This makes thorium safer to work with compared to uranium-235, which is fissile. When we are ready to use thorium as a nuclear fuel, we irradiate it to produce uranium-233, which is a fissile isotope. Thorium reactors produce fewer radioactive waste products than uranium reactors, and no plutonium or curium. These benefits of improved safety and less radioactive waste make thorium reactors tempting alternatives. China, Canada, and India are all investing in thorium reactor research. Xu Hongjie, the director of China's molten salt reactor program, predicts China will have the world's first thorium reactor by 2030.

Key Takeaways

- Nuclear energy is a reliable source of energy available 24-7, 365 days a year. Nuclear energy boosts the economy and is not a significant source of greenhouse gases, nitrogen oxides, or sulfur dioxide.
- The largest uranium deposits are located in Australia, Canada, Russia, and Namibia. Nuclear energy makes up about 5 percent of global society's sources of energy. The percentage is larger in the United States (20 percent) and some other countries.
- A controlled fission reaction produces heat that is used to boil water and produce steam. High-pressure steam turns the blades of a turbine, a transformation of heat to mechanical energy. Next, the mechanical energy is transformed into electricity.
- The main environmental issues of nuclear energy use are 1) the potential for reactor meltdowns and 2) the accumulation and storage of radioactive waste.
- Sharing of reactor designs and safety protocols by the International Atomic Energy Agency helps to prevent future accidents. Next-generation nuclear reactors (at the research and development phase) based on thorium rather than uranium generate less waste and are safer.

13.6 A Look to the Future: Lessons Learned from the *Deepwater Horizon*

What lessons have we learned from the *Deepwater Horizon* explosion and aftermath (see "Case Study: Deepwater Horizon") when oil gushed into the Gulf of Mexico over the course of five months? Even to this day, over a decade later, monitoring of the oil and its effects on the Gulf of Mexico ecosystem continues (see video link: "Restoration of the Gulf of Mexico"). In the months and years following the initial explosion, Congress has passed new legislation and we have improved oil-drilling safety protocols.

A tally of the cleanup costs and the economic impact the spill has had and continues to have on the national and regional economies overrode neither our demand for energy nor our will to drill for oil in the Gulf of Mexico. Nor did the level of environmental degradation, loss of countless organisms, and significant threat to biodiversity motivate the majority of people to boycott petroleum. Today, roughly forty-five to fifty drilling platforms are active in the Gulf of Mexico (see Figure 13.18). Our future challenge is to access sources of energy and at the same time protect the environment. Renewable sources of energy (see Chapter 14) offer a way forward to support this objective.

Change is occurring, but be patient, because fossil and nuclear energies are only slowly decreasing in their shares of the energy market. Energy giants, British Petroleum (BP) included (opening story), are planning for this different future and are heavily investing in greener technologies. BP predicts solar energy's percentage of global power could increase to 21 percent by 2040. To prepare for this future, BP formed a partnership with Lightsource, one of the largest solar developers in the world. By the turn of the next century, BP's name will most likely be more associated with solar panels than with petroleum, and oil spills will fade from memory.

FIGURE 13.18

According to the Bureau of Safety and Environmental Protection, there are currently 1,862 drilling platforms, much fewer than the NOAA reported in 2010, when there were roughly 4,000. Only a fraction (40–50) of these platforms are active. The red dot marks the position of the *Deepwater Horizon*. (A) Location of drilling platforms in the Gulf of Mexico at the time of the *Deepwater Horizon* oil spill. (B) Production trend of crude oil from the Gulf of Mexico.

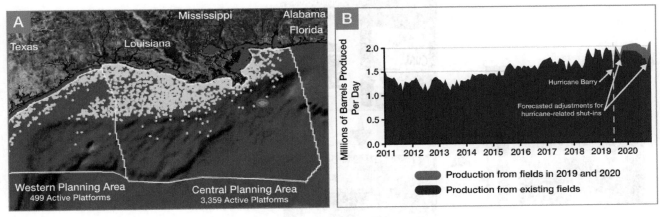

Sources: NOAA; data from EIA, https://www.eia.gov/todayinenergy/detail.php?id=47536#.

 Restoration of the Gulf of Mexico

Listen to NOAA's update on the restoration of the Gulf of Mexico after the *Deepwater Horizon* incident.

View in the online reader

Key Takeaways

- The *Deepwater Horizon* accident informs us of the large-scale destruction petroleum mining can have on massive ecosystems. The presence of drilling rigs in the Gulf of Mexico after the tragedy suggests: 1) Society's dependence on nonrenewable energy overrides any costs of environmental degradation. 2) Because society's demand of energy will continue regardless of environmental effects, alternative and sustainable sources of energy are needed to allow energy use to continue but at the same time protect the environment.
- Renewable energies will continue to increase their shares of the energy market.

FIGURE 13.19 Visual Overview: Nonrenewable Energy Sources
Summarizing figure: There are pros and cons associated with every nonrenewable energy resource (coal—13.2; petroleum—13.3, natural gas—13.4, and nuclear energy—13.5). Society's aim is to meet energy needs (13.1) without damaging the environment or human society (13.6).

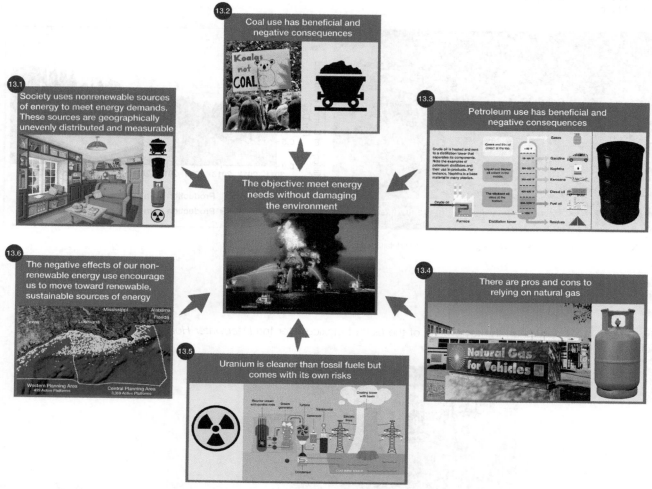

Sources: Joseph Shostell; See previous citations for image credits.

13.7 References

- American Geosciences Institute (AGI). 2018. *Petroleum and the Environment Part 13: Offshore oil and gas.* www.americangeoshciences.org/critical-issues/petroleum-environment.

- Atlas, R. M., and T. C. Hazen. 2011. "Oil biodegradation and bioremediation: a tale of the two worst spills in the U.S. history." *Environmental Science and Technology* 45: 6709–6715.

- Beiriger, J. M., R. A. Failor, and K. V. Marsh. 1986. *Radioactive Fallout from the Chernobyl Nuclear Reactor Accident.* Livermore, California: Lawrence Livermore National Laboratory.

- Brockway, P. E., A. Owen, L. I. Brand-Correa, and L. Hardt. 2019. "Estimation of global final-stage energy-return-on-investment for fossil fuels with comparison to renewable energy sources." *Nature Energy* 4: 612–621.

- Casper, J. K. 2010. *Global Warming Fossil Fuels and Pollution the Future of Air Quality.* Facts on File, Inc. New York: Infobase Publishing.

- Cleveland, C. J. 1992. "Energy quality and energy surplus in the extraction of fossil fuels in the U.S." *Ecological Economics* 6: 139–162.

- Cleveland, C. J. 2005. "Net energy from oil and gas extraction in the United States, 1954–1997." *Energy* 30: 769–782.

- Currie, J., M. Greenstone, and K. Meckel. 2017. "Hydraulic fracturing and infant health: new evidence from Pennsylvania." *Science Advances* 3, no. 12: e1603021.

- Elbaradei, M. 2008. "The Enduring lessons of Chernobyl (Opening Address)." In: *Chernobyl—Looking Back to Go Forward, Proceedings of an International Conference*. Vienna, 6–7 September, 2005.

- Environmental Defence (ED). 2008. *11 Million Litres A Day: The Tar Sands' Leading Legacy*. Toronto, ON: Environmental Defence.

- Environmental Protection Agency (EPA). 2010. *EPA Issues Comprehensive Guidance to Protect Appalachian Communities from Harmful Environmental Impacts of Mountaintop Mining*. EPA.

- Fleeger, J. W., M. R. Riggio, I. A. Mendelssohn, Q. Lin, D. R. Deis, D. S. Johnson, K. R. Carman, S. A. Graham, S. Zengel, and A. Hou. 2019. "What promotes the recovery of salt marsh infauna after oil spills?" *Estuaries and Coasts* 42, no. 1: 204–217.

- Foote, L. 2012. "Threshold considerations and wetland reclamation in Alberta's mineable oil sands." *Ecology and Society* 17, no. 1: 35. https://doi.org/10.5751/ES-04673-170135.

- Galván, K. A., J. W. Fleeger, B. J. Peterson, D. C. Drake, L. A. Deegan, and D. S. Johnson. 2011. "Natural abundance stable isotopes and dual isotope tracer additions help to resolve resources supporting a saltmarsh food web." *Journal of Experimental Marine Biology and Ecology* 410: 1–11.

- Gayral, B. 2016. "LEDs for lighting: basic physics and prospects for energy." *Comptes Rendus Physique* 18: 453–461.

- Geras'kin, S. A., S. V. Fesenko, and R. M. Alexakhin. 2008. "Effects of non-human species irradiation after the Chernobyl NPP accident." *Environ Int* 34: 880–897.

- Hall, C., and C. Cleveland. 1981. "Petroleum drilling and production in the United States: yield per effort and net energy analysis." *Science* 211: 576–579.

- Haney, J. C., H. J. Geiger, and J. W. Short. 2014a. "Bird mortality from the Deepwater Horizon oil spill. I. Exposure probability in the offshore Gulf of Mexico." *Marine Ecology Progress Series* 513: 225–237.

- Haney, J. C., H. J. Geiger, and J. W. Short. 2014b. "Bird mortality from the Deepwater Horizon oil spill. II. Carcass sampling and exposure probability in the coastal Gulf of Mexico." *Marine Ecology Progress Series* 513: 239–252.

- Hyman, D. M., and G. R. Watzlaf. 1997. "Metals and other components of coal mine drainage as related to aquatic life standards." *Proceedings America Society of Mining and Reclamation* 1997: 531–545.

- Incardona, J. P., L. D. Garder, T. L. Linbo, T. L. Brown, A. J. Esbaugh, E. M. Mager, J. D. Stieglitz, B. L. French, J. S. Labenia, C. A. Laetz, M. Tagal, C. A. Sloan, A. Elizure, D. D. Benetti, M. Grosell, B. A. Blaco, and N. L. Scholz. 2014. "Deepwater Horizon crude oil impacts the developing hearts of large predatory pelagic fish." *PNAS*. www.pnas.org/cgi/doi/10.1073/pnas.1320950111.

- Jasperse, L., M. Levin, K. Tsantiris, R. Smolowitz, C. Perkins, J. E. Ward, and S. De Guise. 2018. "Comparative toxicity of Corexit®/oil mixture on the eastern oyster, *Crassostrea virinica* (Gmelin)." *Aquatic Toxicology* 203: 10–18.

- Lee, Y. G., X. Garza-Gomez, and R. M. Lee. 2018. " Ultimate costs of the disaster: seven years after the Deepwater Horizon oil spill." *The Journal of Corporate Accounting and Finance* 29, no. 1: 69–79.

- Lichtveld, M., S. Sherchan, K. B. Gam, R. K. Kwok, C. Mundorf, A. Shankar, and L. Soares. 2016. "The Deepwater Horizon oil spill through the lens of human health and ecosystem." *Curr Envir Health Rpt* 3: 370–378.

- Litz, J. A., M. A. Baran, S. R. Bowen-Stevens, R. H. Carmichael, K. M. Colegrove, L. P. Garrison, S. E. Fire, E. M. Fougeres, R. Hardy, S. Holmes, W. Jones, B. E. Mase-Guthrie, D. K. Odell, P. W. Rosel, J. T. Saliki, D. K. Shannon, S. F. Shippee, S. M. Smith, E. M. Stratton, M. C. Tumlin, H. R. Whitehead, A. J. Worthy, and T. K. Rowles. 2014. "Review of historical unusual mortality events (UMEs) in the Gulf of Mexico (1990–2009): providing context for the multi-year northern Gulf of Mexico cetacean UME declared in 2010." *Diseases of Aquatic Organisms* 112: 161–175.

- Llewellyn, G. T., F. Dorman, J. L. Westland, D. Yoxtheimer, P. Grieve, T. Sowers, E. Humston-Fulmer, and S. L. Brantley. 2014. "Evaluating a groundwater supply contamination incident attributed to Marcellus Shale gas development." *Proceedings of the National Academy of Sciences*: www.pnas.org/cgi/doi.10,1073/pnas.1420279112.

- Mendelssohn, I. A., G. L. Andersen, D. M. Baltz, R. H. Caffey, K. R. Carman, J. W. Fleeger, S. B. Joye, Q. Lin, E. Maltby, E. B. Overton, and L. P. Rozas. 2012. "Oil impacts on coastal wetlands: implications for the Mississippi River Delta Ecosystem after the Deepwater Horizon oil spill." *Bioscience* 62, no. 6: 562–574.

- McNutt, M. K., R. Camilli, T. J. Crone, G. D. Guthrie, P. A. Hsieh, T. B. Ryerson, O. Savas, and F. Shaffer. 2012. "Review of flow rate estimates of the Deepwater Horizon oil spill." *Proceedings of the National Academy of Sciences* 109, no. 50: 20260–20267.

- Murphy, D. J., and C. A. S. Hall. 2011. "Energy return on investment, peak oil, and the end of economic growth." *Annals of the New York Academy of Sciences* 1219: 52–57.

- Obama, Barack. To *Las Vegas Review*, May 20, 2007. https://www.reviewjournal.com/opinion/barack-obama-explains-yuccamountain-stance/.

- Pimental, D., S. Fast, W. L. Chao, E. Stuart, J. Dintzis, G. Einbender, W. Schlappi, D. Andow, and K. Braderick. 1982. "Water resources in food and energy production." *Bioscience* 32, no. 11: 861–867.

- Rico-Martínez, R., T. W. Snell, and T. L. Shearer. 2012. "Synergistic toxicity of Macondo crude oil and dispersant Corexit 9500A$^\circ$ to the *Brachionus plicatilis* species complex (Rotifera)." *Environmental Pollution* 173: 5–10.

- Rohal, M., N. Barrera, E. Escobar-Briones, G. Brooks, D. Hollander, R. Larson, P. A. Montagna, M. Pryor, I. C. Romero, and P. Schwing. 2020. "How quickly will the offshore ecosystem recover from the 2010 Deepwater Horizon oil spill? Lessons learned from the 1979 Ixtoc-1 oil well blowout." *Ecological Indicators* 117: 106593.

- Salehi, M., H. Khajehpour, and Y. Saboohi. 2020. "Extended energy return on investment of multiproduct energy systems." *Energy* 192: https://doi.org/10.1016/j.energy.2019.116700.

- Spier, C., W. T. Stringfellow, T. C. Hazen, and M. Conrad. 2013. "Distribution of hydrocarbons released during the 2010 MC252 oil spill in deep offshore waters." *Environmental Pollution* 173: 224–230.

- Suárez, B., V. Lope, B. Pérez-Gónezm, N. Aragonéz, F. Rodríguez-Artalejo, F. Marqués, A. Guzmán, U. Viloria, J. M. Carrasco, J. M. Martín-Moreno, G. López-Abente, and M. Pollán. 2005. "Acute health problems among subjects involved in the cleanup operation following the Prestige oil spill in Asturias and Cantabria (Spain)." *Environ Res.* 99, no. 3: 413–424.

- Tenenbaum, D. J. 2009. "Oil sands development: a health risk worth taking." *Environmental Health Perspectives* 117, no. 4: A150–A156.

- Thorne, M. C. 2012. "Is Yucca Mountain a long-term solution for disposing of US spent nuclear fuel and high-level radioactive waste?" *J Radiol Prot* 32: 175–180.

- United Nations Development Programme (UNDP) and World Health Organization (WHO). 2009. *The Energy Access Situation in Developing Countries: A Review Focusing on the Least Developed Countries and Sub-Saharan Africa*. New York: United Nations.

- United States Coast Guard (USCG). 2010. *National Incident Commander's Report: MC252 Deepwater Horizon*.

- United States Department of Energy (USDOE). 2012. "Life-Cycle Assessment of Energy and Environmental Impacts of LED Lighting Products Part 2: Manufacturing and Performance." U.S. Department of Energy Efficiency & Renewable Energy Building Technologies Program.

- United States Energy Information Administration (eia). 2021. *Petroleum and Other Liquids.*

- Wassel, R. 2012. "Lessons from the Macondo Well blowout in the Gulf of Mexico." *The Bridge Linking Engineering and Society* 42, no. 3: 46–53.

- Weißbach, D., G. Ruprecht, A. Huke, K. Czerski, S. Gottlieb, and A. Hussein. 2013. "Energy intensities, EROIs (energy returned on invested), and energy payback times of electricity generating power plants." *Energy* 52: 210–221.

- Wollin, K., G. Damm, H. Foth, A. Freyberger, T. Gebel, et al. 2020. "Critical evaluation of human health risks due to hydraulic fracturing in natural gas and petroleum production." *Archives of Toxicology* 94: 967–1016.

CHAPTER 14
Renewable Energy Sources

Case Study: Wind Farms off the Coast of New York

Some thirty miles off the coast of Long Island sits New York's hope for a cleaner, more sustainable future. Here are the future sites of the nation's largest offshore wind farms, and of New York's vision of clean energy (see Figure 14.1). Construction of the first of five offshore wind projects began in 2022. New York's **Climate Leadership and Community Protection Act** of 2019 mandates that 70 percent of New York's electricity will come from renewable sources of energy by 2030, and that the state will reach a zero-carbon-emissions status for all power plants by 2040. All fossil fuel–powered plants will be retired, including natural gas power plants, which currently make up 35.4 percent of the state's energy portfolio (see Figure 14.1).

Each wind turbine is huge, which means the wind farms are enormous. For instance, each wind farm will have an estimated sixty to eighty wind turbines in an 80,000-acre area. Together, the first two wind farms—Empire Wind and Sunrise Wind—will offer 1,700 megawatts (MW), approximately enough to power one million homes. A single rotation of the blades of the newest, largest wind turbines transforms enough **wind energy** to power a home for twenty-four hours. Each blade is nearly as long as the world's largest commercial airplane. New York's sustainable energy plan does not stop there. Additional leases, contracts, and construction will continue, so by 2040, New York's offshore wind energy capacity will reach 9,000 MW (NYSERDA 2019). Analysis of wind speeds suggests New York could potentially generate 92,000 MW of electricity if it has enough wind farms, which means New York's energy plan barely scratches at the surface of what wind energy offers.

Use of offshore wind farms in the United States is still in its infancy. The first one became operational just a few years ago, in 2017, off the coast of Rhode Island. Thus, in many ways, New York's energy initiative is opening the door to this part of the United States energy sector. The United States is literally just at the starting line relative to the numerous offshore wind farms already present in Europe. The potential for growth in the offshore wind industry (and on land) is unprecedented.

Growth of the wind-power industry has been slow in the United States for several reasons. The general notion of changing the energy infrastructure is difficult for a segment of the population to accept. These people are familiar with a society dependent on fossil-fuel technology, and expect to see gas stations, propane tanks, etc. as the norm. Others comprehend the benefits of greener technologies and support the construction of wind turbines—as long as the development is not close to where they live. This is referred to as Not In My Back Yard Syndrome (NIMBYS) (see Chapter 2).

Any decision about a change in energy infrastructure should only occur after collecting and analyzing volumes of data from multiple sectors of society and the environment over decades. In this case, the naysayers of wind technology in New York did not offer a strong enough argument to stop the green-energy initiative. An explanation of New York's "yes" to offshore wind farms lies in the expected outcomes in the areas of improved quality of life, reduced health-care costs, economic growth, and reduced greenhouse gas emissions. Numerous studies indicate a lower life expectancy and poorer quality of life is associated with living in cities with high pollution levels, particularly particulate matter (Pope et al. 2009). For New York, an elimination of fossil fuels will help to prevent the premature death of an estimated 4,000 New Yorkers each year due to air pollution (Jacobson et al. 2013).

Together, the five offshore wind farms will create an estimated 6,800 jobs and boost New York's economy by more than $12 billion. Based on research by Stanford professor Dr. Mark Jacobson, this is a drop in the bucket to the potential growth of the wind industry in New York. In one of his

Climate Leadership and Community Protection Act (CLCPA)

New York's energy law that mandates 70 percent of the state's electricity will come from renewable sources of energy by 2030 and the state will reach a zero-emissions carbon status for all power plants by 2040. The law passed in 2019 and goes into effect in 2022.

wind energy

The energy of wind; an example of a renewable source of energy.

scenarios for offshore wind farms, he suggested New York would need 320,000 full-time workers during construction, and 7,140 annual (permanent) full-time workers for the expected 12,700 offshore wind turbines (Jacobson et al. 2013).

FIGURE 14.1

New York is changing its energy portfolio to rely more on renewable sources of energy and eliminate fossil fuels. A significant part of the plan is the construction of large offshore wind farms. (A) East Coast of the United States showing location of sites for current (under construction, in red) and future (in blue) offshore wind farms. (B) New York welcome sign. (C) An offshore wind farm. (D) New York state's electricity generation by source (2020).

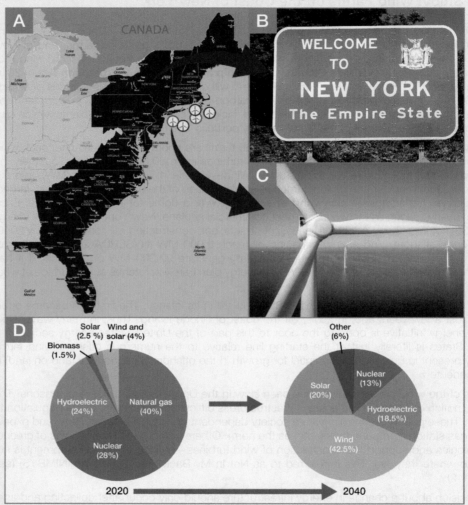

Sources: Joseph Shostell; © Shutterstock, Inc.; data from EIA, https://www.eia.gov/state/print.php?sid=NY#23 and Siemens Power Technologies, Inc., Zero-Emissions Electric Grid in New York by 2040 Study, https://www.nyserda.ny.gov/about/publications/new-york-power-grid-study.

New York's 2019 environmental law, the Climate Leadership and Community Protection Act, supports the development of offshore windfarms. The name of the law hints at its strong role in protecting public health, natural resources, and the environment from the adverse impacts of climate change. Specifically, the law states, "The severity of current climate change and the threat of additional and more severe change will be affected by the actions undertaken by New York and other jurisdictions to reduce greenhouse gas emissions." New York's energy plan supports the Paris Agreement to substantially reduce greenhouse gas emissions to limit global warming (see Chapter 11). The Act goes well beyond replacing fossil fuel–powered electric power plants with wind turbines and solar panels. It also mandates the replacement of all fossil fuel combustion linked to transportation, heating, and cooling. This means the elimination of gas stations. Action undertaken by New York will avert emissions in excess of 163 million metric tons of CO_2 per year. New York's aim is to reduce greenhouse gas emissions by 100 percent by 2050, and at least 40 percent by 2030. As stated by the New York State Senate in Bill S2992B, "Action undertaken by New York to reduce greenhouse emissions will have an impact on global greenhouse gas emissions and the rate of climate change." Every individual and every community can do its own part in solving global environmental problems.

New York's new energy initiative embraces biomass energy (see Section 2), solar energy (see Section 3), and hydroelectric (see Section 4), and geothermal (see Section 5) energies as well. New York is destined to have a cleaner and healthier future. Add the Big Apple to your travel plans; just remember, the longer you wait to visit, the cleaner the air will become.

14.1 The Value of Renewable Energy

Learning Objectives

1. Understand and appreciate the feasibility and benefits of society's transition from a dependence on nonrenewable energies to renewable energies.
2. Compare the capacity factor of different sources of energy.
3. Consider the time scale of society's transition to full use of renewable sources of energy.

New York's transition to a greener energy portfolio comes with many benefits. First and foremost, the action protects ecosystem goods and services through the elimination of many pollution sources. Emissions of carbon dioxide, particulate matter, sulfur dioxide, nitrogen oxides, surface-level ozone, mercury, and a number of other pollutants will essentially cease. With these changes, New Yorkers will experience fewer health issues and their quality of life will improve. Health-care costs will drop, and the economy will be stimulated with the creation of many long-term, full-time jobs and their associated effects.

Yes, New York is leading a pathway of energy change and proving the feasibility of what seemed impossible just a few years ago. The state has an exciting road ahead, but it is just one of fifty states. Is it possible to scale up a similar transition to renewable energies for the entire United States? Dr. Jacobson of Stanford University says it is, and he and his research team have already completed the calculations (Jacobson et al. 2015).

Dr. Jacobson puts forth an ambitious energy plan that is economically and technically attainable. The plan only incorporates renewable forms of energy (i.e., wind, water, and solar). No more coal. No more petroleum. No more natural gas. No more nuclear energy. Jacobson's plan depends on a nationwide shift to electric power and electric power only. This means no gas stoves and no internal combustion engines. Instead, every home would only have electrical appliances, and the only cars would be electric. The change would reduce the number of energy transformations (see Chapter 13) and improve energy efficiency. Our society would meet energy demands while using one-third less energy.

Our Energy Use Is Changing

New York is an example of society's changing energy use. In the case of New York, the target is for renewable energies to provide a minimum of 70 percent of statewide electricity generation by 2040. Dr. Jacobson's feasibility study is more aggressive and expansive; it lays out a set of roadmaps for the elimination of all nonrenewable energies by 2050 in all fifty United States. What is noteworthy about New York's renewable-minded strategy, as well as Dr. Jacobson's suggested transition of the entire United States to a renewable energy economy, is the relatively short time frame. Full adoption of renewable energies requires appropriate infrastructure, technology maturity, and product development. These will take some time, which means it is unrealistic to immediately convert from fossil and uranium fuels to renewables. This is why Jacobson describes a roadmap and projected milestones for the future. What would it take to replace 80 to 85 percent of our nonrenewable sources of energy with renewables by 2030, and 100 percent by 2050? These are very ambitious goals, but let us think broadly and openly about the relative composition of renewable energy sources and the new energy industry infrastructure needed to make this a reality. According to Dr. Jacobson's calculations, the United States can meet almost all of its energy needs with wind energy (half) and solar energy (45 percent) alone. The remainder can be obtained from a combination of geothermal and hydroelectric (traditional hydropower, wave power, and tidal power).

capacity factor

The actual amount of electricity generated divided by the maximum potential or nameplate capacity.

A determination of society's future energy infrastructure (power plants, transmission lines, and so on) accounts for **capacity factor**, which is the actual amount of electricity generated divided by the maximum potential or nameplate capacity. Power plants that run on nuclear, coal, or natural gas have higher capacity factors than wind and solar farms (see Figure 14.2). For example, a nuclear power plant runs at roughly 80 percent to 95 percent of its full capacity throughout the year—close to its maximum electricity output. In contrast, wind farms have monthly capacity factors between 20 percent and 40 percent. What is the relevance of these data? The nameplate capacity given to a wind farm is higher than its average capacity factor. Wind farms such as Empire Wind and Sunrise Wind (see "Case Study: Wind Farms off the Coast of New York") can operate at full capacity, but they don't always reach this capacity, because the required wind speeds don't always prevail. Natural daily and seasonal lulls in wind speed mean electricity generation by wind farms is not always at maximum output. Solar farms have an even greater variability than wind farms; their capacity factors range from about zero to 40 percent. To account for the difference between maximum potential electricity generation and average generation, three to four wind farms would have to replace each nuclear power plant of similar nameplate capacity. There would be an even greater number of solar farms.

Is a full conversion to renewable fuels by 2050 realistic? Is it smart? The answer to the second question is "yes," if the aim is for a healthier, cleaner environment. An answer to the first question depends on who is asked, and if there is sufficient stimulus for support. A stimulus might be the realization of the devastation caused by pollution and habitat degradation, or the incentive of economic gains, or decreased health-care costs, or potential for a higher quality of life (or a maintained quality of life for the rich). The United States Energy Information Administration predicts a much slower transition for the United States to renewable energy sources. The upward trend of renewable energy consumption is clear, as is the downward trend of coal (see Figure 14.3). We actually reached a major milestone in 2019, when renewable energy consumption for generating electricity surpassed coal consumption. Based on these trends and expectations, electricity generation from renewables will double by 2050—to 38 percent, which is still a far cry from the 100 percent mentioned in Dr. Jacobson's feasibility study (USEIA 2020).

FIGURE 14.2
Seasonal variation in generator capacity factors for select fuels and technologies in the United States. The higher-capacity factor value, the closer a fleet of electrical generators is to working at maximum potential.

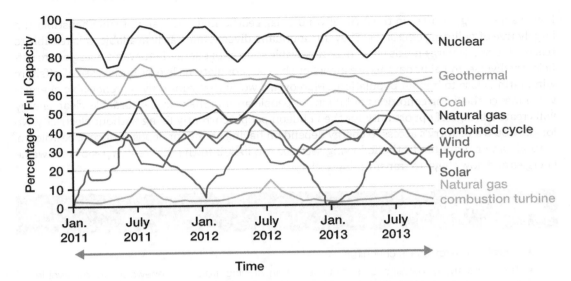

Source: Joseph Shostell; adapted from EIA, https://www.eia.gov/todayinenergy/detail.php?id=14611.

FIGURE 14.3
Based on current trends and expectations, the U.S. Energy Information Administration states electricity generation from renewables will rise from 19 percent in 2020 to 38 percent in 2050. The red circle indicates when electricity generation from renewables exceeded that of coal.

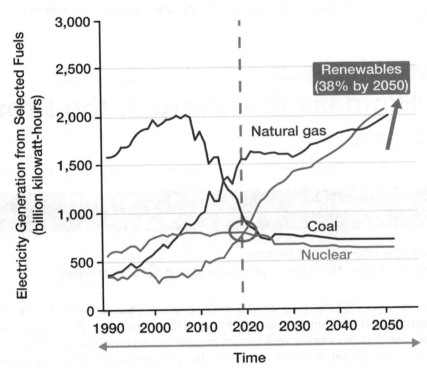

Source: Adapted from EIA, https://www.eia.gov/outlooks/aeo/pdf/AEO2020 Full Report.pdf (page 68).

Overview of Renewable Energy

Renewable energy sources in the form of wind, solar, geothermal, and water are inexhaustible and largely free of polluting emissions. They are abundant, diverse, and easily available. It is feasible to reach all societal energy needs with these renewable sources of energy. Renewable energies are sufficiently diverse and abundant to use anywhere human populations live, or in the case of offshore wind farms, close to human populations. Moreover, a world that runs only on renewable energies will enhance the living conditions of billions of people around the world. Affordable, clean energy will create a bridge of opportunity for the 1.1 billion people currently living without electricity. No longer would a country's access to energy depend on having abundant deposits of coal, petroleum, natural gas, or uranium. In the following sections, we look into the different types of renewable energies and how they are transforming society.

Key Takeaways

- Society's energy use is changing.
- There are many benefits of society fully transitioning from nonrenewable to renewable sources of energy, including reduced emissions of greenhouse gases, nitrogen oxides, and sulfur dioxide, as well as reduced smog, improved health conditions, lower health-care costs, protection of ecosystem services, and an infusion of new long-term jobs to boost the economy.
- It takes time to build the infrastructure needed to support wide-scale use of renewable energies across the various sectors of society.
- Renewable energies (wind, solar, geothermal, and water) are diverse, abundant, and easily available.

14.2 Biomass (Bioenergy), the Pros and Cons

Learning Objectives

1. Describe the various forms of biomass.
2. Assess the value of different forms of biomass as useful sources of energy.

biomass

The total mass of living things within a specific area or volume.

New York's energy portfolio (opening story) includes producing **biomass**—the total mass of living things in a specific area or volume—that can be burned to generate electricity. Since 1986, the State University of New York has worked with rural communities and created a network of twenty universities and commercial partners that focuses on shrub willow as a source of biomass within and outside of New York (Johnson et al. 2018) (see Figure 14.4). Currently, New York has a little over 1,250 acres devoted to growing shrub willow. This weedy, fast-growing plant grows quickly even in poorly drained soils and other marginal areas, and therefore growing it for biomass does not compete for space with food crops. There are other benefits too. Shrub willow crops lessen soil erosion (Duggan, 2005), serve as a wind buffer (Heavey and Volk 2014), provide wildlife habitat (Campbell et al. 2012), and, importantly, are a useful source of energy. They are usually harvested four years after planting, and then every three years thereafter for six to seven cycles. After twenty-two to twenty-five years, replanting commences and the whole process repeats.

FIGURE 14.4
An aisle between dense rows of shrub willow. This shrub is a renewable source of biomass energy.

Source: © Shutterstock, Inc.

What Is Biomass?

Since the time our ancient ancestors first discovered fire, we have used biomass as a source of energy. Biomass is a renewable source of energy. Examples of biomass include wood, sawdust, crops (edible and nonedible parts), algae, animal fat, animal wastes, and decomposing organic matter in landfills (see Figure 14.5).

FIGURE 14.5
Biomass makes up about 5 percent of all U.S. energy consumption (A) and 45 percent of all U.S. renewable energies (B). Examples of biomass (C).

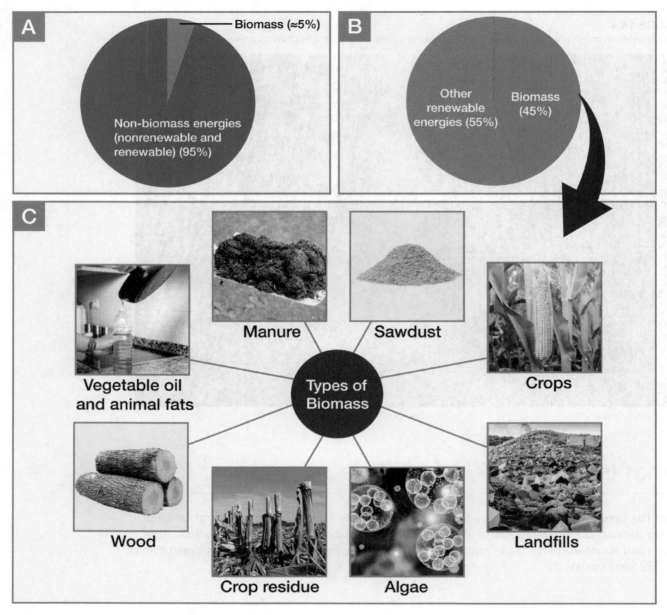

Sources: Joseph Shostell; data from EIA; https://www.eia.gov/energyexplained/biomass/; © Shutterstock, Inc.

biofuels

Fuels produced from biomass.

There are three general ways to transform the potential energy in biomass to a form of energy useful to society (see Figure 14.6). The most common process is to burn the biomass to produce heat for warmth or for cooking. This is the prevalent method in impoverished areas of developing countries, where fossil fuels are not easily accessible, or where there is a lack of capital and technology to build contemporary power plants. The heat from burning biomass may also be transformed into electricity, in a process similar to burning fossil fuels in power plants. In a second way, biomass is placed in an anaerobic digester to produce biogas (mostly methane), which in turn is combusted to generate electricity. Third, biomass is chemically converted to a liquid such as ethanol for use as a transportation fuel. Corn-based ethanol and soybean-based biodiesel are examples of liquid biofuels. These and any other fuels produced from biomass are **biofuels**.

FIGURE 14.6

Examples of using biomass as a source of energy. (A) A large skillet of boiling oil sits atop a burning pile of wood. (B) Human wastes are directed to a sewage treatment plant, where it is used to produce biogas that is transformed to electricity. (C) Crops are converted to ethanol, a liquid fuel for transportation.

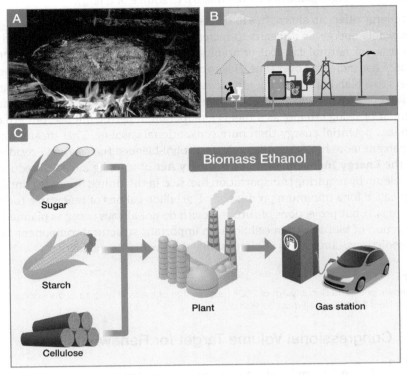

Source: © Shutterstock, Inc.

Benefits of Using Biomass

Biomass is a renewable, cheap fuel and easily accessible by the poor and rich alike. Because biomass is at Earth's surface where we live, we do not have to expend effort, money, energy, or time to extract it from the ground as we do with fossil fuels and uranium. Advanced technology is not required to access the energy stored within many forms of biomass, which means literally anybody can make use of biomass as a source of energy. At least as early as the Neolithic age, humans have used dung for fuel (Mlekuž 2009). Even before humans domesticated animals some ten thousand years ago, our ancestral species *Homo erectus* learned how to control fire and make it from dry biomass on demand. Therefore, the concept of using biomass as a source of energy is deeply rooted in all societies.

Use of biomass as a source of fuel adds economic value to organic wastes. There are many examples in which a need for energy has at least partially solved a waste problem. In Ontario, the city of Waterloo tested the effectiveness of transforming the energy in dog poop to electricity for use in households. In one year, Waterloo's poop project prevented the emissions of about three quarters of a ton of carbon dioxide and generated enough electricity to power fourteen homes. On a much grander scale, Chinese scientists proposed making use of crop residues. For years, Chinese farmers have routinely burned crop residues, and consequently polluted an already-challenged atmosphere with particulate matter and carbon dioxide. To fall in line with the Paris Agreement, China plans to generate no carbon dioxide emissions from agricultural waste by 2030 (MAC 2015). Their proposed plan describes converting rice husks, wheat straw, and soybean straw—all crop residues—to bio-coal (Cheng et al. 2020). Based on their calculations, China would not squander the energy stored in the agricultural waste and instead use the waste to produce approximately 400 million tons of bio-coal, which contains the same amount of energy as 380 million tons of coal. Combustion of bio-coal is still a source of pollution, but this strategy does lessen China's greenhouse gas emissions. Methane captured from landfills and sewage plants and burned to generate electricity is another example of using organic matter (biomass) as a source of energy.

Biomass energy offers an alternative to nonrenewable energies. Nations see biomass and other forms of renewable energy as a means to increase their energy independence and rely less on imports of petroleum, natural gas, coal, or uranium. In the United States and elsewhere, the use of biomass ethanol has increased over time. Have you noticed the signage at the gasoline pump? The label **E10** refers to a blend of 10 percent ethanol and 90 percent conventional gasoline. Then there is **E85**, which is a flex fuel in which ethanol content may range between 51 percent and 85 percent. One clear benefit of using ethanol as a fuel is a reduction in petroleum use, but ethanol-blended fuels contain less potential energy than pure conventional gasoline. That means consumers can use up to 30 percent more fuel when they rely on alcohol-blended fuels. When President George W. Bush signed the **Energy Independence and Security Act** of 2007, he aimed to reduce U.S. dependence on petroleum by requiring transportation fuel sold in the United States to contain renewable fuels. The Act called for a minimum production of 36 billion gallons of renewable fuels per year by 2022 (see Figure 14.7), but projections of future growth do not always occur as planned. Specifically, current production of biofuels from cellulose, an important structural component in plants, falls far short of predictions. Limitations of biomass like this are discussed next.

E10

A blend of 10 percent ethanol and 90 percent conventional gasoline.

E85

A flex fuel in which ethanol content may range from 51 percent to 85 percent.

Energy Independence and Security Act

Calls for a minimum production of 36 billion gallons of renewable fuels per year.

FIGURE 14.7
The Energy Independence and Security Act of 2007 requires that of the total amount of transportation fuel sold yearly, 136 billion liters (36 billion gal) must be biofuel.

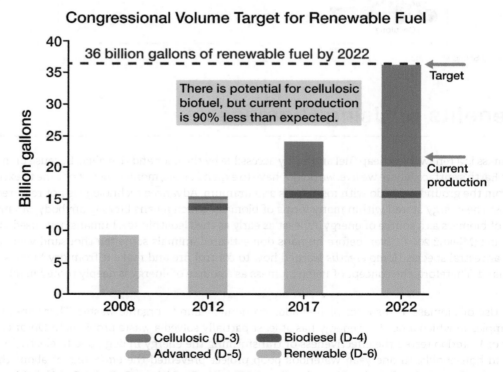

Source: Adapted from Overview for Renewable Fuel Standard, EPA, https://www.epa.gov/renewable-fuel-standard-program/overview-renewable-fuel-standard.

Biomass-Limitations and Environmental Impact

Is biomass a source of greenhouse gases and other air pollutants? Any answer to this question strikes at the heart of biomass's usefulness as a source of energy. The U.S. Environmental Protection Agency classifies biomass as green energy, and any emissions of carbon dioxide from biomass as a natural part of the carbon cycle. For many people, this "green label" seems sufficiently justified and therefore they do not question the value of biomass as a source of energy. However, an analysis of data collected from biomass use would suggest otherwise, because the combustion of biomass does not just emit carbon dioxide, but also particulate matter, nitrogen oxides, and small amounts of sulfur dioxide. Particulate matter from biomass may very well have been some of the first hazards we faced as a young species. We can only imagine how the lungs of our ancient ancestors were exposed to carcinogens created by open fires in primitive huts and in caves. Studies today such as that by Mishra et al. (2002) list indoor air pollution from biomass fires as silent killers. The point is clear: biomass is a source of air pollutants.

Maybe green energy is not always greener. For example, the offshore wind farms discussed in the opening story are far greener sources of energy than biomass. How does biomass compare with fossil fuels? Corn-based ethanol emits 12 percent less carbon dioxide compared to conventional gasoline, and soybean-based biodiesel releases 41 percent less carbon dioxide than conventional diesel (Manuel 2007). Sulfur dioxide emissions are lower as well.

Furthermore, corn, soybean, and sugarcane crops have several limitations as biofuels. In a time of growing human populations and consequent food shortages, these crops take up precious agricultural land. Biofuel crops also come with the negative environmental effects of pesticide and synthetic fertilizer use (see Chapter 8). Corn, soybean, and sugarcane are also energy-intensive crops, which means they require significant energy investments in fuel for large-scale farm machinery, and in the production of genetically modified seeds, synthetic fertilizers, and pesticides. All of these investments detract from the energy value of biofuel crops. For instance, the net energy balance for corn-based ethanol is 25 percent, which means it only yields one-quarter more energy than is required to produce it (Manuel 2007).

Back in 2009, the buzz was about algal fuel. At the time, Sapphire Energy had just sent a Prius hybrid car running on "Green Crude" (algal fuel) on a ten-day, 3,705-mile trip from San Francisco to New York City. Under great hype and expectations, the company secured $150 million from private investors and an additional $104 million in grants and loans from the federal government. Promises were never fulfilled, and a little over a decade later, Sapphire Energy no longer exists. Despite predictions, algal fuel faced several hurdles that prevented it from being useful as a commercial source of energy. The energy costs of isolating oil from algae were too high, and the fuel was not cost-competitive. Do not count algal fuel out just yet, for there is new hope on the horizon. Synthetic Genomics, in partnership with energy giant ExxonMobil, has genetically modified algal cells to produce 100 percent more oil per cell (Ajjawi et al. 2017). The companies promise to produce ten thousand barrels of algal biofuel per day beginning in 2025. Only time will tell if this promise will be kept.

Key Takeaways

- Biomass (i.e., crops, sewage, manure, wood, sawdust, and algae) is renewable and easily accessible. Use of biomass as a fuel adds economic value to organic wastes and lessens our reliance on fossil fuels.
- Biomass is labeled a green energy, yet burning of biomass releases particulate matter, carbon dioxide, nitrogen oxides, and sulfur dioxide.

14.3 Solar Energy, the Pros and Cons

Learning Objectives

1. Understand and appreciate the value of solar energy as a source of energy for society.
2. Identify and understand the benefits and limitations of solar energy use.
3. Comprehend how photovoltaic cells transform solar energy into electricity.
4. Explain the negative effects of mining to obtain materials for solar panels and the need to appropriately manage used solar panels to protect the health of the environment.

In addition to soon having North America's largest wind farms (see "Case Study: Wind Farms off the Coast of New York"), New York possesses the largest solar farm on the East Coast of the United States.

What Is Solar Energy?

solar energy

Renewable, limitless energy from the sun.

Solar energy refers to the limitless, renewable energy from the sun. Every hour, our sun bathes the Earth with enough energy to meet all of society's energy needs for an entire year (Mackay 2013). The sun's short distance from Earth—a mere 150 million km (93 million mi)—and massive size make this possible (see video link: "Potential of Solar Energy ").

 Potential of Solar Energy

Listen to billionaire Elon Musk discussing the potential of solar energy.

View in the online reader

The real source of the sun's energy originates from fusion reactions in its core caused by extreme temperature and pressure conditions. Accounting for only half of the Earth facing the sun at one time, the tilt of the Earth's axis, Earth's spherical structure, and atmospheric reflection and absorption, on average, Earth's surface receives about 163.2 watts per square meter (see Figure 14.8). Given this information, a relatively small part of the world covered with solar panels would harvest enough sunlight to provide for all of society's energy needs. Part of this calculation includes a 20 percent estimated efficiency for solar panels, which is common for higher-end equipment.

FIGURE 14.8

Capturing solar energy. (A) Of the solar energy that reaches Earth, about one-third is reflected back into space, and about one-fifth is absorbed by Earth's atmosphere. The remaining amount (roughly half) reaches Earth's surface. (B) In a solar panel system, photons of light hit the semiconductor membrane of photovoltaic cells (squares in solar panel), exciting electrons and stimulating an electric current. The current can be used immediately or transformed to chemical energy (in batteries) for later use.

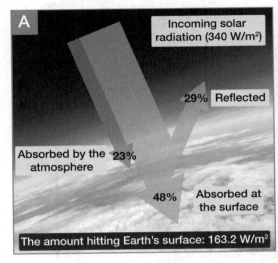
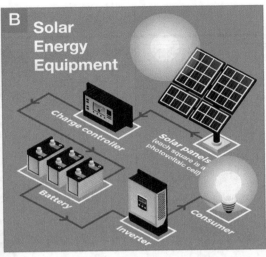

Sources: Joseph Shostell; NASA Earth Observatory, https://earthobservatory.nasa.gov/features/EnergyBalance/page1.php; © Shutterstock, Inc.

How Does a Solar Panel Work?

Solar panels are becoming the norm on rooftops these days because these systems do not take up ground space. How do they collect and transform solar energy into electricity? The answer lies in the functional unit of a solar panel, the **photovoltaic cell** (see Figure 14.9), which has a standard width of about 15.6 cm (6.1 in). Photons bombard the semiconductor material of each photovoltaic cell, knocking electrons loose. The freed electrons are the source of the current. In this way, photons of light are transformed into electricity. Usually, photovoltaic cells are arranged in groups of thirty-six to seventy-two as a **module**, which is more commonly called a solar panel. The amount of electricity a solar panel generates depends on the number of photovoltaic cells (its size) and their efficiency rate.

How many solar panels should be installed in a home? The answer varies depending on the location of the house and how much energy its inhabitants consume (see "Critical Thinking Activity: Calculating the Number of Solar Panels Needed for an Average-sized House in California"). In 2019, the average American home consumed about 877 kWh of electricity per month. This average accounts for a wide range of **solar insolation** (sunlight intensity) and daylight period between high latitudes (where solar insolation is generally lower), and lower sunnier latitudes (see Figure 14.9).

photovoltaic cell

The functional unit of a solar panel.

module

Photovoltaic cells arranged into groups of thirty-six to seventy-two. A solar panel.

solar insolation

Sunlight intensity.

FIGURE 14.9

Solar energy. Based on this solar energy distribution map, the southwest United States receives the most solar energy in the country. The image shows an aerial view of the East Coast's largest solar farm in Long Island, New York.

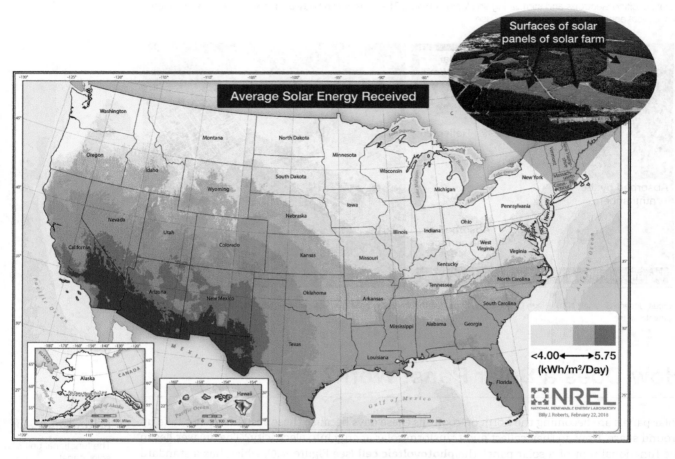

Sources: Joseph Shostell; NREL, https://www.nrel.gov/gis/assets/images/solar-annual-ghi-2018-usa-scale-01.jpg; Brookhaven National Laboratory, https://www.bnl.gov/lisf/.

Critical Thinking Activity: Calculating the Number of Solar Panels Needed for an Average-sized House in California

A homeowner interested in solar energy understands how much energy they consume per month as well as the power output of an average solar panel (about 265 watts). Additionally, the owner considers the number of daylight hours (for example, about twelve hours in April). Based on this information, and assuming the owner is calculating energy needs for the month of April, they would multiply twelve hours by 265 watts to obtain total usage of 3,180 watt hours—3.18 kilowatt hours (kWh)—per day. The product, 3.18 kWh, is multiplied by the number of days in a month. Thus, in this California example, a 265 watt solar panel generates 95.4 kWh in April, which is only about 10 percent of the energy consumed by the average household. In this case, ten solar panels would probably be sufficient to meet the owner's needs for electricity.

There are other methods of generating electricity from sunlight without photovoltaic cells. One way is to concentrate solar energy with the help of mirrors (see A in Figure 14.10). In some **concentrating solar power (CSP) plants**, sunlight hits parabolic (u-shaped) mirrors, which direct the light to collecting tubes filled with synthetic oil. Pipes carry the hot oil through a water tank; steam forms and turns a turbine, which generates electricity. The mirrors are programmed to move with the sun throughout the day, maximizing the amount of solar energy they intercept.

Another type of CSP plant includes a centrally located tower that receives concentrated sunlight from a surrounding circle of flat mirrors (see B in Figure 14.10). The largest CSP plant with a receiver tower in the United States resides in the Mojave Desert, in the state of California. It spans an area of 3,500 acres, contains three receiver towers, and has nearly 175,000 mirrors. At full capacity, the Ivanpah CSP plant generates 392 megawatts (MW) and powers over 100,000 homes.

concentrating solar power (CSP) plants

Solar energy is concentrated with the help of mirrors. The mirrors direct the sunlight to collecting tubes filled with synthetic oil or molten salt.

FIGURE 14.10
Concentrated solar power (CSP) plants rely on mirrors to concentrate the sun's energy. (A) Illustration of parabolic mirrors directing sunlight to receiver tubes filled with oil. (B) A CSP with a central tower receiving concentrated sunlight from surrounding mirrors.

Sources: Joseph Shostell; © Shutterstock, Inc.

Benefits of Using Solar Energy

There are clear benefits to using solar energy. In fact, the argument is very compelling to add solar panels to every house and business. Solar panels are a source of neither greenhouse gasses, sulfur dioxide, nor nitrogen oxides. Use of solar energy does not contribute to global warming, acid rain, or smog. There are also secondary benefits, such as not contributing to future human health issues caused by smog, and the avoidance of property damage due to climate change. Solar energy systems do not require water to generate electricity as fossil fuel and nuclear power plants do.

Solar farms make optimal use of degraded lands too polluted for other purposes. For example, New York's energy portfolio (see "Case Study: Wind Farms off the Coast of New York") includes a solar farm constructed on a superfund site in Long Island. This 32-megawatt solar farm—the largest on the East Coast—transforms enough solar energy to generate electricity for 4,500 homes. Landfills make useful sites for solar farms as well.

Solar farms are more than just protective of the environment; they also reduce energy costs for consumers. Rising costs of energy encourage more and more homeowners to tap into free solar energy to reduce their electric bill while acting sustainably. As always, before a large purchase, it is prudent to conduct a cost–benefit analysis, for example by calculating the number of years it will take to recoup the initial investment in a solar panel system. The cost of installing a solar panel system may range from $10,000 to $50,000, with the average around $20,000. Federal and state tax credits will reduce this amount by at least 30 percent, which means the price drops to no more than $14,000 dollars. How long will it take to pay off a solar investment? The amount of time will vary depending on location, efficiency of photovoltaic cells, and size of the solar panel system. As an example, if installation of solar panels reduces a monthly electric bill by $65, it would take fifteen years to recoup a $12,000 investment.

Solar power systems are modular in design, so they can be sized to meet any energy demand (see Figure 14.11). A homeowner may elect to install five solar panels or fifty, and a solar power plant may have over one hundred thousand. Solar panels are portable and ideal for isolated areas that do not have access to an electric grid system. They provide an affordable, sustainable way to bring electricity to the more than one billion people who currently live without it (Alkin et al. 2017). Standard of living and educational opportunities increase with access to electricity.

Solar Energy Limitations and Environmental Impact

Despite its many advantages, solar energy comes with several challenges, including a solar cell's low energy efficiency and limited number of daylight hours. Even the most efficient solar cells can transform only about 40 percent of the solar energy they absorb, while the remaining 60 percent is lost (King et al. 2007). However, these advanced solar cells are extremely expensive and uncommon. The average efficiency rate for solar cells is closer to 20 percent, and therefore 80 percent of the energy is lost. It looks like we have room for much improvement!

Because solar energy is not constantly available to us, homes with solar panel systems must have at least one additional source of energy besides solar energy. In California, for example, homes with solar panels are connected to the electric grid. During daylight hours and depending on the size of the solar panel system, California homes can partially or totally rely on solar energy to meet energy needs. These homes draw on electricity from the grid at night when there is no solar energy available. Being connected to the electrical grid has other benefits too, such as sending any surplus electricity generated through solar panels to the electrical grid. Homeowners can make a profit doing this. Homes off grid often have solar batteries. The batteries are charged during daylight hours and then are used as a source of energy during the night. Unfortunately, this requires two more energy transformations, one to transform solar energy into chemical energy within the battery and a second to transform the chemical energy to electricity when you use a stove, iPad, or computer at night. Every additional transformation increases energy losses (see Chapter 3). Unlike in California, in Germany there is a growing trend of homes with solar panel systems being connected to the electric grid and also having solar batteries.

Rapid expansion of solar farms has outpaced our knowledge of how the installation of hundreds—or hundreds of thousands—of solar panels will affect wildlife. Will the solar panels take up valuable habitat space? Some of the premier locations for solar farms also support threatened and endangered species. In the arid Southwest, a prime location for solar farms, ecosystems are delicate and sensitive to change. Will installations affect keystone species such as the Agassiz desert tortoise (Lovich and Ennen 2011)? Additional research will help to fill in any gaps in knowledge. Avian mortality is another ecological problem caused by solar farms. An estimated 37,800 to 138,000 birds perish in the United States each year from coming in contact with solar project structures or from exposure to concentrated sunlight (Walston et al. 2016).

In a discussion of creating a zero-carbon future by building solar energy technology infrastructure, scant attention is given to how we can sustainably obtain the minerals and metals needed to construct solar cells. "The world cannot tackle climate change without an adequate supply of raw materials to manufacture clean technologies" (Ali et al. 2017). The materials for solar panels and other renewable technologies do not come from nothing; rather, they originate from mining (see A in Figure 14.11). As the demand for solar panels increases, so too will the demand for aluminum, copper, indium, iron, lead, nickel, silver, and zinc. This information suggests solar energy use is not 100 percent green.

FIGURE 14.11
Use of solar energy takes a toll on the environment. (A) Minerals and metals in solar panels originate in mines that harm the environment. (B) Broken solar panels (such as this one hit by hail) contain toxins harmful to organisms and ecosystems.

Source: © Shutterstock, Inc.

Toxins in solar panels present an end-of-life problem. Environmental scientists are raising the alarm about cadmium, lead, and other toxic metals in broken and worn-out solar panels (see B in Figure 14.11). In the current cradle-to-grave concept, all of the materials in solar panels are eventually lost, and they can pollute aquatic and terrestrial ecosystems. We are just in the infancy of the solar energy industry, and we are already having trouble managing discarded solar panels. The International Renewable Energy Agency states that there are over 250,000 metric tons of used solar panels, and by 2050, the number will increase to 78 million metric tons. Arizona recognizes this growing problem and is attempting to pass legislation to mandate the recycling of solar panels.

Key Takeaways

- Solar energy is renewable, limitless energy from the sun.
- Photovoltaic cells and concentrating solar power plants can transform solar energy into electricity.
- Use of solar energy reduces electricity costs for consumers and does not contribute to global warming, acid rain, or smog.
- There are limits to solar energy's usefulness, such as the low efficiency of solar cells and limited number of daylight hours. Solar energy systems require mined minerals and metals, and therefore negatively affect ecosystems where mines operate. In addition, heavy-metal toxins in each solar panel must be appropriately managed at the end of the panel's lifespan to protect the health of the environment.

14.4 Hydropower, the Pros and Cons

Learning Objectives

1. Explain how we transform the energy in moving water to electricity.
2. Identify the benefits of society's use of hydropower.
3. Give examples of limitations and negative environmental effects of hydropower.

The force of a river's current can overcome even the strongest of swimmers. This fact and our observations of tidal movements, turbulent rivers, and waterfalls inform us of the power of moving water. Over two thousand years ago, creative and ambitious Greeks and Romans saw opportunity here and engineered the world's first hydropower structure—a waterwheel to harness the energy of running water. Many centuries later, with an accumulated knowledge of improved designs and new ideas, we have become quite adept at harnessing the kinetic energy of moving water. In this section, we explore hydropower as a source of electricity.

Hydroelectric Energy

hydroelectricity

The use of hydropower to generate electricity.

Our focus in this section is on **hydroelectricity**—the use of hydropower as a source of electricity (see video link: "Hydropower"). The most common way of transforming the energy of moving water to electricity is to make use of a dam, reservoir, and turbine. The National Inventory of Dams lists approximately 91,500 dams in the United States. A small fraction of these—just a little over 2 percent—are hydroelectric dams (see A in Figure 14.12). The vast majority were constructed for other reasons: flood control, irrigation, and to create aquatic recreational areas (see B in Figure 14.12). Just a handful of states are responsible for generating most of the nation's electricity from hydroelectric dams. Three western states—Washington (28 percent), Oregon (13 percent), and California (9 percent) and one eastern state, New York (11 percent)—generate over 60 percent of the total. New York (opening story) is the clear leader in hydroelectricity generation capacity on the East Coast. The state's hydroelectric dams along with its offshore wind farms, solar power plants, and geothermal sites are examples of why New York is a leader in sustainable energies. In total, the United States obtains 7 percent of its electricity from hydroelectric facilities.

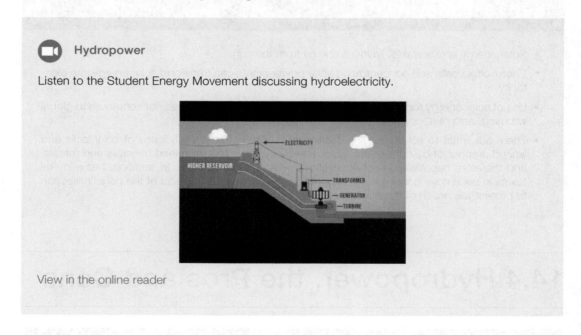

🎥 **Hydropower**

Listen to the Student Energy Movement discussing hydroelectricity.

View in the online reader

FIGURE 14.12

Hydroelectric dams. (A) The United States has approximately two thousand hydroelectric power plants. Symbols indicate different types of hydroelectric dams. The larger the symbol, the greater the capacity. Colors indicate ownership. (B) A breakdown of the number of different types of dams within the U.S.

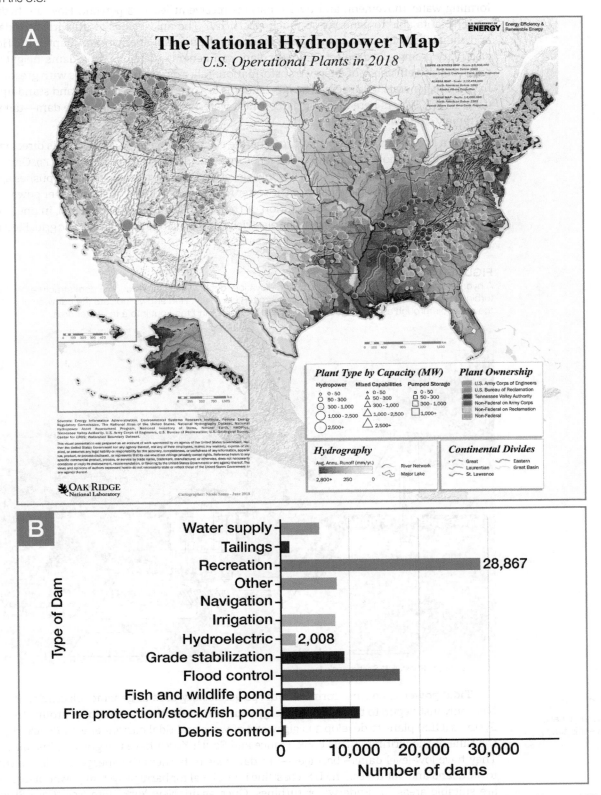

Sources: Oak Ridge National Laboratory, https://hydrosource.ornl.gov/map/2018-national-hydropower-map; Joseph Shostell; data from National Inventory of Dams, https://nid.usace.army.mil/#/.

Hydroelectric dams are distributed unequally outside U.S. borders too, and their distribution reflects the location of natural river systems. At the global level, a little over 16 percent of electricity comes from hydropower. Eight countries receive 90 percent or more of their electricity from transforming water movement, and twelve nations receive at least 75 percent. How are hydroelectric power plants able to generate so much electricity? The answer has to do with how dams work and the ability of dams to store large amounts of potential energy (see Chapter 10). How much electricity a single hydroelectric power plant can generate depends on a dam's height, depth of reservoir, and efficiency of energy transformation. Taller dams and reservoirs with greater volumes have more generating capacity. The largest dams are over 2 km (1.2 mi) long and stand up to 305 m (1,000 ft) tall. Waters here are deep. In contrast, water on the other side of the dam—tail water—is extremely shallow.

For a hydroelectric power plant to generate electricity, water in a reservoir is directed through a gate and into a hollow channel called a penstock inside the dam (see Figure 14.13). Gravity-driven water rushes from a high elevation to a low elevation through the penstock and pushes against the blades of turbines. The movement of the water rotates the turbines. Just like other power plant systems, a generator transforms the rotation of the turbines into electricity. Then, in one final step, a transformer changes the voltage of the electricity and transfers it to the electric grid. Electric power lines carry the electricity to homes and businesses.

FIGURE 14.13

A hydroelectric dam funnels water from a high elevation to a low elevation through a dam structure. Water turns a turbine and a generator converts the kinetic energy to electricity. Red arrows indicate the pathway of water from the reservoir through an intake gate, penstock, to a turbine, and then out into a tail water area.

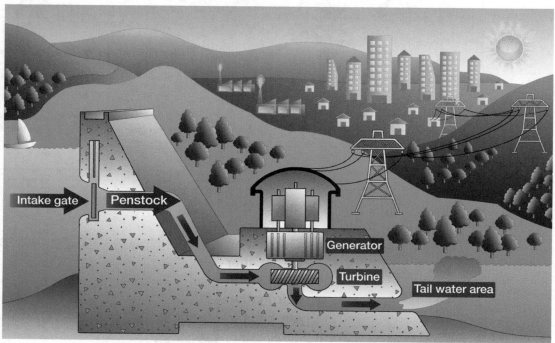

Sources: Joseph Shostell; © Shutterstock, Inc.

tidal power

Tidal energy; the kinetic energy of oceanic tides.

Tidal power is another form of hydropower society uses to generate electricity. It seems we have only just begun to tap into this energy source. By 2050, the international group Ocean Energy Systems (OES) plans to develop 300 gigawatts of wave and tidal current energy (Huckerby 2016). At the time of the writing of this book, France and South Korea have the greatest installed capacity. They have low-level dams—barrages—in tidal areas to harness the energy of tides as they move toward land and out to sea. The U.S. coastline is not ideal for barrage system power plants, but there are suitable areas for underwater turbines. Once again, New York state (see "Case Study: Wind Farms off the Coast of New York") is leading the way in energy technologies. Since 2002, the energy company Verdant has been testing tidal turbine prototypes in New York City's East River. Their efforts have paved the way for the installation of thirty commercial tidal turbines. Tidal turbines are shorter, more durable, and smaller than wind turbines (see Figure 14.14). Verdant's newest—generation five—model consists of a nacelle with 2.5-meter blades attached to a 3-meter pole mounted on the sea floor. Water pushes on the blades of the turbines, and a submerged electrical generator transforms the rotation of the turbines into electricity. The electricity is transferred from the generator to the shore by underwater cables.

FIGURE 14.14
In Scotland, a 1.5 MW tidal turbine is being readied for installation.

Source: Arild Lilleboe/Shutterstock.com

Benefits of Using Hydropower

Hydropower has many advantages over other sources of energy. The raw source of energy in hydropower is water, which is a nontoxic liquid. In many ways, it is the antithesis of benzene and other highly toxic molecules found in fossil fuels. Furthermore, hydropower is renewable. Our use of water as an energy source does not reduce the overall quantity or quality of water. As long as the water cycle continues, we will have the opportunity to rely on this renewable energy source.

Hydroelectric dams have a high efficiency of energy transformation. The efficiency rate of a large dam may be as high as 95 percent, which is much greater than the average solar panel's efficiency (about 20 percent), or even the most efficient natural gas–fired power plant (about 60 percent). After construction, hydroelectric dams need little management and can last for more than one hundred years. They are also the largest and greatest-capacity structures we use to generate electricity. Nine of the world's ten greatest-capacity power plants are hydroelectric. The world's largest power plant is the Three Gorges Dam on the Yangtze River in Hubei Province, China. A little smaller, yet still mammoth, the Grand Coulee Dam on the Columbia River in Washington generates electricity used by eleven U.S. states and Canada.

States and nations with hydroelectric plants enjoy a reliable, domestic source of energy. Reservoirs created with the intention of generating electricity can have other positives. In addition to being a source of energy, they are useful for flood control, irrigation, and recreation, such as fishing, swimming, and boating. For example, the hydroelectric Kentucky dam on the Tennessee River created the largest artificial lake in the eastern United States. Local tourism promotes the recreational value of Kentucky Lake's 160,000 acres, and anglers have reeled in state records of several fish species.

The African Union sees hydropower as a cost-effective way to provide electricity to hundreds of millions of its citizens. Over half of the continent's population does not have access to electricity, and much of the half that does only receives it intermittently. Their Agenda 2063 includes building the largest hydroelectric system to date, substantially greater in size than the Three Gorges Dam. The Grand Inga Dam system is projected to generate forty thousand megawatts and will be constructed over six phases. It is one of the African Union's high-priority projects.

Hydropower—Limitations and Environmental Impact

All sources of energy, including water, have shortcomings. The main disadvantages of using water as a source of energy are the unequal distribution of water resources geographically, displacement of people, loss of cultural heritage, destruction and fragmentation of species habitat, and release of methylmercury and greenhouse gases. Hydroelectric dams, tidal turbines, and barrage-system power plants only exist where water is present. Therefore, states and nations with rich water resources have an enhanced opportunity to construct and rely on hydroelectric power plants.

Dams displace people and destroy cultural heritage. Very likely, the largest displacement came with the construction of the Three Gorges Dam in China, which created a 660 km (410 mi) reservoir. An estimated 1.3 to 2 million people were relocated. Conversion of a river to a reservoir creates a very different aquatic ecosystem, which is often selective for different fish species. A dam also creates an impassable barrier for salmon and other migrating fish. We can offset this barrier to some extent by adding a **fish ladder** (see Figure 14.15). Fish swim against the current and jump through a series of ascending pools (the ladder), thereby circumventing the dam. However, we are failing in our assistance (Brown et al. 2012). Only about 3 percent of Atlantic salmon, American shad, and river herring are able to migrate from the sea through a maze of dams to reach their spawning grounds. Eels and other non-jumping fish species are out of luck with an ascending pools ladder. These fish need an alternative pathway to circumvent the dam.

fish ladder

A route consisting of a series of connected pools at different elevations that allows fish to bypass a dam.

FIGURE 14.15
Fish ladders provide a route for fish to move around dam structures. (A) Fish ladder sign. (B) Water runs down a fish ladder near the Bonneville Power Plant in Oregon.

Source: © Shutterstock, Inc.

The erection of a dam and creation of a reservoir also place aquatic species at risk of mercury uptake and poisoning. Terrestrial areas have naturally occuring mercury—usually in low concentrations—in addition to enrichments of mercury from the burning of fossil fuels. When the terrestrial area becomes flooded, the mercury becomes part of an aquatic ecosystem. Studies show 1.3- to 10-fold greater accumulation of methylmercury in plants and fish within reservoirs for the first three decades after construction (Calder et al. 2016). Methylmercury biomagnifies up the food chain, and it ends up in the tissues of people who eat mercury-contaminated fish (see Chapter 15). Mercury adversely affects heart rate and causes neurological abnormalities. During their first few years, reservoirs also emit a higher amount of greenhouse gases than the formerly unflooded area, as organic debris—now submerged under water—is broken down. Even with these limitations, hydroelectricity is viewed as a viable, carbon-free, and sustainable form of energy beneficial to society.

Key Takeaways

- The most common way of transforming the movement of water into electricity is to hold back a column of water with a dam, and then direct the water from a high to low elevation through turbines.
- Water has several advantages over other sources of energy. Water is nontoxic, renewable, and clean. Hydroelectric dams have a high efficiency of energy transformation and may last for over one hundred years. Finally, reservoirs may serve multiple purposes.
- The main disadvantages of using hydroelectricity are the unequal distribution of water resources globally, displacement of people and loss of their cultural heritage due to flooding, and the destruction of species habitat. Methylmercury and greenhouse gases are concerns when terrestrial areas are flooded.

14.5 Geothermal Energy, the Pros and Cons

Learning Objectives

1. Define geothermal energy and describe its potential as an energy source for society.
2. Explain the benefits of geothermal energy use.
3. Identify the limitations and environmental impact of geothermal energy use.

"No source of green energy is more promising than geothermal." These were the words of Kenyan president Uhuru Kenyatta during his speech on April 28, 2017, with the christening of a 158 MW geothermal power plant. The Okaria V power project funded by Japan is part of Kenya's plan to increase the amount of electricity generated from geothermal energy to 19,200 MW by 2030. Currently, Kenya receives 45 percent of its electricity from transforming geothermal energy (see video link: "Geothermal Energy in Kenya"). While New York (see "Case Study: Wind Farms off the Coast of New York") does not have volcanoes or hot springs like Kenya, geothermal energy does exist here and is included in New York's energy portfolio.

Geothermal Energy in Kenya

Learn more about Kenya's expanding use of geothermal energy.

View in the online reader

What Is Geothermal?

The word **geothermal** originates from the Greek words *geo* (earth) and *thermos* (heat). Therefore, use of geothermal energy means tapping into the heat of the Earth itself. The high temperature of Earth's inner core is on par with the surface of the sun, and it is the primary source of Earth's geothermal energy. This energy is widely available and renewable. About three meters (ten feet) down into the ground, the Earth's temperature is typically stable at 10–15.5°C (50–60°F), which offers warmth during cold weather and coolness during warm weather. Some geographical locations near volcanoes and tectonic plate boundaries have an even greater potential for serving as sources of energy. Subsurface temperatures in these areas are much greater, and hot geysers and hot springs often exist here. The availability of higher temperatures closer to the surface makes these places ideal sites for geothermal power plants. In the United States, the vast majority of these sites are in the west. Around the world, countries with the greatest potential for geothermal power plants exist mainly along the Pacific's Ring of Fire or near other tectonic plate boundaries (see Figure 14.16).

FIGURE 14.16

The top ten countries (labeled on map) transforming geothermal energy into electricity are located along tectonic plate boundaries (dotted lines). (A) Tourists at Lassen Volcanic National Park in California. (B) People enjoying geothermal waters in Iceland. (C) A geothermal power plant in Kenya. (D) In Indonesia, volcanic gas bubbles come up through porous rock in the ocean floor. Indonesia has only just begun to access the estimated 28,910 gigawatts (GW) available to them (Pambudi 2018).

Sources: Paulm1993/Shutterstock.com; Birol Bali/Shutterstock.com; Joseph Shostell; © Shutterstock, Inc.; data from EIA, https://www.eia.gov/energyexplained/geothermal/where-geothermal-energy-is-found.php.

Benefits of Using Geothermal Energy

Geothermal energy use has many advantages over other forms of energy. Geothermal energy is accessible twenty-four hours per day, renewable, and widely available. Society benefits from geothermal energy in three basic ways: direct interaction (direct use), transformation to electricity, and heating and cooling by way of heat pumps.

My best recollection of using geothermal energy is of soaking in the steamy warm waters near Palea Kameni within Santorini's flooded caldera. The Greek island is a lip of a caldera jutting out from the depths of the sea. Taking a bath in a geothermal hot spring is very likely one of the oldest examples of how we benefit from geothermal energy systems (see B in Figure 14.16). A swim in a hot spring and cooking food in a column of hot steam rising from the Earth itself are types of direct geothermal use. Ancient cultures, including those in Greece and China, also used geothermal energy in their district heating systems. In these cases, warm water from the ground (hydro-geothermal) is drawn from the ground and brought into a building as a source of heat. Poland recently formed a partnership with Iceland to further develop district heating systems to help reduce their reliance on coal and therefore mitigate pollution emissions. Poland is the leading exporter and second largest consumer of coal in Europe. It depends on coal-fired power plants for about 80 percent of its electricity. A change from coal to geothermal would help to improve the air quality in Warsaw and other Polish cities.

Geothermal is also an excellent source of energy for generating electricity. Twenty-three countries collectively generate over 80 billion kWh of electricity from geothermal energy. Although only about 0.4 percent of the electricity in the United States comes from geothermal power plants, the United States is the clear leader in geothermal energy use for electricity. Almost all of it comes from California (72 percent) and Nevada (22 percent). The best locations for a geothermal power plant have subsurface temperatures of at least 300°F. Geothermal power plants generate electricity by directing dry or wet steam through turbines. Dry-steam power plants are simple in design and consist of an intake steam pipe, turbines, generator, condenser, and outflow pipe. The design is slightly different for the more common wet-steam hydrothermal power plants, also known as flash steam plants. In these systems, extremely hot water under high pressure is directed to a flash tank at Earth's surface. A rapid decrease in pressure causes the water to boil rapidly into steam. As in dry-stream power plants, the steam turns a turbine (see A in Figure 14.17).

Not all geothermal resources have sufficiently high temperatures for wet- and dry-steam power plants. In these lower-temperature geothermal areas, binary cycle designs are used. Binary cycle geothermal power plants are smaller and a little different from steam plants. In these alternative electricity-generating systems, geothermal steam never contacts a turbine. Instead, the upper part of the pipe containing the geothermal fluid runs adjacent to a second pipe (hence the name binary) in a heat exchanger. Liquid in this second pipe heats up, boils, and forms steam, which moves to a turbine (see B in Figure 14.17). Since 2000, the majority of newly built utility-scale geothermal power plants in the United States have binary cycle designs.

Society further benefits from geothermal energy through the use of geothermal heat pumps. A geothermal heat pump transfers heat between indoors and outdoors. The pump is part of a geothermal pump transfer system, which consists of a hole in the ground, liquid-filled pipes that run from the hole to the building and back, and a pump that moves the water through the pipes. Water perpetually circulates between the hole and the building. Stable subsurface temperatures serve to cool the inside of a house on a hot day and heat the house on a cold day (see C in Figure 14.17).

FIGURE 14.17

Harnessing geothermal energy. (A) An illustration of the workings of a geothermal energy power plant. (B) A binary cycle geothermal power plant. (C) A geothermal heat pump system. The red lines indicate circulating hot water drawn into the house, and the blue lines indicate cold water directed outside and into the ground, where it is heated again.

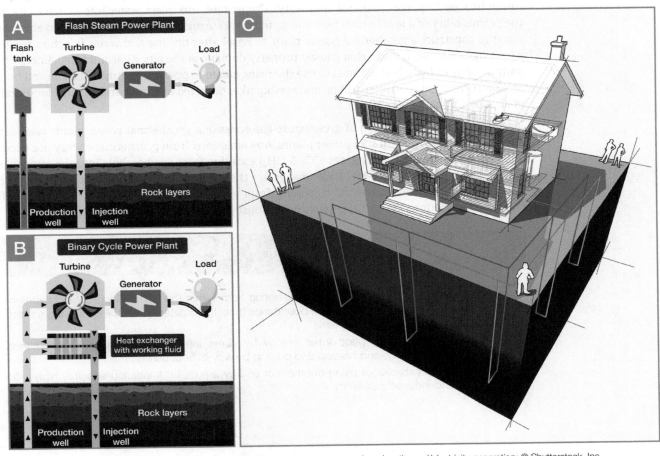

Sources: Data from Office of Energy Efficiency & Renewable Energy, https://www.energy.gov/eere/geothermal/electricity-generation; © Shutterstock, Inc.

Geothermal Limitations and Environmental Impact

The drawbacks of geothermal energy are the unequal distribution of extremely hot areas close to the surface, high startup costs, and induced seismicity. Subsurface temperatures are not uniform (nor are hydrothermal areas) across geographical locations, and some are extremely hot whereas others are just mildly warm. Locations of the greatest subsurface temperatures, known as high-enthalpy resources, offer the best potential for development of geothermal power plants and generation of electricity. States and nations that do not have these areas cannot build large geothermal power plants.

Geothermal systems have high startup costs. The typical investment cost is $4 million per megawatt (Kristjánsdóttir and Margeirsson 2014). Flash steam geothermal turbine systems are larger (average capacity of 30.4–37.4 MW) and more expensive than typically smaller binary cycle turbine systems (average capacity of 6.3 MW) designed for medium-temperature geothermal areas (Tomarov and Shipkov 2017). Approximately half of the developmental cost is for drilling and lining the wells (Capuano 2016). Smaller geothermal heat pump systems for individual houses have steep initial expenses too, but financial investments are easily recouped as time progresses. Post-construction, a geothermal power plant has little upkeep and low running costs—much less than those associated with conventional power plants.

Drilling deep wells of up to five kilometers for the development of a geothermal energy system can induce earthquakes (induced seismicity). Companies also inject water into a well to increase the permeability of a geothermal reservoir or to create steam. Engineers in Switzerland abandoned plans to construct a geothermal power plant in Basel after drilling and water injection triggered a 3.4 magnitude earthquake that caused property damage in the city (Giardini 2009). Energy company Geopower Basel had planned to use the rising steam to power one hundred thousand homes. Similar correlations between drilling and earthquakes occurred in France and El Salvador (Bommer et al. 2006, Cuenot et al. 2011).

In an overall comparison of greenhouse gas emissions, geothermal power plants release just a fraction relative to fossil fuel power plants. Any emissions from geothermal energy use occur as a result of stored greenhouse gases (CO_2 & CH_4) escaping from the borehole into the atmosphere. Research conducted in Italy and Iceland suggests the negligible amount is already part of the carbon cycle, which includes natural degassing from geothermal and volcanic areas and therefore should not be counted as anthropogenic greenhouse gas emissions (Ármannsson 2003).

Key Takeaways

- Geothermal energy is heat energy originating from within the Earth. Geographical locations near volcanoes and tectonic plate boundaries have the greatest potential for serving as ideal sites for geothermal power plants.
- Society benefits from geothermal energy by direct interaction, transforming geothermal energy to electricity, and heating and cooling by way of heat pumps.
- The main drawbacks of using geothermal energy are that it's location specific, high initial costs, and induced seismicity.

14.6 Wind Energy, the Pros and Cons

Learning Objectives

1. Describe the formation of wind and identify the geographical areas with bountiful wind power.
2. Identify, explain, and reflect on the benefits of society's relying on wind energy to generate electricity.
3. Recognize the limitations and environmental effects of using wind energy.

The opening story in this chapter described New York's plan to build the nation's largest offshore wind farms. New York is not the only state evaluating future energy needs, nor is the United States the only nation investing in wind energy technology. Kenya, in Eastern Africa, has come out as a wind-technology leader. They recently created the largest wind farm on the African continent, consisting of 365 wind turbines with a total capacity of 310 megawatts. The Lake Turkana project in northwestern Kenya reduces the need for fossil fuels, and according to the African Development Bank Group, prevents up to 735,000 tons of carbon dioxide emissions annually. In this section, we describe wind energy and the advantages and disadvantages of wind as a source of energy.

Wind Energy: What Is Wind Energy and How Do We Harness It?

Wind is the natural movement of air. It is, for example, the light breeze on your cheek in the fall or the strong gusts of air right before the thunderstorm. Wind is also an artifact of an unequal distribution of solar energy on Earth. Upon heating, parcels of air become less dense and ascend, creating a low-pressure area (see Chapter 5 and Chapter 11). Cooler air then moves in the direction of low pressure. The movement of air in response to differences in temperature and pressure, along with the rotation of the Earth, explains the movement patterns of large convection cells between the equator and poles. Land features and oceans and other large bodies of water also contribute to wind speed and direction. A sea breeze moves from above a cool body of water to a warm, low-pressure area over land in daytime and reverses at night. Offshore winds tend to be stronger and steadier than on-land winds, making coastlines ideal spots for wind farms (see "Case Study: Wind Farms off the Coast of New York").

In the United States, the Great Plains, just east of the Rockies, make another ideal location for wind turbines. Prevailing winds coming from the Pacific move eastward, first hitting the western side of the United States. The winds drop in temperature and release water as they scale the western side of the Rocky Mountains. Then, the prevailing winds rush down the east slope of the Rocky Mountains and continue to travel eastward across the open Great Plains. Observe the wind-speed map of the United States created by the National Renewable Energy Laboratory (NREL) (see Figure A in Figure 14.18). Speeds represent wind moving 80 meters above the ground, which is a common operating height of wind turbines. Notice the purple, red, and blue representing high wind-speed areas mostly on either the east and west coastlines, in the Great Plains, and in the Great Lakes area. Compare these locations of higher wind speeds to established wind farms shown in B in Figure 14.18. Wind turbines are located in high-wind areas, with the majority in the Great Plains. Finally, compare the wind-generating capacity per state. Right now, Texas is a clear leader in harnessing wind energy.

Wind energy accounts for a little over 3 percent of U.S. energy consumption, and it is the primary source of energy for about 8.5 percent of the total electricity generation in the United States (see Figure 14.19). Its share is rapidly expanding. Globally, soaring numbers of wind turbine installations have increased capacity to over 700 GW. This capacity continues to grow in leaps and bounds—sometimes almost 20 percent per year—with the largest increases occurring in China and the Untied States.

FIGURE 14.18

Wind turbines are erected in areas where there is bountiful wind power. Compare average annual wind speeds 80 meters above the ground (A) to the location of wind farms (B). Numbers represent current wind farm capacity per state.

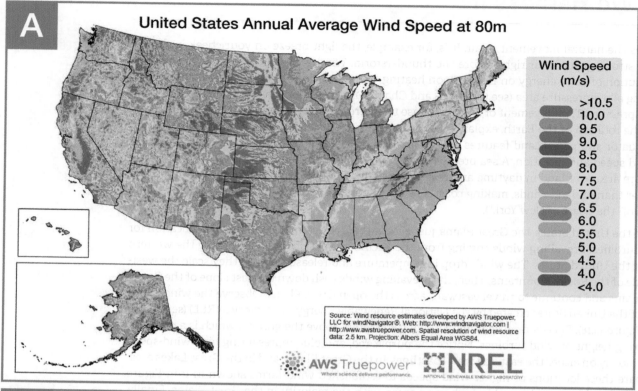

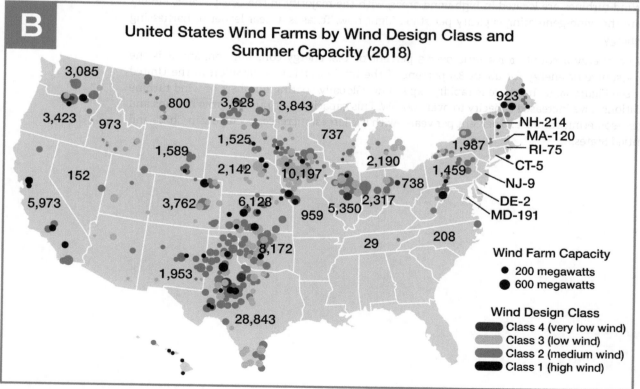

Sources: Adapted from NREL, https://windexchange.energy.gov/maps-data?category=land-based; U.S. Energy Information Administration, Form EIA-860, Annual Electric Generator Report.

FIGURE 14.19
Wind accounts for only a small fraction of all energy sources in the United States (A), and roughly one-fifth of renewable energies (B). The many benefits of wind energy combined with greater demands for energy and concerns about nonrenewable sources of energy have driven a strong increase in wind capacity in the United States since 2000 (C).

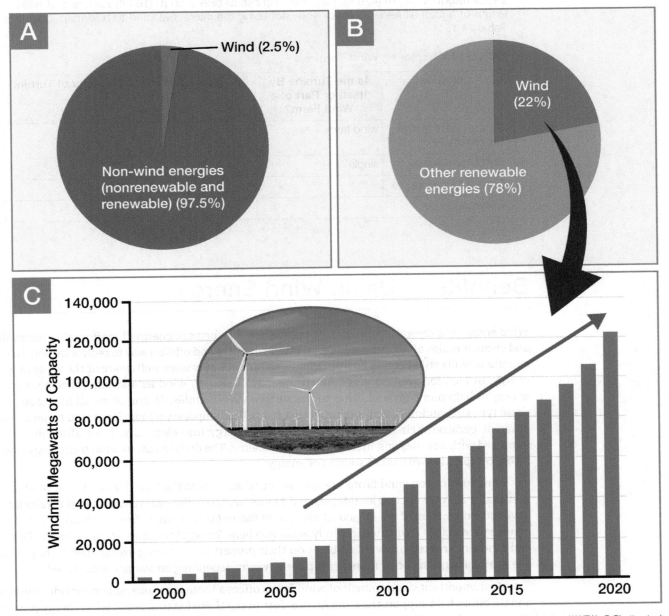

Sources: Joseph Shostell; data from EIA, https://www.eia.gov/energyexplained/us-energy-facts/; data from American Wind Energy Association (AWEA); © Shutterstock, Inc.

Bringing It Closer to Home: Locate a Wind Turbine

As of January 2020, the United States had 63,003 wind turbines with a combined capacity of 100,255 megawatts (MW). In this exercise, go to the interactive map here to locate the closest wind turbine to your home. The light green areas on the displayed map indicate high densities of wind turbines. Type in your city and state into the upper right search bar and click return. This brings you to the desired location. For example, if you type in East Grand Forks, Minnesota, a blue dot signifying a turbine will appear. Hover the curser above the dot to reveal details. The wind turbine in East Grand Forks went online in 2010 and has a total height of 35 m (115 ft). It is also possible to search by project name. For the next search, type Pilot Hill in the "Search by Project Name" box in the upper left and click enter. When you do this, a collection of 103 wind turbines in Illinois is displayed. Hover the cursor over individual dots to gather more information about the turbines. Each of these turbines is much larger than the one in East Grand Forks. For instance, the easternmost turbine, number 3049858, has a rotor diameter of 100 m (328 ft) and a total height of 130 m (426 ft). Each blade in this turbine is 50 m (164 ft) long, almost half the length of a football field. To check your skill using the interactive wind turbine map, complete Table 14.1.

TABLE 14.1 Exploring Wind Turbines

Location	Is the Turbine By Itself or Part of a Wind Farm?	Height of Turbine	Capacity of Turbine
Off the coast of New Shoreham, RI	wind farm		
East Grand Forks	single		
Closest to your home			
Chicago			

Benefits of Using Wind Energy

Wind energy has several advantages over nonrenewable forms of energy. It is affordable, renewable, and clean. It is also often compatible with other land uses and offers a way to reduce carbon dioxide emissions while still meeting energy demands. Our ancestors were well aware of the value of wind energy. In fact, for over 150 years, Americans have relied on wind as a steady, reliable source of energy to help pump ground water to the surface via windmills. At one point, all fifty states had these types of windmills, and some still exist today. Contemporary windmills—wind turbines—are different because their role is to transform wind energy into electricity. Their affordability has improved with new designs, increased size, and scaling. The drop in cost of wind technology makes it cost competitive with other sources of energy.

Wind turbines on wind farms are spaced out, which means the majority of land on wind farms is available for other activities (Meyers and Meneveau 2010). For example, standard turbines that have rotor diameters of 91.1 m (300 ft) are spaced 640 m (2,100 ft) apart from each other. All of this excess space makes farmlands in windy areas excellent for wind turbines. More and more farmers and ranchers are erecting wind turbines on their properties. By selling excess energy they do not use, they can earn $2,000 or more per turbine per year, depending on average wind speeds.

Most important, development of wind farms offers a route to reduce carbon dioxide emissions and therefore help support the Paris Accord. Just in the United States, use of wind energy prevents the release of 201 million metric tons of carbon dioxide annually, and to date it has spurred the creation of 114,000 jobs. Under an energy agenda initiated by President George W. Bush in 2006, one goal of the U.S. Department of Energy is that wind will provide 20 percent of U.S. electricity by 2030 (USDOE 2008). The International Renewable Energy Agency predicts that we will need to generate more than one-third of our global electricity needs from wind power by 2050 (IRENA 2019). This entails increasing the total capacity of onshore and offshore wind farms by three-fold and ten-fold respectively by 2050 compared to 2018. The change would have the effect of reducing 6.3 gigatonnes of carbon dioxide emissions annually. Can society do it? These predictions come with aggressive plans for rapid development.

Wind Energy—Limitations and Environmental Impact

Wind energy does not have many drawbacks. The main disadvantages of wind energy are the unequal geographic distribution of wind currents, costly distribution networks for electricity, release of sulfur hexafluoride (SF_6, a potent greenhouse gas), and mortality and disturbance of wildlife. Wind and solar have some of the same issues. For instance, the usefulness of both sources depends on location and time of day. Average wind speeds in some areas are insufficient for generating electricity (see Figure 14.18). For example, wind speeds for much of the interior southeastern United States are too low to make wind farms economically competitive with other methods of generating electricity. Distribution networks for electricity are an issue as well. Because good wind sites are often remote, transmission lines must be created to transfer the electricity to cities. Installing lines and substations to service them can be costly.

To completely switch from fossil fuels to renewable energies such as wind and solar, all machines (stoves, cars, trains, and so on) would need to be swapped out for electric versions. Changes like this require large financial investments and government incentives. As we wean off of fossil fuels and switch to relying on renewable energies, our demand for electricity and electrical infrastructure increases. So too does demand for sulfur hexafluoride because it is a component in electrical equipment. Emissions of SF_6 into the atmosphere due to maintenance, replacement, and leakage are an issue (Simmonds et al. 2020). SF_6 is no ordinary greenhouse gas; its global warming potential is 23,500 times greater than that of carbon dioxide over a 100-year time span. Scientists are now searching for greener alternatives to SF_6.

A number of investigations into the effects of wind turbines on wildlife have shown that the turbines directly kill birds and bats, and wind farms can disrupt wildlife habitats (Erickson et al. 2001). Any loss of wildlife is a point of concern, but studies have not documented any significant population declines. On average, each windmill kills approximately two birds per year. These numbers pale in comparison to the estimated eighty million avian mortalities on roadways and one hundred million mortalities from domestic cats each year.

Undoubtedly, wind farms would be more common today if everyone were receptive to having a windmill installed within view of their home. A subset of people generally support windmills but consider them eyesores on an otherwise beautiful landscape. Such opposition is referred to as Not In My Backyard Syndrome (NIMBYS). There are certainly many successes in wind farm development, but NIMBYS has obstructed scores of planned wind projects.

Key Takeaways

- The distribution, consistency, and speed of winds are the result of geographical location, proximity to large bodies of water and mountains, differences in temperature and pressure, and Earth's rotation.
- Wind energy comes with many advantages, including reduced carbon dioxide emissions, affordability, and renewability.
- The main disadvantages of wind energy are the unequal geographical distribution of wind currents, costly distribution networks for electricity, release of sulfur hexafluoride (a potent greenhouse gas), and mortality and disturbance of wildlife.

14.7 A Look to the Future: Moving Toward Sustainable Use of Energy

Learning Objectives

1. Compare the costs of different energy technologies.
2. Assess New York's energy strategy for developing a cleaner future.

Personal computers, cell phones, cars, and washing machines are examples of modern-day conveniences that only work with access to energy. Most would agree with me when I state that we do not want to give up these luxuries. However, society's use of energy is also the root cause of many environmental problems. With this realization, we might fall into the trap of thinking we must decide between owning electronic gadgetry or living on a healthy, clean planet. However, this really is not the decision that faces us today, because some forms of energy solve key environmental problems. Our decisions about which forms of energy to use depend on the advantages and disadvantages of each energy source. All forms of energy have pros and cons, but solar, wind, and other forms of renewable energies come with fewer environmental problems compared to nonrenewable sources of energy. Decisions about energy also depend on costs. In this last section, we compare the costs of different energy sources and then revisit the opening case study about New York state.

Current and Future Levelized Costs of Different Energy Technologies

levelized cost

A cost used to compare different energy technologies and that accounts for a power plant's building costs, lifespan, and management and operational costs.

Economists and environmental scientists sometimes use a **levelized cost** approach to compare different energy technologies used for generating electricity. The levelized cost for electricity is "the price at which the generated electricity should be sold for the system to break even at the end of its lifetime" (Papapetrou and Kosmadakis 2022). Cost in this case is referred to as the price of electricity at the point where the power plant connects to the electrical grid. Building costs, operation and management needs, fuel needs, construction time, and expected lifespan can vary greatly among different types of power plants. A levelized cost approach accounts for these differences and allows a way to compare the different methods of generating electricity. How do the different sources of renewable energy compare with nonrenewable energies (see Figure 14.20)?

FIGURE 14.20
Different energy technologies have different costs. Predicted levelized cost of generating electricity in 2025 (bars) and 2040 (dotted lines) using different technologies.

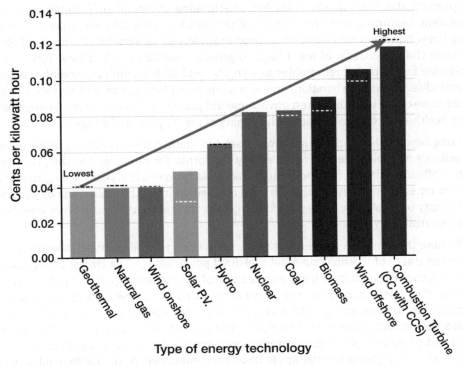

Source: Joseph Shostell; data from EIA, https://www.eia.gov/outlooks/aeo/pdf/electricity_generation.pdf.

Renewable energies are price-competitive with nonrenewable energies. For instance, a levelized cost comparison indicates solar photovoltaic and geothermal as the most economical technologies to generate electricity, significantly less than any technology applied to nonrenewable energy. Furthermore, prices of clean, renewable energies are declining every year, with economies of scale and improved designs. Economies of scale refers to the decrease of the average cost per unit (i.e., a solar panel) as the company increases production. Between 2010 and 2020, the cost of offshore wind, onshore wind, and solar technology systems dropped by 48 percent, 56 percent, and 85 percent, respectively, and continue to decline (IRENA 2021). The cost of electricity from solar photovoltaic technology is expected to decline to about 2.7 cents per kilowatt hour by 2040. Going forward, we predict the largest drop in cost to occur in electricity generated through offshore wind farms. Offshore wind farms such as those being built off the coast of New York (see "Case Study: Wind Farms off the Coast of New York") will pave the way for these reductions (see video link: "Offshore Wind Farms"). By 2040, we also expect onshore wind turbines to be more cost effective at generating electricity than the most advanced natural gas power plants.

Offshore Wind Farms
Observe the construction of a new wind farm off the coast of Yorkshire, England.

View in the online reader

Opening Story Revisited: Wind Farms Off the Coast of New York

New York state has ambitious, yet realistic energy goals. By 2040, the state expects 70 percent of all of their electricity to come from renewable energy sources and 100 percent to be carbon-free. Can it reach these sustainable goals? To do so takes commitment, financial investments, and people with the appropriate skills to install and maintain clean energy technologies. The plan entails transitioning from a current energy portfolio of about one-fourth petroleum to renewable energies such as wind and solar. Additionally, New York is decommissioning some of its nuclear power plants and replacing nuclear energy with renewable energies.

Billions of dollars from a combination of private investors and state funds have helped New York implement the early phases of its forward-thinking energy plan. Visionaries see a return on investment, beginning with the creation of thousands of new jobs and a boost to the state's economy. Greenhouse gas emissions would drop precipitously as would all forms of pollution originating from the combustion of fossil fuels to generate electricity. When New York converts its transportation sector to full renewables as well, this will all but eliminate greenhouse gas emissions, ground-level ozone generation, and emissions of sulfur dioxide and nitrogen oxides—all sources of some of the world's greatest environmental problems. Cleaner air would avert billions of dollars in health-care costs and improve the quality of life for people of all ages.

Looking beyond New York, we see every state and many countries moving in the direction of greater reliance on renewable sources of energy. California, for example, is in the planning stages of building offshore wind farms, and Portugal has already shown it is possible to generate all electricity from renewable energy. In 2016, Portugal reached an important milestone by generating all of its electricity on renewable energy for four days. Portugal is planning to achieve greenhouse gas emissions neutrality by 2050.

Right now, the world is experiencing a change in energy infrastructure. Developed countries are in various stages of mothballing fossil fuel–fired power plants. The largest changes will occur in developing countries. Africa will experience some of the highest population growth in the coming decades. Every person, no matter their country of origin, has the right to a high standard of living and access to clean energy. The African Union's 2063 Agenda describes a bright future for its citizens that is supportive of social cultures and access to electricity for all. The "all" includes the estimated 50 percent of African citizens who currently do not have access to electricity and therefore endure unnecessary hardships in health and education. Agenda 2063 involves the use of renewable energies and supports the United Nations Sustainable Development Goals. Because of the many benefits of clean energy, the market share of renewable energy in global electricity will likely continue to maintain rapid growth. Just in New York, we have witnessed use of solar energy increase by 1,500 percent since 2011. Strong growth of solar, wind, and hydrothermal will continue, and we can expect wind turbines and solar panels to become common sights. Which renewable energies will be most popular? The answer depends on geographical location. Do not forget, every source of energy has advantages and disadvantages, but any shortcomings of renewable energies pale when compared with those of nonrenewables. The question for each of us is, "How will we assist society in making this change?"

Key Takeaways

- A levelized cost approach accounts for differences in building costs, operation and management needs, fuel needs, construction time, and expected lifespan of power plants.
- New York state plans to transition from relying on fossil fuels to renewable sources of energy. They are investing in solar, wind, hydropower, and geothermal technologies.

FIGURE 14.21 Visual Overview: Renewable Energy Sources
Summarizing figure: Society is increasingly making use of renewable sources of energy (14.1), including biomass (14.2), solar (14.3), hydropower (14.4), geothermal (14.5), and wind (14.6). Each has pros and cons but causes fewer environmental problems than any nonrenewable energy source. Renewable technologies are predicted to become even more price competitive (14.7).

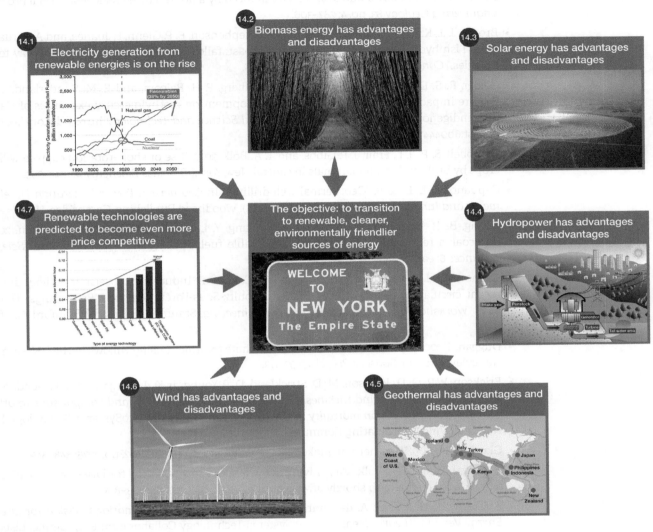

Sources: Joseph Shostell; See previous citations for image credits.

14.8 References

- Ali, S. H., D. Giurco, N. Arndt, E. Nickless, G. Brown, A. Demetriades, R. Durrheim, et al. 2017. "Mineral Supply for Sustainable Development Requires Resource Governance." *Nature* 543: 367–72.

- Alkin, M., P. Bayer, S. P. Harish, and J. Urpelainen. 2017. "Does basic energy access generate socioeconomic benefits? A field experiment with off-grid solar power in India." *Science Advances* 3: e16202153.

- Ajjawi, I., J. Verruto, M. Aqui, L. B. Soriaga, J. Coppersmith, K. Kwok, L. Peach, E. Orchard, R. Kalb, W. Xu, T. J. Carson, K. Francis, K. Kongsfeld, J. Bartalis, A. Schultz, W. Lambert, A. S. Schwartz, R. Brown, and E. R. Moellering. 2017. "Lipid production in *Nannochloropsis gaditana* is doubled by decreasing expression of a single transcriptional regulator." *Nature Biotechnology* 35: 647–652.

- Ármannsson, H. 2003. "CO_2 emission from geothermal plants." *International Geothermal Conference*, Reykjavík, Iceland.
- Bommer, J. J., S. Oates, J. M. Cepeda, C. Lindholm, J. Bird, R. Torres, G. Marroquín, and J. Rivas. 2006. "Control of hazard due to seismicity induced by a hot fractured rock geothermal project." *Engineering Geology* 83, no. 4: 287–306.
- Brown, J. J., K. E. Limburg, J. R. Waldman, K. Stephenson, E. P. Glenn, F. Juanes, and A. Jordaan. 2012. "Fish hydropower on the U.S. Atlantic coast: failed fisheries policies from half-way technologies." *Conservation Letters* 6, no. 4: 280–286.
- Calder, R. S. D., A. T. Schartup, M. Li, A. P. Valberg, P. H. Balcom, and E. M. Sunderland. 2016. "Future impacts of hydroelectric power development on methylmercury exposures of Canadian indigenous communities." *Environmental Science and Technology*. https://doi.org/10.1021/acs.est.6b04447.
- Campbell, S. P., J. L. Frair, J. P. Gibbs, and T. A. Bolk. 2012. "Use of short-rotation coppice willow crops by birds and small mammals in central New York." *Biomass Bioenergy* 47: 342–353.
- Capuano Jr., L. E. 2016. "Geothermal well drilling." In *Geothermal Power Generation Developments and Innovation*: 107–139 (Ed.: DiPippo, R.). Woodhead Publishing. Cambridge, UK.
- Cheng, B., B. Huang, R. Zhang, Y. Chen, S. Jiang, Y. Lu, X. Zhang, H. Jiang, and H. Yu. 2020. "Bio-coal: a renewable and massively producible fuel from lignocellulosic biomass." *Science Advances* 6: eaay0748.
- Cuenot, N., M. Frogneux, C. Dorbath, and M. Calo. 2011. "Induced microseismic activity during recent circulation tests at the EGS site of Soultz-Sous-Forétz (France)." *Proceedings, Thirty-Sixth Workshop in Geothermal Reservoir Engineering*, Stanford University, Stanford, California.
- Duggan, J. 2005. "The potential for landfill leachate treatment using willows in the UK—a critical review." *Resour Conserv Recycl* 45: 97–113.
- Erickson, W.P., G. D. Johnson, M. D. Strickland, D. P. Young, Jr K. J. Sernja, and R. E. Good. 2001. *Avian collisions with wind turbines: a summary of existing studies and comparisons to other sources of avian collision mortality in the United States*. Western EcoSystems Technology Inc. National Wind Coordinating Committee Resource Document.
- Giardini, D. 2009. "Geothermal quake risks must be faced." *Nature* 462, no. 7275: 848–849.
- Heavey, J. P., and T. A. Volk. 2014. "Living snow fences show potential for large storage capacity and reduced drift length shortly after planting." *Agro for Syst.* 88: 803–814.
- Huckerby, J., H. Jeffrey, A. de Andres, and L. Finlay. 2016. *An International Vision for Ocean Energy Version III 2017*. Ocean Energy Systems Technology Collaboration Programme. Lisbon, Portugal.
- International Renewable Energy Agency (IRENA). 2019. "Future of Wind Deployment, Investment, Technology, Grid Integration and Socio-Economic Aspects." International Renewable Energy Agency. Abu Dhabi, United Arab Emirates.
- IRENA. 2021. "Renewable Power Generation Costs in 2020." *International Renewable Energy Agency*. Abu Dhabi, United Arab Emirates.
- Jacobson, M. Z., M. A. Delucchi, G. Bazouin, Z. A. F. Bauer, C. C. Heavey, E. Fisher, S. B. Morris, D. J. Y. Piekutowski, T. A. Vencill, and T. W. Yeskoo. 2015. "100% clean renewable wind, water, and sunlight (WWS) all-sector energy roadmaps for the 50 United States." *Energy Environ. Sci.* 8: 2093–2117.
- Jacobson, M. Z., R. W. Howarth, M. A. Delucchi, S. R. Scobie, J. M. Barth, M. J. Dvorak, M. Klevze, H. Katkhuda, B. Miranda, N. A. Chowdhury, R. Jones, L. Plano, and A. R. Ingraffea. 2013. "Examining the feasibility of converting New York State's all-purpose energy infrastructure to one using wind, water, and sunlight." *Energy Policy* 57: 585–601.
- Jean, J., A. Want, and V. Bulović. 2016. "In situ vapor-deposited parylene substrates for ultra-thin, lightweight organic solar cells." *Organic Electronics* 31: 120–126.

- Johnson, G., T. Volk, K. Hallen, S. Shi, M. Bickell, and J. Heavey. 2018. "Shrub willow biomass production ranking across three harvests in New York and Minnesota." *BioEnergy Research* 11: 305–315.

- Johnson, M. M., S. C. Kao, N. M. Samu, and R. Uria-Martinez. 2020. "Existing Hydropower Assets, 2020." HydroSource. Oak Ridge National Laboratory, Oak Ridge, TN. https://doi.org/10.21951/ EHA_FY2020/1608428.

- King, R. R., D. C. Law, K. M. Edmondson, C. M. Fetzer, G. S. Kinsey, H. Yoon, R. A. Sherif, and N. H. Karam. 2007. "Efficient metamorphic GaInP/GaInAs/Ge multijunction solar cells." *Applied Physics Letters* 90. https://doi.org/10.1063/1.2734507.

- Kristjánsdóttir, H., and Á. Margeirsson. 2014. "Geothermal Cost and Investment Factors." In: *Elsevier Reference Module in Chemistry, Molecular Sciences and Chemical Engineering* (Ed.: Reedijk, J.). Waltham, MA: Elsevier. 21-Jan-15. https://doi.org/10.1016/B978-0-12-409548-9.09464-1.

- Lovich, J. E., and J. R. Ennen. 2011. "Wildlife conservation and solar energy development in the desert southwest, U.S." *BioScience* 61: 982–992.

- Mackay, D. J. C. 2013. "Solar energy in the context of energy use, energy transportation and energy storage." *Philosophical Transactions of the Royal Society A.* https://doi.org/10.1098/ resta.2011.0431.

- Manuel, J. 2007. "Battle of the biofuels." *Environmental Health Perspectives* 115, no. 2: A92–A95.

- Meyers, J. and C. Meneveau. 2010. "Optimal turbine spacing in fully developed wind-farm boundary layers." *Wind Energy* 15: 305–317.

- Ministry of Agriculture of China (MAC). 2015. *The National 13th Five-year Sustainable Development Plan for Agriculture.* Ministry of Agriculture of the People's Republic of China, Beijing, China.

- Mishra, V., R. D. Retherford, and K. R. Smith. 2002. "Indoor air pollution: the quiet killer." East-West Center report 63: https://www.jstor.org/stable/resrep16005.

- Mlekuž, D. 2009. "The materiality of dung: the manipulation of dung in Neolithic Mediterranean caves." *Documenta Praehistorica* XXXVI: 219–245. https://doi.org/10.4312/dp.36.14.

- New York State Assembly Memorandum in Support of Legislation, submitted in accordance with Assembly Rule III, Sec 1(f).

- New York State Energy Research and Development Authority (NYSERDA). 2019. *Fact Sheet Offshore Wind in New York State.* NYSERDA, Albany, NY.

- Pambudi, N. 2018. "Geothermal power generation in Indonesia, a country within the ring of fire: current status, future development and policy." *Renewable and Sustainable Energy Reviews* 81: 2893–2901. https://doi.org/10.1016/j.rser.2017.06.096.

- Papapetrou, M., and G. Kosmadakis. 2022. "Resource, environmental, and economic aspects of SGHE." In: *Salinity Gradient Heat Engines* (Eds.: Tamburini, A., A. Cipollina, and G. Micale). Sawston, UK. Woodhead Publishing.

- Pope, C. A., M. Ezzati, D. W. Dockery. 2009. "Fine-particulate air pollution and life expectancy in the United States." *The New England Journal of Medicine* 360, no. 4: 376–386.

- Samu, N. M., D. Singh, M. Johnson, S. C. Kao, S. Gangrade, S. Curd, and B. T. Smith. 2020. The 2020 National Hydropower Map, Version 1. United States. National Hydropower Asset Assessment Program. Oak Ridge National Laboratory, Oak Ridge, TN. https://doi.org/10.21951/ MapPoster_FY20/1634829.

- Simmonds, P. G., M. Rigby, A. J. Manning, S. Park, K. M. Stanley, A. McCulloch, S. Henne, F. Graziosi, M. Maione, J. Arduini, S. Reimann, M. K. Vollmer, J. Mühle, S. O'Doherty, D. Young, P. B. Krummel, P. J. Frazer, R. F. Weiss, P. K. Salameh, C. M. Harth, Mi-Kyung Park, J. H. Park, T. Arnold, C. Rennick, L. P. Steele, B. Mitrevski, R. H. J. Wang, and R. G. Prinn. 2020. "The increasing atmospheric burden of the greenhouse gas sulfur hexafluoride (SF6)." *Atmospheric Chemistry and Physics.* https://doi.org/10.5194/acp-2020-117.

- Tomarov, G. V., and A. A. Shipkov. 2017. "Modern geothermal power: binary cycle geothermal power plants." *Thermal Engineering* 64, no. 4: 243–250.
- United States Department of Energy. 2008. *Twenty percent wind energy by 2030: Increasing wind energy's contribution to U.S. electricity supply.* Oak Ridge, Tennessee: U.S. Department of Energy.
- United States Energy Information Administration (USEIA). 2020. *Annual Energy Outlook 2020 with Projections to 2050.* U.S. Information Administration, Office of Energy Analysis, U.S. Department of Energy, Washington, DC.
- Walston, L. J., K. E. Lagory, and K. Szoldatits. 2016. "A preliminary assessment of avian mortality at utility-scale solar energy facilities in the United States." *Renewable Energy* 92: 405–414.

CHAPTER 15
Environmental Health and Toxicology

Case Study: COVID-19

"You don't have the right to infect me." "It's not about your life. You do not have the right to risk someone else's life." Such were the strong words of then-New York Governor Andrew Cuomo, who spoke in 2020 about the importance of social distancing because of the seriousness of **COVID-19**, the ease of its spread, and mounting deaths. New York was an initial epicenter of COVID-19 infections in the United States. Just in the state of New York, hundreds of thousands were infected and hundreds died each day during the months of March, April, and May of 2020. In the first thirteen days, the number of infections in New York reached 613 and the first fatality occurred. Nine days later, over 25,000 New Yorkers were infected and the daily death toll exceeded 100. Four days later, the number of infected surged to 52,000 and soon surpassed 100,000. Daily death rates leapt from 100 to over 200 in four days, and then to 400 in another four days. At the peak, thirty-seven days after the first infection and twenty-five days after the first fatality, almost 800 New Yorkers died in one twenty-four-hour period. The number of sick overwhelmed New York's health-care system, and victims' bodies had to be stacked and stored in moveable, refrigerated semi-trailers acting as makeshift morgues (see Figure 15.1). When the number of COVID-19 cases in New York reached 25,000, roughly half of all national cases were in New York alone. This ratio changed as New York's infection curve leveled off and then decreased, while the national and global numbers of infections and deaths continued to rise. By mid-August 2021, the number of confirmed COVID-19 cases around the world reached 206 million, and the number of deaths exceeded 4.3 million. Approximately three months after the initial known outbreak, and after COVID-19 had spread to more than 100 countries, the World Health Organization (WHO) declared it a **pandemic**, a worldwide spread of disease.

As COVID-19 spread across the United States and the world, it became clear that not all communities were equally affected. Both in NYC and elsewhere, a disproportionate number of high-poverty and minority communities had high infection and mortality rates (Boserup et al. 2020, Cyrus et al. 2020). The situation was exacerbated in some communities, such as Flint, Michigan, that had not fully recovered from a prior public health crisis. The Flint community had recently been dealing with lead-contaminated drinking water (Gómez et al. 2018, Hanna-Attisha et al. 2016). Dependable access to clean water is critical for basic human health, even more so during a pandemic (see Figure 15.2).

COVID-19

Disease caused by SARS-CoV-2. The first known outbreak of COVID-19 occurred in late 2019 and continues today, infecting millions of people.

pandemic

A spread of a disease over a large geographical area across multiple countries (can be of global scale) affecting a large number of people.

risk

Possibility of injury or loss.

virus

An ultramicroscopic (20–200 nanometers) infectious agent that has some life-like properties and needs a host cell to reproduce.

SARS-CoV-2

Virus responsible for COVID-19.

zoonotic diseases

Zoonosis; a disease spread between animals and humans.

environmental hazards

A factor in the environment with the potential to adversely affect human health and therefore is considered a threat to humans.

FIGURE 15.1
Global COVID-19 cases and fatalities (A). In the photo (B), a line of refrigerated trucks near Bellevue Hospital in New York City acted as temporary morgues for the hundreds of people who died each day at the initial epicenter of the COVID-19 outbreak in the United States.

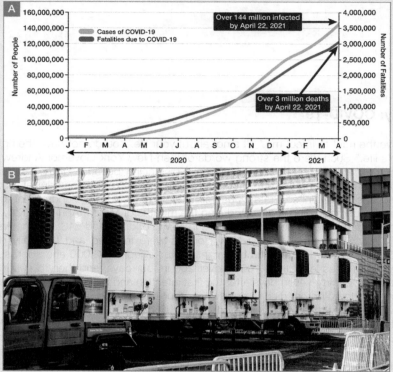

Sources: Joseph Shostell; data from COVID-19 Tracker, https://www.bing.com/covid?vert=graph; Tvalerii eidlin/Shutterstock.com

As the disease moved through the global population in 2020 and 2021, and continues to resurge today, we aimed (and aim) to protect the noninfected human population. We also want to protect those previously infected who are at **risk** of infection again, and, furthermore, to protect against similar events caused by environmental hazards in the future. How can we accomplish these tasks? Minimizing an environmental risk begins with identifying it and where it came from. In the case of COVID-19, we identified and classified a new **virus** (**SARS-CoV-2**), but what was its point of origin? About half of all human diseases, and probably COVID-19 as well, originate from other species. Well-known examples of these **zoonotic diseases** include rabies, avian flu, Lyme disease, malaria, and Ebola. When appropriate and if possible, vaccinations can protect those at risk (see Section 5).

A zoonotic disease and lead-poisoned water are just two of the many examples of **environmental hazards** to health. In this chapter, we explore the full spectrum of environmental hazards, including chemical, biological, physical, and sociocultural hazards. Each can be enhanced or mitigated by anthropogenic activities.

FIGURE 15.2

In Flint, Michigan, which has one of the highest poverty rates among cities in the United States, residents were still recovering from a crisis involving lead-contaminated water when COVID-19 infected their community. A sign states where to drop off water donations (A), and the National Guard distributes bottled water (B). The donated water helped residents avoid drinking lead-contaminated water until the problem with the pipes was fixed.

Sources: Barbara Kalbfleisch/Shutterstock.com; Linda Parton/Shutterstock.com

15.1 Environmental Health and Types of Hazards

Learning Objectives

1. Define environmental health.
2. Explain the connection between socioeconomic status and risk from environmental hazards.
3. Describe how human behaviors and society's activities affect risk from environmental hazards.
4. Identify the four categories of environmental hazards.

Life, inherently, comes with risks. Our health and very lives are continuously threatened from the moment we are born through the end of our days. **Environmental health**, which is the topic of this chapter, is a branch of public health focused on identifying, understanding, and mitigating environmental hazards that affect human health and well-being. An environmental health scientist attempts to address these environmental hazards and therefore improve our lives. Consider what your individual health needs are and the barriers to those needs. Some communities lack access to clean water and fresh, nutritious food; other communities endure polluted air; and still others are at heightened risk from contagious diseases. These factors are not mutually exclusive, and furthermore may be synergistic.

environmental health

A branch of public health focused on identifying, understanding, and mitigating environmental hazards that affect human health and well-being.

The Purpose of Environmental Health

noncommunicable disease

A non-contagious disease.

We study environmental hazards because human life and health are important. Moreover, we value a high quality of life and equal protection of health and well-being for all people regardless of culture, religion, gender, and socioeconomic status. Life, however, does have an end point. Genetics and environmental factors and the interaction between the two limit our life spans. Not counting COVID-19, which killed an estimated three million people in 2020, the leading causes of human mortality at the global level are cardiovascular (heart) disease, cancer, respiratory disease, and dementia (see Figure 15.3). Over 18 million people die from heart disease every year. Somewhat hidden within this group of global data, there are two general trends across countries. In developed countries, including the United States, the leading causes of death are usually long-term, **noncommunicable diseases**. Mirroring what we see at the global level, heart disease, cancers, dementia, and respiratory diseases are usually at the top of the list.

communicable disease

A contagious disease.

In contrast, developing countries suffer more from preventable **communicable diseases**. HIV/AIDS, malaria, and tuberculosis are three of the top seven leading causes of death in Uganda, one example of many developing nations (see Figure 15.3). COVID-19 (see "Case Study: COVID-19") is another example of a communicable disease that disproportionately threatens socioeconomically depressed communities in developed nations and particularly in impoverished developing nations. India and other developing nations have widespread poverty and fragile health-care systems that are easily overwhelmed. Access to personal protective gear, ventilators, and intensive-care beds in these countries is much lower than in wealthy countries. Even health-care systems in wealthy countries were strained to the point of failure under the COVID-19 pandemic wave.

This chapter is in part about how to lower environmental hazards and therefore reduce the risk of these hazards to the human population. We are also increasingly cognizant of how our activities alter the environment in which we live, and have become uncomfortably aware of how this change often increases our exposure to pathogens and other hazards. Are you aware of the different types of environmental hazards?

FIGURE 15.3

Leading human mortality factors in the world (A), United States (B), and Uganda (C) in 2019 (data source: Our World in Data). If the 2020 COVID data were included in this graph, COVID-19 would have ranked as the third-highest cause of death in the United States.

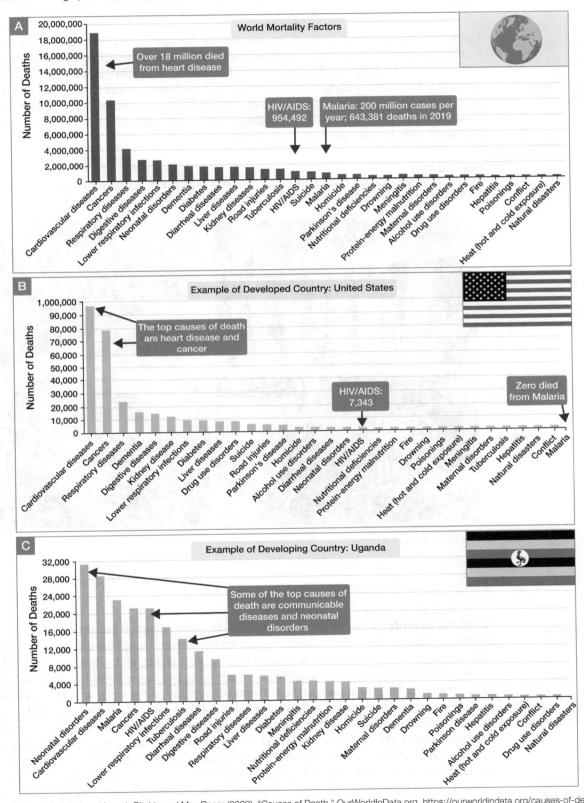

Sources: Joseph Shostell, data from Hannah Ritchie and Max Roser (2020), "Causes of Death," OurWorldInData.org, https://ourworldindata.org/causes-of-death;; © Shutterstock, Inc.

Types of Environmental Hazards

toxicology

The study of the adverse effects of chemical, biological, and physical agents on living organisms.

There are four different types of environmental hazards (see Figure 15.4). They are chemical (see Section 2 and Section 3), biological (see Section 4), physical (see Chapter 11 and Chapter 12), and sociocultural. The ubiquity of environmental hazards explains why Madame de Stael said, "As soon as there is life, there is danger." We humans navigate these hazards throughout our lives, mostly successfully. In a worst-case scenario, an environmental hazard causes death. To better understand these health hazards, we explore **toxicology**, which is the study of the adverse effects of chemical, biological, and physical agents on living organisms.

FIGURE 15.4
Environmental hazards: (A) Chemical (mercury in fluorescent light bulbs), (B) biological (mosquitos that transmit human pathogens), (C) physical (flooding), and (D) sociocultural (vaping).

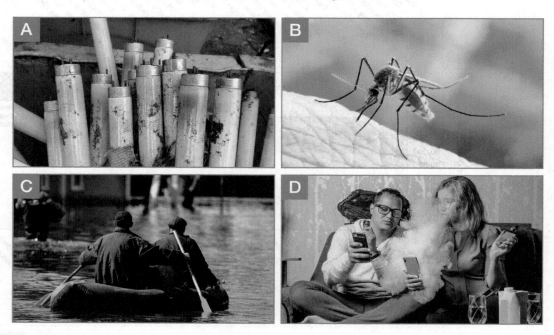

Source: © Shutterstock, Inc.

Chemical Hazards

chemical hazards

Chemicals that threaten human health.

toxicant

Synthetic poison; non-biological poison.

toxin

Poisonous chemical of natural biological origin that is harmful to living things.

Chemical hazards threaten human health. The U.S. Environmental Protection Agency maintains a lengthy database of harmful chemicals (some 875,000 and growing) that can be searched to investigate molecular structure, potential health effects on humans, and other pertinent information. Some of these chemicals are extremely harmful even at low doses, and all are toxic at high enough concentrations. We are exposed to these chemicals at home and at work, in the products we handle, the air we breathe, the water we drink, and even the food we consume. Analysis of human tissues for toxins is the gold standard for measuring exposure (Sexton et al. 2004). For example, Rachel Morello-Frosch's research team detected concentrations of mercury, organochlorine pesticides (OCPs), and polychlorinated biphenyls (PCBs) in human blood (Morello-Frosch et al. 2016). Every one of us has toxins in our tissues. Chemical hazards are further discussed in Section 2 and Section 3. Although some scientists use the terms **toxicant** and **toxin** to differentiate synthetic and natural chemicals, respectively, for clarity in this chapter we refer to all poisonous chemicals as toxins or as toxic substances.

Biological

Biological hazards make up another large group of potential hazards to human health. Common examples of biological hazards include microorganisms such as viruses, bacteria, and protozoa; and macro-sized organisms such as poisonous plants, toxin-producing spiders and snakes, and a variety of insects. A subgroup of biological hazards (bacterial and viral pathogens) can cause lethal diseases or pandemics. Highly contagious infectious diseases can spread rapidly through a population. Another subgroup of biological hazards do not spread from human to human. Examples in this group are allergens such as animal dander or pollen, and noninfectious microorganisms such as *Clostridium tetani*—the bacterial cause of tetanus (which spreads to humans via spores in soil or animal feces). Biological hazards are further discussed in Section 4.

biological hazards

Biologics, in whole or part that threaten human health; viruses, bacteria, fungi, and protozoa, poisonous plants and animals.

Physical Environmental Hazards

A variety of physical hazards in the environment can cause harm to humans. Examples of **physical hazards** include floods, hurricanes, earthquakes, volcanoes, and tornadoes—all topics covered in Chapter 11 and Chapter 12. The enormity and power of some of these physical hazards can cause mass fatalities in just minutes or over the course of days. On January 23, 1556, Shaanxi Province in China experienced an 8 to 8.3-magnitude earthquake, which is estimated to have killed 830,000 people (Yu et al. 2019). Physical hazards also include light pollution, noise pollution, and ultraviolet (UV) and gamma radiation. Perhaps you have smeared on sunscreen to shield your skin from UV radiation? This particular physical hazard is a well-known occupational hazard. UV radiation in sunlight is the reason why construction workers and farmers who frequently work outdoors are at a greater risk of developing skin cancer, premature skin aging, and damage to the eyes.

physical hazards

Physical agents that compromise human health. Examples: flooding, hurricanes, earthquakes, volcanoes, tornadoes, and noise.

Sociocultural

Sociocultural hazards threaten us as well. A growing body of research documents the tight associations between sociocultural factors and health (Marmot and Wilkinson 2006). Certain behaviors help minimize an individual's risk from environmental hazards; other behaviors worsen their effects. Washing hands with clean water, for instance, can prevent the spread of germs to oneself and to others. Choosing the right source of water to drink, and if needed, purifying it, are important too. Behaviors such as overeating, selecting non-nutritious foods, and smoking can worsen the effects of other types of environmental hazards. For instance, smokers are more likely to have severe symptoms of COVID-19 than are non-smokers (Guan et al. 2020).

sociocultural hazards

Sociocultural practices that threaten human life and place humans at greater risk of experiencing chemical, biological, or physical hazards; examples: smoking, lack of access to clean water.

Where we live, our economic status, and acts of environmental injustice also affect our exposure to biological, chemical, and physical hazards. Look to Flint, Michigan (2014–2018) (see "Case Study: COVID-19") with their polluted water. To save money in 2014, the city of Flint changed their source of drinking water from the Detroit Water and Sewerage Department to the Flint River, a highly corrosive source of water. After the switch was made, lead from old water-transport pipes leached into Flint's water supply exposing Flint's residents to elevated levels of lead. A report by the Flint Water Advisory Task Force strongly suggests that the Flint community was neglected because a large portion of the community was black (57%), and 42% lived below the national poverty line (FWATF 2016). We could also compare the effect of COVID-19 on different communities. For example, statistics indicate African Americans were disproportionately affected (Garg et al. 2020). These are examples of environmental injustice (see Chapter 1).

We'll continue to investigate chemical toxins (such as cigarette smoke and lead) in air, water, and soil in the next section.

Key Takeaways

- Environmental health is a branch of public health focused on identifying, understanding, and mitigating environmental hazards that affect human health and well-being.
- Communities do not have equal access to clean water, fresh food, clean air, clean soil, and high-quality health care. As a consequence, different communities have different risks from environmental hazards.
- The four categories of environmental hazards are chemical, biological, physical, and socio-cultural.
- Our behaviors can help to protect us from environmental hazards, or worsen their effects.

15.2 Toxicology and the Threat of Toxic Agents on Human Health

Learning Objectives

1. Identify and understand the categories of toxic chemicals based on their effects on human health.
2. Explain the natural defenses that protect humans from toxic chemicals and other hazards.
3. Understand the underlying causes of variation in the effects of toxic chemicals on people.

Too much of a good thing can kill you. Water, vitamins, licorice, and salt are all examples of everyday items we might ingest without a second thought, yet any of these items can be toxic if taken in excess. In the case of water, for example, drinking water faster than your body can excrete it—about a gallon of water over a three-hour period—can kill you because it dilutes the blood too much. A toxicologist will tell you, "The dose makes the poison" (Bus 2017). An extremely poisonous substance may not be lethal if ingested or absorbed at a sublethal dose, but that dose varies depending on the toxin. Some substances are so lethal that just a tiny amount can kill you. The most toxic substance known is botulinum, a toxin produced by the bacterium *Clostridium botulinum* (Popoff 2014). Ingesting just 30 ng (one billionth of an ounce) can be lethal, and an estimated 234 g (8.25 oz) would be enough to kill everyone on Earth (Dhaked et al. 2010, Peck 2006, Arnon 1997).

Types of toxic substances are described next, followed by their effects on our bodies and our natural defenses.

Types and Effects of Toxic Substances

Toxic agents can be divided into categories based on their common effects on humans and animals. The main types are carcinogens, mutagens, teratogens, neurotoxins, and endocrine disruptors (see Figure 15.5).

FIGURE 15.5
Society has history of using toxic chemicals: (A) Dichlorodiphenyltrichloroethane (DDT), an endocrine disruptor, being sprayed on a soldier during WWII; (B) An old transformer that contains polychlorinated biphenyls (PCBs), which are both carcinogens and endocrine disruptors; (C) a plate of puffer fish, which contain neurotoxins; and (D) plastic containers and cutlery made with bisphenol A and phthalates, both endocrine disruptors.

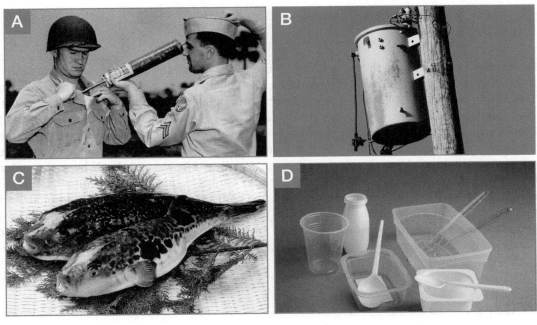

Sources: CDC, Public Health Image Library; © Shutterstock, Inc.

Carcinogens, Mutagens, and Teratogens

Carcinogenic agents (**carcinogens**) increase the probability of developing cancer—the second leading cause of death in the world and in the United States (see Figure 15.3). Cancer is a generic term to describe a group of over 100 diseases commonly defined by uncontrolled division of malfunctioning cells. Masses of cells called tumors can form, and new abnormal cells can also spread and infiltrate tissues and organs elsewhere in the body. Examples of chemical carcinogens are perfluorooctanoic acid (PFOA) in Teflon, benzene in crude oil, arsenic in rice, formaldehyde in particleboard, polychlorinated biphenyls (PCBs) in old transformers, and radon gas. In addition, the category includes biological agents (some bacteria and viruses) and physical agents (such as ultraviolet radiation and gamma radiation). What types of symptoms would alert you to cancer? Lumps under the skin, fatigue, and weight change are three common symptoms, among others. We often see greater incidences of cancer in seniors mainly because of repeated exposures to carcinogens, accumulated DNA damage, and weakened immune systems.

Many, but not all carcinogens, are mutagens. A **mutagen** is an agent that can alter a cell's DNA. If the cell doesn't detect and correct the alteration, it becomes a mutation. Most mutations are harmless, but some can lead to cancer.

Teratogenic agents cause physical or functional defects of the human embryo or fetus. The word **teratogen** originates from the Greek word τέρας (téras) signifying "monster." Thalidomide is probably the best-known example of a teratogen (Ito et al. 2011). Between 1957 and 1962, thalidomide was widely used outside the United States to reduce morning sickness. And, although not approved by the U.S. Food and Drug Administration for use in the United States, thousands of women in the United States were given thalidomide as a part of a clinical trial. An epidemic of birth defects followed, mostly outside of the United States, and more than 10,000 children were born with drastically shortened, malformed limbs. These effects prompted the removal of thalidomide from the drug market in most countries by 1961. Lead is another example of a teratogen because it dis-

carcinogens
Cancer-causing agents.

mutagen
A physical or chemical agent that alters a cell's DNA.

teratogen
Agents that cause physical or functional defects of the human embryo or fetus.

rupts neurological development and reduces fetal growth (Bellinger 2005). Even today, there are environmental sources of lead that can threaten human health. Older homes (built before 1978) often have lead paint, but so do some water pipes (such as those in Flint, Michigan), jewelry, toys, certain imported candies, and soils near airports.

Neurotoxins

neurotoxins

A natural or synthetic chemical that alters the structure and/or function of the nervous system.

Do you care to dine with death? Such is the question when you sit down to "enjoy" a feast of pufferfish. When not prepared correctly (by a trained chef), you may very well succumb to tetrodotoxin. This deadly neurotoxin is 1,200 times more toxic than cyanide. **Neurotoxins** are synthetic or natural chemicals that alter the structure and/or function of the nervous system (Hajeb et al. 2012). Every year, a couple dozen people in Japan suffer from tetrodotoxin poisoning after eating pufferfish, and an unfortunate few die. The first symptoms start within about forty-five minutes of consuming the toxin, beginning with numbness. Paralysis follows, and death by asphyxiation occurs within twenty-four hours. Pufferfish dinners are not common in the United States, but organophosphates and mercury are widely used, and both are neurotoxins. Organophosphates are found in agricultural insecticides (and therefore their residues are found in fruits and vegetables), and some flea-control products and treatments for head lice. The Geneva Convention prohibited the use of neurotoxins as chemical weapons in 1925, but they are still occasionally used by terrorists.

Endocrine Disruptors

endocrine disruptors

Chemicals that mimic or interfere with our body's hormones.

Our furniture, carpets, electrical equipment, nonstick pots and pans, cosmetics, toys, and food contain chemicals that mimic or interfere with our body's hormones. These are **endocrine disruptors** (see video link: "Endocrine Disruptors"). Common types include dioxins, bisphenol A, phthalates, polychlorinated biphenyls (PCBs), dichlorodiphenyltrichloroethane (DDT), and perfluoroalkyl/polyfuoroalkyl substances (PFAS).

 Endocrine Disruptors

Listen to Drs. Heather Patisaul and Andrea Gore discussing endocrine-disrupting chemicals.

View in the online reader

Dioxins are a group of polychlorinated organic molecules produced, for example, by waste incineration, paper-bleaching processes, and pesticide manufacturing. Once emitted into the environment, they accumulate in organisms and biomagnify up the food chain. The dioxin 2,3,5-trichlorphenoxyacetic acid was a key chemical ingredient in Agent Orange, used during the Vietnam War to defoliate forests. An estimated 50 million liters (13.2 million gal) were sprayed in Vietnam between 1962 and 1971.

Bisphenol A (BPA) is a plasticizer, an ingredient to increase the softness and flexibility of plastic containers, such as those used for foods and beverages, and of epoxy resins lining food-containing cans. Exposure most commonly occurs when BPA leaches from the containers into foods or drinks, and then is ingested. A series of studies detected BPA in the vast majority of people (Moura et al. 2019). Just like bisphenol A, phthalates are plasticizers in many commonly used products. Prenatal (before birth) exposure to phthalates is associated with decreased testosterone, progesterone, and thyroxine in children (Wen et al. 2019). One of the recommended methods to protect yourself from BPA and phthalates is to use alternative plasticizers. We can, for example, choose to only use plastics labeled "BPA-free" and avoid eating canned foods. However, BPA substitutes can also show endocrine disruption effects (Moon 2019). BPA-free doesn't mean it's safe. Switching from food stored in plastic containers to food stored in glass containers is the best way to reduce exposure to BPA and BPA substitutes.

PCBs, PFAS, and **DDT** are three particularly troublesome endocrine disruptors. **Polychlorinated biphenyls (PCBs)** are long-lasting (persistent), chlorine-containing compounds found in electrical equipment, lubricants, old televisions, refrigerators and other electrical appliances, plasticizers, and pesticides. **Perfluoroalkyl and polyfuoroalkyl substances (PFAs)** are synthetic, persistent chemicals found in food packaging and various commercial household products (such as nonstick products and paint). Because PFAS have spread into the environment, they can now be found in some drinking water supplies and in the tissues of most animals, including humans. One example in this group, PFOA, was recently highlighted in the movie *Dark Waters*, and is now banned in the United States. It was a chemical ingredient in Teflon, a common nonstick coating for kitchen pans, through 2014 (see "Critical Thinking Activity: An Investigation into the Possible Existence of Toxic Chemicals in Our Bodies"). Dichlorodiphenyltrichloroethane (DDT) is an organochlorine insecticide originally touted as a huge success in the 1940s and 1950s. However, Rachel Carson's publication of *Silent Spring* made the public aware of DDT's toxic effects on a wide variety of nontargeted organisms, from beneficial insects to common robins (see Chapter 1) (Wurster et al. 1965). Of special concern was DDT's ability to persist in nature, biomagnify, and cause the thinning of eggshells, thus lowering reproductive success and decreasing the population size of Peregrine falcons and other predatory bird species (Kolaja and Hinton 1977). Most countries banned DDT in the 1970s and 1980s, and since then these bird populations have recovered.

Bringing It Closer to Home: Am I Exposed to Any Toxic Chemicals?

The United States Environmental Protection Agency monitors hundreds of toxic chemicals that place human lives and the environment at risk. Table 15.1 lists common household items and the toxic chemicals they often contain. Look through the short list and then verify the presence of each toxic chemical on the EPA's inventory list here. To verify the toxins, click on the "Go" button and download a spreadsheet of the TRI chemical list. Scroll through the list to locate the three toxic chemicals listed in Table 15.1. As one final step, state "yes" or "no" under "Do I have this item in my home?"

Use of any of the few products in the table does not necessarily mean you were exposed to toxic chemicals, or exposed at harmful doses. For more information about toxins in your household items, you would have to find out which chemicals were used to produce them. Some chemicals have been prohibited by the Food and Drug Administration for use in human food, but some edible products still contain them. Safrole is an example (Ara 2012). Other toxic chemicals such

---

dioxins

A group of polychlorinated organic molecules produced by waste incineration, bleaching of paper, and manufacturing of pesticides. An example of an endocrine disruptor.

bisphenol A (BPA)

A plasticizer, an ingredient of plastic containers including beverage bottles; a component in metal can coatings.

dichlorodiphenyl-trichloroethane (DDT)

An insecticide that most countries banned in the 1970s and 1980s; example of an endocrine disruptor.

polychlorinated biphenyls (PCBs)

Long-lasting (persistent), chlorine-containing compounds found in electrical equipment, lubricants, old televisions, refrigerators and other electrical appliances, plasticizers, and pesticides. PCBs are endocrine disruptors.

perfluoroalkyl and polyfuoroalkyl substances (PFAs)

Synthetic, persistent chemicals that occur in food packaging and various commercial household products (i.e., nonstick products and paints); endocrine disruptors that are widespread contaminants of drinking water supplies and animal tissues.

as the pesticide Diphenylamine (see Table 15.1) are legally applied to fruit as a postharvest rinse. To protect ourselves from diphenylamine and other toxic chemicals on the outside of apples, we can wash or peel the apples before eating them.

TABLE 15.1 Toxic Chemicals in Household Products

Household Item	May Contain This Toxic Chemical	How Does It Enter My Body (Type of Exposure)?	Harmful Effect(s) of This Toxic Chemical	Do I Have This Item in My Home?	Reference
Apples	Diphenylamine (a pesticide)	Orally (ingestion)	Slightly toxic: alters clinical chemistry		EPA 1998
Spinach, collards, apples, beer, wine, tomatoes, potatoes, cigarettes (released in cigarette smoke), and cured rubber products	Ethylene thiourea (a fungicide)	Inhalation, ingestion, dermal contact	Carcinogen, teratogen, affects endocrine system (thyroid hyperplasia)		NTPDHHS 2016
Herbal products derived from the sassafras tree (e.g., essential oils), and edible spices such as cinnamon, pepper, and nutmeg. Banned as a food additive since 1960, but still detected in some soft drinks.	Isosafrole and safrole (organic compounds), unregulated until 1960	Ingestion, inhalation, dermal contact	Carcinogen		Tisserand and Young 2014; Ara 2012, Kemprai et al. 2019

Critical Thinking Activity: An Investigation into the Possible Existence of Toxic Chemicals in Our Bodies

You probably have toxic chemicals in your body. How can I say this with any level of certainty? What steps of analysis did I take to make such a statement? Consider a process to determine how I was able to reach this conclusion and then read the following story on PFOA. After completion of the story, use evidence and reasoning to determine that there are toxic chemicals in your tissues, and then compare this strategy to the one outlined in Table 15.2.

In 1998, Earl Tennant, a cattle farmer in West Virginia, gave environmental attorney Robert Bilott a call. He explained that 150 of his livestock were dead after drinking from a creek called Dry Run on his property. Earl had dissected his deceased livestock, and discovered all had an enlarged gall bladder, abnormal kidneys, and a very unusual looking spleen (Bilott 2019). All had exhibited bizarre behavior before they died. For example, the cattle were staggering as if in a drunken stupor, and had started kicking (domestic cattle are normally quite docile). Earl had also noticed dead wildlife around Dry Run Creek. He inspected the creek beyond his property and discovered an industrial pipe dumping effluent into it. The source of the effluent was a landfill owned by DuPont.

Bilott began his own investigation, following a trail of data that revealed DuPont had been dumping manufacturing waste into the environment since 1951. One of those chemicals in the waste, perfluorooctanoic acid (PFOA), was being used to produce Teflon and other fluoropolymers at DuPont's Washington Works plant in West Virginia. Hundreds of tons of PFOA had been dumped into the landfill upstream from Tennant's farm.

Bilott had never heard of PFOA, and the chemical wasn't registered with the Environmental Protection Agency. Through his search, he discovered that DuPont had carried out laboratory studies linking PFOA with pancreatic, liver, and testicular cancers in animals, but the company had not disclosed this data to the federal government. DuPont even knew about the presence of PFOA in water moving into Dry Run Creek on Earl Tennant's farm.

Bilott suspected that it wasn't just the Tennant's farm that had been affected. Tens of thousands of people living nearby were very likely being exposed to PFOA in their drinking water. Once these people were informed of the potential contaminant, they began to have their water tested and shared the results with Bilott.

Having gathered an abundance of evidence, Bilott filed and won a federal lawsuit against DuPont on behalf of 70,000 victims. DuPont settled in 2004, for the staggering amount of $300 million. In addition, the Environmental Protection Agency pursued its own investigation, and followed up with its own lawsuit for violating the Toxic Substances Control Act and the Resource Conservation and Recovery Act. The EPA imposed on DuPont $10.25 million in penalties, plus an additional $6.25 million for environmental projects. It was the largest civil administrative penalty in the EPA's history. After winning, Susan Hazen, the EPA's principal deputy assistant administrator for the Office of Prevention, Pesticides, and Toxic Substances, said, "We are pleased that as a direct result of this settlement with DuPont, valuable information will be produced for the scientific community to better understand the presence of PFOA in the environment and any potential risks it poses to the public. We are hopeful that today's action will serve as an important reminder of the importance of timely industry reporting of substantial risk information to EPA." In 2017, Bilott successfully represented 3,500 personal injury cases and recovered an additional $753 million from DuPont in individual damages compensation.

PFOA is sometimes referred to as a "forever chemical" because its strong carbon–fluorine bonds makes it resistant to breakdown in the environment and in the body. Environmental persistence, combined with widespread use and ease of absorption (by ingestion, inhalation, or through the skin), explain why PFOA is found in most people (Lau et al. 2007). The average concentration of PFOA in blood serum of Americans is 4 μg/L, well below the average of 75.7 μg/L in people who were exposed to PFOA in drinking water in Parkersburg, West Virginia (Hoffman et al. 2011). Exposure to PFOA can occur through drinking, showering, or bathing in contaminated water; or by eating contaminated fruits and vegetables (Tillett 2007). Do you know of any toxic chemicals in your water supply?

TABLE 15.2 Determining Whether There Is a Toxic Chemical in Your Body

Questions	Next Steps	
1. The initial question is asked. Are toxic chemicals in my body?	To determine an answer, begin by asking yourself about your potential exposure to chemical hazards. See questions 2 through 8 below.	
2. Follow-up question to ask: Are toxic chemicals in my foods?	To determine an answer, begin by listing the foods you eat and where/how these foods are grown. This can be a challenge because most people purchase their food in a grocery store and are not aware of the origin of their food. Your choices here are to 1) trust the company; 2) investigate each company and only purchase foods after a complete vetting of the source; or 3) grow all of your own food.	
3. Follow-up question to ask: Are toxic chemicals in the products I use?	To determine an answer, begin by listing the products you use and the chemical ingredients in each one (a daunting task!). Cross-check every chemical on your list against the EPA's toxic chemical list (see here). This list comes from the Toxics Release Inventory Program.	
4. Follow-up question to ask: Are toxic chemicals in the water I drink?	To determine an answer, begin by finding out where your drinking water comes from. Is it from a well? Is it from a water tower? Is it from a reservoir? Then, contact the managing agency of your water supply and request water quality data. The only assured way of verification is to send a sample of your water to a certified analytical lab and have the water sample analyzed. This will cost money, but it's worth the expense to best protect your health.	
5. Follow-up question to ask: Are there toxic chemicals in the air I breathe?	To determine an answer, access one of a number of air-pollution search sites. Go to the EPA's MyEnvironment website here. You can also check the EPA's National Air Toxics Assessment here.	

Questions	Next Steps	
6. Follow-up question to ask: Are there toxic chemicals in the soil around my house?	To determine an answer, collect a soil sample and send it to a certified laboratory. They will test for dangerous concentrations of lead and arsenic, among other toxic substances.	
7. Follow-up question to ask: Are there toxic chemicals at my workplace?	To determine an answer, follow the same methods you used to determine the presence of toxic chemicals in your home (e.g., check water, soil, air, products).	
8. Revisiting the initial question (Are toxic chemicals in my body?): The only assured way to really know is to have your own body tested. However, you must know what to screen for. In the case of PFOA, a certified laboratory could analyze a sample and inform you as to the concentration of PFOA.		

Source: (Images) © Shutterstock, Inc.

The Human Body's Defenses

All humans are exposed to toxic chemicals. Type, dose, route of exposure (inhalation, ingestion, dermal contact, or injection), length of time of exposure, and an individual's state of health are all factors in determining the severity of effects of a toxic substance on a person. For example, ricin applied to the skin has no effect, but inhaled is a different matter. Other chemicals are absorbed readily through the skin.

Humans have multiple levels of defense against foreign particles or substances, including toxic chemicals. One of these levels is a set of general, immediate mechanisms that protect the body from invasion. Think of this as your body's first line of defense, similar to a fence around your house that keeps out unwanted "guests." This level consists of two main parts: 1) surface barriers and 2) phagocytic cells such as macrophages, and antimicrobial substances.

The first part of the body's general defenses consists of barriers that keep most foreign substances and particles on the outside of the body. Skin is thick, oily, and difficult to penetrate. Membranes that line the interior surfaces of the body (such as the respiratory system, mouth, stomach, and intestines) are easier to penetrate than skin, but antimicrobial proteins, extreme pH, and the waving action of cilia protruding from some of these membranes offer additional protection.

The second part of the body's general defenses can be triggered by physical trauma, toxic chemicals, heat, or microorganisms that enter the body's internal environment. Blood flow increases to the area, speeding delivery of phagocytic cells that can engulf and dismantle invading microorganisms or particles. Redness and swelling are outward signs of this process, which is called inflammation.

Detection of a foreign substance or particle inside the body triggers yet another level of vertebrate defense, one that is more specific and powerful than the general defenses. Anything that triggers this adaptive response—a toxic chemical, bacterium, virus, parasitic worm, or something else—is called an antigen (see Figure 15.6). There are two parts to this system: humoral immunity and cell-mediated immunity. In humoral immunity, specialized white blood cells called B-lympho-cytes (B-cells) produce antibodies that specifically bind to the invading antigen. Antibody binding facilitates uptake of the antigen by phagocytic cells, and it neutralizes some antigens—preventing them from harming the body in the meantime. In cell-mediated immunity, special immune cells are produced that target and kill infected or ailing body cells. Some of the immune cells that form during adaptive responses are long lived, and these can mount a faster, stronger response if the same antigen is detected in the body again. This capacity is called immunological memory.

FIGURE 15.6

The human body has multiple layers of defense against foreign substances and particles. (A) Skin is a tough barrier that is impenetrable to most viruses, bacteria, and other potential threats. (B) Phagocytic cells engulf and break down anything they recognize as foreign. (C) B-cells and T-cells, antibodies, and phagocytic cells such as macrophages participate in adaptive immune responses that target specific antigens.

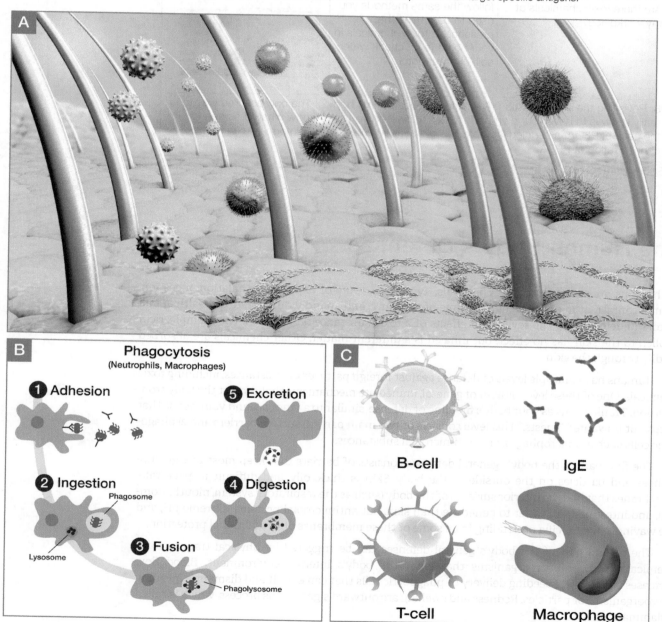

Source: © Shutterstock, Inc.

Not all toxic chemicals trigger an immune response, but the body has other defenses. For example, the liver and kidneys have detoxifying capabilities that can rid the body of many pesticides, food additives, and drugs. Kidneys filter the blood and maintain its composition. They can transfer ionic chemicals directly to urine, which is then excreted. The liver breaks down other toxic chemicals, and can convert some nonionic molecules into ionic forms that are excretable by the kidneys.

Key Takeaways

- Carcinogens, mutagens, teratogens, neurotoxins, and endocrine disruptors are general categories of toxic agents based on their potential effects on human health.
- Differences in dose, route of exposure, length of exposure, health factors, and genetics are the sources of differences in the effects of a toxic substance among individuals.
- The human body has multiple levels of defense against potentially harmful substances and particles: 1) immediate mechanisms that consist of surface barriers and general internal immune defenses; 2) adaptive immunity, which includes humoral responses (that produce antibodies targeting specific antigens), and cell-mediated immunity (that kills infected or ailing body cells); and 3) detoxifying functions of the kidneys and liver.

15.3 Movement, Distribution, and Fate of Toxic Chemicals in the Environment

Learning Objectives

1. Identify the factors that determine a toxic chemical's ability to move through the environment.
2. Use off-gassing as an example to explain the movement of toxic chemicals by air.
3. Describe how the hydrosphere offers a delivery route for toxic chemicals moving through the environment.
4. Compare and contrast bioaccumulation and biomagnification.
5. Evaluate the sources, uptake, concentrations, and mitigation of mercury in the Florida Everglades.

Did you know that watching a movie in your favorite theater potentially exposes you to airborne toxic chemicals? Dr. Roger Sheu of Yale University investigated the movement of toxic chemicals, and how particular sources of these chemicals and their movement through air pollute the local atmosphere. His team tested the air in movie theaters for the presence of benzene and formaldehyde—two carcinogens that are by-products of smoking. Smoking had been banned in these theaters, so the air inside of them was presumably free of these chemicals (Sheu et al. 2020). Contrary to what most people would expect, concentrations of these and other toxic compounds in the air spiked when moviegoers entered the theaters (see Figure 15.7). Volatile organic compounds (VOCs) on smokers' clothes wafted into the air, exposing the other moviegoers to the equivalent of up to ten cigarettes' worth of secondhand smoke per movie. The new term for this environmental hazard is **off-gassing**.

off-gassing

The movement of toxic molecules from one's clothes and other articles into atmosphere.

FIGURE 15.7
Toxic chemicals have many sources, some we hardly expect. Even in theaters where smoking is banned, nonsmoking moviegoers may breathe in the equivalent of 1 to 10 cigarettes' worth of secondhand smoke wafting from the clothes of smokers sitting in the theater. (A) A group of people in a theater. (B) Fumes of a cigarette.

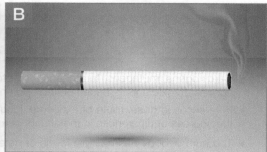

Source: © Shutterstock, Inc.

In this section, we investigate the movement of toxic chemicals and their fate in the environment. The extent of a chemical's movement and its eventual distribution depends on its structure, chemical properties, origin, and how it is released. For example, some chemicals tend to move through the atmosphere, spreading via air-circulation routes; others are highly soluble in water and spread via water movements. As another example, a toxic chemical's stability—its ability to resist degradation—influences the extent of its spread through the environment. A case in point, PCBs used in electronic equipment more than forty years ago persist in the environment, still cycling among air, water, and soil compartments.

Airborne Toxins

Dr. Sheu's study suggests we are exposed to airborne toxic chemicals even in places where we may least expect it. These chemicals exist in a variety of urban and rural areas as well as indoors and outdoors, whether or not our senses detect them. Toxic chemicals released from human activities into the atmosphere degrade environments locally as well as thousands of kilometers away. Airborne movement of these chemicals creates global pollution problems (see "Case Study: COVID-19"). How is this possible? One mechanism involves the tall chimneys of coal-burning power plants that spout chemical pollutants high into the atmosphere. These chimneys—some taller than 305 m (1,000 feet)—are intended to minimize effects of pollutants on the local community. Wind currents at the higher altitude move faster, so they move pollutants emitted from the chimneys over greater distances. As you learned in Chapter 11, carbon dioxide, sulfur dioxide, nitrogen oxides, heavy metals (such as mercury), dioxins, and PCBs are just some of the many examples of anthropogenic chemicals in our atmosphere. Natural sources of some of these chemicals exist, but anthropogenic sources typically emit greater quantities that have a significant impact on natural processes.

Waterborne Toxins

Water offers another major delivery route for toxic agents (see Chapter 10). Some atmospheric pollutants mix with water, then fall to Earth's surface in precipitation. For example, sulfur dioxide and nitrogen oxide react with water and oxygen to form acids that lower the pH of rain (acid rain). Surface runoff from precipitation carries pesticides, fertilizers, and various household and industrial chemicals into storm drains that connect to waterways. These waterborne toxins pollute drinking water supplies, threaten water recreational activities, and degrade natural aquatic habitats.

Heavy rains can cause streams and rivers to swell and then overflow, so water floods through residential neighborhoods, industrial areas, and agricultural lands. Floodwaters that absorb household and industrial chemicals can spread them across large areas. Flooding is particularly worrisome for communities near toxic waste sites. For example, in 2017, torrential rains from Hurricane Harvey flooded the San Jacinto Waste Pits superfund site in the city of Houston (EPA 2017). These pits contain carcinogenic dioxins and other toxic chemicals created through industrial processes (such as chlorine bleaching in paper mills) (Iyer et al. 2016). Floodwaters carried chemicals from the pits to the San Jacinto River. Waters also swept through residential areas close to the superfund site.

Sewer systems and sewage treatment systems can be overwhelmed during flooding, and this results in untreated sewage flowing directly into waterways. Drought causes problems too, because toxic compounds that end up concentrated in the smaller volume of water can create deadly hotspots.

Food Chains and Ecosystems

Some toxic chemicals can accumulate in organisms (bioaccumulation) and increase in concentration (biomagnification) up food chains (see Chapter 1). Harmless, dilute concentrations of these chemicals in the air or water may reach dangerous concentrations within organisms. Chemicals that bioaccumulate and biomagnify include mercury, lead, cadmium, PCBs and other organochlorides, polycyclic aromatic hydrocarbons (PAHs), perfluorooctanoic acid (PFOA), and DDT. In a more detailed example, we look into the movement and fate of mercury in the Florida Everglades, the largest subtropical ecosystem in the United States (see Figure 15.8).

Covering 1.3 million acres (5,260 km^2), the intricate network of lakes, rivers, marshes, and forests in the Everglades is home to innumerable fish and wildlife. In this biodiversity hotspot, we find the endangered whooping crane and Everglade snail kite, the vulnerable American manatee, the majestic bald eagle and American alligator, the fearsome-looking great barracuda, and the mysterious endangered Florida panther. In the late 1980s, scientists were surprised and alarmed to detect dangerously high concentrations of mercury in fish and wildlife of the Everglades. The concentrations of mercury in fish were substantial enough to warrant fish-consumption advisories for the public.

What troubled the scientists was the lack of a clear origin of the toxic chemical. Why would high concentrations of mercury exist in the Everglades? Few roads exist, buildings are almost nonexistent, and only a small number of people live there. To determine when the mercury started accumulating in the Everglades, researchers checked for mercury in local sediments collected at different depths, and also tested feathers of birds that had been collected in the region and sent to museums (Frederick et al. 2005). They discovered that there was a sudden onset of mercury in birds collected in the 1970s and 1980s—a time frame consistent with mercury data from the sediments. Groups of researchers considered possible sources of mercury, for instance from local burning of agricultural fields, pollutants blown from the East Coast of the United States, and air pollution traveling long-distance from Africa. Furthermore, they found mercury chloride, which generally deposits within about 120 kilometers (75 mi) of its source. Approximately 92–96 percent of local mercury emissions originated from medical waste incinerators and municipal waste combustion. Once known, these sources were targeted and mitigated, so local mercury emissions dropped by 93 percent, and the concentration of mercury in fish and wildlife dropped by 85 percent. These successes have lowered (but not eliminated) mercury contamination in the Everglades because mercury is persistent in the environment and does not break down or degrade.

FIGURE 15.8

Persistent toxic chemicals that accumulate in organisms (bioaccumulation) increase in concentration up the food chain (biomagnification). Persistent chemicals move through ecosystems in the same pathway as nutrients (colored arrows), so they end up most concentrated in the tissues of top carnivores. This example shows a subtropical aquatic ecosystem. Which organisms are likely to have the highest amounts of toxic chemicals in their tissues?

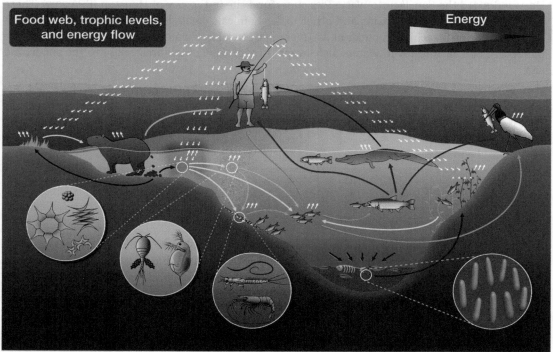

Source: © Shutterstock, Inc.

Mercury is a naturally occurring element in the environment, a neurotoxin, and a mutagen. The majority of mercury released to the atmosphere is in the relatively unreactive elemental form. It has a residence time of one year, giving it plenty of time to travel great distances across the globe via air. Within the atmosphere, elemental mercury usually loses electrons to form a highly reactive form of mercury, which is deposited on water or land, where it can move into food webs. In aquatic areas, specialized bacteria at the bottom of the food chain convert the mercury to methylmercury. Zooplankton feed on the bacteria and further concentrate mercury. Zooplankton are ingested by small fish, and they, in turn, by larger fish. As it moves up the food chain, the methylmercury becomes more and more concentrated: Top predators can have concentrations of mercury millions of times higher than those of lake, river, and ocean waters (Zillioux et al. 1993). Methylation of mercury can also occur in water-logged soils (Eklöf et al. 2018).

Human exposure to mercury usually occurs by ingestion of mercury-contaminated fish and shellfish. The worst recorded mercury poisoning happened in Minamata, Japan, after industrial waste flowed into Minamata Bay and contaminated the fish community. Over 1,700 people who subsisted on fish died from mercury poisoning (see video link: "Minamata Disaster").

The fate of toxic chemicals in organisms also depends on the degree of the chemical's solubility in water. Water-soluble toxic chemicals readily move through the aqueous environment of blood and tissue fluids, yet need assistance to cross cell membranes to enter cells. Lipid-soluble toxic chemicals including methylmercury can easily move across a cell's membrane and can concentrate in fat tissues. Less common, people can be exposed to mercury by vapor inhalation of elemental mercury, for example after an old mercury-containing thermometer breaks (Broussard et al. 2002).

Key Takeaways

- Toxins can be airborne or waterborne. Living things are at risk from these toxins.
- Atmospheric pollutants can undergo chemical reactions, mix with water, and then fall to Earth's surface in precipitation.
- Once mobile, some toxic chemicals can accumulate in species and magnify (biomagnification) in food chains.

Minamata Disaster
Listen to professor of environmental health, Dr. Jack Caravanos at City University of New York, discussing the mercury contamination in Minamata, Japan.

View in the online reader

15.4 Biological Hazards

Learning Objectives

1. Identify categories of biological hazards.
2. Summarize the global impact of biological hazards on human health.
3. Explain the difference between a contagious disease and an infectious disease.
4. Understand the cause and significance of rising resistance among pathogenic species.

Although there is a relatively small possibility of life on Mars, as explorers and inquisitive creatures we want to determine this with certainty. Does life exist on this neighboring world? Answering this question presents a dilemma, as recognized by the National Research Council. "How can NASA use human ingenuity and creativity on Mars to search for life when that life (if it exists) may pose a threat to astronaut health and safety (and therefore the success of a human mission) as well as to Earth's biosphere?" (NRC 2002).

Extensive planning and great care are taken prior to every NASA mission. Although there is a remote chance of life on our sister planets, it is logical to consider the possibility of biological hazards given the many we deal with on our own planet. SARS-CoV-2 and many other biological hazards threaten humans on Earth. In this section, we introduce different types of biological hazards, infectious diseases, and antibiotic resistance.

Types of Biological Hazards

The virus named SARS-CoV-2 (see "Case Study: COVID-19") is responsible for the ongoing COVID-19 pandemic. It is just one example of a biological hazard, but one that caused the loss of millions of lives. A biological hazard is any living organism—or substance from a living organism—that harms human life. Viruses, bacteria, fungi, protozoa, dander, pollen, and poisonous plants and animals can be biological hazards (see Table 15.3).

TABLE 15.3 Common Biological Agents and the Diseases They Cause

Disease	Causative Biological Agent	Average Number of Infected Per Year	Average Number of People Who Die Each Year
Influenza A	Virus: H1N1, H3N2	3–5 million	290,000–650,000
COVID-19	Virus: SARS-CoV-2	84 million (for 2020)	1.8 million (for 2020)

Disease	Causative Biological Agent	Average Number of Infected Per Year	Average Number of People Who Die Each Year
Cervical cancer	Virus: Human papillomavirus (is sexually transmitted)	570,000	311,000
Hepatitis	Virus: HBV, HCV	325 million	1.3 million
Poliomyelitis (polio)	Virus: *Enterovirus C*	33 (dropped from 350,000 in the late 1980s)	<1
Malaria	*Plasmodium*	228 million	446,000
Rabies	Virus: *Lyssavirus* (95 percent transmitted from dog bites)	As high as 29 million (number of people bitten by animals)	59,000
Acquired immunodeficiency syndrome (AIDS)	Virus: human immunodeficiency virus	Total number infected: 37.9 million (1.7 million added per year)	770,000 died of illnesses related to AIDS
Dengue fever	Virus (with mosquito vector): *Flavivirus*	100–400 million	22,000
Smallpox	Virus: *Orthopoxvirus*	0 (50 million in 1948; eradicated now)	0
Tuberculosis (TB)	Bacteria: *Mycobacterium tuberculosis*	10 million	1.5 million

hepatitis

Hepat = liver, *itis* = inflammation; inflammation of the liver; often caused by viral agents.

A good majority of the biohazards listed in Table 15.3 infect hundreds of thousands to hundreds of millions of people each year. Three in particular—hepatitis, malaria, and dengue fever—are worrisome due to the sheer number of people infected (see Figure 15.9). In 2019, we added COVID-19 to this list. On average, at any one time, 325 million people in the world suffer from virus-caused **hepatitis** (*hepat* = liver, *itis* =inflammation). The name of the disease describes the targeted organ, essential to the production of bile, removal of toxic chemicals, storage of carbohydrates, and many other critical functions necessary for maintaining normal body processes. Of the five hepatitis viruses, B and C are the most common and are transmitted from person to person via infected body fluids. Vaccination programs are helping to reduce the number of new cases, but 1.3 million people still die from hepatitis each year.

FIGURE 15.9
Biological hazards affect hundreds of millions of people each year. (A) Dengue fever rash on a baby's back. Mosquitos transmit the virus that causes this illness. (B) In Mali, a young boy lays on a bed under an insecticide-treated net that protects him from disease-carrying mosquitos.

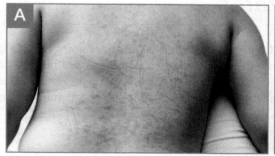

Source: © Shutterstock, Inc.

Hundreds of millions of people also suffer from malaria and dengue fever. **Malaria** is caused by a single-celled parasite that is transmitted to humans by mosquitos. The disease is widespread in tropical and subtropical parts of the world. Approximately 445,000 people die of malaria each year. People who have malaria usually feel extremely sick. Common symptoms are high fever and shaking chills. Malaria and many other diseases are entirely preventable with the proper awareness and protection (see "Critical Thinking Activity: What Hazards Place Me at Risk When I Travel Internationally?"). When traveling in areas where malaria is common, cover your entire body with clothing, and use an effective mosquito repellant, head netting, and bed netting. Another protective strategy is to take antimalarial pills (Malarone).

Dengue fever is also transmitted to humans by mosquitos, but the agent of disease is a virus. This disease is on the rise, and currently infects an upward estimate of 400 million people. Up to 3 billion of the world's population in over sixty countries are at risk from this disease (Wang et al. 2020). People who get dengue fever often have a fever. Other common symptoms include nausea, vomiting, rash, aches, and pains. Control of the mosquito vector, use of protective clothing, and development of a vaccine are imperative to control this extensive disease.

> **malaria**
>
> A disease caused by a protozoan (*Plasmodium*) and transmitted to humans by a mosquito vector; widespread in tropical and subtropical parts of the world.

Infectious Diseases

A contagious disease (also called a communicable disease) is transmitted from person to person through direct contact. All contagious diseases are infectious, which means they are caused by pathogens—disease-causing microscopic organisms such as viruses, bacteria, protozoans, and fungi. However, not all infectious diseases are contagious. COVID-19 is an example of a contagious and infectious disease (see Figure 15.10) because the viral agent that causes it (SARS-CoV-2) easily spreads from one person to another. In contrast, tetanus is a noncontagious infectious disease. The bacterial agent of this disease, *Clostridium tetani*, can only infect humans by crossing the boundary layer of skin, for example through a puncture wound caused by a rusty nail. The resulting infection cannot pass from person to person and thus is not spread through a handshake or coughing. Other diseases such as diabetes are noninfectious because they result from lifestyle or genetic factors, not pathogens.

Scientific research and the culmination and application of that research in the form of vaccinations, improved sanitation, and sewage treatment plants, in addition to appropriate hygiene (such as handwashing) lessen the spread of infectious disease. Although our war on pathogens has successes, we are a long way from conquering infectious diseases (Drexler 2010). On average, approximately one-fourth of all deaths globally are caused by infectious diseases. Just in the few seconds it took to read the previous sentence, six people in the world contracted tuberculosis (TB); and in the time it takes you to read this paragraph, another child dies from malaria.

One in nine children under the age of five die from diarrheal diseases caused by rotavirus, *Salmonella typhi* (the bacterial agent of typhoid fever), *Shigella* bacteria, and *Vibrio cholerae* (the bacteria that cause cholera) (Levine et al. 2020). Victims of any of these diseases suffer from three or more loose stools per day, and they are at risk of severe dehydration that can be fatal. Contaminated drinking water, insufficient sanitation, poor hygiene habits, and a general lack of proper nutrition place an estimated 2.5 billion people at risk of diarrheal diseases (see Figure 15.11). The vast majority of childhood deaths related to these diseases—upward of 80 percent—occur in Africa and South Asia (UNICEF 2016). Working toward achieving the United Nations, fourth Millennium Development Goal, the total number of deaths due to diarrheal diseases is on a decline, with the aim of having the overall under-five mortality rate from diarrheal disease be less than 26 per 1,000 live births for any country (UN 2017).

FIGURE 15.10
COVID-19 is a contagious disease that spreads easily from person to person in tiny droplets released from the respiratory tract. In the photo, a man wears a protective mask and looks on as a nearby person coughs with no mask.

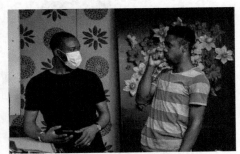

Source: © Shutterstock, Inc.

FIGURE 15.11

Approximately one-third of the people in the world are at a high risk of infectious diarrheal diseases. Most but not all live in Africa and South Asia. As shown in the schematic, there are multiple contamination pathways. Typhoid fever and cholera are examples of diseases spread through contamination.

Source: © David Snyder/CDC Foundation, adapted from https://www.cdc.gov/healthywater/pdf/global/programs/globaldiarrhea_la_508c.pdf.

In the United States and other developed nations, the probability of contracting a diarrheal disease is far lower than in developing countries. Nevertheless, there are many infectious diseases in developed nations too. Foodborne illnesses are of particular concern. One in six Americans, for example, get sick from eating contaminated food each year (CDC 2018) and of these, about 3,000 die. Roughly, 18 percent of these cases are the result of pathogens. The big three are *Salmonella* (bacteria), *Listeria* (bacteria), and *Toxoplasma* (protozoan). Right now, an estimated 40 million Americans are infected with *Toxoplasma gondii*. For most, there are no symptoms, as long as their immune systems remain healthy. In people with weakened immune systems, there can be severe symptoms, including blurred vision, poor coordination, confusion, and seizures. Outbreaks of these and other foodborne illnesses result from eating raw or undercooked meat, fruits and vegetables irrigated with contaminated water, improper handling of foods, and poor hygiene.

Zoonotic diseases are those that can spread from animals to humans. The **Centers for Disease Control and Prevention** (CDC) predicts that zoonotic diseases make up more than 60 percent of all known infectious diseases. Rabies is an example of a zoonotic disease distinct to mammals and, in the United States, is most often carried by bats, skunks, foxes, and raccoons (see Figure 15.12). COVID-19, with its hypothesized animal vectors—horseshoe bats and pangolins—is probably a zoonotic disease as well.

FIGURE 15.12
The rabies virus spreads by direct contact with an infected mammal. Most human cases of rabies in the United States are the result of bites from a rabid animal.

Source: © Shutterstock, Inc.

Centers for Disease Control and Prevention (CDC)

The national public health agency of the United States.

Antibiotic Resistance

Species are evolutionarily dynamic, which means they have the capacity to respond to a changing environment over time. In general, how quickly a species responds depends on its generation time (the time between consecutive generations) and the rate at which mutations accumulate in its genome. Many bacteria have short generation times, which means their populations can grow—and change—much more rapidly than can human populations.

Our advances in the development of new antibiotics and vaccines and the overuse of antibiotics are pushing pathogens to evolve and to become resistant (see Figure 15.13). Antibiotics act as environmental pressures. Bacteria susceptible to the antibiotic die. Resistant bacteria survive and increase in number because of natural selection (see Chapter 4). Their resistance poses one of our greatest challenges to protecting humans against biological hazards. According to the U.S. Centers for Disease Control and Prevention (CDC), antibiotic resistance is to blame for an estimated 23,000 deaths in the United States each year. Globally, an estimated 700,000 people perish from infections with resistant pathogens (O'Neil 2016), and new resistant strains continue to arise. As an example, **Plasmodium** *falciparum*, the most virulent of four protozoan species that cause malaria, is now highly resistant to chloroquine, a drug that was highly effective during the 1960s and 1970s (White 2004). Thus, we don't have many drugs for protozoan parasites. Over-prescribing antibiotics by general medical practitioners is part of the problem because these prescriptions are associated with an increase and often unnecessary use of antibiotics. Physician-targeted interventions to improve antibiotic prescriptions can be effective in reducing the overall number of prescriptions (van der Velden et al. 2013).

Plasmodium

A protozoan genus, which includes five species that cause malaria; these species use mosquito and human hosts to complete their life cycle.

FIGURE 15.13

Pathogens can become resistant to antibiotics. This graph shows trends of antibiotic resistance in *Neisseria gonorrhea*, the bacterial pathogen that causes the sexually transmitted disease called gonorrhea.

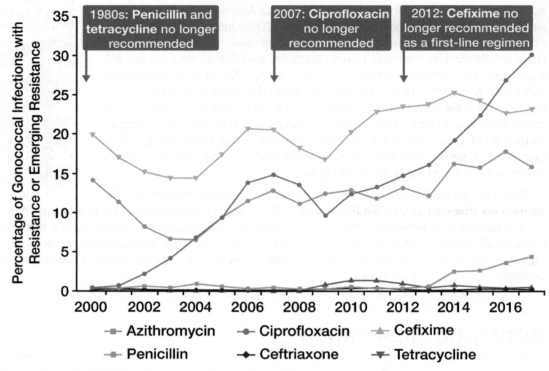

Source: Adapted from CDC, https://www.cdc.gov/drugresistance/pdf/threats-report/gonorrhea-508.pdf.

Key Takeaways

- Viruses, bacteria, protozoa, fungi, animals, and plants can be biological hazards.
- Hundreds of millions to billions of people suffer from biological hazards, and many millions die from these hazards every year.
- Communicable diseases are transmitted from person to person through direct contact.
- Our advances in the development of new antibiotics and vaccines and over-prescription of antibiotics are pushing pathogens to rapidly develop resistance.

15.5 Risk Assessment and Management

Learning Objectives

1. Recognize and understand the steps of risk assessment.
2. Explain why it is a challenge to assess risks.

3. Describe how we determine the level of acceptable risk.

4. Summarize and present examples of mitigating environmental hazards.

Governors across the United States began to issue orders in March of 2020 to minimize the risk of coronavirus exposure to people and to mitigate the spread of coronavirus. Orders were given to close bars, dine-in restaurants, and gyms, and classes were moved to online formats. Forty-three governors issued statewide stay-at-home orders in response to the coronavirus pandemic. The shutdowns plus the banning of large gatherings of people helped to reduce the spread of the coronavirus and save lives. State health departments continually monitored the spread of the coronavirus and reported cases of COVID-19 to the Centers for Disease Control and Prevention. When the number of new COVID cases in states began to level off and decline, governors began to reopen their states. Risk assessment was part of their reopening strategy.

On Friday, April 24, 2020, Georgia governor Brian Kemp and Michigan governor Gretchen Whitmer reopened their states, long closed due to the COVID-19 pandemic. They led a charge of state reopenings. By late May, all states were open to some degree. What methods did the governors and their workgroups use to assess the risks related to reopening? Was it challenging for governors to assess these risks? How did they manage these risks, and what level of risk was deemed acceptable? In this section, we investigate answers to these and other questions related to risk assessment and management.

Risk Assessment: Identify the Hazard and Estimate the Risk

Without doubt, we consider human lives, human health, and human well-being to have significance. These realizations push us to identify hazards that threaten humans, and when found, to mitigate these hazards. Risk assessment and risk management are important parts of environmental health. **Risk assessment** is a process used to evaluate risks associated with a particular hazard or activity. **Risk management** is the process of identifying, evaluating, selecting, and implementing actions to reduce risk. The protection process often begins with a question. We may ask, for example, if there are health risks associated with a particular activity, product, chemical, or organism. We might ask the question: "What is the risk associated with attending a concert during a pandemic?" or, "What are the risks to human health when using gasoline, pesticides, or coal?" Risk, in each of these cases, is defined as the potential to cause harmful effects on human health. An assessment of health risks (risk assessment) begins with a well-constructed and thought-out plan. Initially, in the planning and scoping phase of assessment, a risk assessor asks several questions (who, what, when, where, how) to gather information and make an early judgement.

The Environmental Protection Agency uses risk assessment to estimate the threat an environmental stressor poses to ecological health and on human health. In risk assessment, a stressor may also be referred to as an environmental hazard. Risk assessment has four general parts (see Figure 15.14), beginning with risk identification—a determination of whether a stressor has the potential to cause health problems. For instance, this step determines if a stressor has the potential to increase the incidence of cancer, nervous system damage, or other negative health effects. Data from human trials are valuable in this first step of assessment, but because of ethical concerns of testing chemicals and other stressors on humans, assessors often rely on data from animal models. Animals, especially mammals, have similar anatomies and physiologies to humans. Dogs, mice, and rabbits and other animals also suffer from some of the same diseases as humans. However, participating scientists are expected to follow strict procedures and only perform experimentation when there are no other alternatives.

risk assessment

A process used to evaluate risks associated with a hazard or activity.

risk management

The process of identifying, evaluating, selecting, and implementing actions to reduce risk.

FIGURE 15.14
We carry out risk assessment and risk management to protect human health from environmental hazards. (A) What drives risk assessment? (B) Risk assessment process.

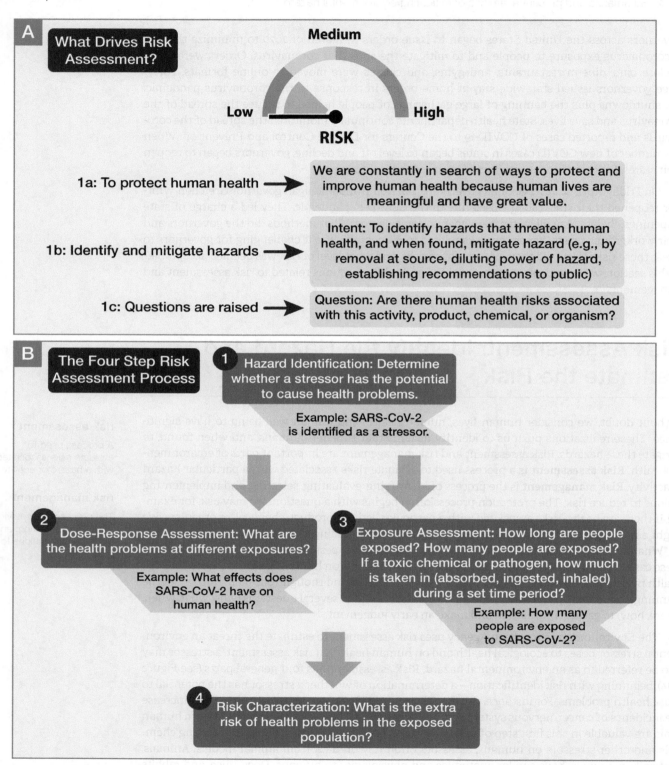

A What Drives Risk Assessment?

Medium

Low   **RISK**   High

1a: To protect human health → We are constantly in search of ways to protect and improve human health because human lives are meaningful and have great value.

1b: Identify and mitigate hazards → Intent: To identify hazards that threaten human health, and when found, mitigate hazard (e.g., by removal at source, diluting power of hazard, establishing recommendations to public)

1c: Questions are raised → Question: Are there human health risks associated with this activity, product, chemical, or organism?

B The Four Step Risk Assessment Process

1 Hazard Identification: Determine whether a stressor has the potential to cause health problems.

Example: SARS-CoV-2 is identified as a stressor.

2 Dose-Response Assessment: What are the health problems at different exposures?

Example: What effects does SARS-CoV-2 have on human health?

3 Exposure Assessment: How long are people exposed? How many people are exposed? If a toxic chemical or pathogen, how much is taken in (absorbed, ingested, inhaled) during a set time period?

Example: How many people are exposed to SARS-CoV-2?

4 Risk Characterization: What is the extra risk of health problems in the exposed population?

Sources: Joseph Shostell; © Shutterstock, Inc.

There are limitations to animal models because animal physiology differs from human physiology in some respects. A mouse may have a different response to a toxic compound than a human has. Furthermore, dosages used on animal subjects can be much higher than what humans might be exposed to in the real world. It's important to note that negative effects caused by high doses in a laboratory do not imply that lower concentrations are also toxic (see Figure 15.15). This is a common misconception by the public. Another misconception is that things we routinely use are not toxic. Everyday things including water and salt can be toxic at high doses. While it is exceedingly rare, drinking a lot of water in a very short period of time can be lethal.

In the second part of risk assessment, dose response, scientists assess any health problems associated with exposure to different doses. Similar to the risk identification step, in the dose-response step, there is often insufficient data from humans. Once again, animal models are used as a source of data. At this stage, different groups of mice or rats may be exposed to varying concentrations of a chemical stressor. In the third step of the risk assessment process, scientists address the question of length (time) of exposure.

The last step of the risk assessment process is risk characterization, in which the risk is evaluated based on dose-response assessment and exposure assessment data for a specific situation. An assessor combines and interprets the information gathered from these earlier stages of the assessment process and determines the likelihood that an environmental stressor could cause harm to nearby people. In effect, risk characterization synthesizes an overall conclusion about risk that is complete, informative, and useful for decision makers (Omenn et al. 1997). For example, risk characterization of the lead disaster in Flint, Michigan (see "Case Study: COVID-19"), described that the risk of lead to the people exceeded an acceptable threshold.

One of the functions of the EPA is to establish and periodically review National Ambient Air Quality Standards (NAAQS) for recognized pollutants, including lead. In one of many examples and under the authority of the Clean Air Act, the EPA completed a risk assessment of a smelter plant in Herculaneum, Missouri (EPA 2006). To give some context here, the Herculaneum lead smelter plant is one of the largest in the world. As part of the assessment, the EPA mapped out potential exposure routes and then tested for lead in air, soil, dust, and blood, and used a model to correlate blood lead levels with IQ loss in children. At the time of the assessment, 37,562 people lived within 10 km (6.3 mi) of the plant. Soil samples collected from over 900 residential locations had concentrations of lead ranging from 53 mg/kg to 23,350 mg/kg. Concentrations of lead in soil of 400 mg/kg or above are considered a soil lead hazard. One of the recommended mitigation measures from the assessment process was to remove soil from the most contaminated properties.

We also use risk assessment in the process of vaccine development. A risk may concern a vaccine itself or address the failure of the vaccine to control a disease. The risk of the vaccine to human health is compared to the benefit of disease prevention. If a disease is near global eradication, risk of the vaccine to a human population can exceed the risk of the disease. In this case, immunization policy changes, as it did with the smallpox vaccine in the United States. After smallpox was eradicated in the U.S., routine vaccination against smallpox stopped. In cases of lethal disease outbreaks such as COVID-19 (see "Case Study: COVID-19"), the risk of a vaccine to human health is normally considered less than the risk of the disease, and the vaccine is administered. In the United States, a vaccine must be licensed by the United States Food and Drug Administration before it is used in a vaccination program. Vaccines undergo extensive safety evaluations in the laboratory, in animal models, and in human clinical trials before they are licensed.

FIGURE 15.15
We often use laboratory animals to test the toxicity of chemicals. (A) An LD50 curve, as shown here, indicates the dose that is lethal to half of the population tested. Can you tell which of the two chemicals is more toxic? (B) A white rat undergoing testing.

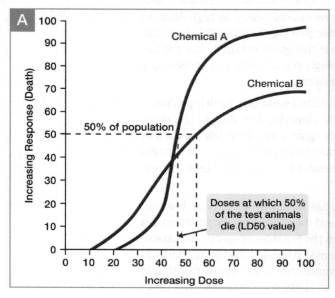

Source: Joseph Shostell; © Shutterstock, Inc.

The Top Predictors of Health Risks Are Location, Poverty, and Lifestyle

People contend with premature death, distress, and disability no matter where they live (Singh & Singh 2008). However, there is a relationship between geographical region and influence of specific categories of hazards. For example, infectious diseases are disproportionately more common in impoverished areas, where people suffer from malnutrition, live in conditions of poor sanitation, and do not have access to water treatment. By contrast, in developed countries, noninfectious, noncommunicable diseases—specifically cardiovascular disease and cancer—cause a much greater loss of life. Thus, key health risks for people in developed countries are linked to lifestyle: whether they smoke, what they eat, and their degree of physical activity.

Where we work and where we live within a geographical region are also good predictors of our health risk. For instance, and understandably, living close to a lead smelter facility presents an increased health risk, no matter what part of the world you live in.

Why Is It a Challenge to Assess Risks?

There are many challenges to assessing risks beyond what has already been mentioned about extrapolating from testing on laboratory animals. A lack of knowledge of a risk, cost of assessment, vast number of new products and chemicals in need of vetting, restrictions and ethics of testing, and complexities of dosages, exposure time, and synergistic effects of multiple hazards create a heavy workload for risk assessors.

Just like the popular phrase, "you only know what you know," an assessor bases decisions on accrued knowledge. At the most basic level, we assess only what we know about or what we think exists. We can't, for example, assess our risk of a new zoonotic virus in the Congo until we know it exists. Assessments take coordination, time, personnel, and money to complete accurately. Who funds the assessment? Individuals don't have the money, the time, nor the expertise to appropriately conduct risk assessments. However, federal tax dollars do cover expenses for the workings of the Environmental Protection Agency. The agency conducts risk assessments on our behalf.

Key challenges for risk assessors also exist surrounding length of exposure and exposure to mixtures of biological, chemical, physical, and sociocultural hazards (Sexton and Hattis 2007). Cumulative risks, either simultaneous or sequential, add layers of complexities to risk assessments. Conventional risk assessments focus on exposure to one stressor at a time. In reality, we are constantly exposed to multiple hazards. A group of people could be exposed to radon, tobacco smoke, and asbestos. Would their risk of developing lung cancer be higher than another group only exposed to radon? In fact, exposure to these three hazards is multiplicative and not simply additive (Erren et al. 1999, Morrison et al. 1998). Rigorous assessments of cumulative risks are needed to improve our understanding of the interactive effects of multiple stressors on human health.

Perceived Risk Versus Actual Risk

When the governors elected to reopen their states during the COVID-19 pandemic, they made a decision based on a judgement of acceptable risk. State economies were faltering, businesses had temporarily or permanently shuttered their doors, unemployment had skyrocketed, and families were struggling to keep food on the table. In this case, the governors accepted the risk of potential loss of life from COVID-19 when they reopened their states.

When perception of a risk and actual risk are equal, governors, lawmakers, and policy makers put forth cost-effective measures to control risks. This is ideal. In contrast, when judgements are not based on valid information or undue human irrationality creeps in, the chance of making poor decisions increases. Social media and news channels can influence our perceptions of risks by reporting murders more often than the number-one killer in the world: heart disease. An irrational fear of a hazard may cause us to have a perception of risk that is greater than the actual risk, which leads to overprotection. Should this occur, we waste resources. The reverse could occur as well, where perception of risk is less than actual risk. When this happens, the public is underprotected.

Managing Risk

Risk assessment is not the endpoint. Once we identify and evaluate risks, we seek to lessen them and, if possible, eliminate them. Minimizing and removing risks is part of risk management. Federal and state governments have major roles in risk management. They establish and give authority to agencies, propose and pass laws, and create health-care programs. Landmark federal laws intended to protect human health from hazards include the Clean Water Act, Clean Air Act, Superfund Act, and **Food, Drug, and Cosmetic Act**.

Food, Drug, and Cosmetic Act

A federal law passed in 1938. Together with its thirty amendments, the Act gives the U.S. Food and Drug Administration the responsibility of overseeing the safety of food, cosmetics, drugs, and medical devices.

Toxic Substances Control Act (TSCA) of 1976

Federal law, passed in 1976 that authorizes the EPA to regulate new and existing chemicals.

Frank Lautenberg Chemical Safety for the 21st Century Act (LCSA)

Federal act, passed in 2016; requires the EPA to evaluate existing chemicals with clear, enforceable deadlines; supports transparency of information about chemicals for the public and risk-based assessments.

When needed, the federal government creates laws and agencies for managing environmental stressors. For example, the EPA formed in 1970 to improve the U.S. government's response to environmental problems. Both the Clean Water Act and Clean Air Act give authority to the EPA to implement pollution-control programs and therefore regulate (manage) pollutants to protect human health and the environment. Among the many noteworthy acts, the **Toxic Substances Control Act (TSCA) of 1976** authorizes the EPA to maintain and update a list of chemical substances manufactured, processed, or imported in the United States (over 83,000 chemicals). The Act requires manufacturers, processors, and distributors of chemical substances to report to the EPA when they find out that a chemical substance presents a substantial risk to people or the environment. In 2016, the **Frank Lautenberg Chemical Safety for the 21st Century Act(LCSA)** amended the TSCA, adding additional requirements for evaluating chemical substances and conducting risk-based chemical assessments.

Another federal agency, the Centers for Disease and Control and Prevention (CDC), safeguards human health against hazards by promoting health and supporting disease-prevention measures. When the CDC formed in 1946, its primary responsibility was to prevent malaria from spreading across the United States Prior to World War II, malaria was still considered a major public health problem. Under guidance of the CDC and in collaboration with state and local health agencies, approximately 4.7 million houses were sprayed with insecticides, and potential mosquito breeding sites were drained. As a result of these measures, by 1949 malaria was no longer a major public health problem in the United States.

Critical Thinking Activity: What Hazards Place Me at Risk When I Travel Internationally?

What risk are we comfortable with when we travel? To what lengths are you willing to go to reduce your risk of hazards? What is an acceptable risk to you? Months before I travel internationally, I refer to the Centers for Disease Control and Prevention (CDC) to see if they have any recommendations to help protect me from harm. For example, if you plan to travel to Colombia, what vaccines and medicines should you consider? Go to the CDC's Traveler's Health website here. Click on "Find out which vaccines are recommended or required for the countries you plan to visit." In the selection box under "For Travelers," choose "Colombia" and click "Go." A map of Colombia pops up, along with any current outbreak alerts. Underneath the map, observe "Travel Health Notices." In summer of 2020, travelers were warned about COVID-19 (Health Notice Level 3) and cautioned about dengue fever (Watch - Level 1). Scroll down further on the web page to "Vaccines and Medicines." Here, the CDC recommends all travelers to Colombia should be up to date on routine vaccinations (measles, mumps, rubella, diphtheria, tetanus, pertussis, varicella, polio, and flu). Furthermore, most travelers are advised to receive vaccines for hepatitis A and typhoid. Depending on length of stay and planned activities, travelers to Colombia may also need protection against hepatitis B, malaria, rabies, and yellow fever. Click on the "Clinician View" icon toward the upper right of the web page. This version presents much of the same information with additional details. Scroll down to the "Non-Vaccine-Preventable Diseases." Here, three additional vector-borne diseases are listed, including Chagas disease, dengue, and zika. As you can see, it takes time to plan for safety on an international trip, and the knowledge of potential hazards allows us to determine possible protective measures—and decide whether the trip is worth the associated health risks.

Now, apply what you have learned and select a country other than Colombia that you would like to visit. Determine the health risks and recommendations for vaccines and medicines. England? China? Cambodia? They are all great to visit, just prepare accordingly to protect your health.

The Food and Drug Administration (FDA) is another example of federal agency that regulates issues critical to health. Founded in 1908, the FDA ensures the safety of drugs, cosmetics, and the nation's food supply. Passage of the Federal Food, Drug, and Cosmetic Act of 1938 gave authority to the FDA to set standards for food and perform inspections of factories. It also enabled the FDA to legally request evidence regarding the safety of newly developed drugs.

Because the types of risk people face vary by region and nation, so do the management plans to ameliorate risks. For example, in developing countries where infectious diseases are to blame for a disproportionately high number of deaths, risk managers try to improve sanitation, offer vaccinations, and improve water treatment. In developed nations, where noninfectious, noncommunicable diseases pose the greatest threats to health, more resources are invested to promote proper nutrition and exercise. COVID-19 was an exception to this trend. In all areas of the world, government risk management plans included enforcement of social-distancing guidelines, quarantining people as needed, shutting down businesses, and restricting travel (see Figure 15.16). These measures were intended to slow the spread of disease (a risk to humans) and prevent hospitals from being overwhelmed with patients. Public health officials called it "flattening the curve."

FIGURE 15.16
Common strategies taken to reduce risk of COVID-19 included (A) wearing of masks, (B) quarantine, and (C) social distancing. (D) By enacting these measures, governments hoped to flatten the infection curve and therefore not overwhelm their health-care systems.

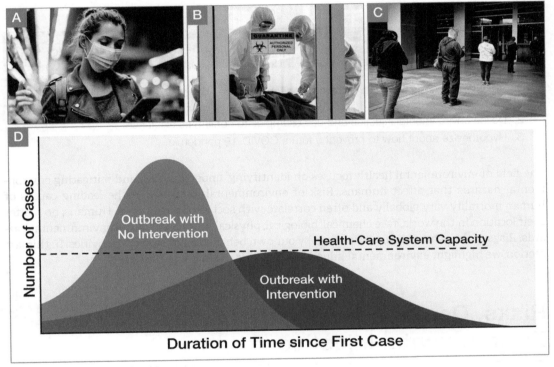

Source: © Shutterstock, Inc.; Joseph Shostell

Key Takeaways

- We use risk assessment and risk management to identify, evaluate, and mitigate environmental hazards that affect human health and well-being.
- The main steps of risk assessment are 1) determination of whether a stressor has the potential to cause health problems, 2) determination of dose response, 3) determination of exposure, and 4) risk characterization.
- There are many challenges to assessing risks. Challenges include a lack of knowledge of a risk, cost of assessment, vast number of new products and chemicals in need of vetting, restrictions and ethics of testing, and complexities of dosages, exposure time, and synergistic effects of multiple hazards.

- Social media can influence our perception of risks. Ideally, the perceived risk matches the actual risk.
- We mitigate risks to protect the public. For instance, legislation, policy, and federal agencies help to protect citizens from environmental hazards.

15.6 A Look to the Future: Environmental Injustice and the Likelihood of Future Pandemics

Learning Objectives

1. Articulate an understanding of the connection between anthropogenic activities and environmental hazards.
2. Define environmental injustice and use examples to confirm its existence.
3. Hypothesize about how to prevent a future COVID-19 pandemic.

The field of environmental health focuses on identifying, understanding, and mitigating environmental hazards that affect humans. Risk of environmental hazards and the leading causes of human mortality vary globally and often correlate with socioeconomic status. Humans, no matter their location in the world, face chemical, biological, physical, and sociocultural environmental hazards. Risks of these hazards are influenced by our own behaviors and society's activities. In this last section, we highlight environmental injustice and revisit the opening case study.

Risks, Degraded Ecosystems, and Environmental Injustice

Risks from environmental hazards increase with degraded ecosystems. All life, including human life, depends on intact, fully functioning ecosystems and the goods they provide. Clean air, clean water, clean soil—indicators of Mother Nature's health—are essential to human well-being. Society's nonsustainable activities negatively affect Earth's ecosystems and increase our exposure to toxic chemicals, pathogens, and physical hazards. For a variety of interconnected reasons—from poor infrastructure, insufficient sanitation, and political instability, to inadequate food supplies and underdeveloped health-care systems—peoples of the world have unequal protection against these hazards. We recognize this for what it is: environmental injustice. At times, environmental injustice can also be the result of location in a community and/or socioeconomic factors. For example, during 2020, the Navajo Nation in New Mexico suffered from over half of the COVID-19 cases in the state, yet they only make up 11 percent of the state's population (see video link: "COVID-19 in the Navajo Nation"). The pandemic exacerbated already existing inequalities and health-care inequities. Houses in Navajo communities are often overcrowded, and many do not have plumbing. These conditions make it challenging to follow recommendations of public health officials to wash hands and to practice social distancing. Poverty is widespread in the Navajo Nation too, which often makes it challenging to purchase hand sanitizers and masks to reduce the spread of the coronavirus. Chronic underfunding of Navajo Nation's health-care system is another source of the problem. There are many ways we can help to reduce environmental injustice, beginning with raising awareness about it. Empowering communities through education and by including them in the decision-making process of environmental issues are important too.

 COVID-19 in the Navajo Nation

Listen to CNN's coverage of COVID-19 spreading through the Navajo Nation.

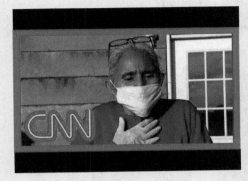

View in the online reader

Opening Story Revisited: Comparing Pandemics

Humans face many environmental hazards, and COVID-19 is not the first viral disease to spread through the human population. Each year, many millions of Americans are infected with a flu virus (influenza), and about 35,000 of those infected die. We are very nervous about COVID-19 because it has a much higher death rate and it's much more infectious. We enacted extreme measures to slow its spread, including temporarily closing businesses, shifting schools to an online format, imposing strict travel guidelines, and issuing stay-at-home orders. Entire sports seasons were canceled, restaurants shut down, and people were asked to adhere to strict social distancing guidelines. For the majority of us—those less than 104 years of age—this is the first time we have experienced such restrictions. However, these measures are not unprecedented. Similar measures were implemented during the "Spanish flu" influenza pandemic of 1918–1919 (Taubenberger and Morens 2006). The 1918 flu ravaged the world population, killing an estimated 50 million people, including 675,000 Americans (Johnson and Mueller 2002, Pambuccian 2020). Measures that were introduced then, like now, helped people survive the deadly pandemic. One difference in disease management between 1918 and 2020 is our capability to synthesize and distribute billions of vaccines in a relatively short period of time (see Figure 15.17). The availability of large numbers of effective vaccines saved many lives during the COVID-19 pandemic. Compared to 1918, today we have a better healthcare system and a greater understanding of how viruses work. Looking to the future, environmental scientists suggest that we should expect an increased likelihood of experiencing infectious disease events (Marani et al. 2021).

FIGURE 15.17
Vaccinations protect us from biological hazards such as H1N1 and SARS-CoV-2. A patient receives a vaccine.

Source: © Shutterstock, Inc.

Key Takeaways

- Society's nonsustainable activities negatively affects Earth's ecosystems and increase our exposure to toxic chemicals, pathogens, and physical hazards.
- COVID-19 is not the first pandemic to spread through the human population.
- Looking to the future, we expect infectious diseases to increase in frequency.

FIGURE 15.18 Visual Overview: Environmental Health and Toxicology
Summarizing figure: Environmental health (15.1) is a branch of public health dealing with toxicology (15.2); movement, distribution, and fate of toxic chemicals (15.3); biological hazards (15.4); and risk assessment and management (15.5). It helps us to prepare for future threats to human health (15.6).

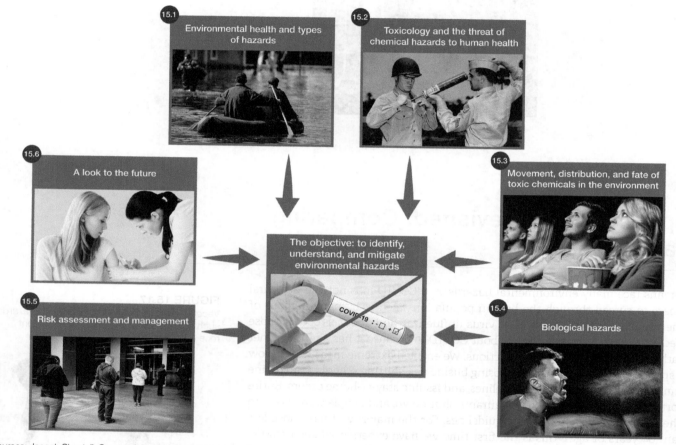

Sources: Joseph Shostell; See previous citations for image credits.

15.7 References

- Ara, S. A. 2012. *Determination of Safrole and Isosafrole from Soft Drinks Using Gas Chromatogram*. Doctoral thesis. Department of Pharmacy, East West University, Dhaka, Bangladesh.

- Arnon, S.S. 1997. "Human tetanus and human botulism." In: *The Clostridia: Molecular biology and pathogenesis* (Eds.: Rood J. I., B. A. McClane, J. G. Songer, and R. W. Titball) London: Academic press.

- Bellinger, D. C. 2005. "Teratogen update: lead and pregnancy." *Birth Defects Research (Part A)* 73: 409–420.

- Bilott, R. 2019. *Poisoned Water, Corporate Greed, and One Lawyer's Twenty-Year Battle Against DuPont.* New York, NY: Atria Books.

- Boserup, B., M. McKenney, and A. Elkbuli. 2020. "Disproportionate impact of COVID-19 pandemic on racial and ethnic minorities." *Am Surg* 86, no. 12: 1615–1622.

- Broussard, L. A., C. A. Hammett-Stabler, R. E. Winecker, and J. D. Ropero-Miller. 2002. "The toxicology of mercury." *Laboratory Medicine* 33, no. 8: 614–625.

- Centers for Disease Control (CDC). 2018. CDC and Food Safety. U.S. Department of Health and Human Services. https://www.cdc.gov/foodsafety/pdfs/CDC-Food-Safety-2018-H.pdf

- Cyrus, E., R. Clarke, D. Hadley, Z. Bursac, M. J. Trepka, J. G. Dévieux, U. Bagci, D. Furr-Holden, M. Coudray, Y. Mariano, S. Kiplagat, I. Noel, G. Ravelo, M. Paley, and E. F. Wagner. 2020. "The impact of COVID-19 on African American Communities in the United States." *Health Equity* 4.1: 476–483.

- de Staël, Madame. Germany (New York, 1814), 2:315; JMN 6:37.

- Dhaked, R. K., M. K. Singh, P. Sing, and P. Gupta. 2010. "Botulinum toxin: bioweapon and magic drug." *Indian J Med Res* 132, no. 5: 489–503.

- Drexler, M. 2010. *What You Need to Know About Infectious Disease.* Washington, DC: National Academies Press.

- Eklöf, K., K. Bishop, S. Bertilssonm, E. Björn, M. Buck, et al. 2018. "Formation of mercury methylation hotspots as a consequence of forestry operations." *Sci Total Environ* 613–614: 1069–1078.

- Environmental Protection Agency (EPA). 1998. *R.E.D. Facts Diphenylamine.* EPA-738-F-97-010.

- Environmental Protection Agency. 2006. *Lead Human Exposure and Health Risk Assessments and Ecological Risk Assessment for Selected Areas. Pilot Phase External Review Draft Technical Report.* Office of Air Quality Planning and Standards, U.S. Environmental Protection Agency. Research Triangle Park, NC.

- Environmental Protection Agency (EPA) 2014. *Framework for Human Health Risk Assessment to Inform Decision Making.* EPA/100/R-14/001. www.epa.gov/raf.

- Environmental Protection Agency (EPA) 2017. *Record of Decision San Jacinto River Waste Pits Harris County, Texas.* EPA Region 6, Dallas, TX.

- Erren, T. C., M. Jacobson, and C. Piekarski. 1999. "Synergy between asbestos and smoking on lung cancer risks." *Epidemiology* 10: 405–411.

- Frederick, P., D. Axelrad, T. Atkeson, and C. Pollman. 2005. "Contaminants research and policy: the Everglades mercury story." *National Wetlands Newsletter* 27, no. 1: 3–6.

- Garg, S., L. Kim, M. Whitaker, A. O'Halloran, C. Cummings, R. Holsteinm, M. Prill, S. J. Chai, P. D. Kirley, N. B. Alden, et al. 2020. *Hospitalization Rates and Characteristics of Patients Hospitalized with Laboratory-Confirmed Coronavirus Disease 2019-COVID-NET, 14 States, March 1–30, 2020.* Centers for Disease Control and Prevention.

- Gómez, H. F., D. A. Borgialli, M. Sharman, K. K. Shah, A. J. Scolpino, J. M. Oleske, and J. D. Bogden. 2018. "Blood lead levels of children in Flint, Michigan: 2006–2016.: *J Pediatr* 197: 158–164.

- Guan, W. J., Z. Y. Ni, Y. Hu. et al. 2020. "Clinical characteristics of coronavirus disease 2019 in China." *N Engl J Med.* https://doi.org/10.1056/NEJMoa2002032.

- Hajeb, P., H. C. Mei, W. N. Noordin, and N. A. Mahyudin. 2012. "Make the deadly yellow puffer fish a safe food to eat." *Journal of Food, Agriculture and Environment* 10, no. 3&4: 72–77.

- Hanna-Attisha, M., J. LaChance, R. C. Sadler, and A. Champney Schnepp. 2016. "Elevated blood lead levels in children associated with the Flint drinking water crisis: A spatial analysis of risk and public health response." *Am J Public Health* 106, no. 2: 283–290.

- Hoffman, K., T. F. Webster, S. M. Bartell, M. G. Weisskopf, T. Fletcher, and V. M. Vieira. 2011. "Private drinking water wells as a source of exposure to perfluorooctanoic acid (PFOA) in communities surrounding a fluoropolymer production facility." *Environmental Health Perspectives* 119, no. 1: 92–97.

- Huang, C., Y. Wang, X. Li, L. Ren, J. Zhao, Y. Hu, L. Zhang, G. Fan, J. Xu, X. Gu, Z. Cheng, T. Yu, J. Xia, Y. Wei, W. Wu, X. Xie, W. Yin, H. Li, M. Liu, Y. Xiao, H. Gao, L, Guo, J. Xie, G. Wang, R. Jiang, Z. Gao, J. Wang, and B. Cao. 2020. "Clinical features of patients infected with 2019 novel coronavirus in Wuhan, China." *The Lancet* 395: 497–505.

- Ito, T., H. Ando, and H. Handa. 2011. "Teratogenic effects of thalidomide: molecular mechanisms." *Cellular and Molecular Life Sciences* 68: 1569–1579.

- Iyer, R., J. Aggarwal, and B. Iken. 2016. "A review of the Texas, USA San Jacinto Superfund site and the deposition of polychlorinated dibenzo-p-dioxins and dibenzofurans in the San Jacinto River and Houston ship channel." *Environ Sci Pollut Res* 23: 23321–23338.

- Johnson, N. P., and J. Mueller. 2002. "Updating the accounts: global mortality of the 1918–1920 'Spanish' influenza pandemic." *Bull Hist Med* 76: 105–115.

- Kemprai, P., B. P. Mahanta, D. Sut, R. Barman, D. Banki, M. Lal, S. P. Saikia, and S. Haldar. 2019. "Review on safrole: identity shift of the 'candy shop' aroma to a carcinogen and deforester." *Flavour Fragr Journal* 35: 5–23.

- Kolaja, and Hinton. 1977. "Effects of DDT on eggshell quality and calcium adenosine triphosphatase." *J Toxicol Environ Health* 3, no. 4: 699–704.

- Lau, C., K. Anitole, C. Hodes, D. Lai, A. Pfahles-Hutchens, and J. Seed. 2007. "Perfluoroalkyl acids: a review of monitoring and toxicological findings." *Toxicol Sci* 99, no. 2: 366–394.

- Levine, M. M., D. Nasrin, S. Acacio, Q. Bassat, et al. 2020. "Diarrhoeal disease and subsequent risk of death in infants and children in low-income and middle-income countries: analysis of the GEMS case-control study and 12-month GEMS-1A follow-on study." *Lancet Global Health* 8, no. 2: E204–E214.

- Marani, M., G. G. Katul, W. K. Pan, and A. J. Parolari. 2021. "Intensity and frequency of extreme novel epidemics." *PNAS* 118, no. 35: e2105482118.

- Moon, M. K. 2019. "Concern about the safety of Bisphenol A substitutes." *Epidemiology* 43: 46–48.

- Morrison, H. I., P. J. Villeneuve, J. H. Lubin, and D. E. Schaubel. 1998. "Radon-progeny exposure and lung cancer risk in a cohort of Newfoundland fluorspar miners." *Radiat Res* 150: 58–65.

- Moura, H. S. R. P., P. R. S. Rocha, A. A. Amato, and F. F. Sodré. 2019. "Quantification of bisphenol A in urine samples from children studying in public schools from the Brazilian capital." *Microchemical Journal* 152: 104347. https://doi.org/10.1016/j.microc.2019.104347

- Morello-Frosch, R., L. J. Cushing, B. M. Jesdale, J. M. Schwartz, W. Guo, T. Guo, M. Wang, S. Harwani, S. E. Petropoulou, W. Duong, J. Park, M. Petreas, R. Gajek, J. Alvaran, J. She, D. Dobraca, R. Das, and T. J. Woodruff. 2016. "Environmental chemicals in an urban population of pregnant women and their newborns from San Francisco." *Environ Sci Technol* 50, no. 22: 12464–12472.

- National Research Council (NRC). 2002. *Safe on Mars: Precursor Measurements Necessary to Support Human Operations on the Martian Surface.* Washington, DC: The National Academies Press. https://doi.org/10.17226/10360.

- Omenn, G. S., A. C. Kessler, N. T. Anderson, P. Y. Chiu, J. Doull. et al. 1997. *Framework for Environmental Health Risk Management.* The Presidential/Congressional Commission on Risk Assessment and Risk Management Final Report Volume 1.

- O'Neil, J. 2016. *Tackling Drug-Resistant Infections Globally: Final Report and Recommendations.* The Review on Antimicrobial Resistance. Report commissioned by the UK Prime Minister.

- Pambuccian, S. 2020. "The COVID-19 pandemic: implications for the cytology laboratory." *Journal of the American Society of Cytopathology.* https://doi.org/10.1016/j.jasc.2020.03.001.

- Peck, M.W. 2006. "Clostridium botulinum and the safety of minimally heated, chilled foods: an emerging issue?" *J Appl Microbiol* 101, no. 3: 556–570.

- Popoff, M. R. 2014. "Botulinum neurotoxins: more and more diverse and fascinating toxic proteins." *The Journal of Infectious Diseases* 209: 168–169.

- Sexton, K., L. L. Needham, and J. L. Pirkle. 2004. "Human biomonitoring of environmental chemicals: measuring chemicals in human tissues is the "gold standard" for assessing people's exposure to pollution." *American Scientist* 92, no. 1: 38–45.

- Sexton, K., and D. Hattis. 2007. "Assessing cumulative health risks from exposure to environmental mixtures—three fundamental questions." *Environmental Health Perspectives* 115, no. 5: 825–832.

- Sheu, R., C. Stönner, J. C. Ditto, T. Klüpfel, J. Willams, and D. R. Gentner. 2020. "Human transport of third hand tobacco smoke: a prominent source of hazardous air pollutants into indoor non-smoking environments." *Sc. Adv.* 6: eaay4109.

- Singh, A. R., and S. A. Sing. 2008. "Diseases of poverty and lifestyle, well-being and human development." *Mens Sana Mongr* 6, no. 1: 187–225.

- Taubenberger, J. K., and D. M. Morens. 2006. 1918 Influenza: the mother of all pandemics. *Emerg Infect Dis* 12: 15–22.

- Tillett, T. 2007. "Research helps clean up a water supply." *Environ Health Perspect* 115: A134.

- Tisserand, R., and R. Young. 2014. *Essential Oil Safety, Second Edition A Guide for Health Care Professionals.* London, UK: Churchill Livingstone.

- United Nations Children's Fund (UNICEF). 2016. *The State of the World's Children 2016. A Fair Chance for Every Child.* New York, NY: United Nations.

- Van der Velden, A., M. Duerden, J. Bell, J. Oxford, A. Altiner, et al. 2013. "Prescriber and patient responsibilities in treatment of acute respiratory tract infections—essential for conservation of antibiotics." *Antibiotics* 2: 316–327.

- Wang, W., A. N. Urbina, M. R. Chang, W. Assavalapsakul, P. Lu, Y. Chen, and S. Wang. 2020. "Dengue hemorrhagic fever—a systemic literature review of current perspectives on pathogenesis, prevention and control." *Journal of Microbiology, Immunology and Infection.* https://doi.org/10.1016/j.jmii.e0e0.03.007.

- Wen, H., H. Huang, T. Tsai, and S. Wang. 2019. "Phthlates." In: *Health Impacts of Developmental Exposure to Environmental Chemicals (Ed.: Kishi, R. and Grandjean, P.).* London, UK: Springer Nature.

- White, N. J. 2004. "Antimalarial drug resistance." *J Clin Invest* 113, no. 8: 1084—1092.

- World Health Organization (WHO). 2003. Update 74-Global Decline in Cases and Deaths Continues. https://www.who.int/csr/don/2003_06_05/en/.

- Wurster, C. F., D. H. Wurster, and W. Strickland. 1965. "Bird mortality after spraying for Dutch elm disease with DDT." *Science* 148, no. 3666: 90–91.

- Yu, J., T. Sim, C. Guo, Z. Han, J. Lau, and G. Su. 2019. "Household adaptation intentions to earthquake risks in rural China." *International Journal of Disaster Risk Reduction* 40. https://doi.org/10.1016/j.ijdrr.2019.101253.

- Zhang, C., W. Zheng, X. Huang, E. W. Bell, X. Zhou, and Y. Zhang. 2020. "Protein structure and sequence reanalysis of 2019-nCoV genome refutes snakes as its intermediate host and the unique similarity between its spike protein insertions and HIV-1." *Journal of Proteome Research* 19: 1351–1360.

CHAPTER 16
Solid and Hazardous Waste

Case Study: Sailing through the Great Pacific Garbage Patch

In 1997, on his return to the coast of California after racing in the Transpacific Yacht Race, Charles Moore sailed into a seemingly endless stretch of floating plastic garbage. After his trip, Captain Moore described what he had witnessed. "There were shampoo caps and soap bottles and plastic bags and fishing floats as far as I could see." He and his crew were the first to discover the immense Pacific Garbage Patch (see Figure 16.1). Huge in scale, the patch is estimated to cover an area of 1.6 million km^2 (617,760 mi^2), about four times the size of California (Lebreton et al. 2018). Remove from your mind the image of concentrated trash in a **landfill**, because the swirling mass of plastic in the Northern Pacific Ocean is more akin to a peppered soup. The plastic is spread out—a little less than one piece per square meter of water. To some, this number might seem inconsequential, but in total, the floating garbage patch consists of trillions of plastic pieces ranging in size from 50 microns (μm) to a few centimeters, with an average between 500 μm and 1 mm. The various shapes of the pieces—shards, fibers, and quasispheres—attest to the original products and the physical toll of waves and solar radiation. Plastic is fairly impervious to breakdown in the environment, so it can persist for decades (plastic bags), hundreds of years (plastic bottles), or longer (plastic pipes). Waves and UV light break larger pieces into bits, but plastics (unlike organic materials) don't get broken down into their molecular components, much less molecules that can be used by living things. In some cases, it is possible to discern letters and words that offer clues to the origin of the fragments. Based on language inscriptions, one-third of the plastic comes from Japan, one-third from China, and lesser amounts from nine other countries (Lebreton et al. 2018). Concentrations of plastics decrease exponentially with depth, from a maximum of 0.212 plastic pieces per cubic meter of water (1 piece per 56 gallons) in the upper surface waters to less than 0.001 pieces per cubic meter at depths of 2 km (1.2 miles) (Elias et al. 2018). These numbers are conservative, because the research group that carried out this survey ignored plastic pieces that were smaller than 500 μm (Egger et al. 2020).

FIGURE 16.1

The Pacific Garbage Patch is the world largest garbage dump. Waste discarded on land enters rivers and makes its way to ocean coastlines, where it is swept out to sea by a rotating ocean current called a gyre. Waste also originates from cruise ships, fishing vessels (especially discarded nets), and oil rigs. (A) Floating waste off the coast of Panama. (B) Plastic waste on the sea floor.

Sources: Fotos593/Shutterstock.com; © Shutterstock, Inc.

Upon making the Great Pacific Garbage Patch discovery, Captain Moore, who is a researcher and oceanographer, pondered over questions relevant to all of us: "From where does this plastic originate?" and, "How does it end up in the ocean?" Decades after plastics are synthesized and sold to consumers—many in one-time-use products—their remnants remain in nature. Yearly global production of plastics reached 369 million metric tons in 2020, and is projected to increase

---

landfill

A waste disposal site on land; covered with soil when full.

waste

Undesired materials generated by society.

waste disposal

The final destination of wastes that are not recycled, composted, reused, or recovered. This is the least desirable endpoint in a waste management hierarchy strategy.

municipal solid waste (MSW)

Waste from residences and institutions (e.g., schools, small businesses, prisons).

yearly in the foreseeable future. Due to poor waste management, a small fraction of the total (4.8–12.7 million metric tons) makes its way into rivers, and ultimately, into the oceans (Jambeck et al. 2015).

A large proportion of plastic waste in the Garbage Patch comes from commercial fishing activities (i.e., abandoned fishing nets), but a significant amount also comes from land-based activities. Plastic cups, bottles, bottle caps, forks, shampoo bottles, detergent containers, straws, bags, toys, and countless other structures, both broken and whole, are cast aside after use and swept into streams and rivers. Smaller and then progressively larger rivers act as conveyor belts that move the plastic all the way to ocean coasts (see Figure 16.1). From coastlines, the waste is taken up by a slow-moving, giant whirlpool of water—a gyre—that covers an area of 20 million square kilometers (7.7 million mi^2). Hence, the ocean literally takes out society's trash. Over the course of months to years, the plastic circulates in the gyre and gradually moves to the gyre's more static center. The center, with its concentrated mass of plastic, is the location of the Great Pacific Garbage Patch.

Lingering, nonbiodegradable plastic is harmful to the oceanic ecosystem in several ways, well beyond aesthetics. Marine mammals, birds, and fish mistake colorful bottle caps and plastic debris for food (see Figure 16.2). For example, on Kure Atoll, northwest of Hawaii, in the middle of the North Pacific, black-footed albatross (*Phoebastria nigripes*) parents feed plastic debris to their chicks. We think the propensity to ingest plastic occurs because one of this species' preferred food sources is flying fish egg masses, which float and are similarly colorful. Necropsies of chicks showed that between 18 percent and 94 percent of their stomachs were packed with plastic debris (Hyrenbach et al. 2017). Hundreds of thousands of albatrosses are dying of starvation with their stomachs full of plastic.

FIGURE 16.2
Plastic waste in the ocean threatens marine life and ecosystem functioning. (A) A Laysan albatross with a stomach full of plastic (notice the intact cigarette lighter). (B) A sea turtle mistakes a plastic bag for a jellyfish. (C) Fish tangled in an abandoned net.

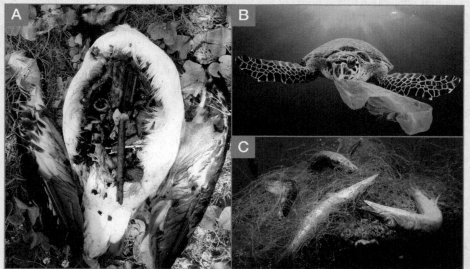

Sources: NOAA, https://marinedebris.noaa.gov/multimedia/photos/impacts#prettyPhoto; © Shutterstock, Inc.

There are other dangers associated with plastics because they contain toxic chemicals included at time of production, and they sorb (take up) toxic chemicals from the surrounding seawater (Mendoza and Jones 2015). Carcinogenic polycyclic aromatic hydrocarbons (PAHs) and polychlorinated biphenyls (PCBs) are examples of some of the toxic chemical groups (see Chapter 15) manufactured by society, indirectly deposited in the oceans, and adsorbed by floating plastic. It is reasonable to assume that some of the sorbed chemicals (lipophilic pollutants) will easily transfer to biological membranes of marine organisms that ingest the plastic particles. Bioaccumulation of toxic chemicals such as PCBs in organisms and the biomagnification of these substances in the food chain are other harmful effects (see Chapter 1). Because of the presence of toxic chemicals in plastics, ingestion of plastic by marine invertebrates, birds, fish, and mammals leads to severe health problems. In mammals, for example, PCB exposure can lead to abnormalities in the reproductive system, low birth weight, and cancer.

The presence of plastics can disrupt ecosystem functioning (see Figure 16.2). The more than 1,200 marine species coming into contact with plastic can also become entangled by discarded nets, which make up a large proportion of plastic in garbage patches. To make matters worse, the Great Pacific Garbage Patch is not the only floating mass of plastic. There are patches of garbage in each of the world's five giant gyres: in the North Pacific, South Pacific, North Atlantic, South Atlantic, and Indian Oceans. Furthermore, within each of these large areas there are smaller patches of garbage. What we observe at the ocean's surface is only about half of the plastic litter, because the rest sinks and accumulates on the ocean floor (Elias 2018). However, Robert Moore suggests the percentage on the bottom is closer to 99 percent. Assessing the amount of plastic in the depths of the oceans is a major challenge, and we have only just begun to collect data. Researchers at the University of California's Scripps Institute of Oceanography analyzed sediments off the coast of southern California. Their sediment core represented materials that settled on the ocean floor between the years 1834 and 2009. They noted an exponential increase in plastic deposition over time, and a doubling every fifteen years (Brandon et al. 2019). This is the result of a throwaway culture that accelerated post-World War II (see Figure 16.3).

FIGURE 16.3
Of all of the plastic produced between 1950 and 2009 that is not still in use, more than 79 percent has been discarded, 12 percent has been incinerated, and less than 9 percent has been recycled (Data from Geyer et al. 2017).

Sources: Joseph Shostell; data from Geyer et al., "Production, use, and fate of all plastics ever made." Sci Adv, 3 (2017). Retrieved from https://pubmed.ncbi.nlm.nih.gov/28776036/ ; © Shutterstock, Inc.

While we recognize the negative effects of throwaway plastics, other forms of plastics come with many benefits. Thousands of companies depend on plastics in their daily business activities. Thanks to plastics, planes, trucks, and cars are all lighter, but still durable, allowing us to reduce fuel use without sacrificing safety. Plastic packaging saves shipping and energy costs because it is lighter than other forms of packaging. The issue of plastic waste is more about improving efficiency, less use and more reuse, and recycling than the elimination of plastic altogether. Key to the solution is rethinking how our own actions can help change our throwaway culture. Furthermore, all types of plastics are not equally damaging to the environment, and some are organic-based and biodegradable.

TABLE 16.1 All of Society's Waste (Billons of Tons per Year)
There are many categories of waste. Industrial, municipal, and hazardous wastes are the most common.

Type of Waste	Description	Examples	Amount Generated by U.S. Each Year
Industrial waste	Waste produced by industrial activity	• Mining • Agriculture • Coal combustion • Oil and gas production • Manufacturing	Estimated to be as high as 7.6 billion tons
Municipal solid waste	Nonhazardous solid waste from homes, schools, small businesses, hospitals, prisons, nursing homes, stores, restaurants, etc.	• Plastic • Glass • Yard trimmings • Wood • Paper and paperboard • Textiles • Food • Rubber and leather	298 million tons in 2018
Hazardous waste	Toxic, chemically reactive, flammable, or corrosive; can originate from multiple sources	• Wastes from processing of coal • Wastes from manufacturing pesticides • Petroleum refinery wastewater treatment sludge • Discarded commercial chemical products (e.g., unused pharmaceuticals) • Wastes with dioxins	29 million tons in 2017
Radioactive waste	Waste that emits subatomic particles or energy from radioactive decay. Although this radiation is hazardous to life, the EPA does not list radioactive waste in its definition of hazardous waste.	• Spent nuclear fuel from nuclear reactors	2,000 tons

Sources: Data from EPA, https://www.epa.gov/sites/default/files/2016-03/documents/industrial-waste-guide.pdf; EPA, https://www.epa.gov/facts-and-figures-about-materials-waste-and-recycling/national-overview-facts-and-figures-materials; EPA, https://cfpub.epa.gov/roe/indicator.cfm?i=54; Scientific American, https://www.scientificamerican.com/article/nuclear-waste-lethal-trash-or-renewable-energy-source/; and https://www.energy.gov/ne/articles/5-fast-factsabout-spent-nuclear-fuel.

In this chapter, we look into society's solid waste stream, including types of **wastes**, methods of **waste disposal**, as well as waste management, reduction, and elimination. Most waste is classified as **municipal solid waste (MSW)** from residences and institutions, industrial waste, or hazardous waste (see Table 16.1), and all three are discussed in this chapter. (The less common (<0.1 percent) radioactive waste is mentioned in Chapter 13.)

16.1 Society's Waste

Learning Objectives

1. Describe society's waste stream.
2. Provide evidence of society's creating more waste than what the environment can handle.
3. Explain the benefits of reducing society's waste stream.

A bobbing plastic bottle cap in the ocean, a used notebook in a trash can, and a broken love seat in a landfill are examples of waste, signs of inefficiency, and loss of valuable resources. Every citizen of every country generates waste. Americans, for example, produce an average of 2 kg (4.5 lbs) of garbage (MSW) every day (see Figure 16.4), and that amount is climbing. In 2020, Americans together generated over 270 million tons of municipal solid waste (MSW), which is almost a 210 percent increase from 1960. Part of this increase is due to a larger U.S. population, but this does not completely explain the increase in waste generation over the decades. Since 1960, the U.S. population has grown from 179 million to 333 million, or by 86 percent. Therefore, the rate of waste generation far exceeds the rate of population growth, and the average American produces more garbage today than in the previous decades. Higher-income countries, including the United States, have higher per-person daily averages than lower-income countries. According to the World Bank, a meager 16 percent of Earth's population generates 34 percent of its waste.

Across the world, more than eleven billion tons of MSW are collected each year. This form of easy-to-observe, tangible waste (plastic bottles, grass clippings, etc.) is just one fraction of society's total waste.

All wastes are part of a large **waste stream**—spanning the life of waste from formation to endpoint. Within the main stream, we can follow individual waste types (in their own, smaller waste streams) to their final destination; for instance, a landfill, incineration, or recycling.

waste stream

The pathway of wastes from origin to endpoint.

FIGURE 16.4

As of 2017, the average American generates 2.05 kg (4.51 lbs) of waste per day, which is much higher than the global average of 0.74 kg (1.63 lbs) per day. Over the course of a lifetime, that works out to almost 60,000 kg (132,300 lbs) of garbage! Images illustrate the weight of cumulative waste at specific years.

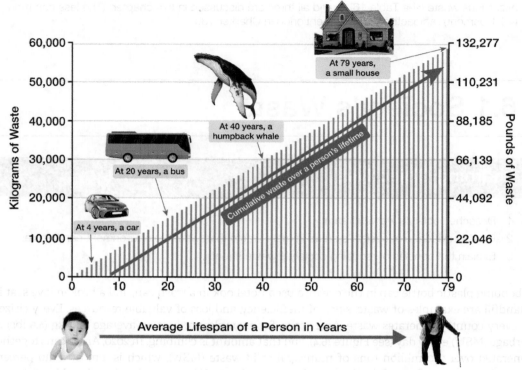

Sources: Joseph Shostell; data from EPA, https://www.epa.gov/facts-and-figures-about-materials-waste-and-recycling/national-overview-facts-and-figures-materials#:~:text=Per capita MSW generation increased,Food: Material-Specific Data; © Shutterstock, Inc.

Are We Creating Too Much Waste?

How did we get to this point? Over ten thousand years ago, our forefathers didn't worry much about waste; then they gave up their nomadic lifestyle and settled in one place. Even then, waste was not much of an issue. As long as the density of people remained low, the natural environment could easily absorb and degrade any wastes they generated. Over the course of time, human populations began to realize the limits of what Mother Nature could degrade naturally, the connection between wastes and illness, and the need to manage waste.

For instance, at the beginning of the twentieth century, residents of large American and European cities were fed up with smelly, unaesthetic, and unsanitary piles of horse manure and all-too-frequent horse carcasses on city streets (see Figure 16.5). A single horse produced an average of 9 kg (20 lbs) of manure and two pints of urine every day. Chicago alone had 74,000 horses, and Manhattan had 130,000, approximately one horse for every fifteen people (Tarr and McShane 2008). Every manure pile provided habitat space for egg-laying flies and fostered development of larvae, pupae, and adult flies that spread disease. If not for the dawn of the horseless carriage, horse-drawn carriages may well have been banned from city limits. Thus, certain anthropogenic activities generate piles of organic waste that threaten human health.

FIGURE 16.5

As these late-nineteenth-century photos of (A) a double-decker carriage-bus in London and a New York City street (B) with and (C) without horse manure indicate waste (manure in this case) can be a problem in society, especially in densely populated urban areas. Today, there are many signs that waste generation is increasing across the globe. The graph (D) depicts predicted waste generation through 2050.

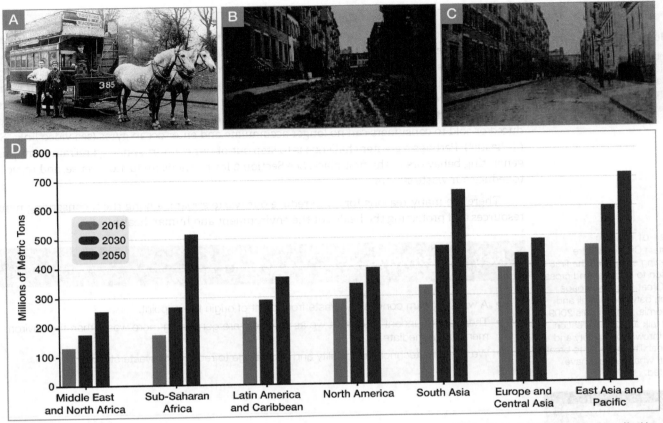

Sources: Atlas Obscura, https://www.atlasobscura.com/articles/the-first-global-urban-planning-conference-was-mostly-about-manure; Internet Archive, https://archive.org/details/streetcleaningdi00wari/page/n29/mode/2up; data from The World Bank, https://datatopics.worldbank.org/what-a-waste/trends_in_solid_waste_management.html.

What are the signs of creating too much waste? Any evidence of waste's accumulating faster than it degrades would be a good starting point. When the accumulation reaches a level that compromises ecosystem functioning and the environment's ability to provide ecosystem services, then we have surpassed nature's resiliency. Is there evidence of accumulated waste and the negative effects of that waste on ecosystems? Peer-reviewed journal articles suggest that all terrestrial biomes and aquatic life zones are struggling to maintain themselves as society's waste accumulates in them. For example, microplastics are now widespread in rivers, lakes, and oceans (Zarfl et al. 2011, Free et al. 2014). Microplastics are negatively affecting life zones because they accumulate contaminants and are often ingested by fish, birds, mammals, and other animals.

Look also for evidence in marginalized and impoverished communities, because these communities suffer disproportionately from pollution. More than two billion people lack access to sewage treatment facilities and solid waste collection services. General poor health and incidences of diarrheal diseases can be good indicators of waste accumulation beyond what can be appropriately managed in a particular city, town, or region.

Can We and Should We Reduce the Waste Stream?

industrial waste

Nonhazardous solids, liquids, semisolids, and gaseous wastes generated by industrial activities.

We have the technology and know-how to reduce our waste stream right now. The most effective strategy is to reduce waste at the point of origin (see Section 4). For instance, we could make a big dent in our waste stream by weaning ourselves off petroleum products. If we all drove electric cars, we would eliminate most new **industrial waste** generated from petroleum mining and at refineries. We could replace all petroleum-based plastics with plant-based materials, so a large part of municipal solid wastes would become biodegradable. Petroleum-based plastics that are not produced or sold to consumers can no longer accumulate and enter ocean gyres (see video link: "Seas of Plastic"). Perhaps a greater challenge is to step out of our comfort zone and refrain from waste-generating behaviors in the first place. See Section 2 for methods (reduction, reuse, and recycling) to reduce our waste stream.

There are many reasons for us to reduce our waste stream, among them conserving natural resources and protecting the health of the environment and human health.

Seas of Plastic

Captain Charles Moore (opening story) was the first person to discover and cross the Great Pacific Garbage Patch between Hawaii and California. Listen to his 2009 TED talk about the creation of a throwaway society and the inability of nature to break down what humans have created.

View in the online reader

Key Takeaways

- A waste stream contains all waste from point of origin to endpoint.
- There are abundant signs that we as a society are generating more waste than the environment can remediate.
- We have the technological ability and knowledge to reduce the waste stream.

16.2 Municipal Solid Waste (MSW)

Learning Objectives

1. Identify the waste streams of municipal solid waste.
2. Explain the benefits of having an integrated solid waste management strategy.
3. Explain why waste disposal is the last and least desirable step of waste management.
4. Provide examples of laws that help to ensure waste management.
5. Identify the pros and cons of landfills.

To manage the vast amount of waste we generate, we have to classify wastes into broad categories based on origin and properties. Discarded plastic beverage bottles and straws are examples of municipal solid waste (MSW) that can end up in ocean gyres (see "Case Study: Sailing through the Great Pacific Garbage Patch"). These wastes originate from homes, small businesses, office buildings, prisons, restaurants, and other sources.

Municipal Solid Waste Has Many Waste Streams with Multiple Endpoints

The EPA recognizes more than ten main waste streams for municipal solid waste generated in the United States (see A in Figure 16.6). Wastes that make up these streams are highly visible because we take them out in kitchen garbage, for example. According to the EPA, one-fourth of these wastes consist of paper and paperboard. Food (15 percent), plastics (13 percent) yard trimmings (13 percent), and metals (9.4 percent), make up other major categories. Most of these wastes end up in one of four general endpoints: **recycling**, **composting**, **energy recovery**, and landfill (see B in Figure 16.6). Recycling and composting, which are forms of **recovery**, reduce the overall waste stream. It is most unfortunate that more than half of America's MSW ends up in landfills. Keep in mind, EPA's data for municipal solid waste do not include waste lost to the environment; they are based solely on records of what is collected (and reported).

recycling

Converting waste into reusable material and new products.

composting

The natural process of recycling organic matter such as lawn cuttings and food scraps under aerobic conditions to produce compost, nutrient-rich, and decayed organic matter. Compost can be used as fertilizer to improve soil structure.

energy recovery

Energy recovery from waste.

recovery

Removal of useful materials from the waste stream prior to disposal. Recycling and composting are examples of recovery.

FIGURE 16.6
Main municipal solid waste (MSW) streams in the United States (A) Amounts of the different types of municipal solid wastes generated each year. (B) Municipal solid waste endpoints. Most MSW generated in the U.S. end up in landfills.

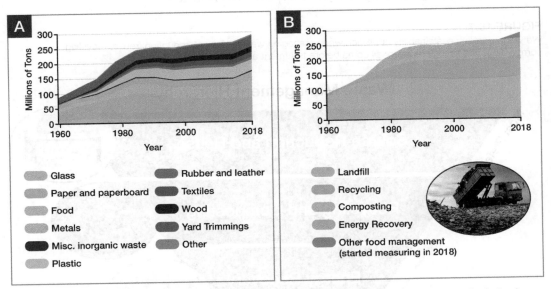

Sources: Joseph Shostell; data from EPA, https://www.epa.gov/facts-and-figures-about-materials-waste-and-recycling/national-overview-facts-and-figures-materials; © Shutterstock, Inc.

Generation of waste has increased drastically over the last century—more than 200 percent overall just since 1960. The amount of increase varies by the waste stream. For example, glass waste had the smallest increase (about 70 percent). On the other end of the spectrum, plastic waste increased by 9,000 percent, textile waste by close to 900 percent, wood waste by almost 500 percent, and food waste by more than 230 percent. What happens to these wastes? The amount of waste generated tells just part of the story.

Managing Municipal Solid Waste

Management of waste has not changed much over thousands of years. We recycle it, leave it where it lays, burn it, or bury it. On the whole, our ancient and more recent ancestors were quite frugal and embraced reuse and recycling as part of their economy. During the late Stone Age—some

11,650 years ago—populations living in the Sahara Desert region found new uses for broken stone tools they carried with them across a sea of sand. These stones served as a source for stone flakes that were used to fashion blades or other functional tools (Close 1996). During the first part of the first millennium in what is now Great Britain, Romans recycled broken glass to produce new glass objects (Sainsbury 2018). More recently, throughout the colonial period, materials were constantly reused. Old clothing was mended until unpresentable and then converted to rags or stuffing in furniture (Zimring 2009). Similarly, blacksmiths forged new goods from metal scraps. In contemporary Japan, people still practice kintsugi, the mending of broken pottery with gold. It is a different way of looking at what we in the west would consider waste.

Most industrialized countries today make use of a comprehensive approach to managing municipal solid waste (MSW) called **integrated solid waste management**. The aim of this strategy is to manage solid waste in ways that best benefit human health and the environment. Integrated solid waste management includes source reduction, recovery (recycling and composting), treatment, and, when necessary, safe disposal. In this management system, waste is separated into streams. For example, in many urban areas, recycling trucks pick up recyclables at the curbside and haul them to a transfer station and recycling center. This is big business! The global recycling and recovery market is valued at around $400 billion—an amount that gives credence to the adage, "one person's garbage is another one's treasure." Sustainability-minded waste managers follow a **waste management hierarchy**. In descending order, they strive for source reduction and reuse, followed by recovery (recycling and composting), and disposal (see Figure 16.7).

integrated solid waste management

Managing solid waste to best benefit human health and the environment. Includes source reduction, recycling, composting, treatment, and, when necessary, safe disposal.

waste management hierarchy

Management of waste striving for the following in descending order of preference: source reduction and reuse, recycling/composting, recovery, and disposal.

FIGURE 16.7
We want to take a sustainability approach when managing wastes. Source reduction, reuse, recycling, composting, and energy recovery all come before treatment and disposal.

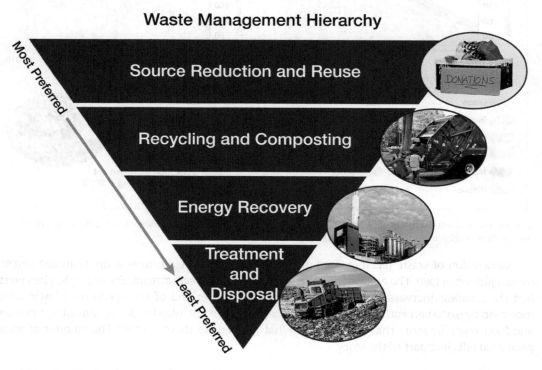

Sources: Data from EPA, https://www.epa.gov/smm/sustainable-materials-management-non-hazardous-materials-and-waste-management-hierarchy; © Shutterstock, Inc.; ImagineStock/Shutterstock.com

Preventing Waste Formation

Source reduction, better known as waste prevention, is the most effective way to reduce waste generation. There are many ways to achieve source reduction. A redesign, selective purchase, or a more efficient manufacturing process can eliminate wastes before they are formed. Newer product models may contain overall less material and more environmentally friendly components. For example, advances in technology, upgrades in equipment, and decades of experience allowed manufacturers to redesign aluminum cans so they now contain 30 percent less aluminum. Companies can also improve the efficiency of using resources by analyzing their design, manufacturing, and transportation processes. New production equipment may demand less energy and require a smaller amount of raw materials than old equipment, while still permitting a company to maintain or exceed quota. This does not necessarily mean that old equipment is immediately replaced. Rather, older equipment models are calibrated for peak efficiency, and then when they fail, the older models are replaced with newly designed models that use less energy and require less materials.

Businesses and consumers can support source reduction through selective purchasing. A company also reduces waste by minimizing packaging. Consumers support source reduction by including sustainability in their decision-making process. If we wanted to be one of these consumers, we would only buy what we needed, and refuse to buy products that would generate waste that is not recyclable or compostable. Whenever possible, we would refuse single-use items, even when they were free. Rather than drinking water from a plastic bottle, we would sip from a reusable container (remember, many recyclable containers end up in landfills or in ocean gyres). Rather than using throwaway plastic bags, we would pack our purchased items in reusable cloth bags. The message here is to refuse and reduce as much as possible. Reuse fits here as well. Reuse refers to finding other uses for objects after their original function has been fulfilled. In our house, we use large cat litter containers, purchased some twenty years ago, to store ecological field equipment. They have handles, stack nicely, and are quite durable.

Decisions and leadership by individuals have ripple effects through a population and can effect real change. In Africa, Wangari Maathai's Mottainai campaign highlighted the issue of plastic waste (see Figure 16.8). The positive effects of her efforts in sustainability were recognized internationally multiple times (see Chapter 9).

source reduction

Waste prevention; the most effective way to lessen waste generation.

FIGURE 16.8
The environmental efforts of Wangari Maathai (A) had many positive effects, such as the planting of millions of trees across Africa, and the eventual (six years after her death) banning of plastic bags in Kenya. (B) Even with this change, plastic and other forms of solid waste continue to plague Kenya—evidenced by a man standing amidst garbage on Kenya's coast.

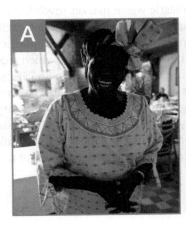

Sources: Joseph Sohm/Shutterstock.com; © Shutterstock, Inc.

Recycling and Composting

Recycling and composting help to reduce the overall waste stream before disposal. Almost 94 million tons of materials were recovered by way of recycling and composting from America's MSP waste stream in 2018. Another 34 million tons were incinerated to recover energy in a process called **waste-to-energy**. Even after recycling, composting, and energy recovery, 146 million tons of waste remained and were disposed of in landfills. Ideally, all waste should be recycled or composted, but this is not happening. On a letter-grade scale, we receive an F to a D-depending on the material.

The highest recycling rates are for paper (68 percent) and ferrous metals (33 percent). At over 65 million tons per year, paper and paperboard (cardboard) make up the largest waste stream of MSW in the United States. Generation of paper and paperboard waste peaked in the 1990s and has decreased since then (see A in Figure 16.9). Newspaper circulations have been on a steady decline, and most people now prefer to send documents electronically. It is faster, cheaper, and conserves space. Overall, Americans have become better stewards of paper. Since 1960, U.S. recycling of paper products has increased by 805 percent, so a smaller amount is ending up in landfills (a decline of 30.8 percent since 1960).

Generation of food waste continues to accelerate. In 2018 alone, more than 63 million tons were generated, and only 2.5 million tons of it (6 percent) was composted. Most (56 percent) ended up in landfills (see B in Figure 16.9). In fact, food waste is the single largest component of MSW in landfills (see video link: "Food Waste"). The problem is escalating in part because we are generating more food waste per capita every year. The United States Food and Drug Administration estimates we are wasting somewhere between 30 percent to 40 percent of the nation's food supply, which is equal to a loss of about $189 billion per year. To combat this trend, the USDA, EPA, and FDA formed a partnership with the Food Waste Reduction Alliance (FWRA). This partnership hopes to reduce the millions of tons of food lost and wasted in the United States every year. One way the partnership does this is by increasing the donations of healthy nutritious food to those in need. Very often, excess high-quality food ends up as waste in landfills and never makes it to consumers.

Plastic is the third largest category of municipal waste, after paper and food. Plastic waste generation has increased by 9,000 percent since 1960, and reached 35.7 million tons in 2018 (see C in Figure 16.9). Three-fourths of this waste ends up in landfills. Significant amounts of plastic are lost to the environment, ending up in rivers and entering ocean gyres (see "Case Study: Sailing through the Great Pacific Garbage Patch"). Less than 9 percent of plastic is recycled. Furthermore, this estimate is likely considerably lower when the route of recycled material is traced from recycling bins in stores and colleges to sorting centers and to shipments abroad. Plastic from the United States ends up in other countries, where it is re-formed into new products and then resold. The value of plastic waste as a commodity supports a substantial plastic waste market involving 123 exporting nations. Until the end of 2017, China was the main importer (>50 percent) of the world's nonindustrial plastic waste. This all changed when China banned the import of most plastics because as much as 70 percent of the imported plastic ended up buried or mismanaged, which triggered a series of environmental problems (Wen et al. 2021). The ban redirected waste to Southeast Asian countries (Wang et al. 2019). The resulting large increases in imported wastes led Thailand and Malaysia to impose their own bans. Generally, developing countries lack recycling facility infrastructure to process and manage their own wastes, so they are ill-prepared to handle waste imported from other countries. A refusal of plastic waste may compel wealthy exporters to rethink the plastic trade network and motivate them to process the waste domestically (Wang et al. 2019).

FIGURE 16.9
Generation and endpoints of America's municipal solid waste. (A) Paper and paperboard, (B) Food waste, (C) Plastic waste, (D) Yard trimmings, (E) Ferrous Metal Waste. Legend: blue = generated waste, yellow = landfilled, orange = recycled or composted, grey = combusted for energy recovery.

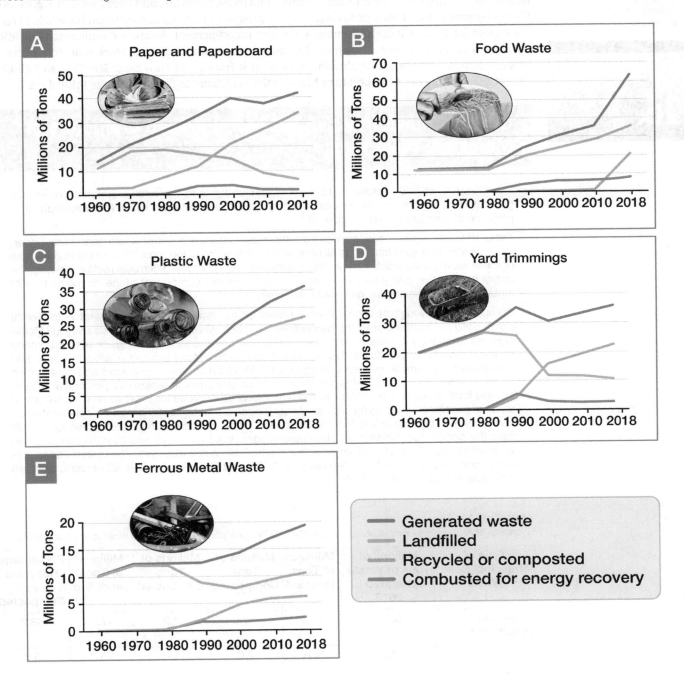

Sources: Data from EPA, https://www.epa.gov/facts-and-figures-about-materials-waste-and-recycling/guide-facts-and-figures-report-about#Materials; © Shutterstock, Inc.

The United States generates almost as much yard waste as plastic waste (see D in Figure 16.9). The way we manage yard trimmings, however, is very different. Unlike petroleum-based plastics, yard trimmings such as leaves can be composted and broken down naturally by decomposers. From 1960 to 2018, yard trimming waste increased 76 percent, to more than 35 million tons. However, during this same period, we considerably reduced the amount of this waste that ended up in landfills. By the mid-1990s, twenty states had banned yard waste from landfills. Today, that number has increased to twenty-six states (NERC 2017).

Food Waste

Food wastes are clogging up landfills. Listen to an explanation of why this is happening.

View in the online reader

Each year, the United States generates millions of tons of metal waste, and this amount is steadily increasing. In 2018, we generated 25 million tons. Almost 19 million tons of this amount is ferrous metals (iron and steel) found in cans, appliances, furniture, and tires (see E in Figure 16.9). Limited primary resources, cost savings, and the prospect of energy conservation have helped recycling rates for ferrous metals to increase by over 12,000 percent. Another 6 million tons of MSW consists of nonferrous metals such as aluminum, copper, lead, and zinc. More than 60 percent of this nonferrous metal waste is aluminum, most of it from aluminum cans. See "Critical Thinking Activity: Generation and Endpoints of Municipal Solid Waste" to further analyze MSW data.

Critical Thinking Activity: Generation and Endpoints of Municipal Solid Waste

The objective of this exercise is to explore and understand the relative amounts of wastes generated (by weight) and endpoints of each waste stream category within MSW through interpretation of data presented in Table 16.2.

Table 16.2 lists the waste categories from the most to least amount of waste generated. Paper, food, plastic, and yard trimmings all have values above 35 million tons. Society generates more of these wastes than waste in any other categories. Iron-containing (ferrous) metals make up the last of the top five categories. Ferrous waste is the largest component of the 25 million tons of metal waste that Americans generate every year.

Compare the rankings of each category based on the amount of waste generated to weight combusted or landfilled, or to the percentage recycled. What does this analysis tell you? Rankings would change if, instead, they were based on combustion, landfilling, or the percentage recycled. Food and plastic wastes are significantly less in total amount relative to paper and paperboard, yet Americans combusted and landfilled significantly more food and plastic than paper. It seems the United States does a poor job recycling plastic waste (8.7 percent) and composting food waste (5.7 percent). Do the data reveal other areas for improvement? What about areas of excellence? Recycling and composting rates are less than 20 percent for six waste categories and 40 percent or less for nine categories. Paper, yard trimmings, and nonferrous metals have the highest recycling/composting percentages, but they are all less than 70 percent. Can we improve our efficiency and increase these rates? Most definitely, yes. The United States currently recycles or composts 32 percent of its MSW, but Germany recycles 68 percent. How are they able to accomplish this feat?

TABLE 16.2

Endpoints of America's municipal solid waste in 2018. MSW categories are listed from most to least abundant.

Type of Municipal Solid Waste	Millions of Tons of Waste Generated in 2018	Millions of Tons Recycled	Millions of Tons Composted	Millions of Tons Combusted	Millions of Tons Landfilled	Percentage Recycled or Composted
Paper and paperboard	67.4	46.0	N/A	4.2	17.2	68.2
Food waste	45.4	N/A	2.6	7.6	35.3	5.7
Plastic	35.7	3.1	N/A	5.6	26.9	8.7
Yard trimmings	35.4	N/A	22.3	2.6	10.5	63.0
Ferrous metals (iron and steel)	19.2	6.4	N/A	2.3	10.5	33.7
Wood	18.2	3.1	—	2.8	12.2	17.2
Textiles	17.0	2.5	N/A	3.2	11.3	14.8
Glass	12.3	3.1	N/A	1.6	7.6	25.0

Type of Municipal Solid Waste	Millions of Tons of Waste Generated in 2018	Millions of Tons Recycled	Millions of Tons Composted	Millions of Tons Combusted	Millions of Tons Landfilled	Percentage Recycled or Composted
Other (combination of smaller categories)	4.6	—	—	0.7	3.0	21.3
Rubber and leather	4.2	1.7	N/A	1.7	0.8	40.4
Misc. inorganic waste	4.1	—	N/A	0.8	3.3	—
Aluminum	3.9	0.7	N/A	0.6	2.7	17.2
Nonferrous metal besides aluminum (copper, lead . . .)	2.5	1.7	N/A	0.1	0.7	67.3

Source: Data from EPA, https://www.epa.gov/facts-and-figures-about-materials-waste-and-recycling/national-overview-facts-and-figures-materials#NationalPicture.

Disposal Is the Last and Least Desirable Step of Waste Management

On July 10, 2010, a landfill collapsed in Quezon City, Philippines, killing 278 people. More recently, in 2015 a construction waste pile collapsed in Shenzhen, China, leading to the death of seventy-seven people (Yang et al. 2017). Accidents like these are preventable when waste is carefully managed, access to the disposed waste is restricted, and safety guidelines are followed and enforced. Wandering through and scavenging in U.S. landfills is explicitly prohibited. In addition to protecting people from the potential harm of accumulated wastes, it is also very important to protect natural ecosystems. Whenever possible and where municipal solid wastes accumulate, the aim is to isolate those wastes from the environment as much as possible. They are deposited in carefully designed **sanitary landfills** that have clay and plastic membrane liners (see Figure 16.10), leachate collection systems, and ongoing monitoring systems. Leachate is the contaminated liquid formed from water passing through waste of the landfill. Sanitary landfills are mostly located in wealthier countries.

sanitary landfills

A landfill that has a liner or other structure to help separate the waste from the environment.

FIGURE 16.10
A landfill is the final resting spot for much of society's waste. The general principle is to isolate the waste from the environment as much as possible by laying down a base liner, collecting and treating leachate, collecting methane (which can be used as a source of energy), and sealing the landfill when full. (A) Installation of a plastic membrane on top of a clay base. (B) A closed landfill with 1.5 m (5 ft) of topsoil covering previously deposited waste.

Sources: © Shutterstock, Inc.; Michael Vi/Shutterstock.com

leachate

A liquid that contains leached matter. Leachate emitted from landfills is a slurry of pollutants.

The idea of safely disposing of solid waste in space (a landfill) blocked off from Mother Nature is naïve, because no landfill is truly isolated from the environment. **Leachate**—a liquid slurry of leached matter containing heavy metals and other pollutants—seeps through landfill liners into ground and surface waters. Landfills are also a source of greenhouse gases, mainly methane. Yet as long as society supports cradle-to-grave product designs, landfills will continue to exist, stocked with valuable resources classified as waste. Just in the United States, an estimated $1.4 billion of recyclables are lost to landfills each year (Powell and Chertow 2018). Then there are the disposal costs, estimated at about $11 billion per year. Society's strategic sustainability goal is to steadily eliminate ill-designed (cradle-to-grave) products and to incrementally increase our capacity to capture resources from the waste stream.

There is sufficient evidence to indicate that landfills cause environmental problems. In addition to a shortage of land available for waste disposal, clay and plastic liners at the bottom of landfills cannot permanently prevent leachate from migrating out of them. Clay liners crack. Plastic liners break down when they come into contact with various chemicals, and eventually develop holes, rips, and stress cracks. The United States Geological Survey (USGS) collected and analyzed leachate from twenty-two landfills in twelve states; the agency identified more than one hundred different contaminants in these samples, including an array of pharmaceuticals and household chemicals (Masoner et al. 2015). Six of the landfills did not even have liners, and these released untreated leachate directly into groundwater. Another landfill discharged untreated leachate directly into a river, and three others applied it to nearby soil as a fertilizer. The remaining twelve landfills continuously discharged leachate to wastewater treatment plants. Wastewater treatment plants are unable to mitigate the full range of these contaminants, which include PFOA and other forever chemicals (Hamid et al. 2017) (see Chapter 15). Currently, the majority of forever chemicals in the leachate are released from wastewater plants into the environment. Some wastewater plant managers are now rejecting leachate from landfills over concern of forever chemicals. Targeting and removing forever chemicals from leachate and wastewater remains a challenge.

Just like any other hole with a limited amount of space, every landfill will eventually fill with waste. After an MSW landfill is full and can no longer accept additional wastes, it needs to be stabilized and monitored over the long term. Consider the Puente Hills Landfill, which accepted waste from Los Angeles from 1956 through 2013. Now, the 1,365-acre, 152 m (500 ft) high pile of refuse is covered by 1.5 m (5 ft) of soil, and there are plans to convert part of the site into a community park. Gas produced from the buried, decomposing organic material is collected, and this powers roughly 50,000 homes. By covering the waste, we are also masking the unpleasant evidence of a wasteful society.

Another form of waste treatment and disposal is incineration. Check out "Critical Thinking Activity: To Burn or Not to Burn Wastes", and weigh the pros and cons of this strategy.

waste-to-energy facility

A facility that recovers energy in waste through one of a variety of methods, including combustion and anaerobic digestion.

Critical Thinking Activity: To Burn or Not to Burn Wastes

In a world of accumulating waste, incineration offers an option to eliminate solid wastes and free up much-needed landfill space. Incinerated waste also serves as a source of energy. For instance, the Montgomery County incineration plant in Maryland, which burns 1,800 tons of waste daily, is an example of a **waste-to-energy facility**. Incineration reduces the volume of waste by 90 percent and supplies 52 megawatts of energy—enough to power 37,000 homes. On the downside, combusting municipal solid waste releases dioxins, mercury, lead, and sulfur oxides into the atmosphere. In essence, the wastes were never eliminated; rather, most of the solid waste was converted to gaseous waste. Is the trade-off worthwhile? How do we make such a comparison? Thousands of people in Maryland are fed up with the state's accepted practice of waste incineration. They want to stop trash incineration and develop zero-waste alternatives. What do you think? Do you support waste incineration? Before finalizing your answers to these questions, check out the innovative and sustainable solutions for dealing with solid waste offered by the company InEnTec (see here). InEnTec uses Plasma Enhanced Melter technology to convert waste into Syngas, which can be used to produce fuels such as ethanol and hydrogen.

State and Federal Laws Help to Ensure Effective Waste Management

The **Resource Conservation and Recovery Act (RCRA)** authorizes the Environmental Protection Agency to regulate municipal, industrial, and hazardous solid waste. Subsection D of the Act covers municipal solid waste and other forms of nonhazardous solid waste. For example, it establishes criteria for designing, operating, and monitoring municipal landfills to best protect human health and the environment. Under RCRA, open dumping is banned. **Open dumping** refers to the disposal of waste in ravines, empty lots, and other unapproved dumping areas (see Figure 16.11). In addition, the statute prohibits the open burning of waste save for agricultural waste and a few other exceptions. Waste management practices listed in the RCRA were designed to protect the health of floodplains, endangered and threatened species, and underground drinking water sources. For example, the Act states that a landfill shall not be located in a wetland area unless there is no alternative, and landfill operators must control disease vectors (e.g., rodents and flies).

FIGURE 16.11
Open dumps exist around the world. (A) One of the many roadside dumps in California. (B) A small fire in an open dump next to a river, in Europe.

Sources: Richard Thornton/Shutterstock.com; © Shutterstock, Inc.

RCRA also sets required and recommended solid waste separation and recovery practices based on number of people and market. As an example, in residential areas with more than 500 families, used newspapers must be collected at curbside. If there is a market, RCRA recommends the collection of cans, glass, and mixed paper. In addition to following federal guidelines, states can establish more stringent regulations as well as incentives for adhering to best management practices. Ten states and Guam elected to develop **bottle laws** to encourage recycling. In Vermont, for instance, a consumer pays an extra fee called a deposit when they purchase a carbonated soft drink, beer, or wine. Upon returning the container—a bottle, jar, or can composed of glass, metal, or plastic—they receive a refund. The refund amount varies across states from two cents to fifteen cents. Cents on the bottle or other container can really add up. Vermonters who return 100 liquor bottles worth 15 cents each, and 100 plastic soda cans worth 5 cents each, will collect twenty dollars.

Resource Conservation and Recovery Act (RCRA)

Federal law that gives authority to the Environmental Protection Agency to manage solid wastes. Subtitle D covers nonhazardous industrial waste; Subtitle C covers hazardous waste.

open dumping

The disposal of waste in nonapproved areas.

bottle laws (bottle bills)

Statutes to encourage recycling. A consumer pays an extra fee called a deposit when they purchase a beverage. Upon returning the container—a bottle, jar, or can composed of glass, metal, paper, or plastic, they receive a refund.

Under the **Marine Protection, Research, and Sanctuaries Act**, dumping of solid waste in the oceans is prohibited. Internationally, the **London Protocol** bans waste dumping and intentional waste incineration at sea. The United States is one of almost ninety nations that support the London Protocol.

New environmental laws and policy shifts can quickly reduce the generation of waste. More than 125 countries have either banned or taxed the use of nondegradable plastic bags. China banned them in large cities in 2020, and its ban is expected to be nationwide in the next few years. Only two U.S. states, California and New York, have passed laws banning the use of plastic bags. Plastic bag waste generation has substantially declined in those locations where bans have taken effect. For example, in California, coastal cleanup crews have observed a 94 percent drop in plastic grocery bag litter between 2008 and 2017.

Key Takeaways

- Municipal solid waste (MSW) has multiple endpoints. Depending on type (i.e., plastic, paper, and food) and location of municipal solid waste, it may be recycled, composted, used in waste-to-energy, or deposited in a landfill.
- The United States has an integrated solid waste management approach, and waste managers follow a waste management hierarchy, yet, overall, recycling and composting rates are quite low. Large volumes of valuable resources are lost to landfills.
- Preventing waste formation, also referred to as source reduction, is the most efficient and cost-effective option to reduce the volume of MSW.
- Subsection D of the Resource Conservation and Recovery Act covers MSW. It establishes criteria for designing, operating, and monitoring municipal landfills. RCRA also sets required and recommended solid waste separation and recovery practices, and it bans open dumping.

16.3 Industrial Solid Waste

Learning Objectives

1. Compare and contrast industrial waste and municipal solid waste.
2. List and describe the main methods of industrial waste management.
3. Explain the benefits of using an industrial ecology approach to managing industries.

The slogan "Made in America" is powerful because it points out the relationship between manufacturing, American jobs, and the health of the American economy. Technology-driven manufacturing allows mass production of many of the different products we use—apparel, paper, and plastic products, for example. Manufacturing is just one of the industrial sectors at the heart of the U.S. economy, and like all industrial sectors in the United States and abroad, it generates waste (see Figure 16.12). Our many and various needs and wants are met by these industries. For example, to satisfy a desire for an apple we rely on the agricultural industry. What about a gold engagement ring? We then count on the mining industry. The utility industry helps to heat our homes, the construction industry makes the existence of our homes possible, and the transportation industry allows for airline travel to our favorite vacation destination. These large industry sectors consist of subsectors, such as the juice industry within the agriculture sector, and coal mining within the mining sector.

FIGURE 16.12
Examples of industrial waste. (A) A semisolid slurry of industrial waste empties from a pipe into a river. (B) Coal ash waste in China. (C) Gold-mining waste in Guyana. (D) A large mining truck releases waste rock into a dump in New Zealand.

Sources: © Shutterstock, Inc.; humphery/Shutterstock.com

Industrial wastes are generally less visible than MSW, so people tend to be less knowledgeable about them. For example, an industrial farmer understands agricultural waste and a mining manager understands mining waste, but people outside these industries tend to have little understanding of the types and volume of wastes they generate. By some estimates, industrial waste accounts for most of society's waste (over 95 percent) (Mervis 2012); other estimates (Krones 2016) consider it on par with MSW because 90–97 percent is water.

Types and Volume of Industrial Waste

Types and volume of waste vary by industrial subsector. With gold mining, for example, 99.9 percent of all mined material ends up as rock waste and tailings. Potash mining (potassium ore) generates the same type of waste but less of it (10 percent). Construction waste includes insulation, electrical wiring, tree stumps, roofing tiles, lumber, and any other material used in the construction of a house or building. Agricultural waste consists of field and process residues in the form of stems, leaves, stalks, and roots. Within the agricultural industry, the juice industry accumulates large volumes of peel waste, and the coffee industry generates large amounts of coffee pulp.

Management of Industrial Waste

Federal and state laws mandate that industries manage wastes effectively and safely. The general principles of dealing with industrial waste are similar to those for municipal solid waste. Reduction, reuse, and recycling are all part of industrial waste management. Effective, cost-efficient, and safe waste management is about planning and organizing; clear labeling of wastes, routine and up-to-date safety training, and basic good housekeeping help protect workers and the environment. These practices help companies avoid accidents such as spills, so they save money in the long run.

Source Reduction (Waste Prevention)

Having less materials at the source translates to less waste generation. Source reduction is accomplished through more efficient designs, advances in technology, and elimination of unnecessary materials. In the hospitality industry, for example, small plastic shampoo and conditioner bottles are being phased out. Marriott International and InterContinental Hotels Group elected to replace the bottles with wall-mounted dispensers. This simple change eliminates the production of hundreds of millions of small plastic bottles each year, reduces waste, saves money, and protects the oceans (see "Case Study: Sailing through the Great Pacific Garbage Patch"). Such source reductions also conserve natural resources and energy.

Recycling of Industrial Waste

The conventional view of the economy is linear, from source to waste. In contrast, the recommended sustainable approach is a circular economy (see A in Figure 16.13) in which wastes are used as raw materials for manufacturing new products. A circular economy works when there is an economic benefit to recycling. One industry's waste must be seen as valuable by another industry (see Figure 16.13). This is becoming common practice to reduce costs and improve sustainability. For example, Ford and Volvo manufacture seats for their cars with fabric made from recycled plastic bottles. Ford has also partnered with McDonald's and now utilizes their waste—the skin of coffee beans, a by-product of coffee roasting—as a raw material for automobile parts such as headlamp housings. In a third example, coal ash waste from coal-fired power plants is often used as a base material in concrete production (Mangi et al. 2019). An estimated 40 percent of the 110 million tons of coal combustion residues produced every year benefit another industry. To encourage use of industrial waste, nonprofit organizations and state and local governments have enacted materials exchange programs. A company can use these programs to source raw materials in waste generated by another company.

FIGURE 16.13

A circular economy. (A) In a circular economy wastes are used as raw materials for manufacturing new products. As an example, discarded leaves from the pineapple industry (B) serve as raw material in the textile industry. (C) A worker dries fibers from pineapple leaves.

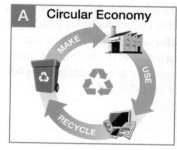

Source: © Shutterstock, Inc.

Treatment and Final Disposal of Industrial Waste

Treatment helps to reduce the volume and toxicity of waste before final disposal, and both can make waste more amenable to recycling. Industrial waste may be treated physically, chemically, or biologically. Grinding, shredding, and filtering are three of the many types of physical treatments. In chemical treatment, the chemical composition of the waste is altered through the addition of a chemical reagent, heating, or both; biological treatment relies on microorganisms to break down the waste. The properties of the waste determine which type of treatment or combination of treatments is appropriate. Regulation and treatment of nonhazardous industrial waste fall under Subtitle D of the Resource Conservation and Recovery Act (RCRA).

Disposal is the last—and least desirable—waste management practice. Nonhazardous industrial waste is deposited in an **industrial landfill** or injected into a deep well and then monitored under federal guidelines in addition to any state guidelines. An industrial landfill in the United States must have a minimum capacity of 300,000 metric tons. The goal of this stage of management is to protect the natural environment from contamination during long-term storage. Operators of industrial landfills report on the quantity and type of waste they receive, and they measure and report greenhouse gas emissions from the landfill. Today, industrial landfills in the United States emit 8.1 million metric tons of greenhouse gases every year, far less than the 89.2 million metric tons coming from municipal solid waste landfills (see Figure 16.14). Reporting of greenhouse gas emissions from industrial landfills is part of the EPA's Greenhouse Gas Reporting Program.

By the way, the remaining 60 percent of the 110 million tons of coal residue generated in the United States each year and not used by another industry is disposed of in an industrial landfill or stored in a **surface impoundment**. Surface impoundments are natural or artificial ponds widely used by industries to store and treat wastewaters. Note that residue of coal combustion (coal ash) contains toxic metals such as arsenic, mercury, cadmium, and lead, so its classification as nonhazardous waste by the EPA concerns environmental scientists.

> **industrial landfill**
>
> A disposal site on land for industrial waste.

> **surface impoundment**
>
> A natural or artificial pond used by industries to store and treat wastewaters.

FIGURE 16.14
In the United States, municipal landfills generate far more greenhouse gases than do industrial landfills. Values represent total 2019 emissions of greenhouse gases from waste sources in millions of metric tons of greenhouse gas equivalents (CO_2e). The United States releases more CO_2e from landfills than any other country.

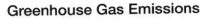

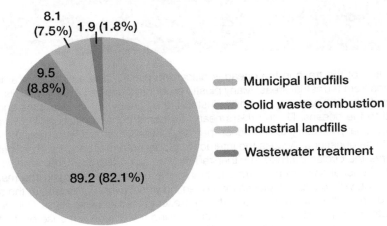

Greenhouse Gas Emissions

- 8.1 (7.5%)
- 1.9 (1.8%)
- 9.5 (8.8%)
- 89.2 (82.1%)

- Municipal landfills
- Solid waste combustion
- Industrial landfills
- Wastewater treatment

Sources: Joseph Shostell; data from EPA; https://www.epa.gov/ghgreporting/ghgrp-waste.

Deep injection wells are another route of disposal for liquid waste. More than 740,000 of these wells are scattered across all fifty states and territories of the United States The premise is to store wastes deep underground, far from humans and groundwater. However, these wells can corrode and leak. Of the six types of injection wells, the vast majority (>70 percent) are simple, unsophisticated ones constructed to receive stormwater and other fluids. Another 25 percent (class II wells) receive liquid wastes from the oil and gas industries. The remaining 5 percent store a variety of industrial and municipal liquid wastes, including nonhazardous, hazardous, and radioactive wastes.

> **deep injection wells (deep well disposal)**
>
> Wells that contain liquid wastes injected deep into the ground. These wastes include nonhazardous, hazardous, and radioactive liquids.

website

Bringing It Closer to Home: Determining Greenhouse Gas Emissions from Landfills and Industries

Landfills are one of the many sources of greenhouse gases driving rapid climate change, one of the greatest environmental problems the world faces today. The goal of this exercise is to determine the total greenhouse gases generated by industries and landfills in your home state. Go to the EPA's Greenhouse Gas Reporting Program (GHGRP) website. Use the dropdown menu under "Select a State" to select your state. A new page shows the number of facilities reporting greenhouse gas emissions and the total emissions for the entire state. Use the interactive state map to locate the industrial source of greenhouse gas emissions closest to your home.

Industrial Ecology

industrial ecology

A management approach that views industries as connected with nature. In this approach, industries are considered ecosystems with energy flow and nutrient cycles.

One approach to encouraging sustainable growth is to view industries as not separate from nature. In this approach (**industrial ecology**), industries are considered ecosystems, complete with energy flow and nutrient cycles. Similar to nature, industries have matter and energy, and the origin of these is the natural world. The premise of industrial ecology is to acknowledge how industries work, and to make them compatible with natural ecosystems through change and innovation. Industrial ecologists use natural ecosystems as models for industry and see parallels between the two. For instance, food webs (see Chapter 4) in natural ecosystems exemplify how all matter is useful. Nothing is wasted. Based on this structure and associated function, in industrial ecology, industrial processes are seen as circular rather than as linear. In the circular approach, one process makes use of another's leftover, unusable materials. The approach encourages innovation and efficient use of resources at all stages, and its practice is part of sustainable growth.

Bringing It Closer to Home: Determining How Much Plastic Is Discharged from Rivers into the Ocean

A good portion of the trash in the ocean is discarded plastic, and a significant amount of this plastic comes from terrestrial areas. Many plastic products (such as bottles, utensils, and plates) are not recycled and never reach landfills; instead, they are swept into streams and rivers and transported to the oceans. Do the rivers near your home contain plastics? How much plastic does an individual river carry to the ocean per day? In this exercise, you have the opportunity to answer these questions. Access the interactive global map managed by The Ocean Cleanup here. Observe the circles outlined in either red or blue along the coastlines of each continent. These mark the locations where rivers empty into the ocean. By enlarging the map at any of these areas, you will access the plastic load of an individual river. For example, the sole red dot near Wilmington on the eastern U.S. coastline represents the Delaware River. Center this dot on your computer screen and then enlarge either by using the dial on a mouse or double-clicking on the map. At some magnification, you will trigger the software to present a series of numbers, each one representing the amount of plastic carried by an individual river. Keep magnifying until you discern the name of the river: Delaware River. The Delaware River dumps in excess of 125,000 kg (275,578 lbs) of plastic into the ocean every year. Confirm this by noting the current numerical value on the map.

Now, locate a river close to where you live and then follow its course to the coastline. At the intersection with the coastline, notice the dot and then magnify and note the plastic load. For example, if you live in the Mississippi River basin, you can focus on the Southwest Pass in Louisiana. The plastic load here should be significantly less than the Delaware River's. Record the name of the river and plastic load in Table 16.3. How does the amount of plastic in the river you selected compare to the Delaware River? The Delaware River carries water and plastic from Maryland, New Jersey, Pennsylvania, and New York. Now, with two data points collected from the United States, compare these plastic loads to two international rivers: the Ulhas River in West India and the Rio Guamá near Belem, Brazil, in northeastern South America. Record the emissions of plastics for each of these rivers in Table 16.3. The Ulhas River is one of the most polluted rivers in the world. Expect the emissions of plastics to be exceptionally high. Finally, choose one additional river and enter this information into Table 16.3 as well. What do these numbers tell you about plastic entering the ocean?

TABLE 16.3 Emissions of Plastics from Rivers into the Ocean

River	Location in World	Discharge of Plastics Per Year
Delaware River	Maryland, USA	128,600 kg (checked 4/4/22)
Home river:_____		
Ulhas River	West India	
Rio Guamá	Brazil	

Key Takeaways

- The volume of solid waste from industries (industrial waste) is equal to or greater than that of municipal solid waste.
- Reduction, reuse, and recycling are all part of industrial waste management. Source reduction is the most cost-effective method to reduce waste generation.
- In industrial ecology, natural ecosystems are models for industry. The idea is to emulate natural ecosystems, in which all matter is useful and nothing is wasted.

16.4 Hazardous Waste

Learning Objectives

1. Explain why we manage hazardous waste differently than we do MSW waste.
2. Summarize how a hazardous site becomes designated as a superfund site.
3. Describe how hazardous wastes are managed.

Close to four decades later, residents of Bhopal, India, still bear emotional and physical scars from experiencing the world's worst **hazardous waste** incident. Just after midnight on December 2, 1984, white smoke escaped and fanned out from Union Carbide's pesticide factory. An estimated 30 to 45 tons of methyl isocyanate blew with the wind, down the alleys of the densely populated slums surrounding the plant (see Figure 16.15). Smoke that contained this toxic chemical seeped into the shoddily built homes and killed people as they slept. Those fortunate enough to wake coughed and gagged as they ran for their lives in whatever attire they wore. Some died as they ran. Eyes burned, mucus dripped, and lungs failed. That night, an estimated 2,500 people died, and over time the number climbed to over 20,000 (Lapierre and Moro 1991). More than 200,000 people were exposed to varying levels of methyl isocyanate, some as high as 1,400 times more than the recommended safety standard determined by the U.S. Occupational Safety and Health Administration (Dhara and Dhara

hazardous waste

Wastes from manufacturing and industrial processes or discarded commercial products that exhibit at least one of four characteristics: ignitability, toxicity, corrosivity, or reactivity.

2003). About 100,000 people remained chronically ill after the accident, suffering from respiratory ailments, eye problems, and skin irritation. Bhopal's tragic tale continues to this day (see video link: "Bhopal Gas Tragedy"). The factory site and waste disposal sites were never remediated. Hundreds of tons of discarded hazardous waste remain, causing birth defects and a host of health issues for the current generation of Indians living nearby. With every passing year, seasonal monsoon rains spread the waste further to contaminate an ever-widening area of soil and groundwater.

Bhopal Gas Tragedy
Listen to an explanation of the world's worst hazardous waste incident. It is referred to as the Bhopal Gas Tragedy.

View in the online reader

FIGURE 16.15

The world's worst hazardous waste accident occurred at the Union Carbide pesticide plant in Bhopal, India, when methyl isocyanate gas drifted into the surrounding residential community. (A) An old storage tank at the now-abandoned plant. (B) One of the many homes near the pesticide plant.

Sources: © Shutterstock, Inc.; arindambanerjee/Shutterstock.com

Methyl isocyanate is an example of a chemical used in the pesticide industry, and it meets the description of hazardous waste as determined by the EPA. That description is narrow. Many compounds and materials that threaten human health are not on the EPA's hazardous waste list, but most are regulated under other statutes. A toxic material is also excluded from EPA's definition of hazardous waste if the EPA has insufficient information about the material. Classification is important because it determines how materials are managed and where they are disposed of. For example, recall from earlier in the chapter that toxin-containing coal ash is currently listed as non-hazardous, which means it can legally be disposed of in industrial landfills and be used as a filler in cement.

Under the Resource Conservation and Recovery Act (RCRA), waste is deemed hazardous if it meets the EPA's definition of solid waste, is not covered by other statutes, and exhibits at least one of four characteristics: ignitability, toxicity, corrosivity, or reactivity. For ignitability, consider the ability of a material (i.e., compressed gas) to cause fire. A substance is toxic if it is harmful to human health or the environment. The third characteristic, corrosivity, refers to corrosive materials such as aqueous solutions of either very low or very high pH. The last characteristic, reactivity, refers to chemical instability—the tendency to undergo spontaneous, violent change. Among many examples, hazardous waste comes from pesticide manufacturing, aluminum production, lead processing, coking, and petroleum refining.

Household waste can contain materials with hazardous characteristics, but they are excluded from the EPA's hazardous materials list. Residential paints, cleaners, oils, batteries, and pesticides, again not categorized as hazardous waste, still need to be used, stored, and disposed of properly to protect human health and the environment. When they are no longer useful, they have recommended routes of disposal that differ from those for regular garbage. At certain times of the year, communities often have a special collection day.

Contaminated Sites (Superfund Sites)

Abandoned sites contaminated with hazardous wastes present a threat to human health and the environment. Such sites are proposed to the EPA for consideration as **superfund sites**. A superfund designation places a site on the National Priorities List. Sites on this list are prioritized by the EPA for investigation and, if needed, remediation (see Figure 16.16). The United States currently has over 1,300 superfund sites, and the number continues to grow as new sites are identified. The Comprehensive Environmental Response, Compensation and Liability Act (CERCLA) of 1980, better known as the superfund law, came about in response to a rising cancer death rate in the U.S. population, substantial damage to natural resources due to pollution by toxic chemicals, and expansion in production of hazardous chemicals. Losses of agriculture due to chemical contamination were in the many hundreds of millions of dollars, and there were thousands of hazardous dumpsites in need of costly remediation. The signing of the Comprehensive Environmental Response, Compensation and Liability bill by President Jimmy Carter to create CERCLA was intended to offer a means to clean up hazardous sites as well as leaks and spills from hazardous waste accidents.

The existence of so many superfund sites for a prolonged period signifies a huge backlog in remediation of sites. Some superfund sites have been on the National Priorities List for over four years. The main roadblock to these projects is insufficient funding. Back in 1995, the average remediation cost per superfund site was $20–30 million, and the average cost is substantially higher today. Estimated cost to remediate all existing superfund sites exceeds current funding levels. In 2022, the Infrastructure and Jobs Act reinstated a superfund tax that will raise an estimated $14.5 billion for the superfund program by 2031.

FIGURE 16.16
California's Sulphur Bank Mercury Mine is one of more than 1,300 superfund sites in the United States in need of remediation.

Source: EPA, https://www.ecosacramento.net/2016/08/epa-5-year-review-of-the-aerojet-superfund-site/.

superfund sites

A federally recognized abandoned or mismanaged site contaminated with hazardous wastes that is given priority for remediation.

Bringing It Closer to Home: Finding Superfund Sites in Your State

Upon hearing about the existence of hazardous sites recognized by the federal government, one of our first inclinations is to know how close we live to one of these sites. We are also interested in the type of hazardous waste found at the closest sites, and whether this waste threatens us personally. To access the Environmental Protection Agency's Superfund National Priorities List Where You Live Map, go here. The table on this website lists all of the superfund sites in alphabetical order, beginning with Atlas Tack Corporation in Fairhaven, Massachusetts. Instead of scrolling through this extensive list, select your home state in the search box above the table and click Go. An easier method is to search by zip code. You can also search by map. To do this, scroll down the screen until you see a colored map of the United States Enlarge the map to focus on the city where you live. For instance, if you live in Tucson, Arizona, and enlarge that part of the U.S. map, you will find a yellow square indicating a hazardous site. Click on the square to gather information. It says it is in the Tucson International Airport area, and there are several links. Click on the Site EPA ID (AZD9807375390) to find additional information. Here you ascertain that the site is contaminated with organic and metallic compounds, primarily trichloroethylene and hexavalent chromium, and, furthermore, the site overlays Tucson's source of drinking water. Continue to read about the origin of the hazardous waste (Air Force missile-manufacturing plant) and state of cleanup (not begun) and then return to the interactive U.S. map and investigate the superfund site closest to your home.

brownfield sites

Properties contaminated
with hazardous waste and
generally cleaned up by
state and tribal
governments, rather than
by the federal government.

Hosts of other sites are contaminated with hazardous waste, but at lower amounts than what would qualify a superfund site. These can be proposed as **brownfield sites** and are generally cleaned up by state and tribal governments, rather than by the federal government.

Electronic Waste (E-waste)

electronic waste (e-waste)

Discarded whole and
broken electronic
products.

We live in a technologically enhanced culture. Electronic gadgetry is available to us daily. A wireless earbud relaying on-demand music, a Fitbit watch, a smartphone, and a lightweight portable laptop are examples of commonly owned electronic devices in contemporary life. They seem essential to our lives, and companies are designing and producing an ever-larger array of new products for us. On average, working Americans spend over $2,000 each year on electronic products, and our demand for electronic gadgetry is increasing. High consumption rates of electronic products, from electronic toys to computer monitors, in combination with the short life cycles of typical electronics, and few repair options for broken electronics products, have created an **electronic waste (e-waste)** problem.

Just in 2019, the world generated almost 54 million metric tons of electronic waste. A mere 17 percent was collected and recycled. The remainder is not tracked, so it ends up either in landfills or elsewhere. Electronic waste generation varies by location, and is highest in Asia (46 percent of total) (see Figure 16.17). The Americas and Europe each generate roughly half of Asia's total. Electronic waste is accumulating at an extremely fast rate, increasing approximately 3 percent to 4 percent per year. Electronics contain hazardous materials such as mercury, lead, cadmium, arsenic, and brominated flame retardants (BFRs), and therefore present risks to human health and the environment. The global community is ill prepared to handle these wastes, because fewer than half of the world's countries have established policy, legislation, or regulations for managing E-waste (Forti et al. 2020). No federal law exists in the United States that requires recycling of electronic waste, and therefore a significant number of consumer electronic devices are tossed in garbage cans and end up in municipal solid waste landfills. The closest law is the Resource Conservation and Recovery Act of 1976, which covers some electronic waste such as cathode ray tubes of monitors. Still, an estimated 40 percent of consumer electronics waste is recycled (EPA 2019b). Twenty-five U.S. states have electronics recycling laws. Most of these laws place the financial responsibility for recycling on the manufacturers and require manufacturers to take back their electronic products at end-of-life (Esenduran et al. 2016).

FIGURE 16.17
Globally, the generation of electronic waste is accelerating. The amount of E-waste produced varies by region, and is highest in Asia. Red and green bars indicate electronic waste generated and recycled, respectively, in Mt, millions of metric tons. Per capita generation of electronic waste in kilograms (kg) per year is in parentheses.

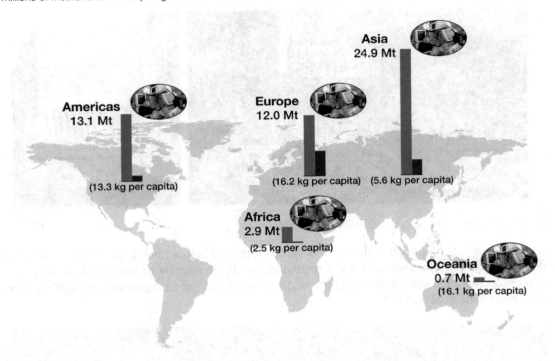

Asia
24.9 Mt

Americas
13.1 Mt

Europe
12.0 Mt

(13.3 kg per capita)

(16.2 kg per capita)   (5.6 kg per capita)

Africa
2.9 Mt
(2.5 kg per capita)

Oceania
0.7 Mt
(16.1 kg per capita)

Sources: Data from Forti et al. 2020, https://collections.unu.edu/eserv/UNU:7737/GEM_2020_def_july1.pdf; © Shutterstock, Inc.

How Are Hazardous Wastes Managed and Disposed Of?

Hazardous waste undergoes special management, as stipulated by the RCRA. Extra precautionary measures apply to hazardous waste from formation to disposal, and include transportation, treatment, and storage. Under the RCRA, an entity that generates hazardous waste is responsible for reporting it, labeling it, recycling it, and disposing of it. For example, when shipped or hauled off-site, all hazardous waste has to be clearly labeled with placards (see Figure 16.18). Transportation of hazardous waste through public areas falls under the jurisdiction of the Department of Transportation and is covered in the Hazardous Materials Transportation Act (HMTA). All personnel working with hazardous waste are required to first complete safety training. Shippers are required to have a hazardous materials safety permit. They are also responsible for identification of the hazardous waste, training of personnel, shipping papers, placarding, emergency response information, and any incident reporting. Stiff penalties are imposed for violating transport regulations for motor vehicles on interstate and intrastate highways, or by rail, aircraft, or vessel. Individuals are subject to fines of up to $250,000, and the amount increases to $500,000 for companies.

FIGURE 16.18

Vehicles transporting hazardous waste are required to display placards identifying the type of hazards posed by their cargo. (A) Placard on train car. (B) Placards on truck.

Sources: © Shutterstock, Inc.; Lost_in_the_Midwest/Shutterstock.com

Where is hazardous waste shipped and how is it treated before final disposal? As needed and depending on type, hazardous waste is treated physically, chemically, or biologically to meet the applicable treatment standards. After recycling and treatment, remaining wastes are disposed of in a hazardous materials landfill.

Key Takeaways

- Under RCRA, waste is deemed hazardous if it meets the EPA's definition of solid waste, is not covered by other statutes, and exhibits at least one of four characteristics: ignitability, toxicity, corrosivity, or reactivity.
- Careful management of hazardous waste can minimize its threats to human health and the environment.
- Society's high consumption rate of electronic products in combination with the typically short lifespan of these products has created an electronic waste (E-waste) problem.
- CERCLA offers a process to prioritize and, when needed, remediate hazardous sites.
- More precautionary measures are required for hazardous waste than for other forms of waste. These measures apply from the waste's formation to its disposal, and include rules for transportation, treatment, and storage.

16.5 A Look to the Future: Saving the Oceans from Plastic Waste

Learning Objectives

1. Recognize the obstacles to protecting the ocean from plastic waste.
2. Review and summarize the Great Pacific Garbage Patch story, and predict the future state of the patch.

Source reduction, product reuse, recycling, and energy recovery go a long way in diminishing the waste stream. Without these strategies, solid wastes would pose an even greater threat to human health and the health of the environment than they do now. This integrated waste management approach is not working as well as it could, however. A much greater percentage of waste ends up in landfills or in the environment than is recycled or composted. So what do we do?

First, recognize the success stories and understand how far we have come on the path toward sustainability. New technologies and experience have allowed us to create more environmentally safe products with less materials. Our efforts to reduce and reuse are helping us create a circular economy, but the scope of these actions fall short, particularly when compared to the escalating problem of valuable resources lost to landfills—and oceans. The system is failing mainly because too much waste is being produced in the first place. Not enough people and companies are engaged in the problem, and governmental support to develop and enforce legislation for reducing solid waste is underwhelming.

A keen observer of waste trends asked the question, "Why has the responsibility of waste control fallen more on the shoulders of individuals rather than on governments? Look where we are today. Active engagement in recycling with almost a religious fervor by numerous people still results in those same people directing usable resources to landfills. The system is broken, is it not?" The person went almost as far as saying, "Recycling is a sham." These are not empty words uttered in frustration. They have merit because waste generation is a real problem.

One of the best strategies for our world of 7.8 billion people is for each of us to think globally and act locally. Have reverence for resources and only consume what is needed, and regret when we create waste. Individuals in leadership positions can carry this strategy into their professional lives and make large-scale change.

Opening Story Revisited: Pacific Garbage Patch

Saving the ocean from plastic waste begins with an acknowledgment that the Pacific Ocean has become a sink for society's waste. Many of us will never cross the ocean by ship, so we must trust the accuracy of scientific data instead of observing the Great Pacific Garbage Patch with our own eyes. Thousands of research studies attest to society's waste's accumulating in the oceans, causing harm to marine life, and disrupting the ability of the oceans to function normally and to provide important ecosystem services, such as producing healthy fish communities. Once we acknowledge or bear direct witness, the next step is to understand the relevance of the situation. Before acting to solve any problem, the logical course of action is to first ask if the problem is worth solving. Is it? Are oceanic ecosystems worth protecting? Don't mistake the question for a plea for help. Posing the question helps us to contemplate the relevancy of the oceans. Whether a person is individualistic, biocentric, or ecocentric, this type of thinking will lead to understanding the interconnectedness of terrestrial and marine ecosystems, and the dependence of all life on a healthy Earth, which is 71 percent ocean. After acknowledgment and determination of relevancy comes action.

There are many ways that individuals can protect the oceans from further damage. The recommendations are to rethink, reduce, reuse, and recycle. To rethink is the most important, because to extricate ourselves from a throwaway lifestyle we must rethink our daily routines and adopt more sustainable behaviors.

Scientists have also considered how to prevent plastic from accumulating in the oceans in the context of our current throwaway culture. Of the many questions they asked, four stand out. The first two are, "What is the origin of the plastic waste?" and "How does the plastic travel from its point of origin to the oceans?" We have already answered these. An estimated 70 percent to 80 percent of plastic originates from land and reaches the oceans by rivers (Li et al. 2016). The third question asked about the ideal locations to remove plastic from the oceans. We have an answer to this question too. Two researchers from the Imperial College of London used computer modeling of the movement of plastic to determine the optimal locations to remove plastic from the oceans (Sherman and Sebille 2016). Their findings suggest the primary locations are off the coast of China and in the Indonesian Archipelago (Sherman and Sebille 2016), rather than in the gyres. Other scientists argue it is preferable to focus on the rivers and remove plastic before it reaches the ocean. The last question was, "How can we remove plastic from water?" Eighteen-year-old Boyan Slat thought he had an answer to that question. He invented a device called the Interceptor that can remove plastic from water, and founded a nonprofit environmental group called The Ocean Cleanup. He and his team of ninety researchers, engineers, and scientists designed and built functional Interceptors and deployed two of them in polluted rivers in Indonesia and Malaysia (see Figure 16.19). Boyan plans to deploy Interceptors in 1,000 of the world's most polluted rivers. These rivers are responsible for carrying up to 80 percent of the plastic to the oceans.

FIGURE 16.19

The Interceptor at work in the Klang River, Indonesia. The arrows represent floating garbage coming into contact with the Interceptor's arm, which directs the garbage to a conveyor belt on the boat. The garbage is conveyed to a temporary storage site on the Interceptor. The majority of the plastic collected by the Interceptor is recycled and used to manufacture new products.

Source: Najmi Arif/Shutterstock.com

Bringing It Closer to Home: Tracking Trash

Citizen scientists are everyday people who contribute to science, whether they have a degree in science or not. Through the Marine Debris Tracker Program, citizen scientists—students and people of all walks of life—can identify debris anywhere in the United States, log its location, and help remove it. Visit this link to learn more about the Marine Debris Tracker app and OR&R's Marine Debris Program (noaa.gov). Click on "How to use the Marine Debris Tracker App." Read the directions on how to get started, download the free app to your phone, and begin to track debris. Once you find trash, enter what you observe, recording the number of items in each debris category and state of removal.

Key Takeaways

- Protecting ocean ecosystems from plastic waste begins with an acknowledgment that the oceans have become sinks for society's waste.
- Reducing, reusing, and recycling help to protect the oceans.
- New inventions can remove garbage from aquatic ecosystems.

FIGURE 16.20 Visual Overview: Solid and Hazardous Waste
Summarizing figure: To protect human health and the environment from the effects of society's waste (16.1), we must better manage municipal solid waste (16.2), industrial solid waste (16.3), and hazardous waste (16.4), both now and in the future (16.5).

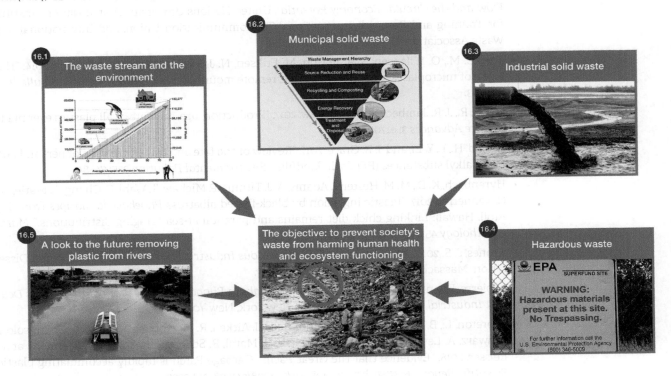

Sources: Joseph Shostell; See previous citations for image credits.

16.6 References

- Bogner, J., R. Pipatti, S. Hashimoto, C. Diaz, K. Mareckova, et al. 2008. "Mitigation of global greenhouse gas emissions from waste: conclusions and strategies from the Intergovernmental Panel on Climate Change (IPCC) Fourth Assessment Report. Working Group III (Mitigation)." *Waste Manag Res* 26, no. 11. https://doi.org/10.1177/0734242X07088433.

- Brandon, J. A., W. Jones, and M. D. Ohman. 2019. "Multidecadal increase in plastic particles in coastal ocean sediments." *Sci Adv* 5: eaax0587.

- Close, A. E. 1996. "Carry that weight: The use and transportation of stone tools." *Current Anthropology* 37, no. 3: 545–553.

- Egger, M., F. Sulu-Gambari, and L. Lebreton. 2020. "First evidence of plastic fallout from the North Pacific Garbage Patch." *Scientific Reports* 10: 7495. https://doi.org/10.1038/s41598-020-64465-8.

- Elias, S. A. 2018. "Plastics in the Ocean." In: *The Encyclopedia of the Anthropocene, volume 1* (Eds.: DellaSala, D. A. and M. I. Goldstein) Elsevier Inc.

- Environmental Protection Agency (EPA). 2019a. *News Releases from Region 09. EPA Resolves Clean Water Act Violations with Honolulu and Waste Management at Waimanalo Gulch Landfill.* EPA.

- Environmental Protection Agency (EPA). 2019b. *Advancing Sustainable Materials Management: 2017 Fact Sheet.* EPA 530-F-19-007. EPA Office of Land and Emergency Management, Washington, DC.

- Esenduran, G., E. Kemahlioğlu-Ziya, and J. M. Swaminathan. 2016. "Take-back legislation: consequences for remanufacturing and environment." *Decision Sciences* 47, no. 2: 219–256.

- Forti, V., C. P. Baldé, R. Kuehr, and G. Bel. 2020. *The Global E-Waste Monitor 2020 Quantities, Flow, and the Circular Economy Potential.* United Nations University/United Nations Institute for Training and Research/International Telecommunication Union, and International Solid Waste Association. Bonn/Geneva/Rotterdam.

- Free, C. M., O. P. Jensen, S. A. Mason, M. Eriksen, N. J. Williamson, and B. Boldgiv. 2014. "High levels of microplastic pollution in a large, remote mountain lake." *Marine Pollution Bulletin* 85: 156–163.

- Geyer, R., J. R. Jambeck, and K. L. Law. 2017. "Production, use, and fate of all plastics ever made." *Science Advances* 3: e1700782.

- Hamid, H., L. Y. Li, and J. R. Grace. 2017. "Review of the fate and transformation of per- and polyfluoroalkyl substances (PFASs) in landfills." *Environmental Pollution* 235: 74–84.

- Hyrenbach, K. D., M. M. Hester, J. Adams, A. J. Titmus, P. Michael, T. Wahl, C. Chang, A. Marie, and C. Vanderlip. 2017. "Plastic ingestion by black-footed albatross *Phoebastria nigripes* from Jure Atoll, Hawaii: Linking chick diet remains and parental at-sea foraging distributions." *Marine Ornithology* 45: 225–236.

- Krones, J. S. 2016. *Accounting for Non-Hazardous Industrial Waste in the United States.* Dissertation. Massachusetts Institute of Technology.

- Lapierre, D., and J. Moro. 1991. *Five Past Midnight in Bhopal: The Epic Story of the World's Deadliest Industrial Disaster.* Warner Books. New York, New York.

- Lebreton, L., B. Slat, F. Ferrari, B. Sainte-Rose, J. Aitken, R. Marthouse, S. Hajbane, S. Cunsolo, A. Schwarz, A. Levivier, K. Noble, P. Debeljak, H. Maral, R. Schoeneich-Argent, R. Brambini, and J. Reisser. 2018. "Evidence that the Great Pacific Garbage Patch is rapidly accumulating plastic." *Scientific Reports* 6: 4666. https://doi.org/10.1038/s41598-018-22939.

- Li, W. C., H. F. TSE, and L. Fok. 2016. "Plastic waste in the marine environment: A review of sources, occurrence and effects." *Science of the Total Environment* 566–567: 333–349.

- Mangi, S. A., M. H. W. Ibrahim, N. Jamaluddin, M. F. Arshad, and S. W. Mudjanarko. 2019. "Recycling of coal ash in concrete as a partial cementitious resource." *Resources* 8, no. 99. https://doi.org/10.3390/resources8020099.

- Masoner, J. R., D. W. Kolpin, E. T. Furlong, I. M. Cozzarelli, and J. L. Gray. 2015. "Landfill leachate as a mirror of today's disposable society: pharmaceuticals and other contaminants of emerging concern in final leachate from landfills in the conterminous United States." *Environmental Toxicology and Chemistry* 35, no. 4. https://doi.org/10.1002/etc.3219.

- Mendoza, L. M. R., and P. R. Jones. 2015. "Characterization of microplastics and toxic chemicals extracted from microplastic samples from the North Pacific Gyre." *Environ Chem.* https://doi.org/10.1071/EN14236.

- Mervis, J. 2012. "Garbology 101: Getting a grip on waste." *Science* 337, no. 6095: 668–672.

- Northeast Recycling Council (NERC). 2017. *Disposal Bans and Mandatory Recycling in the United States.* NERC. Brattleboro, VT.

- Powell, J. T., and M. R. Chertow. 2018. "Quantity, components, and value of waste materials landfilled in the United States." *Journal of Industrial Ecology* 23, no. 2: 466–479.

- Sainsbury, V. A. 2018. "When things stopped travelling: Recycling and the glass industry in Britain from the first to fifth century CE. In: *Things that Travelled Mediterranean Glass in the First Millennium AD* (Eds.: Rosenow, D. M. Phelps, A. Meek, and I. Freestone). UCL Press.
- Sherman, P., and E. van Sebille. 2016. "Modeling marine surface microplastic transport to assess optimal removal locations." *Environmental Research Letters* 11: 014006. https://doi.org/10.1088/1748-9326/11/1/014006.
- Tarr, J. A., and C. Mcshane. 2008. "The horse as an urban technology." *Journal of Urban Technology* 15, no. 1: 5–17.
- Wang, C., L. Shao, M. K. Lim, W. Chen, and J. W. Sutherland. 2019. "Structure of the global plastic waste trade network and the impact of China's import ban." *Resources, Conservation and Recycling* 153. https://doi.org/10.1016/j.resconrec.2019.104591.
- Wen, Z., Y. Xie, M. Chen, and C. D. Dinga. 2021. "China's plastic import ban increases prospects of environmental impact mitigation of plastic waste trade flow worldwide." *Nature Communications.* https://doi.org/10.1038/s41467-020-20741-9.
- Yang, G., Y. Yin, B. Li, W. Wang, N. Zhang, C. Yan, and Z. Xiao. 2017. "Investigation and dynamic analysis of the long runout catastrophic landslide at the Shenzhen landfill on December 20, 2015, in Guangdong, China." *Environmental Earth Sciences* 76, no. 13. https://doi.org/10.1007/s12665-016-6332-8.
- Zarfl, C., D. Fleet, and E. Fries. 2011. "Microplastics in oceans." *Marine Pollution Bulletin* 62: 1589–1591.
- Zimring, C. A. 2009. *Cash for Your Trash: scrap recycling in America.* Rutgers University Press.

CHAPTER 17
Sustainable Community Development and Urbanization

Case Study: Goliaths among Metropolises—Tokyo, Japan, and the Pearl River Delta, China

Tokyo is the second largest **metropolitan area** in the world. It is a **megalopolis**. Approximately 37 million people live and work in the Tokyo and Greater Tokyo area, collectively referred to as Japan's capital region (see Figure 17.1). The expansion of Tokyo proper caused it to merge with surrounding cities to create an enormous urban area that contains one-third of Japan's population. Even with careful urban planning and a sophisticated **mass transit system**, Tokyo struggles with issues common to many large metropolitan areas: sprawl and expensive real estate.

Tokyo was greatly influenced by Japan's postwar reconstruction and revitalization phase, known as the "Japanese Economic Miracle." In less than a decade, Japan's economy transformed from agriculture-based to industry-based (Pernice 2007). The change occurred as waves of citizens migrated from rural to urban areas, in the process overwhelming the structural layout of Japanese cities. The result was an uncontrolled spread of low-density housing units (example of **urban sprawl** or **sprawl**) with inadequate services for occupants. In response to the growing sprawl, Japan passed the New City Planning Act in 1968. Under this law, Tokyo denotes all municipality lands (local government lands) as either lands to be urbanized within ten years, or lands designated for rural conservation (Terada 2017). The law ends up saving green spaces, which become "islands" surrounded by developed urban areas. In addition, agricultural areas are protected by the Productive Green Land Act, which supports farmers who want to continue to grow crops in increasingly urbanized areas. Under this Act, farmers pay greatly reduced land taxes even though surrounding land prices are escalating. Some urban planners see the model created by these Acts as promoting a reasonable balance of green areas, agricultural areas, and developed urban areas.

FIGURE 17.1
Tokyo and the Greater Tokyo area in Japan make up one of the largest urbanized areas of the world. (A) Akihabara, the historic electronic district in Tokyo where people can shop for anime, manga, and video games. (B) A clear view of Tokyo's sprawl. The urban area extends well beyond the city's skyline.

Sources: ESB Professional/Shutterstock.com; YAO23/Shutterstock.com

metropolitan area

A large, densely populated urban center (the city proper) surrounded by less-populated communities. The center and surrounding communities are integrated economically, socially, and industrially.

megalopolis

A very large metropolis.

mass transit system

A system used to transport large numbers of people; examples: fleet of buses, fleet of taxes, light-rail system, and subway system.

urban sprawl

See *sprawl*.

sprawl

Uncontrolled spread of low-density urban development on the outskirts of a city.

city

A densely settled area larger than a town.

Pearl River Delta

The largest urbanized area in the world; home to 65 million people in southern China.

urbanization

The increasing number of people living in urban areas.

urban flight

Exodus of city residents from the city to the suburbs.

community

A group of people living in the same location.

Then, beginning in 2002, Tokyo unveiled its green initiative to make the **city** more environmentally friendly. Based on an analysis by Solidiance, a corporate strategy consulting firm, Tokyo's strategy has worked. Tokyo has emerged as the greenest city of the Asia-Pacific Region, and fifth greenest city globally. Solidiance's study evaluated greenhouse gas emissions, energy use, transportation, green space, environmental governance, water, and wasted space. Among the data this study revealed: More than 8 percent of Tokyo's buildings are green-certified, and the city releases 25 percent less carbon dioxide than it did in 2000. These data confirm that large urban areas can evolve and become more environmentally friendly.

Tokyo is leading the way in green infrastructure and effectively dealing with historically created sprawl, but it has yet to solve the problem of escalating real estate costs. As Tokyo grew, competition for premium land within the city's limits increased and the value of land skyrocketed. High housing costs in Tokyo continue today. For instance, a new apartment in downtown Tokyo costs about thirteen times the average citizen's annual salary, which explains the high volume of commuters who live in more affordable housing outside the city and travel to work in Tokyo daily. Commuting is facilitated by a wonderfully efficient and sophisticated mass transit system and roads free of parked cars (it is illegal to park on most public roads). Bicycles help most commuters make the last leg of their journey from the transit station to their home. Unique among cities, Tokyo also enjoys low unemployment, low crime rates, and good income equality.

FIGURE 17.2

The Pearl River Delta (PRD) in southeast China (A) is the largest urbanized area on the planet. (B) The area consists of eight large primary cities and many smaller areas that have merged as a goliath metropolis—a megalopolis. Circles represent the relative size and location of the primary cities in the PRD. (C) Residents of Shenzhen test and enjoy new electronics at the Sony Exposition. (D) A bridge-tunnel system across the Pearl River Estuary connects Zhuhai and Macao to Hong Kong.

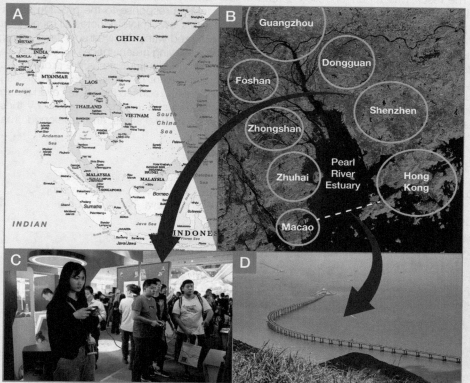

Sources Joseph Shostell; © Shutterstock, Inc.; USGS, https://eros.usgs.gov/image-gallery/earthshot/pearl-river-delta-china; Sorbis/Shutterstock.com

Astoundingly, Tokyo's size is now overshadowed by an even larger urbanized area in southern China. The **Pearl River Delta** (PRD) is home to over 65 million people (see Figure 17.2). Back in 1979, Chairman Deng Xiaoping initiated a new course for the PRD, eventually transforming it from small towns and disconnected cities to a productive and seamless monstrosity with a financial sector (Hong Kong), technology hub powerhouse (Shenzhen), trading hub (Guangzhou), manufacturing areas (Foshan and Dongguan), and entertainment hub (Macao). Shenzhen, a city of roughly 13 million—just one cog in this economic center—is larger than any U.S. city. By comparison, New York City has 8.7 million people, and forty-four U.S. states have smaller populations than this single Chinese city.

Tokyo and the Pearl River Delta are examples of cities experiencing rapid **urbanization**. Today, more than 55 percent of the world's population lives in urban areas, a stark contrast to the early 1960s (see Figure 17.3). Japan is one of the world's most urbanized nations (92 percent), ahead of both the United States (82 percent) and China (60 percent), although the latter is gaining quickly.

The United States does not have any megalopolises, but many of its urban areas are already experiencing increasing low-density development (sprawl). According to the research group Smart Growth America, Atlanta tops the list of large American cities for sprawl (SGA 2014). Several factors contribute to this dubious distinction. For example, rising real estate values in Atlanta's inner city are pricing out low-income families (Lanari 2019). These families are leaving the central urban areas and moving to the suburbs in droves. An exodus of city residents is called **urban flight**. As another example, an inadequate mass transit system and generally poor sidewalk areas hinder the connectivity of the metropolitan Atlanta area (Gaither et al. 2016). By comparison, New York City is a compact, low-sprawl metropolitan area.

In this chapter, we explore **community** development and urbanization, and look into urbanization dynamics, urban sprawl, and strategies for developing sustainable communities and cities.

FIGURE 17.3

Urbanization. (A) Globally, urbanization has increased steadily since the 1960s. Japan, the United States, and China have all contributed to this change. Images of rural (B) and urban (C) China.

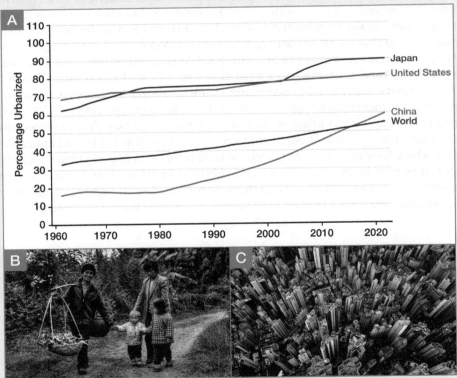

Sources: Data from The World Bank, https://data.worldbank.org/indicator/SP.URB.TOTL. IN.ZS?locations=US; Grigvovan/Shutterstock.com; © Shutterstock, Inc.

17.1 Urbanization Dynamics

Learning Objectives

1. Compare and contrast historical and current urbanization in the United States, in other countries, and globally.
2. Identify, analyze, and comprehend the drivers of (and obstacles to) urban growth.
3. Understand and discuss the origin of slums and the challenges they present.
4. Explain why cities are sources of pollution and summarize the connection of this pollution to global environmental issues.

Large cities and megalopolises such as Tokyo and the Pearl River Delta draw workers away from rural areas (see "Case Study: Goliaths among Metropolises—Tokyo, Japan, and the Pearl River Delta, China"). The migration can severely diminish the pool of workers skilled in traditional labor practices, including agriculture and fishing. In China, the lure of economic gain, cosmopolitanism, and modernity have helped to create a large migrant population—about one-fifth of China's workforce, women and men included (Chiang et al. 2015). City dwellers earn about three times the salary of their rural counterparts. Migrants often send their wages to the families they leave behind to cover general family expenses, tuition of family members, and medical care (Zhu et al. 2012).

People may live in urban or rural areas, but what defines an area as being **urban** or **rural**? Who determines these distinctions? The definition of what qualifies as an urban area varies internationally. In Sweden, it is defined as an area with at least 200 people; in Canada it is 1,000; in Japan, only settlements of at least 30,000 are considered urban. In the United States, the Census Bureau has defined urban areas as those with at least 50,000 people and a density of 1,000 people per square mile. Smaller populations (2,500 to 49,999) are considered "urbanized clusters," and areas with less than 2,500 people are rural. Currently, more than 82 percent of the U.S. population live in urban areas, and this number continues to increase yearly. Figure 17.4 shows America's urbanization trend over the last 230 years. Increasing urbanization in America reflects the global trend. More than half of the world's population lives in urban environments, a massive increase from 2 percent back in 1800. High-income nations such as those in Western Europe, as well as the United States, Canada, Australia, and others, have more than 80 percent of their population living in urban areas. In contrast, lower-income nations in central Africa and southern Asia have largely rural populations. Apply your knowledge of urban and rural areas by completing the "Bringing It Closer to Home: Determining Whether My Family, Friends, and I Live in an Urban or Rural Area" exercise.

urban

A city area. In the U.S., an urban area is defined as an area with a population of 2,500 or more. This value is further broken down into urbanized and urbanized clusters. Urbanized implies an area with a population size of 50,000 or more and a density of at least 1,000 people per square mile. An urbanized cluster area has a population of at least 2,500 but less than 50,000.

rural

Countryside; in the United States, a rural area is defined as an area with a population with less than 2,500 people.

FIGURE 17.4

Urbanization. (A) Long-term urbanization trend in the United States. Images of rural (B) and urban (C) United States.

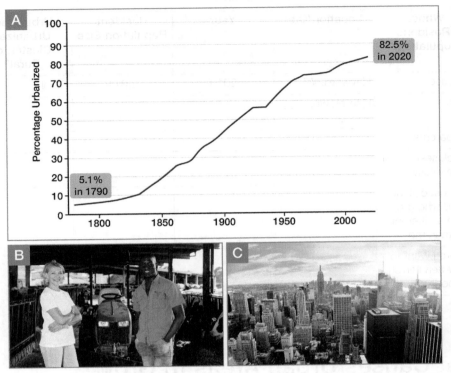

Sources: Joseph Shostell; data from U.S. Census Bureau, https://www.census.gov/dataviz/visualizations/005/; © Shutterstock, Inc.

Bringing It Closer to Home: Determining Whether My Family, Friends, and I Live in an Urban or Rural Area

The goal of this exercise is to determine the size of the population where you, your family members, and your friends live, and whether these areas are considered urbanized, urbanized clusters, or rural. Go here to access data collected and maintained by the United States Census Bureau. Areas with populations of 50,000 or more are urbanized, and those with 2,500 to 49,999 are listed as urbanized clusters. All other areas are categorized as rural. Scroll down the page to the list of states. As a trial, determine the population size of Hayward, Wisconsin. To do so, click on Wisconsin, which brings up an Excel spreadsheet of all resident populations within the state of Wisconsin, listed in alphabetical order. Scroll down the list to Hayward and follow the row to the most recent column. At the time of writing this book, the table was only updated to 2019. In 2019, Hayward had 2,311 residents and therefore was listed as rural. Now repeat the process for your hometown area—listed under the column "Mine" in Table 17.1. Record the location, year, resident population size, and whether the area is urbanized, an urbanized cluster, or rural. Again, repeat the process for your parents, closest out-of-state relative, best friend, and location where you would like to live in the future. Disregarding the practice entry, do you notice any trend in the data? Does this trend mirror the larger trend in the United States, in which 82 percent of the population lives in urban areas?

TABLE 17.1 Urban, Urban Cluster, or Rural?

Whose Resident Population?	Location/City	Year	Resident Population Size	Urbanized, Urbanized Cluster, or Rural?
Practice	Hayward, WI	2019	2,311	Rural
Mine	Hometown:_____ _____			
My parents				
My closest out of state relative				
My best college friend who grew up in a different city than me				
Where I want to live when I finish school				

What Causes Urban Areas to Grow?

megacities

Cities with ten million or more inhabitants.

The year 2007 was the first time in recorded history that more people in the world lived in urban areas than in rural areas. What is driving this change? As stated in the opening story, the prospect of higher wages lures migrants into urban areas. Migrants are lured to urban areas for other reasons too, including to improve access to health care and education. Internal growth (natality) and reclassification also cause urban areas to expand. A combination of limited availability of land, uneven distribution of resources, and an increasing human population result in a greater number of people living close to each other. No matter where we live, it is common to observe other people as we conduct our day's activities. City dwellers encounter hundreds to thousands of people every day just walking down the street or when using public transportation. In this age of urban expansion, we are witnessing the dawn of **megacities** that contain 10 million people or more. These cities were outliers in the mid-1970s, when only four existed. Today there are thirty-four and more will be added soon.

The relative importance of natural population increase (birth rate > death rate), migration, and reclassification on urban growth depends on a country's demographic transition stage. All countries go through stages of demographic transition, so all are in one of these stages (see Figure 6.12). Migration is most important in the early stages, and then diminishes in its influence in later stages. Therefore, migration plays only a small role in urban growth in the United States and other late-stage countries. On the other hand, the influence of natural increase is small in stage I, swells to a high point in stage III, and then declines. For example, natural increase is the primary determinant of urban growth in India and Mexico (both in stage III) and in the United States (in stage IV). Between 67 percent and 83 percent of urban population growth in these three countries is explained by natural increase (Jiang and O'Neil 2018). Finally, reclassification has the greatest impact in the last two stages. For instance, almost 28 percent of urban growth in the United States is due to a redefining or reclassification of what an urban area is (Jiang and O'Neil 2018). See "Critical Thinking Activity: Exploring Urbanization Rates across the World".

Critical Thinking Activity: Exploring Urbanization Rates across the World

More of the global population lives in cities (urbanization) than in rural areas. This percentage has been increasing over time, and it varies greatly among nations. By visiting interactive graphs provided by the World Bank here, we can explore national and global urbanization trends since 1960.

Accessing this web page displays an interactive graph of global urbanization. First, note the title of the graph: "Urban population (% of total population)." The title does not mention "world," but the upper part of the graph line is labeled "WORLD." Noting this label is important because we can graph data of any of the world's countries, and multiple lines can be displayed on one graph. Hover the cursor on the lowest part of the graph line above 1960. Doing so displays three pieces of information: location, time, and percentage urbanized. Data that pops up shows that 33.611 percent of the world's population was urbanized in 1960. This information is recorded in Table 17.2. Next, move the cursor up the graph and determine global urbanization in 1990. You should see 43.029, which means 43.029 percent of the world's population was urbanized in 1990. Record this data in Table 17.2. Repeat the process for the most current year. A comparison of these three data points supports a large increase of global urbanization since 1960. What is pushing this trend?

Global data trends often mask national trends. The next part of this exercise is to explore urbanization trends of individual countries. Move down the page below the graph to display a table listing the most recent urbanization value for each of the world's countries. Scan the list to identify the three countries with the lowest values, and then record these values in Table 17.2. Also record the values for the United States, Canada, China, and India. These data support high urbanization in the U.S. and Canada (both over 80 percent) and lower values for China (low 60s) and India (mid 30s). The lowest urbanized countries, such as Burundi, Liechtenstein, and Papua New Guinea, all have urbanized values in the teens. Why is there such a disparity in urbanization among countries?

TABLE 17.2 Urbanization

Country	Year	Percentage of Total Population Urbanized
Global	1960	33.6
Global	1990	
Global	2020	
United States	Current year _____	
Canada	Current year _____	
China	Current year _____	
India	Current year _____	
_____ (country with the lowest urbanization)	Current year _____	
_____ (country with the 2nd lowest urbanization)	Current year _____	
_____ (country with the 3rd lowest urbanization	Current year _____	

Urbanization Comes with Land-Use Change That Threatens Ecosystem Goods and Services

The rate of urbanization is increasing faster than the rate of population growth, basically tripling for every doubling of the population. This growth places urbanization as a major driver of landscape change, so it impinges on the ability of the environment to maintain ecosystem goods and services. In the forested Midwest, for example, this change begins with the clearing of trees and removal of shrubs and smaller plants. Fox dens are filled in, endemic flowers uprooted, and carnivore hunting grounds destroyed. Nesting sites for hummingbirds and the multitude of other birds disappear. What remains is a denuded landscape with poor biodiversity. In the next phase of development, machinery levels the ground to pave the way for buildings and roads. Such changes diminish the environment's ability to absorb rainwater and prevent flooding. Conversion of rural to urban areas, and the increased number of impervious structures in the form of rooftops, roadways, sidewalks, and parking lots, make the overall land surfaces less permeable to water. Consequently, rainwater bypasses its natural absorption into soils, and instead moves rapidly into streams and rivers, causing peak flows and flooding (see Figure 17.5). To explore structures impervious to water in your home community, see "Bringing It Closer to Home: Exploring the Degree of Surface Impervious to Water in Your Community".

Bringing It Closer to Home: Exploring the Degree of Surface Impervious to Water in Your Community

A surface impervious to water does not allow water to pass through. Rooftops, roads, and driveways are examples of these structures in urban areas. Their presence prevents the natural vertical movement of water into the soil. The question we entertain here is, "What percentage of land surface is covered by structures impervious to water in your home community?" To accomplish this task, go to the Multi-Resolution Land Characteristics Consortium's website here. To the left of the displayed map of North America, click on "Contents" (in green). Double-click on "NLCD Impervious Surface" to display a series of selections. Click (places check mark in box) on the box in front of "2019 CONUS Impervious Surface." Doing so highlights impervious ground. Click on "Legend" in the upper left part of the screen to display a legend relating color to degree of imperviousness. Stronger hues of red indicate surfaces with high imperviousness. First use the interactive map to view Los Angeles (in southern California). Zoom in on Los Angeles and then move the map until you see Los Angeles centered on your screen. Based on the high percentages of red and purple, structures impenetrable to water cover much of the surface area in and around Los Angeles. Click on "Contents" on the upper left-hand side of the screen. Under "NLCD Land Cover," click on "2019 CONUS Land Cover." Again, click on "Legend" to reveal a description of all the other colors on the map. Much of the area outside of Los Angeles is tan/brown color, indicating shrub/scrub. Now zoom in on your home community to investigate the degree of surface impassable to water.

Urbanization also increases erosion and sedimentation in rivers (Chin 2006), which results in the loss of valuable soils, the disruption of fisheries, and reduced aquatic biodiversity. Terrestrial areas are at risk too. Urbanization threatens some areas with the richest biodiversity on the planet. The most desirable areas to live—picturesque valleys and enchanting coastal regions, for example—are already home to numerous endemic species. These species and the communities and ecosystems they create provide critical ecosystem services, from soil formation and pollination to climate control. Urbanization also claims valuable agriculture land and therefore threatens food security (Wu et al. 2011).

FIGURE 17.5
Urbanization threatens ecosystem goods and services. (A) Roofs, roadways, parking lots, driveways, and other structures that are impervious to water can cover a large percentage of the ground in a city. The graph displays the relative proportions of these structures in a typical city. (B) Impervious structures cover a large percentage of the ground in the metro Atlanta region. (C) City structures impervious to water increase runoff and decrease infiltration of water into the ground. (D) Natural movement of water after rain event.

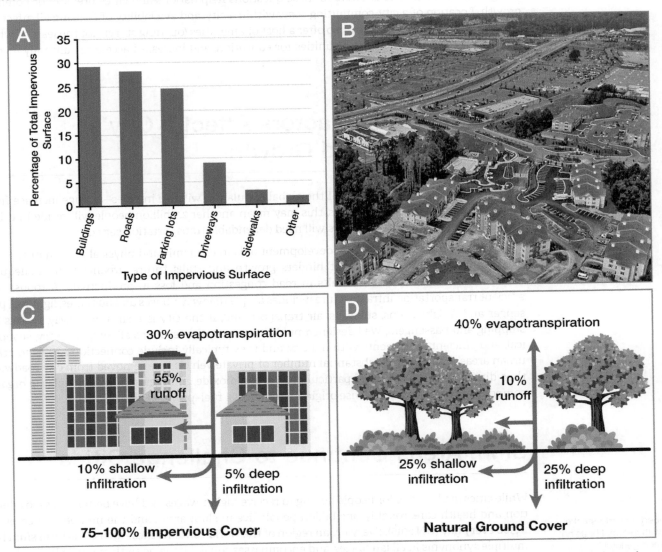

Sources: Joseph Shostell; data from USGS, https://pubs.usgs.gov/of/2007/1008/ofr2007-1008.pdf; USGS, https://www.usgs.gov/media/images/impervious-surfaces-and-water; and EPA, https://www3.epa.gov/npdes/pubs/nps_urban-facts_final.pdf; © Shutterstock, Inc.

Environmental Factors and Technology Influence Urban Growth

Analogous to a seed, a city will grow and flourish under the right set of environmental conditions. Both require water, a source of food, clean air, and habitat space. Different from a seed, a city can control large regions beyond itself to obtain essential resources for its existence and growth. For example, a city wields its technology to tap deep aquifers, and to transform multiple sources of energy into needed electricity and heat. As our forefathers did before us, we settle in areas with abundant resources and on or near transportation routes. Some of the world's largest urban areas are strategically located adjacent to rivers, large lakes, or oceans. These sites are efficient transportation hubs, and as a result became hubs for manufacturing and trade.

Why do cities grow at different rates, and why do they continue to grow even after a country is highly urbanized? The answers to these questions help nations and cities prepare for potential growth. Location of a city, commuting costs within a city, and availability of housing all affect the size of a city (Muth 1969). Cities also offer a host of amenities (opening story), not the least of which are higher salaries, greater opportunities for education, and increased access to culturally diverse activities.

Transportation Factors Affect a City's Development and Growth

By 2050, an estimated 68 percent of the global population will live in cities—a huge increase from today's 55 percent. By the numbers, this may mean another 2.3 billion people will reside in urban areas. These and other city dwellers will need dependable transportation services.

Just as strong transportation development aids in economic and physical growth of the city, weak transportation development hinders growth and stalls future urbanization. Inadequate transportation infrastructure results in road congestion and loss in productivity. A robust and efficient transportation infrastructure includes ample roadways, buses and bus lanes, light rail, passenger and freight trains, subways, air transport, and, if the city is near a waterway, vessels for shipping and passengers. Well-designed public transportation systems allow quick, easy, economical, and efficient movements within a city, and they typically include connection routes to other urban areas. As a result, a substantial number of private vehicles are removed from city roadways, thus diminishing emissions of particulates, carbon dioxide, nitrogen oxides, and volatile organic compounds that would otherwise originate from fossil fuel–powered vehicles.

Slum Areas Continue to Challenge Cities

slum

Crowded, poverty-stricken area with informal housing units and general deteriorating infrastructure.

While cities are beacons for people hoping to receive higher wages and have better access to education and health care, roughly one billion people live in slum areas, and the number increases by 16,500 every day (UN 2016). Every urban region of the world contains these areas. The term **slum** has multiple synonyms in all languages, and encompasses squalid housing settlements in India, shanty towns of Rio De Janeiro, Brazil, as well as high-poverty areas in America. Although *slum* is a widely used word, it can be considered a derogatory term when it connotes people. We prefer to use the United Nation's definition of *slum*, which only refers to characteristics of living condition. No matter the location, slums do possess some similar features. They are crowded, poverty-stricken areas containing informal housing units and general deteriorating infrastructure (see Figure 17.6). Slum residents are often deprived of basic rights and services and are the victims of environmental injustice. They might lack access to clean water and sanitation facilities, and generally lack security. Looking from the outside in, slums are perceived as disadvantageous to urban areas because they are seen as not contributing to production or the economy. Slums also are not attractive. They reduce property values of adjoining areas and serve as nexuses for crime.

FIGURE 17.6
Slums and poverty occur in every metropolis. (A) Homeless man in Los Angeles. (B) Children in Patna, Bihar State, India. (C) A shanty town in Rio De Janeiro, Brazil. (D) A young homeless boy in Bissau, Guinea-Bissau, West Africa.

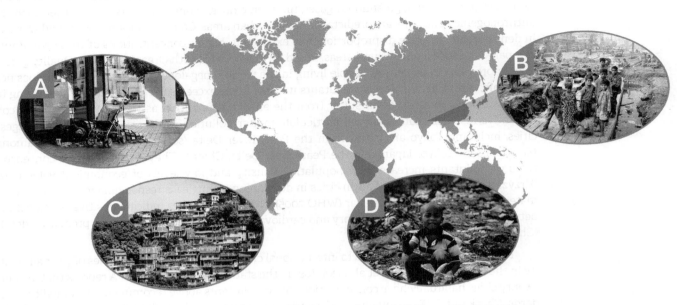

Sources: Andrew V Marcus/Shutterstock.com; © Shutterstock, Inc.; Yury Birukov/Shutterstock.com; TLF Images/Shutterstock.com

What do slums look like in the United States? They can be described as areas where a good proportion (>40 percent) of the resident population has an income below the poverty line. Educational opportunities are lower here than in other areas, infrastructure is deteriorating, and crime is more common. In 2020, the poverty line was an annual income of $13,465 for one person and $26,246 for a family of two adults and two children. These are well below the starting salaries of college graduates entering traditionally high-paying fields such as software engineering, or the lower-paying fields of history, English, and elementary education.

In the latter part of the twentieth century, the United Nations began to move away from the goal of eliminating slums, since this appeared impossible, and instead began a program to upgrade slum areas. The United Nations' Sustainable Development Goal 11 (see Chapter 11 Section 1) states, "By 2030, ensure access for all to adequate, safe, and affordable housing and basic services and upgrade slums." Great strides have been made in reducing the proportion of the global population living in slum areas. Even so, growing populations and swelling urban areas have increased the absolute number of slum-dwellers.

The environmental issues surrounding slum areas are complex due to underlying poverty and inadequate access to basic services. Slum residents rarely have the resources and the education to effectively advocate for themselves and to protect themselves from discrimination, in all of its forms. Dhaka, Bangladesh, for example, is one of the poorest urban areas in the world contending with the challenges of building infrastructure to meet the needs of a growing population. Sanitation and water services are key problems here (UNEP 2005). Only a small percentage of the low-income communities of Dhaka have access to a safe, dependable sanitation system (Alam et al. 2020). On top of this, more than 50 percent of slum residents do not have access to clean drinking water (Rahman et al. 2011).

Cities Are Sources of Pollution

Cities are paradoxical. On one hand, they are beacons of opportunity. On the other hand, they are the largest energy consumers on the planet. Cities consume roughly 75 percent of the energy society uses—much of it carbon-based—and consequently, they are responsible for the majority of global greenhouse gas emissions (Whiteman et al. 2011, Martos et al. 2016). Sources of pollution tend to be concentrated in urban centers, so these areas are front and center in discussions of pollution. Particulate matter, greenhouse gases, nitrogen oxides, ozone, solid waste, and other forms of anthropogenic pollutants are predictably high in urban areas. Consequently, residents and workers in dense urban areas are disproportionately exposed to higher concentrations of these pollutants compared to those living in rural areas. Based on the World Health Organization Air Quality guidelines, more than 95 percent of people living in the world's megalopolises breathe air that does not meet safe, recommended levels. Pollutants in these areas exceed safety standards. Those living in close proximity to a city often suffer from the effects of pollution as well. An international collaborative research team analyzed particulate matter pollution in fifty-six of the world's largest cities, including Tokyo and cities from the Pearl River Delta (see "Case Study: Goliaths among Metropolises—Tokyo, Japan, and the Pearl River Delta, China"). They concluded that concentrations of pollutants increase with population density and low levels of economic development (Krzyzanawski 2014). Polluted air in cities in developing countries is responsible for killing an estimated two million people per year (WHO 2005). Numerous studies indicate positive relationships between air pollution and respiratory and cardiovascular diseases, and, in turn, to premature death (Chen et al. 2017, Arbex et al. 2012).

Poor air quality is not limited to international cities. There are many examples of poor air quality in the United States (Yaya et al. 2020). Just in the state of California, the EPA reports that around twenty cities habitually have concentrations of air pollutants above recommended air quality standards. Check out EPA's air-quality statistics report to find out which cities have poor air-quality in California and other states (see here).

Because pollution does not respect city boundaries, cities serve as sources of pollution that degrades air, water, and soil resources far outside of city boundaries. All of the major environmental issues (climate change, acid rain, eutrophication, etc.) we face are connected to urban areas, and therefore solutions to these issues must focus on cities.

Key Takeaways

- We are in a trend of global urbanization.
- The lure of higher wages and better access to education and health care attracts migrants to urban areas. Urban areas also expand because of internal growth (natality) and reclassification.
- Slums are crowded, poverty-striken areas that have insufficient infrastructure to provide basic services received and enjoyed elsewhere.
- Urban areas are sources of pollution.

17.2 Urban Sprawl

Learning Objectives

1. Identify the causes of urban sprawl.
2. Understand and discuss the negative effects of urban sprawl.
3. Describe mechanisms to reduce the need for urban sprawl.

A fair number of people in the United States say, "I grew up in the **suburbs**." They are referring to a sparsely occupied urban area relative to a denser population in the city proper (see Figure 17.7). The phrase became increasingly common after postwar suburbanization began with the implementation of William Levitt's design for communities on the outskirts of cities. These communities had mass-produced identical housing units on small lots (Kotkin et al. 2015). Home prices in the new suburbs were lower than inner-city housing, which drew in home buyers, resulting in an expansion in home ownership across the United States. The move generated a new concept of a city that had a high density of people living and working at the center and a lower density of people at the outskirts. Today, some people prefer to live in housing developments even further out than the suburbs—in the **exurbs**—where land is more affordable, lots are larger, and there are fewer people (Berube et al. 2006).

suburbs

A part of urban sprawl; urban area that is sparsely populated relative to a denser population in the city proper.

exurbs

Housing developments beyond the suburbs. They usually consist of single-family houses on larger plots of land.

FIGURE 17.7
Examples of urbanization. (A) Suburbs are less populated than central areas of large cities. A suburb in Sydney, Australia surrounds high-rise towers. (B) A small number of nations and special administration regions are fully urbanized. Macao is one example.

Sources: © Shutterstock, Inc.; Jack Hong/Shutterstock.com

The idea of sprawl from America's east coast cities spreading west and merging with the sprawl of west coast cities advancing east seems far-fetched, but we have witnessed expanding urban sprawls of neighboring cities merge. When this happens nationally, full urbanization occurs. This means that the entire county is one huge city. A handful of smaller nations and regions around the world have already reached 100 percent urbanization. This short list includes the special administration regions of Hong Kong and Macao (see "Case Study: Goliaths among Metropolises—Tokyo, Japan, and the Pearl River Delta, China"), Gibraltar, and seven others. Sprawl of each of these urban areas is limited by geographic or political boundaries. For instance, Gibraltar has an area of only 6.7 square kilometers (2.6 mi²), but it cannot expand because Spain abuts it to the immediate north, and the English Channel to the south. Growth of Gibraltar's population can only occur by increasing the number of people per square area (density) and through the construction of taller buildings (see "Critical Thinking Activity: Observation and Analysis of Gibraltar—a Fully Urbanized Territory"). Sprawl is not an option. Decades of economic and population growth in Macao has turned this former Portuguese colony into a gambling capital and one of the most densely populated areas in the world. About 700,000 people live on this 12.7 square-mile (32.9 km²) peninsula. Sprawl is not an option for Macao because it is surrounded by water. The new tunnel and bridges across the Pearl River Delta connecting Macao to mainland China will likely increase the region's economic activity, and thus prompt further internal growth and vertical construction.

Critical Thinking Activity: Observation and Analysis of Gibraltar—a Fully Urbanized Territory

A migrant who moves from a rural community to a dense urban environment notices the change in the landscape and land use as they approach the border of the city and then the city's center. Grasslands and forests transition to sidewalks, roads, and buildings. Even if you have not grown up in the city, very likely you have visited one and observed its dense structure. Fewer people have visited fully urbanized nations or territories such as Gibraltar, just south of Spain. Gibraltar has a certain appeal for its mixed Spanish and English cultures, as a transportation hub for greater Europe, and its proximity to the northern tip of Africa. The question we are interested in with this critical thinking activity is, "How does a nation or territory continue to evolve urban structure when new undeveloped land is no longer available?" An analysis of Gibraltar—a completely urbanized territory of Britain—provides us with a unique opportunity to explore a fully urbanized area without actually traveling there. To get started, visit the United States Geological Survey's Earthexplorer here. Click and drag the map until you have placed Spain in the center. Enlarge the map and center the southern tip of Spain in the center of the map. Continue this process until you see a label for Gibraltar. Stop when the entirety of Gibraltar fits on your computer screen and you can observe the northern border of Gibraltar where it connects to Spain. The large green section of vegetation that runs laterally from north to south covers the west side of a 1,400-foot tall (426 m) massive rock that consists of limestone. Further magnify the satellite image and find the following: airport (next to the northern border), beach (middle of west coast), athletic fields (next to airport), housing developments, large ships docked, and harbor full of yachts. All but the taller limestone rock areas are completely developed. Everything is condensed. Did you observe Winston Churchill Avenue—the road that intersects the runway? This road to Spain closes every time a plane arrives or departs. How does the territory's structure compare to your community's?

What Are the Issues of Urban Sprawl?

Urban sprawl brings forth a host of issues—environmental, social, and economic—that challenge cities (see Figure 17.8). Valuable greenspace and species habitat are destroyed, causing biodiversity in these areas to plummet. Sprawl swallows forests and agricultural lands, thus fragmenting natural ecosystems and threatening food security (Miller 2011, Marzuki and Jais 2020). Another significant issue is the rise in costs of basic services. Relative to the city center, which harbors a high-density population of people, costs of basic services are higher in low-density developments. Costs of sanitation, water, and policing all increase per individual. Sprawl raises the cost of infrastructure and public services by as much as 40 percent (Litman 2015). For example, there are additional costs of policing in sprawled areas because police travel longer distances.

FIGURE 17.8
Negative effects of sprawl. (A) Sprawl causes deforestation, loss of species habitat, and swallows up valuable farmland. A farmer looks to the outskirts of a city encroaching on his farmland. (B) Urban centers with job opportunities, expensive housing, and an inadequate public transport system encourage workers to live in the suburbs and drive their personal vehicles to work. The results are air pollution, traffic jams, and loss of productivity. In the photo, commuters are stuck in San Diego's afternoon rush hour.

Sources: © Shutterstock, Inc.; Hairem/Shutterstock.com

Housing in suburbs is typically not within walking distance of places of work. There is also inadequate public transport to assist residents of the suburbs. Therefore, urban sprawl creates an army of commuters dependent on vehicles for attending work (see B in Figure 17.8). Because gas-powered engines still dominate roadways, exhaust from most of these commuter vehicles contains air pollutants. Tailpipes release greenhouse gases—predominantly carbon dioxide—that contribute to accelerated climate change. Exhaust also contains sulfur dioxide that contributes to acid rain, and particulate matter associated with respiratory ailments (see Chapter 11). Released nitrogen oxides weaken immune systems, and, like sulfur dioxide, contribute to acid rain. Emitted volatile organic carbons are linked to cancer. In sum, a large commuter population driving-internal combustion vehicles creates serious air-pollution problems detrimental to human health and the environment.

More cars and trucks on the roads causes congestion, traffic delays, and parking problems (see B in Figure 17.8). Commuters in large metropolises can spend up to twice as long in traffic relative to commuters living in other areas. Drivers in Boston spend over 160 hours per year on the road. That is almost seven entire days, or twenty eight-hour workdays. Time wasted in traffic is responsible for the loss of billions of dollars from the economy every year.

Often overlooked are the psychological and social costs of commuting. The unpredictability of commute time due to traffic can cause commuters to become frustrated and angry. People who can least afford to commute end up with the longest commutes and less family time. In this situation, owning a reliable car becomes a necessity, and the financial burden would not exist if sufficient affordable housing existed in the city center where jobs are.

Why Does Urban Sprawl Exist?

Not every city experiences the same degree of growth (see Figure 17.9). What factors favor urban sprawl? Consider San Francisco and Atlanta, cities that have taken very different paths in urban development (Leyk et al. 2020). San Francisco's surrounding geography constrains growth at the city's periphery. Located at the northern tip of a peninsula, San Francisco is bounded by waters of the Pacific Ocean and San Francisco Bay on three sides, and it has limited space to the south due to permanently protected state and national parks. As a result, since 1950, San Francisco has undergone a strong densification trend and comparatively modest sprawl. *Densification* refers to the increasing number of people and built structures in a given area. In contrast, the nontopographically constrained city of Atlanta has undergone modest densification and a huge amount of sprawl that has resulted in major deforestation and species habitat loss (Miller 2012).

An analysis of 1,200 urban areas around the world identified several key drivers of urban sprawl (OECD 2018). Geographic, demographic, social, technological, and economic factors, in addition to policy-driven decisions, affect the development of sprawl. The absence of geographical barriers to a city's growth at its periphery is a main factor (Atlanta is an example). Expensive housing and high crime rates within the city center also push workers to live in the suburbs. Fuel-efficient cars and low gas prices make commuting an economically viable option for many families.

Land-use regulations, building height restrictions, and **zoning laws** also encourage sprawl. Under these restrictions, what options does a city with a growing population have other than growth at its periphery? Height restrictions for new buildings in Washington, DC, were implemented to preserve the city's historical character, but these same restrictions also contribute to shortages in office space and housing. Zoning laws that separate residential, industrial, and commercial areas are intended to protect human health and residential property. Residential zoning laws define the type of housing allowed in particular areas (e.g., certain percentages of single-family homes, apartments, and so on). The vast majority of U.S. cities maintain single-family zoning, which creates urban communities of single-family homes. In many areas of California, for example, suburban homes tend to be packed like sardines as close as possible to the property lines, but no matter how close these homes are to each other, they still create low-density communities. Of course, there are different zoning laws in different parts of the United States. Some zoning laws increase the minimum lot area for houses and in doing so, further increase sprawl. For example, in the suburbs of the New Jersey Highlands, we have witnessed a growth of spacious subdivisions

zoning law

An ordinance or law that defines how a zone can be used. For instance, they dictate type, size, and shape of buildings permissible in a section (zone) of the city.

because the minimum lot size has increased significantly since 1975. Between 1975 and 2002, the required minimum lot area for houses has doubled. The result is an expansion of low-density residential areas (O'Neill 2011). These low-density communities (i.e., sprawl) might appeal to the many Americans who place a high value on privacy, but these communities are spread out over much larger areas than needed. To house our increasing population, we are going to have to increase the density of residential units in our cities.

FIGURE 17.9
Urban sprawl continues to expand in some cities but not others. Geographical barriers can impede urban sprawl. (A) San Francisco Bay, the Pacific Ocean, and state and federal parks bordering San Francisco inhibit future sprawl. (B) Atlanta—the poster city for urban sprawl—has no natural geographical barriers.

Source: © Shutterstock, Inc.

Better Solutions

There are solutions to sprawl. These solutions focus on mechanisms that can increase housing density in the city center, for example by repealing antidensity regulations, changing zoning laws, and supporting affordable housing within city limits. Cities can review their building height restrictions and reconsider what is acceptable (see Figure 17.10). In other words, they can decide to build up rather than out. Allowing construction of taller buildings can provide living space for more tenants, reducing demand for land outside the city, supporting the preservation of green space within the city. A percentage of housing units in these taller buildings—enough to serve demand—would be available to and affordable for lower-income families.

FIGURE 17.10

Repealing building height restrictions allows vertical growth and densification within cities. (A) In the District of Columbia, current height caps are 29 m (95 ft) for residential buildings and 39.6 m (130 ft) for office buildings, but discussions are ongoing to change these restrictions. Compare the short, boxy buildings of the District of Columbia to (B) the skyscrapers in the less height-restricted New York City.

Sources: Anton_Ivanov/Shutterstock.com; © Shutterstock, Inc.

There is a need to reevaluate zoning laws to meet the housing needs of our ever-increasing population, and to do so equitably. Zoning and land-use rules across the country inhibit the ability of communities to counter urban sprawl. Neighborhoods may well lift restrictions of single-family houses with incentives from local, state, and federal governments. These incentives can be in the form of grants or waived development fees. In Portland, Oregon, for example, property owners do not have to pay expensive development fees that can be in excess of $15,000 when they build an accessory dwelling unit on their property. An accessory dwelling unit is an independent residential unit that is smaller than the main house. The next section discusses additional strategies for preventing urban sprawl and developing sustainable communities and cities.

Key Takeaways

- Land-use regulations, building height restrictions, and zoning laws are some of the many factors that encourage sprawl—the unregulated spreading of urban developments into undeveloped areas surrounding a city.
- Urban sprawl results in environmental, social, and economic issues that challenge cities.
- There are solutions to urban sprawl. These solutions focus on mechanisms that block anti-density regulations, change zoning laws, and support affordable housing within city limits.

17.3 Strategies for Developing Sustainable Communities and Cities

Learning Objectives

1. Identify and understand strategies for the development of sustainable communities and cities.
2. Explain how urban planning and zoning are essential to ensure urban areas meet challenges.

3. Defend the use of smart growth and green design theory in urban development.

4. Discuss environmentally friendly transportation networks that meet the needs of large, dense urban populations.

Urban sprawl is not all doom and gloom. Tokyo's growth (see "Case Study: Goliaths among Metropolises—Tokyo, Japan, and the Pearl River Delta, China") and research on the positive impacts of urban agriculture demonstrate that urban sprawl is not always incompatible with nature (Terada 2017). A strong sense of environmental ethics and the acceptance and practice of maintaining urban gardens in the Tokyo area are deeply rooted in Japanese culture dating back to the seventeenth century, when samurai households kept gardens (Brown 2009). In contemporary Tokyo, community involvement in growing vegetables in city gardens—urban agriculture—makes use of plots of land that are considered too irregular or small for development. These plots become actively managed green spaces that help protect food security, ameliorate urban heat island effect (see Figure 17.13), and offer fresh, nutritious food to urbanites. In this light, urban sprawl offers opportunities for creating healthy, resilient, and sustainable communities. In this section, we look into strategies for developing sustainable communities and cities. For instance, the strategy of implementing urban agriculture in Los Angeles and other metropolises offers resilience to a community, promotes social inclusion, teaches environmental stewardship, and creates a method for the poor to earn money. This section covers urban planning and zoning, environmental ethics and community property, green designs, and transportation.

Urban Planning and Zoning

urban planning

A planning process for an urban area that considers where people will live and work, and the infrastructure required for those people.

zoning

An urban planning method used to divide land into areas called zones. Each zone allows specific types of land use.

redlining

A discriminative zoning practice causing segregation and environmental injustice.

Everyone lives somewhere. Right now, over 55 percent of the world's population lives in urban settings, but this percentage is increasing each year. By 2050, we predict a doubling of the urban population (UN 2016). **Urban planning** and **zoning** ensure urban areas meet numerous challenges they face. Poorly designed and mismanaged urban areas often have insufficient infrastructure, inadequate basic services, and encourage inequality and segregation (see "Critical Thinking Activity: Reducing Roadblocks to Healthy Community Development"). Urban planners—those who practice urban planning—are interested in where people will live and work in the future, and the systems (such as sanitation and transportation) those people will require. Progressive urban planning involves gathering information from all community groups to ensure plans accommodate the diversity of needs typical of communities. Urban planners also aim to design livable communities that have a sense of culture, and that have safe connections between work, residential areas, schools, hospitals, and retail stores. As discussed in Section 3, later in this section, urban planners often advocate mixed land uses.

Critical Thinking Activity: Reducing Roadblocks to Healthy Community Development

Useful, healthy, ethical planning and zoning is inclusive of all community members and stakeholders. It fosters opportunities for all groups of people regardless of race, gender, or socioeconomic status. The urban designs of today's cities are the result of former planning and zoning regulations, and many have been fostering exorbitant housing costs, racial disparities, and environmental injustice. The question we entertain in this critical thinking exercise is, "How do decisions about planning and zoning made between the 1930s and the 1970s negatively affect city growth, racial equity, and environmental justice? Secondly, how do city planners and community members overcome these issues?" Building positive change in community design begins with an understanding of the evolution of the community, which may include analyzing decades of historical data. Beginning in the 1930s, the federal government—through the passing of the National Housing Act of 1934—began to survey American cities to identify areas of investment based on demographics, specifically race. This discriminative practice is known as **redlining**. Go here to view infamous redlining maps of Minneapolis and Saint Paul created in the 1930s. Observe the various color-coded areas of the maps marked with letters. Green and blue were designated "Best" and "Still Desirable" as investment areas, and yellow areas were considered "Definitely Declining" because they were near areas that had predominantly African American or Asian residents (red areas designated "Hazardous"). Now, analyze the red areas more closely and determine why the people living there are disproportionately exposed to environmental threats (environmental injustice, see Chapter 2). As a hint, identify the business/industrial areas marked with crossed lines. In just about all cases, areas where African Americans and Asians lived ("Hazardous" investments) adjoined business/industrial areas that are sources of pollution. Cities are still dealing with the legacy of such discriminatory practices. To prevent further racial discrimination and to promote environmental justice (see Chapter 1), governments are beginning to review and change zoning laws. Minneapolis progressive mayor Jacob Frey and the Minneapolis City Council recognized the influence and bias of redlining maps, and began to redesign their city. In 2020, Minneapolis opened up areas that had been zoned for single-family residences to other types of housing—including affordable housing. To learn more about how government segregated America's communities and promoted environmental injustice, read Richard Rothstein's *The Color of Law* (2017) and listen to Terry Gross's interview of Richard Rothstein here.

FIGURE 17.11

Urban planners use advanced technology, including 3-D modeling, to envision future city growth.

Source: © Shutterstock, Inc.

Zoning laws have considerable power to influence densification and the spread of sprawl. For instance, they dictate type, size, and shape of buildings permissible in a section (zone) of the city. Because zoning laws regulate land use (see Section 2), it is important to create and uphold zoning laws that support sustainable development.

Today's urban planners have state-of-the-art software that helps them visualize urban designs that meet the economic, growth, diversity, and sustainability goals of the city. ArcGIS Urban is one of several examples of software used by urban planners for visualizing projects (see Figure 17.11). These software products overlay satellite imagery and can calculate the number of households and jobs a hypothetical building project can provide (see video link: "ArcGIS Urban—Transforming Urban Planning and Design").

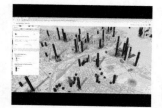
Environmental Ethics and Community Property

Urban areas include community property—shared space that all residents have a right to access. How does environmental ethics (see Chapter 2) apply to these open-access areas? Harden (1968) would have us believe that common areas have no rules, and individual actions outweigh the community good—a view that can result in the tragedy of the commons (see Chapter 2). Anthropologist Mark Moritz does not accept this selfish view for common pastoral areas in rural Cameroon (Moritz 2016), and perhaps the same is true for community property sites in the city. Urban communities with a strong sense of identity can be strong environmental stewards of vacant or commonly owned and openly used areas. Community groups and organizations can leverage their power and finances to protect open areas, even against the intentions of city administrations. For example, on behalf of the community, the Bronx Land Trust in New York City purchased community garden areas to protect them from future housing development (Kim 2016). The mission of this Trust is "to preserve, improve, and promote community managed open spaces for the benefit of all." Environmentally ethical city officials can use their positions of influence to protect open areas of the city. For example, in New Orleans, a city-led project targets vacant city lots for greening to reduce the volume of storm water.

How an urban community uses its common spaces is based on how its members perceive the value of land in general. Does the land have intrinsic value, instrumental value, or neither? Land with intrinsic value implies the land has value just for existing, and therefore, ought to be preserved for its own sake. In contrast, instrumental value implies the land has value because it is useful for some human purpose (i.e., recreational value). Community members who do not identify land as either intrinsically valuable or instrumentally valuable are less likely to engage in environmental stewardship of vacant lots and community-owned land.

Smart Growth

smart growth

An urban development theory that attempts to maximize the benefits of urban infrastructure and simultaneously preserve green space and protect agricultural lands.

new urbanism

A human-scaled urban design movement that supports complete, compact, and connected communities.

Smart growth can alleviate many urban problems. The basic concept of smart growth theory is to maximize the benefits of urban infrastructure and simultaneously preserve green space and protect agricultural lands (Kolbadi 2015). This approach to development creates compact, walkable, mixed-use urban areas supportive of economic activity while preserving open spaces (see video link: "Smart Growth in America"). Smart growth can also be controversial and political because stakeholders have different ideas about land use, and because smart growth can affect existing communities. For example, the addition of a sidewalk may improve the walkability of an urban area that doesn't have one, but property owners may protest the idea.

Smart growth is seen as a means to combat urban sprawl because it emphasizes mixed land use, compact building designs, and densification. Mixed development areas have some combination of residential units, retail and grocery stores, office spaces, health clinics, and so on, all within walking distance (see Figure 17.12). The **new urbanism** movement supports smart growth. New urbanism is a design movement toward complete, compact, and connected communities (Steuteville 2018). Proponents of this movement advocate for residents of cities and towns to have their living needs be within a five-minute walk radius of their homes. Critics of new urbanism point out that new urbanism does not try to preserve nature (Kelbaugh 2015). As a result, open spaces, streams, grasslands, and forests in new urbanism designs tend to be smaller than necessary.

FIGURE 17.12
A mixed-use development optimizes use of a limited area—a principle of smart growth. (A) An example of vertical growth in West Palm Beach, Florida, with residential units above retail stores. (B) In London, a mixed-use area with residences, shopping, offices, and a health clinic.

Sources: © Shutterstock, Inc.; William Barton/Shutterstock.com

Creating a smart growth area influences transportation in two general ways. It creates a sufficient conglomeration of people to prompt a city to invest in a transit hub and connect this vibrant area to other nodes in its transport network. Sales and property taxes of mixed-use zones stimulate the local economy. A pedestrian-friendly, mixed-use development has a diverse range of available activities and therefore significantly reduces a person's need for a car for daily events (Ewing et al. 2011). As a consequence, traffic congestion wanes and air pollution declines.

Green Design

A green-designed city encourages a blend of nature and society. A network of wide sidewalks and car-free zones creates a walkable environment. Home, shopping, and work areas are close, and, importantly, the layout and elements of the city are as harmonious as possible with Mother Nature.

What does **green design** mean at the single-building level (see video link: "Green Building Design")? We expect to see one or more common features that constrain negative environmental impacts: efficient heating and cooling, efficient use of energy, conservation of water, and inclusion of native vegetation (greenery). Natural materials are emphasized during construction, and internal spaces are designed to maximize natural lighting. Green-designed buildings give businesses and homeowners financial advantages, and they have smaller carbon footprints relative to conventionally designed (non-green) buildings. The development of the Leadership in Energy Environmental Design (**LEED**) rating program by the U.S. Green Building Council standardized the model for green buildings. We use this system to rate a building's design and performance. LEED is now a widely used and accepted method of rating the environmental friendliness of new buildings. There are four levels of certification, from Certified (**LEED certified**), the base level, through Platinum, the highest level.

Smart Growth in America
Listen to why the city of Hamilton in Ohio earned a Smart Growth Achievement award.

View in the online reader

green design
Building design that minimizes negative environmental impacts through efficient heating and cooling, efficient use of energy, conservation of water, and inclusion of native vegetation.

LEED
Leadership in Energy Environmental Design; a rating program by the U.S. Green Building Council.

LEED certified
Certification by the LEED rating program.

Green architecture saves money and energy. Across the United States, there are many good examples of LEED Platinum–certified buildings. The new Kaiser Permanente San Diego Medical Center hospital in San Diego, California, is one example (see A in Figure 17.13). College campuses are often at the forefront of green-designed building as well. Penn State University's childcare center at Hort Woods exemplifies a green design. The center has a roof garden to grow vegetables used by onsite chefs. Recycled materials and FSC-certified wood are used in construction, and natural ventilation and lighting are emphasized. Rainwater is collected and used to flush toilets. Green-designed residential homes are becoming more common today too. These homes are more energy efficient than the average home, typically including insulated roofs, solar panels, double- or triple-paned windows, energy-efficient appliances and lighting, among other features that support sustainability (see B in Figure 17.13). Does your residence have these features?

Internationally, the Oasia Hotel Downtown in Singapore is an outstanding example of a green-designed building (see "Critical Thinking Activity: Visiting the Park Royal in Singapore"). Built in 2016, this tall, mixed-use building has a veneer that provides support for twenty-one different species of creeping vines. The vines lend a natural look and smell to an otherwise steel and glass urban environment. The total area covered by creeping vines, combined with thirty-three native species of trees and shrubs in sky gardens inside the building, exceeds the building's footprint many times over.

Critical Thinking Activity: Visiting the Park Royal in Singapore

To begin this exercise, write down what you expect to observe when staying in a common hotel in a metropolis. Consider construction materials, lighting, ambiance, and smell. What does it feel like when you enter the lobby area? What about the street view of the hotel? Most important, what about the relative areas of impervious structures compared to green spaces? Only after you have jotted down your expectations of this conventionally designed hotel, go to the video link "Park Royal" and take a tour of the green-designed Park Royal. Compare and contrast the two hotels.

 Park Royal

Listen to Wong Mun Summ, founding director of WOHA, describing Park Royal's green design.

View in the online reader

FIGURE 17.13
Green-designed buildings are examples of how to minimize the impact of urban development on nature. (A) In 2017, Kaiser Permanente San Diego Medical Center Hospital became the first LEED Platinum-certified hospital in the state of California. (B) Penn State University's Child Care Center, also LEED certified. (C) A green-designed house.

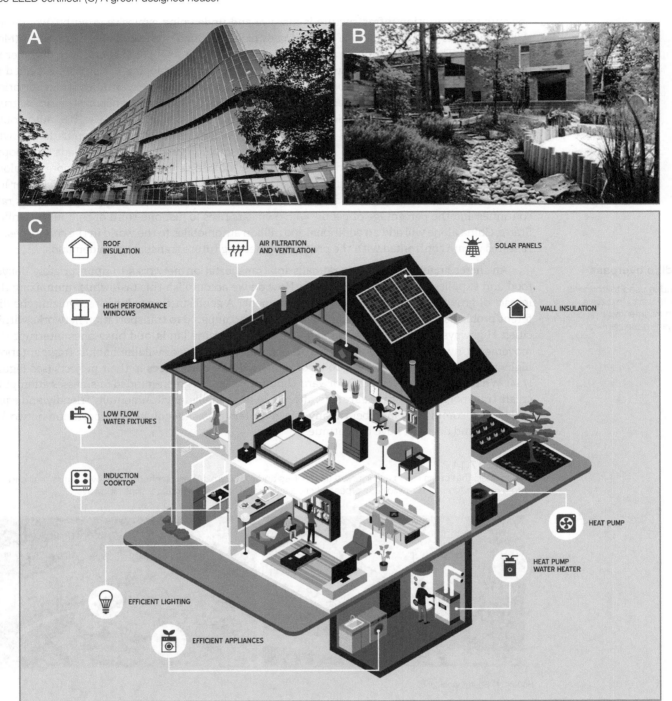

Sources: Roaming Panda Photos/Shutterstock.com; Image courtesy of Penn State; © Shutterstock, Inc.

Transportation

Society's transportation infrastructure is massive and undergoing explosive growth. Twenty-one million kilometers (13 million mi) of roads already exist—enough to circle the Earth 524 times (Meijer et al. 2018). These roads support an ever-growing fleet of automobiles that currently number 1.4 billion, and that are projected to swell to two billion by 2035. Developing nations are expected to undergo most of the new growth, both in number of automobiles and expansion of transportation networks. Comparatively, developed nations possess a more complete transportation infrastructure, so the number of automobiles is growing more slowly. For instance, the U.S. automobile market is relatively maxed out; its much smaller growth trend matches slow population growth and replacement of older vehicles. There are about 275 million cars on America's roads for a population of roughly 331 million, or about 83 vehicles per 100 people (83 percent). A far more populous China (1.41 billion), where we predict continued explosive growth, has only about 19 vehicles per 100 people. China's vehicle population is growing at a rate of about 6–11 percent per year. If this rate continues and the percentage of people who own cars rises to just one-third of that in the United States, China alone will add an additional 300 million automobiles to the world in the coming years. It seems we are confronted with the problem of meeting future transportation demands.

wildlife overpass

A bridge used to connect wildlife areas that have been fragmented by human-made barriers.

An increasingly urbanized world calls for transportation networks to appropriately deliver food and supplies and support commerce. How do we accomplish this task while minimizing the impact of growth of this sector on the environment? A good starting point is recognizing the different problems associated with roads between cities compared to transportation networks within cities. Highways and interstates fragment forests and prairie lands, and busy ones interrupt the movement of wildlife between habitats. To help solve the issue of wildlife habitat fragmentation, highway developers are beginning to incorporate **wildlife overpasses** in their projects (see Figure 17.14). What about urban settings? Forward-thinking cities and green-minded businesses attempt to create transport networks that are safe, affordable, dependable, environmentally friendly, and equitable for all community members. Many urban centers have inadequate transportation networks, but that trend does not have to continue.

FIGURE 17.14
Wild animals that cross roads risk injury to themselves and to drivers. (A) An elephant steps over a guardrail and onto a road in Africa. (B) A wildlife overpass offers a safe travel route for animals across highways.

Source: © Shutterstock, Inc.

A city with a well-planned transportation infrastructure offers plenty of alternatives to driving personal cars. Ample, safe routes for pedestrians and bike lanes free of dangerous motorized vehicles encourage walking and biking—transportation options that do not produce greenhouse gases. A fleet of taxis, buses, and dependable light rail and subway systems strategically link residential and industrial areas.

Fossil fuel–powered vehicles are the root of traffic pollution problems. Traffic-related pollution will disappear if we replace these vehicles with electric cars. Therefore, green-minded cities invest in infrastructure that supports electric cars, such as plug-in stations at strategic nodes throughout the city (see Figure 17.15). More and more people have an interest in developing sustainable urban areas. There are a growing number of cities offering incentives for building green, and that support the use of green infrastructure. For example, some car-congested cities (London, and soon New York City) are offering tax incentives for people to use mass transit instead of personal automobiles (see Chapter 18). Mass transit is better for the environment than individual cars. Emissions of volatile organic compounds, nitrogen oxides, and carbon dioxide all significantly decrease per passenger mile when people choose to use the public transportation system rather than drive their personal vehicle.

FIGURE 17.15
A solar-powered electric car charging station in San Iodefonso, Spain. It is free to use.

Source: Juan Enrique del Barrio/Shutterstock.com

Key Takeaways

- Strategies for developing sustainable communities and cities include smart growth, green design, and fossil fuel–free public transportation systems that serve the needs of all community members.
- Urban planning and zoning are essential to ensure urban areas meet numerous challenges they face. Poorly designed and managed urban areas have insufficient infrastructure and inadequate basic services, and encourage inequality and segregation.
- Environmental ethics is an important part of managing and utilizing shared community property. Urban communities can be strong environmental stewards of vacant, shared, and open-use areas.
- The basic concept of smart growth theory is to maximize the benefits of urban infrastructure while simultaneously preserving green space and protecting agricultural lands. It is seen as a means to combat urban sprawl by encouraging densification in cities via mixed-use areas and tall building designs.

- Green design encourages a blending of nature and society. The general aim is to constrain negative environmental impacts through efficient heating and cooling, efficient use of energy, conservation of water, and inclusion of native vegetation.
- Environmentally friendly transport systems ameliorate environmental impacts. For these systems to be successful and used by the public, they need to be safe, affordable, reliable, and equally accessible to all community members.

17.4 A Look to the Future: Urbanization Trends, Poverty, and Environmental Degradation

Learning Objectives

1. Distinguish past from projected regional urbanization trends.
2. Recognize the contributions of migrant workers to urbanization and the connection between their welfare and environmental issues.
3. Consider the strategies Atlanta could use to curtail further sprawl.

This is the time of urbanization. By 2050, another 2.3 billion people will live in urban areas, and an estimated two out of every three people will call a city their home. The dynamics of these rapidly growing urban areas are paradoxical because they offer great prosperity, but they are also sites of the greatest inequalities. Urban areas are beacons of opportunity because they promise greater availability of jobs, higher wages, and a better standard of living than rural areas. Densely populated areas create demand for local products and services, so they foster local economic growth. These are all positives. On the other hand, urbanization is outpacing city infrastructure. The result is unaffordable housing, environmental injustice, and urban sprawl.

The challenge facing today's urban planners (and governments at all levels) is to provide sufficient affordable housing, basic services, and equal opportunities for all people. Ethical, community-minded urban planning and zoning will ensure future urban areas meet the needs of our growing population. Smart growth and green design can maximize the benefits of urban infrastructure while at the same time protect green space and agricultural lands important for food security. In this last section of the chapter, we will analyze and hypothesize about the coming regional shifts in urbanization, and then further explore the Pearl River Delta (see "Case Study: Goliaths among Metropolises—Tokyo, Japan, and the Pearl River Delta, China") and the future of Atlanta, Georgia.

Urbanization Rates Are Shifting Regionally

Developed, wealthier nations were the first to experience the mass movement of populations from rural to urban areas (urbanization). In contrast, Africa and Asia are only recently becoming urbanized, and the pace of this trend is changing the relative proportions of urbanization in the different regions of the world. We are witnessing (and projecting the continuation of) some of the fastest urbanization trends in these areas (see Figure 17.16). Looking to the future, Asia's proportion of the world's city dwellers is predicted to rise a few percentage points, to 52 percent, by 2050 (Science 2016). During the same period, urbanization in Africa is projected to increase by almost another two-thirds, so this continent will end up with more than 21 percent of the world's city-dwellers. These urbanization dynamics have captured the attention of urban planners, who are wondering how Africa will accommodate this new and unprecedented growth.

FIGURE 17.16
Urbanization trends in different regions of the world. Predicted values are to the right of the dotted line.

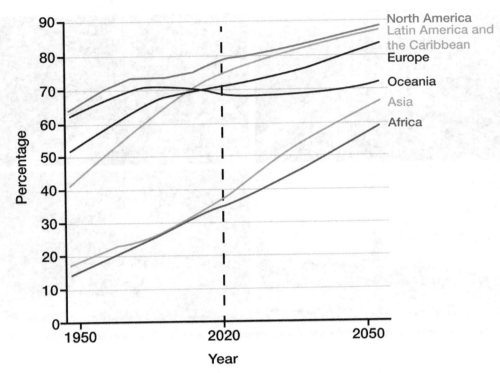

What is driving urbanization in sub-Saharan Africa? This region lacks a well-developed manufacturing sector, which is the driving factor for urbanization in other regions. For example, in China, rural people migrate to urban areas for the promise of employment in manufacturing plants. The classic explanation of migration—farmers moving into cities to work in factories—has occurred in many regions of the world, but it does not explain urbanization in sub-Saharan Africa. The answer is not clear, but there are hints. Surveys of people in African cities show a surprisingly high number of farmers living within city limits. They make up between 9 percent and 40 percent of the urban population, percentages much higher than in other regions of the world (Henderson and Turner 2020). Dr. Vernon Henderson suggests that farmers in Africa may be choosing to live in cities to increase the opportunities for their family members as well as to find employment during the off-season (Henderson and Kriticos 2018).

Do sub-Saharan cities have the necessary infrastructure and finances to support rapid urbanization (see Figure 17.17)? Public transportation services, sewage treatment plants, solid waste pickup, and health care all have associated costs. Without well-planned urban designs, a greater percentage of urban dwellers will live in slums and experience environmental injustice. Can African nations effectively inhibit urban sprawl and adequately protect biodiversity hotspots? Biodiverse West African forests, eastern coastal forests (Tanzania/Kenya), Madagascar, and the southern tip of Africa all support some of the most unique and species-rich ecosystems on the planet. They are also areas of projected urbanization. It is because of the underlying connections between urban infrastructure, poverty, and environmental degradation that our sustainability goals intentionally address urban development, human welfare conditions, and environmental protection simultaneously.

FIGURE 17.17

Nigeria, Africa, has one of the fastest-growing populations in the world, and it is struggling with urbanization. (A) Skyline view of the central business district of Lagos Island. (B) Traffic congestion at Idumota Market in Lagos, Nigeria. (C) Plastic garbage from Lagos degrades coastal habitat. (D) There are fewer than 400 iconic lions remaining in Nigeria, all of them protected in two national parks. Today, most people who observe lions only do so in parks.

Sources: Tayvay/Shutterstock.com; Santos Akhilele Aburime/Shutterstock.com; Alucardion/Shutterstock.com; © Shutterstock, Inc.

Opening Story Revisited: Migrants, Poverty, and Environmental Degradation

We only have fragments of data about the millions of migrant workers who are the unsung heroes of China's rapid urbanization and economic growth. Here, we take the time to become more acquainted with this undoubtedly important population.

The exact number of people living in China's metropolises is difficult to determine. In addition to the official resident population, there is a "'floating" population of migrant workers critical to urban productivity (see Figure 17.18). Migrant workers are discriminated against: They are exploited in their jobs and, unlike nonmigrants, have little protection from the conditions they face, including a disproportionate exposure to pollution (a form of environmental injustice). The COVID-19 pandemic has revealed new evidence about how this population of workers is further victimized (Li et al. 2021). Although they are often one of the first groups impacted by contagious diseases, they often have no health care. Border-control restrictions implemented to slow the spread of COVID-19 severely inhibit migrant travel, sometimes completely. Thus, as a consequence of the pandemic, incomes of migrants fell, as did the amount of money they were able to send home to their families. Migrant wages keep families back home economically afloat; without them, both migrants and their families may slide into poverty.

The global community has an opportunity to develop and strengthen policies to protect the rights of migrants, provide needed health and social services, and, in doing so, help protect the environment. China's migrant population also has a higher incidence of poverty compared to the rest of China. Remember, poverty and environmental protection are not mutually exclusive. Poverty is both a cause and an outcome of environmental degradation. The impoverished have immediate survival needs that must take precedence over long-term environmental policies such as the protection of forests from deforestation, or fish communities from overfishing. Because incidences of poverty are higher in China's migrant population compared to the rest of China, assisting this group is important for the migrants and the environment. However, sustainable use of land minimizes flooding, maintains soil integrity, and safeguards water resources; therefore, it supports agriculture, increases food security, and improves access to nonpolluted drinking water. We reach sustainability by eradicating poverty, raising the living conditions of the poor, and engaging in environmental stewardship.

Opening Story Revisited: Atlanta's Future

What about Atlanta? In the opening story, the city was described as having more sprawl than any other large American city. Does Atlanta have an urban design planned that will benefit all residents and prevent further sprawl? Atlanta's Department of City Planning thinks it does. It is ambitious, calling for sweeping changes that will support increased density within the city center. If the plan is completely implemented, there will be new streetcar lines, subways, and light rail transit connected to walkable communities. Transit buses will have dedicated lanes. These systems are promised to be efficient and dependable. The new city design also promises to convert old train tracks to bike lanes that are free of automobiles. In addition to these transportation changes, the city is in the process of passing new ordinances to create more affordable urban housing. For instance, one ordinance supports the creation of more flexible accessory dwellings such as garage apartments and basement apartments (both are not permitted now). Another ordinance that mostly eliminates a requirement of having at least two parking spaces for every new single-family home will free up expensive real estate ($40,000 per parking space), thus reducing housing costs. Atlanta is just one of many American cities planning to encourage population growth in the city center. If Atlanta—the city with the most sprawl in the United States—can truly change as planned, shouldn't we expect improved designs for all of our cities (see video link: "Principles for Building Better Cities")?

 Principles for Building Better Cities

Listen to Peter Calthorpe discussing seven principles for building better cities.

View in the online reader

FIGURE 17.18

Migrants are an essential part of China's work force in many sectors of the economy. (A) Migrant workers assembling electric fans in a manufacturing plant. (B) A group of migrant workers leaves a construction site after a long day of labor. (C) Migrants take on exceptionally dangerous jobs such as window-washing. Each of these four workers is held up by a single rope—hence their name, "spider men." (D) Two migrant workers heft large sacks of train luggage from a train station.

Sources: humphery/Shutterstock.com; zhaoliang70/Shutterstock.com; TonyV3112/Shutterstock.com; humphery/Shutterstock.com

Key Takeaways

- Asia and Africa are expected to have the greatest rate of urbanization in the coming decades.
- Migrant workers and their families often face discrimination in China. The workers are exploited in their jobs and have little protection from the conditions they face, including a disproportionate exposure to pollution.
- Poverty and environmental degradation are interrelated.
- Atlanta's city planners have proposed sweeping changes to Atlanta's transportation system. These and proposed ordinance changes, if passed, will encourage more people to live in the city.

FIGURE 17.19 Visual Overview: Sustainable Community Development and Urbanization
Summarizing figure: Sustainable community development and urbanization takes into account urbanization dynamics (17.1), strategies to prevent urban sprawl (17.2), smart growth (17.3), and the needs of tomorrow's larger urban populations (17.4).

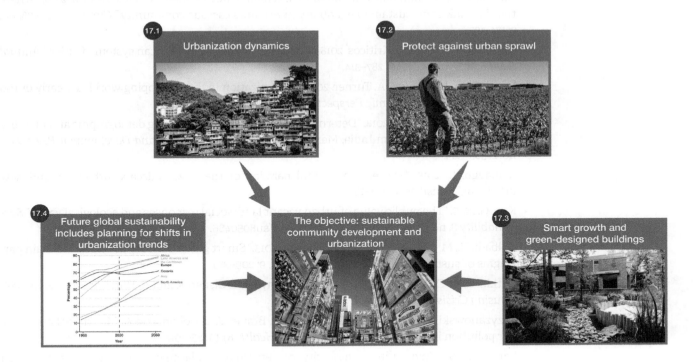

Sources: Joseph Shostell; See previous citations for image credits.

17.5 References

- Alam, M., F. Sharior, S. Ferdous, A. Ahsan, T. Ahmed, et al. 2020. "Strategies to connect low-income communities with the proposed sewerage network of the Dhaka sanitation improvement project, Bangladesh: a qualitative assessment of the perspectives of stakeholders." *Int J Environ Res Public Health* 17, no. 19: 7201; https://doi.org/10.3390/ijerph17197201.

- Arbex, M. A., U. P. Santos, L. C. Martins, P. H. N. Saldiva, L. A. A. Pereira, and A. L. F. Braga. 2012. "Air pollution and the respiratory system." *J Bras Pneumol* 38, no. 5: 643–655.

- Berube, A., A. Singer, J. H. Wilson, and W. H. Frey. 2006. *Metropolitan Policy Program Finding Exurbia: America's Fast-Growing Communities at the Metropolitan Fringe*. The Brookings Institution. Washington, DC.

- Brown, S. A. 2009. *Just Enough: Lessons in Living Green from Traditional Japan*; Kodansha International: Tokyo, Japan.

- Chen, R., P. Yin, X. Meng, C. Liu, L. Wang, X. Xu, J. A. Ross, L. A. Tse, Z. Zhao, H. Kan, M. Zhou, 2017. "Fine particulate air pollution and daily mortality. A nationwide analysis in 272 Chinese cities." *Am J Respir Crit Care Med* 196: 73–81.

- Chiang, Y., E. Hannum, and G. Kao. 2015. "It's not just about the money: gender and youth migration from rural China." *Chin Sociol Rev* 47, no. 2: 177–201.

- Chin, A. 2006. "Urban transformation of river landscapes in a global context." *Geomorphology* 79: 460–487.

- Ewing, R., M. Greenwald, M. Zhang, J. Walters, R. Cervero, L. Frank, S. Kassa, and J. Thomas. 2011. "Traffic generated by mixed-used developments-A six-region study using consistent built environmental measures." *Journal or Urban Planning* 137, no. 3. https://doi.org/10.1061/(ASCE)UP.1943-5444.0000068.

- Gaither, C. J., D. Himmelfarb, S. Hitchner, J. Schelhas, M. Shepherd, and K. C. Binita. 2016. "Where the sidewalk ends: sustainable mobility in Atlanta's cascade community." *City & Society* 28, no. 2: 174–197.

- Henderson, J. V., and S. Kriticos. 2018. "The development of the African system of cities." *Annual Review of Economics* 10: 287–314.

- Henderson, J. V., and M. A. Turner. 2020. "Urbanization in the developing world: too early or too slow?" *Journal of Economic Perspectives* 34, no. 3: 150–173.

- Jiang, L., and B. O'Neill. 2018. "Determinants of urban growth during demographic and mobility transition: evidence from India, Mexico, and the U.S." *Population and Development Review* 44, no. 2: 363–389.

- Kelbaugh, D. 2015. "The environmental paradox of the city, landscape urbanism, and new urbanism." *Consilience* 13: 1–15.

- Kim, G. 2016. "The public value of urban vacant land: social responses and ecological value." *Sustainability* 8, no. 5: 486. https://doi.org/10.3390/su8050486.

- Kolbadi, N., M. Mohammadi, and F. Namvar. 2015. "Smart growth theory as one of the main paradigms of sustainable city." *Int J Life Sci* 5, no. 9: 209–219.

- Kotkin, J., W. Cox, M. Lind, M. Winograd, A. Snyder, T. Cisneros, and R. Harrison. 2015. *America's Housing Crisis*. Chapman University Press.

- Krzyzanowski, M., J. S. Apte, S. P. Bonjour, M. Brauer, A. J. Cohen, and A. M. Prüss-Ustun. 2014. "Air pollution in the mega-cities." *Curr Envir Health Rpt* 1: 85–191.

- Lanari. 2019. "Envisioning a new city center: time, displacement, and Atlanta's suburban futures." *City & Society* 31, no. 3: 365–391.

- Leyk, S., J. H. Uhl, D. S. Connor, A. E. Braswell, N. Mietkiewicz, J. K. Balch, and M. Gutmann. 2020. "Two centuries of settlement and urban development in the United States." *Sci Adv* 6: eaba2937. https://doi.org/10.1126/sciadv.aba2937.

- Li, T., Z. Li, Y. Pan, and X. Wang. 2021. "Frangibility and potentiality: migrant worker families in China during COVID-19." *China Journal of Social Work* 14, no. 2: 100–132.

- Litman, T. 2015. *Analysis of Public Policies that Unintentionally Encourage and Subsidize Urban Sprawl*. Victoria Transport Policy Institute. Victoria, BC. Supporting paper commissioned by LSE Cities at the London School of Economics and Political Science, on behalf of the Global Commission on the Economy and Climate for the New Climate Economy Cities Program.

- Martos, A., R. Pacheco-Torres, J. Ordóñez, and E. Jadraque-Gago. 2016. "Towards successful environmental performance of sustainable cities: intervening sectors. A review." *Renew Sust Energ Rev* 57: 479–495

- Marzuki, A., and A. S. Jais. 2020. "Urbanization and the concerns for food security in Malaysia." *Planning Malaysia* 18, no. 3: 202–217.

- Meijer, J. R., M. A. J. Huigbregts, K. C. G. J. Schotten, and A. M. Schipper. 2018. "Global patterns of current and future road infrastructure." *Environmental Research Letters* 13: 064006. http://doi.org/10.1088/1748-9326/aabd42

- Miller, M. D. 2012. "The impacts of Atlanta's urban sprawl on forest cover and fragmentation." *Applied Geography* 23: 171–179.

- Moritz, M. 2016. "Open property regimes." *International Journal of the Commons* 10, no. 2: 688–708.

- Muth, R. F. 1969. *Cities and Housing*. University of Chicago Press. Chicago.

- Oliveri, R. C. 2016. "Single-family zoning, intimate association, and the right to choose household companions." *Florida Law Review* 67, no. 4: 1401–1453.

- O'Neill, K. 2011. From middle to upper class sprawl? Land use controls and changing patterns of real estate development in Northern New Jersey. *Annals of the Association of American Geographers* 101 (3): 609–624.

- Organisation for Economic Co-operation and Development (OECD). 2018. *Rethinking Urban Sprawl: Moving Towards Sustainable Cities*. OECD. Paris, France.

- Pernice, R. 2007. Urban sprawl in postwar Japan and the vision of the city based on the urban theories of the Metabolists' projects. *Journal of Asian Architecture and Building Engineering* 6 (2): 237–244.

- Rothstein, R. 2017. *The Color of Law A Forgotten History of How Our Government Segregated America*. Economic Policy Institute. Washington, DC.

- Science (authorless). 2016. "Rise to the City." *Science* 352, no. 6288: 906–907.

- Smart Growth America (SGA). 2014. *Measuring Sprawl* 2014. Smart Growth America Improving Lives by Improving Communities. Washington, DC.

- Steuteville, R. 2018. 25 *Great Ideas of New Urbanism*. Congress of New Urbanism. Washington, DC.

- Terada, T. 2017. "Urban sprawl or co-existence with nature: lessons from Japanese urban-rural mixture." *2017 IFLA Asia Pacific Regional Congress*.

- United Nations (UN). 2016. *Habitat III New Urban Agenda Draft Outcome Document for Adoption in Quito*. United Nations Conference on Housing and Sustainable Urban Development.

- United Nations (UN) Habitat. 2016. *Slum Almanac 2015 2016 Tracking Improvement in the Lives of Slum Dwellers*. Participatory Slum Upgrading Programme. UN-Habitat.

- United Nations Human Settlements Programme (UNHSP). 2019. *The Story of Shenzhen Its Economic, Social and Environmental Transformation*. United Nations Human Settlements Programme (UN-Habitat). Nairobi GPA Kenya.

- United States Supreme Court (USSC). 1926. *Village of Euclid v. Ambler Realty Co.* 272 U.S. 365. U.S. Supreme Court.

- Whiteman, G., D. R. de Vos, F. S. Chapin, V. Yli-Pelkonen, J. Niemelä, and B. C. Forbes. (2011) "Business strategies and the transition to low-carbon cities." *Bus Strateg Environ* 20, no. 4: 251–265.

- World Health Organization (WHO). 2005. *WHO Air Quality guidelines for particulate matter, ozone, nitrogen dioxide and sulfur dioxide*. Global update 2005. World Health Organization, Geneva.

- Wu, Y., X. Zhang, and L. Shen. 2011. "The impact of urbanization policy on land use change: a scenario analysis." *Cities* 28, no. 2: 147–159.

- Yaya, O. S., O. G. Awolaja, I. M. Okedina, and X. V. Vo. 2020. "Air quality level in California US State: persistence and seasonality." *Theoretical and Applied Climatology* 142: 1471–1479.

- Zhu, Y., W. Zhongmin, M. Wang, Y. Du, and F. Cai. 2012. "Do migrants really save more? Understanding the impact of remittances on savings in rural China." *The Journal of Development Studies* 48, no. 5: 654–672.

CHAPTER 18
Sustainable Economics

Case Study: Singapore's Use of Sustainable Economics

Nestled next to Malaysia and near the bustling economies of China and India, Singapore has adeptly used its geographical position and **sustainable economics** for success (see Figure 18.1). It is nurturing a sustainable economy underpinned by positive **economic growth** (increased capacity of economy to produce goods and services) that is environmentally friendly and socially responsible. A nation's **economy** refers to its system of production, distribution, and consumption of goods and services. The total value of the goods and services Singapore produces—the **gross domestic product (GDP)**—is massive ($392 billion) despite its being smaller than the city of Lexington, Kentucky. For comparison, a much larger United States (13,500 times larger) has a GDP of $21.4 trillion, which is only about fifty times more than Singapore's. This small island nation enjoys one of the leading gross domestic products (GDP) per capita ($65,234 USD). Compare China's per capita GDP of $9,608. Singapore supports a thriving air transport industry that receives over 60 million passengers per year, and the nation's premier port—the world's busiest—is the envy of Southeast Asia. It is also one of the cleanest countries in Asia. How has Singapore had such phenomenal economic success relying on a sustainable economic strategy?

Their blueprint for prosperous growth reflects lessons learned from a history of environmental degradation exacerbated by colonization in the nineteenth century, occupation during World War II, poor infrastructure, and population growth. By the mid-nineteenth century, Singapore had lost 90 percent of its forests and the prized Singapore River and its tributaries were heavily polluted. In 1950, Singapore was a poor developing nation of one million people. While impoverished, it grew to close to two million by the time of its independence in 1965. These earlier years were a reckoning, for every additional person required resources in a very limited area. For example, it became apparent that there was not enough physical space for everyone to own a car. Between 1961 and 1975, the number of privately owned cars swelled from about 70,000 to 275,000, and projected growth indicated the trend would continue for the foreseeable future. Where would these cars park and how would they affect pollution and traffic? Water and air pollution worsened, and the number of privately owned vehicles increased so much that vehicle congestion, smog, and general dismal air quality were negatively affecting living conditions and economic prosperity. Cognizant of these facts, Singapore began to implement economic tools that nudged its citizens and companies to be environmentally responsible while pursuing their goals (MSE 2016).

Singapore's long-term sustainable economic plan aims to build a green economy, lower the nation's carbon footprint, and become a zero-waste nation. As part of this plan, in 2003, Singapore implemented **congestion pricing** to reduce traffic congestion and its related air pollution. In congestion pricing, drivers are charged fees based on speed of traffic, time of day, and location in the city. Electronic gantries located at every road entering the inner city detect windshield-mounted transponders and then instantly charge car owners as they pass (see Figure 18.2). Financially conscious drivers tend to avoid peak traffic times, or they use Singapore's public transportation system. The result is a substantial reduction in traffic and the smog it produces. Nitrogen dioxide and particulate matter in Singapore's air have declined by 18.7 percent and 13.7 percent, respectively. The rate of childhood asthma has also declined—by 50 percent (Simeonova et al. 2019).

sustainable economics

A sustainable economy underpinned by positive economic growth that is environmentally friendly and socially responsible.

economic growth

Increased capacity of economy to produce goods and services.

economy

A system of production, distribution, and consumption of goods and services.

gross domestic product (GDP)

The total value of the goods and services produced in a nation.

congestion pricing

Drivers are charged fees based on speed of traffic, time of day, and location in a city. Economic tool intended to reduce traffic and associated pollution.

FIGURE 18.1

Despite steady population growth and being an economic powerhouse, Singapore has become one of the cleanest cities in Asia. (A) Location of Singapore in Southeast Asia. (B) Singapore's population growth from 1950 through 2020. (C) Aerial view of Singapore with cargo ships in the background waiting to enter the world's busiest maritime port.

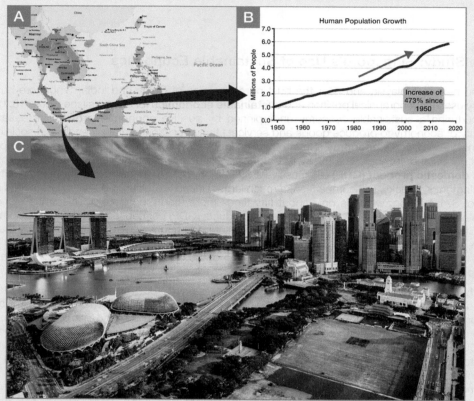

Sources: © Shutterstock, Inc.; Joseph Shostell; data from https://www.worldometers.info/world-population/singapore-population/; gnohz/Shutterstock.com

Singapore's congestion pricing model was well ahead of the global community, but its success has inspired other countries to try it. Now, this economic tool is being tested in London, Stockholm, Milan, and soon will be in New York City as well. A seven-month pilot study in Stockholm resulted in the decline of inner-city traffic by 20–25 percent. A single day after the end of this study, they made the system permanent.

FIGURE 18.2

Singapore uses congestion pricing to limit the number of cars on roads and, indirectly, to reduce air pollution. (A) A street sign informs drivers of the days and times that congestion fees are collected. (B) An electronic toll-collection gantry (ERP = electronic road pricing) on one of the eighty entry points into central Singapore. Implementation of this economic tool has significantly reduced traffic congestion.

Source: © Shutterstock, Inc.; EQRoy/Shutterstock.com

Respiratory illnesses, air pollution, and lost productivity are all examples of **externalities**—side effects endured by other members of a population. Costs of these effects (**external costs**), including health care and environmental remediation, are not included in the cost of owning and driving a car, at least not in most countries. The typical price of a car only accounts for **internal costs**—costs associated with producing, marketing, shipping, and selling. If external costs were included in the market price, more Americans would opt out of vehicle ownership.

In 1991, Singapore implemented two additional economic tools to encourage greater use of public transportation and further reduce pollution and traffic congestion. These tools require car owners to cover the full cost of driving. The Land Transport Management Authority maintains a tightly controlled vehicle quota system. It determines the number of vehicles permitted in Singapore, and through a bidding system has created an effective supply and demand tool that has driven down the rate of growth in vehicle ownership and helped free up road space in the city center (see Figure 18.3). Prior to owning a car in Singapore, one must first purchase a Certificate of Entitlement (COE), but only a limited number of these certificates are available each year (the quota set by the Transport Authority). Prospective buyers place bids for available COEs. Bids always exceed the number of available COEs, and bids can exceed the market value of a car. The COE and several other lofty fees, plus congestion pricing, encourage many Singaporeans to forgo car ownership (see Table 18.1). The growth rate of vehicle ownership has dropped from a historical high of 9 percent to zero percent today. Less than 10 percent of Singaporeans own cars, well below American cities such as New York City (45 percent), Philadelphia (70.5 percent), Orlando (91.8 percent), and Frisco, Texas (98 percent).

TABLE 18.1
What are the expenses to register and own a brand new Toyota Camry that has a market value of $35,000 (USD)?

Estimated Breakdown of Costs for a Toyota Camry	Singapore USD (SD) USD= United States dollar SD = Singapore dollar	California USD
Sticker price of car at dealership	35,000 (47,950)	35,000
Excise tax (customs duty) of 20%	7,200 (9,864)	N/A
Certificate of entitlement	34,558 (47,304)	N/A
Additional registration fee	32,979 (45,130)	N/A
Additional fees/tax	3,245 (4,442)	3,175
Estimated total	112,982 (154,652)	38,175

Singapore's National Environment Agency (NEA) regulates the emissions of six pollutants in vehicular exhaust. The government also wallops car owners with heavy fines ($2,000–$5,000 SD) for violating vehicle emission laws, or for failing to recycle or remove a vehicle from Singapore when its associated COE expires (ten years after purchase). Drivers who give up their COE prior to the full ten years are entitled to a rebate. In essence, with congestion pricing, COEs, excise taxes, and vehicular exhaust fees, Singapore has monetized externalities related to vehicle ownership such that owners shoulder the unseen costs of their car use. Recycling the car at the end of use supports a **circular economy** and conserves limited resources and space. A circular economy is the antithesis of the conventional, linear approach of take, make waste, and dispose (see Chapter 16).

externalities

Costs to other members of society not covered by the user of some product or service. This is also referred to as external cost.

external costs

Costs not covered in the market price on account of externalities.

internal costs

Costs used in the determination of the market price of a product; the cost of production (energy, materials, labor), marketing, shipping, and other expenses involved in bringing the product to market.

circular economy

An economy based on the design of sustainable products and services, supportive of reusing, repairing, and recycling products. Materials and energy from old, worn-out products funnel into the production of new products.

FIGURE 18.3

Singapore's Land Transport Authority controls the number of vehicles in the country. Purchasing a Certificate of Entitlement (COE) is required prior to car ownership, but the Authority offers only a limited number of COEs per year. Hopeful car owners must place bids for one of the available COEs. Because there are always more bids than available COEs (the established quota), the amount paid for a COE can easily exceed the market value of a car. (A) Supply and demand of COEs from 2002 through 2021. The green bars indicate the yearly quota of COEs for small cars. The purple line indicates the average cost of a COE in a given year, again for small cars. (B) Graphed relationship between the quota and price of COE. When quota is high, demand is low; conversely, when the quota is low, the demand is high. This relationship is an outcome of demand (the number of bids) always exceeding supply (quota). (C) An image of a Honda Civic, an example of a small common car in Singapore.

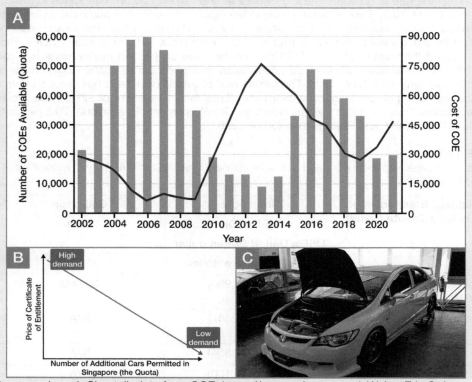

Sources: Joseph Shostell, data from COE, https://coe.sgcharts.com/; Walter Eric Sy/ Shutterstock.com

Singapore also sees air pollution, greenhouse gas emissions, and the effects of climate change as existential threats. It is a tiny country bounded by water—and is therefore unable to relocate its people to other areas in the country. Rising sea levels due to climate change, in particular, impose a major environmental threat for Singapore. Much of Singapore is no more than 49 feet (15 m) above sea level. As a response to the threat of rising sea levels and flooding, it has signed the Paris Accord and pledged to curb greenhouse gas emissions. In 2021, Singapore began using economic tools to incentivize its citizens to purchase electric cars instead of internal combustion engine vehicles. In essence, the rebate reduces the cost of car ownership between $9,000 and $20,000. The goal is to phase out fossil fuel–powered cars by 2040.

Events in Singapore demonstrate that a booming economy and environmental stewardship are not mutually exclusive. In this chapter, we explore sustainable economic topics, including the economic value of the environment (see Section 1), cost of environmental degradation (see Section 2), and development of a sustainable economy (see Section 3) for the benefit of present and future generations (see Section 4).

18.1 The Economic Value of the Environment

Learning Objectives

1. Explain why ecosystem goods and services are necessary for economic growth.
2. Compare and contrast economic theories.
3. Assess society's progression toward a sustainable economy.

Our opening story provides examples of how an economy can have positive effects on the environment. In Singapore and elsewhere, economic tools are applied to incentivize sustainable behavior. Think beyond money, for **economics** is less about money and more about the study of people and the choices they make. Individuals, companies, and governments all use economics when making decisions. For instance, before the Singapore government capped the number of vehicles, built a system of electronic toll gantries, and improved a public transport system, it first weighed the cost of the suggested changes against the benefits. It decided the benefits outweighed the costs. Economics comes with two main assumptions: resources are finite and everything has a cost. An **economic resource** is anything used to produce goods and services in the economy. Laborers (people), land, raw materials, water, oil, buildings, and tools are all examples of resources, as are ecosystem goods and services. Our global economy is dependent on all of these resources.

economics

Social science interested in the production, distribution, and consumption of goods and services.

economic resource

Anything used to produce goods and services within an economy.

The World's Economies Rely on Ecosystem Goods and Services

The world's economies rely on ecosystem goods and services. Many economists and environmental scientists agree that one of our greatest challenges may well be dealing with the economic invisibility of nature. Trees, wetlands, pollinators, and other components of natural, healthy ecosystems provide valuable services to us free of charge. For instance, the water cycle (i.e., rainfall) supports a global agricultural industry that produces hundreds of billions of dollars of food each year (see Chapter 1). Without a monetary value assigned to an ecosystem service to align with other priced services and goods of an economy, society will continue to grapple with the true value of the service—and the ecosystem itself. Somewhat in contrast, society does place monetary values on ecosystem goods, also known as natural goods or **natural capital** (resources from the environment). In fact, the supply and demand of natural goods help drive the economy. The economy works because things—goods—have prices.

A steady supply of services and goods stems from healthy, resilient, and biodiverse ecosystems. Therefore, maintaining Earth's ecosystems is in our best interest, and in the interest of our economies (see "Critical Thinking Activity: Deep Wisdom in a Children's Book"). Singapore (see "Case Study: Singapore's Use of Sustainable Economics") came to this conclusion, for example, by observing the link between the productivity of its fisheries and the health of coastal waters. Singapore's 120 coastal aquaculture farms, which provide 85 percent of the country's local food-fish production, relies on a healthy marine ecosystem. Environmental degradation caused by oil spills, heavy nutrient inputs, and harmful algal blooms negatively affects the productivity of these aquacultures. Singapore also reasoned it was much easier to attract foreign investors if it had an aesthetically inviting, green city. Their **sustainable development** plan has helped to lure more than

natural capital

Natural resources; resources from the environment.

sustainable development

Development supportive of society and the environment for today and the future such that the environment can indefinitely maintain ecosystem services.

7,000 multinational companies to its financial center, now the world's fourth largest. Sustainable development refers to development—including economic growth—that both supports society and protects the environment for today and the future. Singapore is often called the garden city, or the city within a garden, because approximately 50 percent of it is carefully maintained green space. Very similarly, a healthy, pollution-free ecosystem encourages tourism.

Critical Thinking Activity: Deep Wisdom in a Children's Book

Seasoned primary school teachers have an arsenal of tools in their "education belt" before they stroll into the classroom. Children's books are examples of these tools. One in particular, *The Lorax* by Dr. Seuss (1971), breaks down the complexities of the relationship between economic growth and the environment. The aim of this critical thinking exercise is to interpret the meaning and value of *The Lorax* to primary school children (see Figure 18.4). To begin, listen and watch Hollywood actor Danny DeVito read *The Lorax* here. Next, answer the following questions:

1. Why has the young entrepreneur failed to acknowledge the long-term value of truffula trees to his business operation?
2. What might the Lorax have done to assist the entrepreneur in helping to maintain a forest of truffula trees? Like many a good book, *The Lorax* has been controversial. The logging industry points out that the book portrays its activities unfairly because this industry plants new trees, and its plans include the long-term presence of forests. Do you agree?

FIGURE 18.4
Deep wisdom in a children's book. (A) Actor Danny Devito poses next to Dr. Seuss's character, the Lorax, which he voices in the movie *The Lorax*. (B) In Montreal, a rally of protestors display the Lorax and express their outrage against environmental pollution.

Sources: Featureflash Photo Agency/Shutterstock.com; themajestic/Shutterstock.com

Economic Theories and Sustainability

classical economic theory (CET)

An economic theory that approaches the determination of product value based on production costs alone. CET preceded neoclassical economics.

There are strong ties between economic growth and the environment. These ties may seem invisible because ecosystem services are free, and we have always relied on nature's goods and services. Economic growth expands the size of the economy, and when equally shared, across the population, raises everyone's standard of living. However, economic growth is not equally shared and there are many examples of nonsustainable economics pertaining to both classical and neoclassical economic theories. **Classical economic theory (CET)**, brought forth by Karl Marx, Adam Smith, Thomas Malthus, and other economists, relies on a narrow, objective approach to determine a product's value. According to this theory, the value of a Honda Civic would reflect the cost of production, which, more or less, is the cost of the car's components, the labor used to piece the car together, and the cost of energy used during the production process.

Then, beginning in the 1870s, **neoclassical economic theory** took hold and began to account for the subjective cost a person places on a product they desire. Classical economic theory could not account for the market value of a product, which could be higher than the production costs. As it turned out, consumers were willing to pay more for a product in short supply. Neoclassical economics lacks concepts of sustainability, social inclusion, and ethics. In societies without these three goals, the divide between the poor and rich continues to grow, and economic growth comes with the expense of environmental degradation. Both classical and neoclassical economics are only concerned with the production, distribution, and consumption of goods and services. These theories are short-sighted because society will eventually pay for the aftermath of a linear economy, and that price will be severe. This linear, nonsustainable approach to economics is described as "take-make-waste" or "cradle-to-grave."

Ecological economics describes an economy of a sustainable society that incorporates human well-being, health of ecosystems, and environmental justice (see video link: "Ecological Economics"). Ecological economists point to the undue harm to ecosystems that occurs when the goal is only production. They advocate for prices that fully capture the costs of all goods and services—including external costs (see "Case Study: Singapore's Use of Sustainable Economics"). This approach fosters a **green economy**, which is circular rather than linear and places value in recycling and the regeneration of ecosystem goods (see Figure 18.5). Ecological economics prefers to use the **Genuine Progress Indicator** (GPI) rather than GDP because it measures vital environmental and social factors in addition to the production of goods and services.

FIGURE 18.5
Linear vs. circular economies. (A) Classical and neoclassical economic theories describe a linear "take-make-waste" approach to economic growth. (B) In contrast, in ecological economics, a circular, green economy drives economic growth.

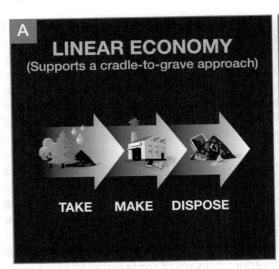
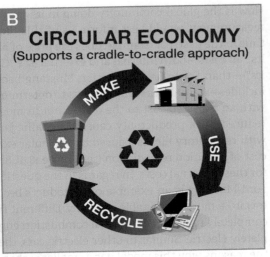

Source: © Shutterstock, Inc.

When a town, city, or nation adopts an ecological economics perspective and therefore acknowledges the dependence of sustained economic growth on resilient, healthy ecosystems, it strives to move toward a sustainable economy. Furthermore, our understanding of the interdependence of environmental systems encourages widening this objective to include the global environment in perpetuity. The aim is to maintain economic growth and simultaneously nurture and protect the local and global environments for the equal benefit of current and future generations.

---

neoclassical economic theory

An approach to economics that accounts for the subjective cost a person places on a desirable product in addition to production cost.

ecological economics

A subdiscipline of economics that is concerned with human well-being, health of ecosystems, and environmental justice in addition to the production, distribution, and consumption of goods and services.

green economy

A circular economy, which places value on recycling and the regeneration of ecosystem goods.

Genuine Progress Indicator

A metric of a country's economic growth and overall well-being; based on the value of products and services including negative externalities (i.e., environmental pollution and social distress).

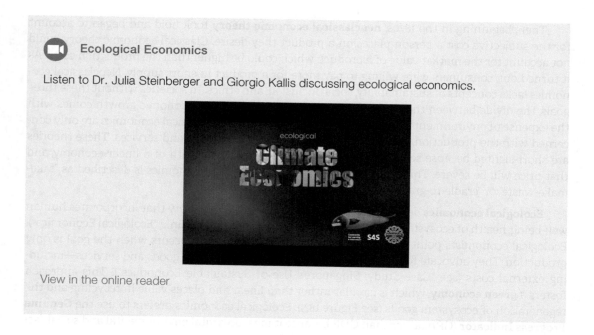

Ecological Economics

Listen to Dr. Julia Steinberger and Giorgio Kallis discussing ecological economics.

View in the online reader

A Measurement of Our Progress Toward a Sustainable Economy

cost–benefit analysis

An evaluation of a project (or action) by comparing its total estimated costs to its total benefits.

How is the global community doing in its progress toward a sustainable economy? What type of measurement would best inform us of this progress? *Progress* means where we are relative to a time in the past. For example, does the price of a Ford Mustang in the 2020s more adequately reflect its full costs—both internal and external (see "Case Study: Singapore's Use of Sustainable Economics")—than Ford's first-generation Mustang back in the early 1960s? A **cost–benefit analysis** that includes externalities would help us to determine the answer to this question. A new vehicle comes with an expected cost to the owner, but in most countries this price does not include the cost of reduced work productivity caused by traffic jams. Nor does it cover health-care costs associated with respiratory illness (caused by vehicular exhaust), the cost of traffic accident fatalities, or the cost of pollution remediation (see Figure 18.6). Singapore is the country that most closely accounts for these external costs. In regards to the question about the Ford Mustang, the answer is "yes." The Ford Mustang is an example of a product's becoming more sustainable and supporting progress toward a more sustainable economy. Different from the Mustang models of the 1960s, which each completely relied on an internal combustion engine, the Mustang Mach-E, released in 2022, is completely electric. Similar to other electric cars, the Mach-E has no tailpipe emissions. This is one of the reasons why this model has a smaller carbon footprint than any of Ford's earlier Mustang models.

FIGURE 18.6
Automobile production, distribution, and consumption are part of the economy. (A) People with sufficient finances can purchase the vehicles of their choice, and in doing so, play a role in driving the economic engine. The price consumers pay accounts for materials and energy used in production and distribution but does not account for external costs such as (B) remediating emissions from tailpipes or (C) health care associated with respiratory illness caused by this pollution.

Sources: MikeDotta/Shutterstock.com; © Shutterstock, Inc.

Waste production and energy use are two additional indicators of society's progress toward a greener economy. Keeping to the theme of cars, does the production of cars today generate less waste than it use to? Yes. Again, we return to the example of the Ford Mustang. Ford has significantly reduced the amount of waste (during production) per vehicle going to landfills. Today's Mustang models also contain more sustainable materials than did the Mustang models of the 1960s. Since 2008, every Mustang has had sustainable soybean-based foam rather than petroleum-based materials in its seat cushions, backs, and headrests. What about energy? Does the Ford Company use less nonrenewable energy to manufacture its Mustangs than the Ford Company did in the past? Yes, Ford's Sustainability Committee has helped the company to set and obtain goals of reducing the Ford Company's reliance on nonrenewable energy. During the 1960s, Ford only relied on nonrenewable energy to run its operations, but this has changed. By the time of writing this book, Ford was close to reducing its nonrenewable energy use by one-third. By, 2035, Ford plans to be completely reliant on renewable energy.

In ecological economics, a green society places monetary value on recycling and regeneration; ideally, the life of every product from concept to endpoint would be circular, and no waste would be generated. How are we doing on recycling cars? It is not 100 percent, but compared to other products, the percentage is relatively high. In the United States, more than 95 percent of the vehicles that reach the end of their lifespans are recycled. A greener economy encourages sustainable management practices in auto-salvage yards, and fewer discarded vehicles in waste sites. All points of the manufacturing process and the use of the product would support a healthy environment and continued economic growth.

Key Takeaways

- A nation's economy is its system of production, distribution, and consumption of goods and services. The raw materials for the products we use come from the environment, and ecosystem services such as soil formation, pollination, and water purification are required by multiple industries. Therefore, a nation's economy depends on ecosystem goods and services.

- Ecological economics, unlike classical and neoclassical economic theories, places monetary value on sustainability, social inclusion, and ethics.

- Although we are currently facing many environmental challenges around the world, evidence supports that the global community as a whole is progressing toward a sustainable economy.

- GDP measures total market value of produced goods and services. GPI (Genuine Progress Indicator) also includes environmental and social factors.

18.2 The Cost of Environmental Degradation

Learning Objectives

1. Comprehend the limited ability of nature to assimilate wastes and replenish goods, and the association of these limits with external costs.
2. Explore why it is challenging for companies to remain competitive when they absorb external costs.
3. Explain external costs related to municipal solid waste, climate change, and agriculture.

high-throughput economy

A nonsustainable, linear economy with an emphasis on maximizing production and increasing economic growth. Based on a take-make-waste approach.

Today's global **high-throughput economy**—a linear economy that emphasizes maximum production and economic growth—is a far cry from a sustainable circular economy. In fact, Daniel O'Neill discovered that no modern country runs a full steady-state economy, which is an economy in which resource use is steady and within ecological limits (O'Neill 2015). O'Neill analyzed ten years of data and used sixteen indicators to determine how close 180 nations were to running steady-state economies. His findings support those by other authors as well as evidence of environmental degradation observed with our own eyes. The collective footprint of human activities—direct and indirect—exceeds the capability of the world to replenish goods and assimilate wastes. Our former and current economic strategies are pushing Earth at least 50 percent beyond its capabilities (Borucke et al. 2013). In this section, we evaluate some of the costs of our environmental footprints (see "Bringing It Closer to Home: Calculating My Ecological Footprint"). Notice that "footprints" is in plural form. This is because the total cost of human environmental impacts is an aggregate of the cost of smaller footprints on specific natural resources such as water and environmental factors such as climate (see Figure 18.7).

Bringing It Closer to Home: Calculating My Ecological Footprint

All of us have an ecological footprint from our daily activities. There are direct and indirect effects from our selection of foods, water and energy use, the type of home we inhabit, and the transportation we use. The seemingly negligible impacts of our individual actions become colossal when pooled with those of the rest of humankind. If everyone followed your routine activities and decisions, what would our collective ecological footprint be? Would it be less than, equal to, or greater than what the world could replenish and assimilate? To begin your assessment, go to the Global Footprint Network here. Click on the footprint in the middle of the screen where it states, "TAKE THE FIRST STEP." Answer thirteen questions about your food, home, trash, and transportation to obtain your results. The results are given in number of Earths needed if everyone in the world followed your style of living. Did you score within the capabilities of what Earth can sustain?

Now, determine how well your data compares to others living in your country. Select "EXPLORE YOUR DATA." Click on your home country. These data look a little different from those of your individual calculation. On the left, in green, is a numerical value representing the biocapacity per person. In the middle, in red, is the ecological footprint per person for the selected country. If this value is greater than the biocapacity per person, then the country's activities are exceeding the threshold of what Earth can provide. You may find that your individual footprint follows your nation's trend. However, if you live a sustainable lifestyle, well within Earth's ability to regenerate and assimilate, your ecological footprint will be significantly less than the average. In one last step, click on "solutions" to further your understanding of solutions. Read the text under "City" and "Energy" and then click on "Learn More" under "City" and "Energy."

FIGURE 18.7
Humankind's total environmental footprint consists of many significant footprints, each with its own cost to the environment and human welfare.

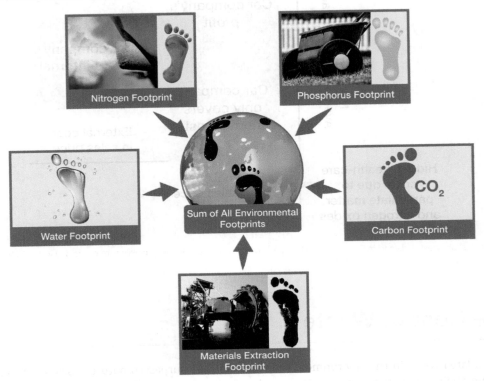

Sources: Joseph Shostell; © Shutterstock, Inc.

In today's economy, it is easy for corporations to direct the external costs of their actions onto natural ecosystems and society (see Figure 18.8). Doing so creates a lean bottom line and gives the company a competitive edge against economically and socially responsible companies. All else being equal (e.g., no subsidies), a company that absorbs external costs of their products is economically disadvantaged. For example, a car company may choose to be environmentally responsible and decide to cover health-care costs related to particulate matter and nitrogen oxides emissions (external costs), but they also want to maintain their same profit margin. Therefore, they increase the price of their car, thus passing these external costs to the consumer. The increase means the company will lose price-competitiveness—and potential customers. A second car company may decide to cover external costs but elect to not raise the price of their car. They maintain their price-competitiveness (and customers), but their profit margin decreases. In both scenarios, the car company puts itself at an economic disadvantage relative to other companies that are not as socially responsible.

Companies generally disregard ownership of externalities, and this disregard contributes to society's overall environmental footprint. Very similarly, consumers ignore the environmental effects of the products and services they value and use. In our current economic system, most consumers favor the purchase of the cheapest products, which are typically the least sustainable.

FIGURE 18.8
Externalities associated with cars and other products are rarely covered in the price consumers pay. (A) Market price does not include external costs; (B) True cost does.

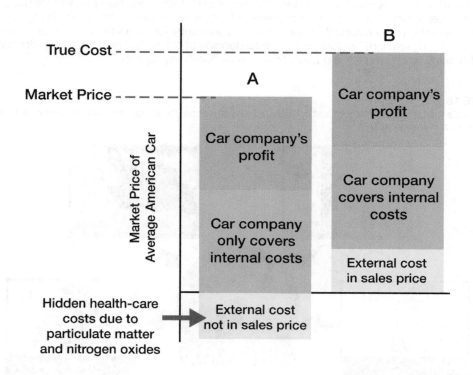

Sources: Joseph Shostell; data from Brand, C., and Hunt, A., 2018. The health costs of air pollution from cars and vans. Technical Report. DO: 10.13140/RG.2.2.25409.86886.

The Cost of Waste

Accumulated waste in the environment indicates we have surpassed nature's assimilative capacity—the ability of nature to break down and assimilate waste without detrimental effects. No matter how you analyze it, municipal solid waste (MSW) and other forms of waste cost money. There are direct costs of managing it, and there are external costs of not managing it effectively. Globally, we produce over two billion tons of MSW annually, and this number is projected to increase to 3.4 billion tons (a 70 percent increase) by the middle of this century (see Chapter 16). How much MSW we generate varies geographically and correlates with gross domestic product (GDP). As GDP per person increases, so does waste.

In waste management, there are infrastructure investments and operational expenses. Waste employees receive a wage for their labor, and trucks used in wealthier areas to haul waste can cost upward of $250,000 each. These trucks transport waste from residences to a transfer station—a temporary storage area—or directly to a landfill. A basic transfer station is an investment of $500,000, and a new landfill requires several times this amount or more depending on size and ability to compost, incinerate, and recover (transform) energy that otherwise would have been lost in waste. Who covers these expenses (see Figure 18.9)? According to the World Bank, local governments shoulder about half of these costs, 10–25 percent are covered by the private sector, and, on average, 20 percent is subsidized by the central government. A **subsidy** is a form of support to an industry, business, or individual, usually in the form of cash or a tax reduction. User fees and money earned from selling recyclables further contribute to covering waste management costs. A basic waste management service in Southeast Asia (see "Case Study: Singapore's Use of Sustainable Economics") charges roughly $100 per metric ton. This amount is far less than the estimated $375 of environmental damage caused per metric ton of untreated waste released to the environment (McKinsey 2016). Open dumping, which accounts for the endpoint of fully one-third of all global MSW, is not only a huge environmental problem, but also a costly financial mistake.

subsidy

Form of governmental support to an industry, business, or individual, usually in the form of cash or a tax reduction.

FIGURE 18.9

Municipal solid waste (MSW) is a conglomeration of used and broken down products that have long-term management costs, and whose contents can have negative effects on the environment and human health. Bearers of internal and external costs of municipal solid waste cover costs of a variety of MSW endpoints (landfilled, open dumping, composted/recycled, & incinerated). Percentages represent the relative amounts of global MSW going to each end point.

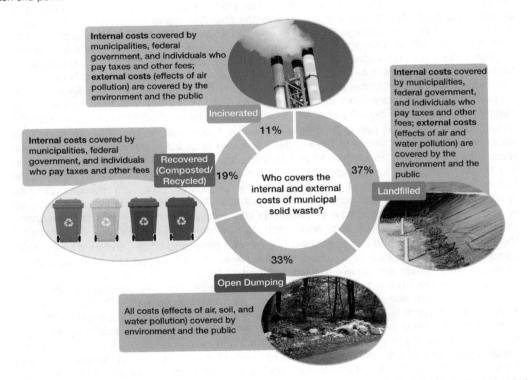

Sources: Joseph Shostell; © Shutterstock, Inc.; data from The World Bank, https://datatopics.worldbank.org/what-a-waste/trends_in_solid_waste_management.html.

In the United States, landfill managers charge an average fee (a "tipping" fee) of about $55 per ton of garbage disposed at their landfills. Then there are the collection fees, which vary across states and urban areas. For instance, NYC pays about $100 per ton to collect refuse and $200 per ton to collect recyclables. Profitability is a key challenge to the U.S. recycling system, more so now because there are fewer international buyers of America's recyclables. In response to increases in waste, rising waste management costs, and a threatened recycling system, lawmakers introduced a bill (the Recovery Act) in 2020 to establish a recycling infrastructure program within the Environmental Protection Agency (H.R. 2020). If this had passed, $500 million over five years would have helped states strengthen their recycling infrastructure and promote recycling programs (an example of subsidies). Some of the provisions of the bill, such as funding for battery recycling programs and recycling education (more subsidies), did make it into the $1.2 trillion infrastructure bill passed by Congress and signed by President Joseph Biden in 2021.

Similar to the United States, Singapore (see "Case Study: Singapore's Use of Sustainable Economics") separates recyclables from other solid waste; however, Singapore's recycling rate (60 percent) is double the United States' and triple New York City's. Different from New York City, where residents do not cover expenses related to waste collection, households in Singapore are charged a uniform fee for waste collection services. In Singapore, post-recycling, sanitation trucks collect all remaining solid waste and haul it to four waste-to-energy incineration plants. The ash produced by incineration is then hauled to waiting barges parked at the Tuas Marine Transfer Station for shipment to the Semakau Landfill—an extension of Pulau Semakau Island located 25 km (15.5 mi) south of Singapore (see "Critical Thinking Activity: Indirect Cost of Municipal Solid Waste (MSW) in Singapore").

Critical Thinking Activity: Indirect Cost of Municipal Solid Waste (MSW) in Singapore

Singapore has a large population in a limited geographical area, so solid waste management is an extra challenge. In this exercise, we analyze the effectiveness of Singapore's management strategy for MSW. This strategy involves the closing of all landfills in Singapore and shipping solid waste to a different island. Decades later, the now-closed landfills still incur costs related to protecting land and water resources from potential leaks. Incinerating all nonrecyclable MSW reduces its overall volume by 90 percent, and some energy is recovered. However, an assessment by National University of Singapore states these benefits are outweighed by the air pollution that the incinerators produce (Tan and Khoo 2006). The ash from incineration is dumped offshore at the Semakau Landfill, which has a capacity of 63 million cubic meters (82 million yd^3). The landfill is part of the sea, enclosed by a rock wall. An impermeable membrane lines the bottom of the landfill to protect the water and local biodiversity. Do you think these measures are sufficient to contain MSW? Is there any evidence of MSW ash contaminating the environment and causing indirect costs? Use one or all three of the search suggestions below to locate peer-reviewed papers that provide an answer. They are: researchgate.net, scholar.google.com, and your school library's databases (such as jstor). For ResearchGate, go to your search engine bar and type in "ResearchGate" followed by these words with one space between each one: municipal, solid waste, ash, toxic; then click Enter. Browse the results for those marked with a green box containing R^G, select a promising article, and then speed-read (browse) its abstract, which is a summary of the paper. What is apparent is that many items in your search results are papers that are not part of ResearchGate.net. These can be useful too, if they are from a bona fide, peer-reviewed source. For your second search, go to scholar.google.com and type in the same search terms that you used for ResearchGate and click Enter. The result is a list of many thousands of peer-reviewed works. Like before, browse through the top entries and select those that are promising. Narrow your search by adding in Semakau Landfill. If you locate a promising abstract and have access to a full paper, read the paper. Lastly, use your school's library to access peer-reviewed information. Almost all schools have access to searchable databases. One particularly useful one is jstor.org. Again, enter key terms and click on Search. Now armed with search results, answer the initial question: Is there any evidence of MSW ash contaminating the environment and causing indirect costs?

The Cost of Climate Change

What is the cost of climate change? Having an excess of carbon dioxide and other greenhouse gases in the atmosphere has economic consequences. The domino effect of warmer air temperatures followed by melting of glacial ice sheets and rising sea levels is probably the most recognized consequence of anthropogenic greenhouse gas emissions. Singapore (see "Case Study: Singapore's Use of Sustainable Economics") sees rising sea levels as an existential threat. It's low elevation places it at risk of inundation and the resulting loss of property, livelihoods, and lives. To protect its assets and culture, Singapore has already spent hundreds of millions of dollars, and pledges to spend billions more. In 2008, at a cost of $226 million, it constructed a 350-meter-long (380 yd) barrage across the Marina Channel to protect low-lying urban areas from high tides. The barrage also secures a long-lasting source of freshwater with a new freshwater reservoir that has a surface area of 240 ha (590 ac) (Moh and Su 2009). Singapore has also invested in the Changi East Project, which is a 1,080 hectare extension of its current airport to further boost economic activity (Chu et al. 2009). The ambitious project, which claims land from the sea, began in 1991 and is projected to be completed in 2030. When finished, a new airport terminal will be built 5.5 m (18 ft) above sea level, which will protect the airport against future flooding caused by rising sea levels.

At the same time Singapore began this project, Professor Samuel Fankhauser from the London School of Economics and Political Science took on the daunting task of estimating monetary damage of global warming (1992). He analyzed dryland loss, capital loss, coastal wetland loss, species and ecosystem losses, effects on agriculture, shift of forests, effects on fisheries, changes in the energy industry, change in water demand, effects on human health, largescale migration of displaced people, and natural disasters (droughts and floods). His calculated estimate was equal to about 1.3–1.5 percent of the world's **gross national product (GNP)**, which includes the total monetary value of products and services at home (GDP) and abroad. Another model by Nordhaus and Boyer (1999) estimates climate damage to the global economy at 0.267 percent of the Gross Domestic Product. If we input the World Bank's 2019 estimate of global GDP ($87.75 trillion) into Nordhaus's and Boyer's equation, climate change costs $234 billion annually. Damage from hurricanes accounts for a substantial amount of this cost in some years (Frame 2020).

> **gross national product (GNP)**
>
> Total monetary value of production and services at home.

External Costs of Agricultural Activities

The economic challenge of making a living in national and global markets incentivizes farmers to boost their crop yields using techniques that often have a relatively low direct cost. Indiscriminate application of cheap pesticides and irrigation that depends on an infinite supply of "free" water have severely disrupted ecosystem functioning in agricultural areas, as well as in ecosystems that connect with them. The question for us here is, what is the economic impact of these common agricultural practices on the environment, human health, and future farming?

A host of studies documents the increase in pesticide use among farmers to prevent losses of their crops to pests. Initial applications typically increase crop yield by 20–30 percent, and thereby increase the farmer's income from market crops. However, the burden of unsustainable pesticide use (see Chapter 8) in the United States, and elsewhere has far-reaching economic implications (see Figure 18.10). Just in the United States, each year pesticide use costs $1.1 billion in health care for those afflicted with exposure-related illnesses and diseases. Another $1.5 billion, again per year, is attributed to crop losses caused by pests that have evolved resistance to pesticides. Pesticides that drift to unintended crops also cause $1.1 billion in crop losses. Bird deaths caused by consumption of pesticide-contaminated prey contributes another $2.2 billion in losses annually. Added to these yearly indirect costs is the $2.0 billion for remediating pesticide-contaminated groundwater (Pimentel 2009). Finally, long-term productivity of soil and crops declines with ongoing application of pesticides.

FIGURE 18.10

Agriculture is vital to every nation. In the current global economy, agricultural products consumers purchase have many external costs not covered in the market price. The arrows point to some of the main external costs. All dollar amounts reflect annual costs in the United States.

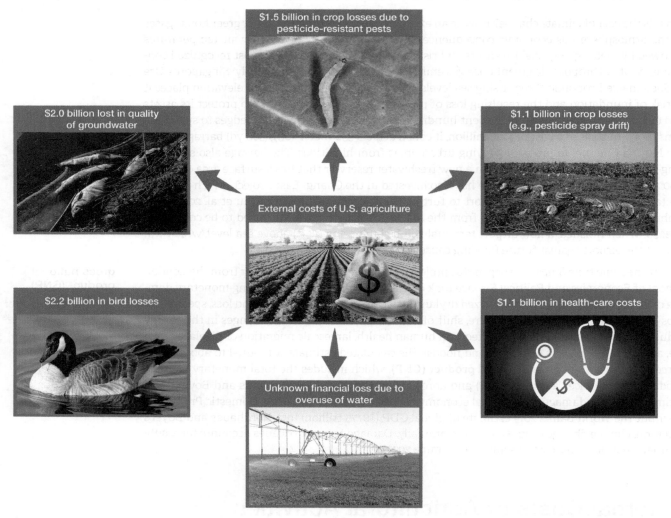

Sources: Joseph Shostell; © Shutterstock, Inc.; data from Pimentel D. 2009. Environmental and economic costs of the application of pesticides primarily in the United States. In *Integrated Pest Management: Innovation-Development Process* (Eds): Peshin, R., and Dhawan, A. K.). Springer Science +Business Media. New York City, New York.

The environment and future farming also bear the indirect costs of overuse of water. A case in point is the historical overuse of the Ogallala aquifer in the high plains of the United States (see Chapter 8 and Chapter 10). The aquifer serves agricultural communities in Colorado, Kansas, Nebraska, New Mexico, South Dakota, Oklahoma, Texas, and Wyoming, and it also supports 30 percent of U.S. agricultural production, valued at $20–35 billion per year (USDA 2020). The water table has been dropping dramatically, and the loss of this economic resource would be devastating to the 32,000 farms overlying the Aquifer and the national population for which they grow food. Beginning in 2011, the federal government's Ogallala aquifer Initiative (delivered through the USDA) infuses funds—a form of subsidy—to farms with the overall goal of reducing water withdrawals from the aquifer. Needed equipment and knowledge provided by the federal government (USDA) help keep agricultural businesses in the area competitive yet sustainable.

There are more indirect costs associated with products and services other than municipal solid waste, pesticide use, water use, and climate change. We would be remiss to not at least mention the effects of deforestation on biodiversity, which undermines the future value of medicine, and the financial impacts of air pollution, water pollution, and soil pollution. Who is covering the costs of acidification of the world's oceans and the pending loss of coral reefs? And, equally important, what are the costs of resources and services required to assist those in poverty, diminished health, and in social distress as a result of nonsustainable economics? These are clear economic challenges, and as you see in the next section (see Section 3), we are engaging in economic solutions.

Key Takeaways

- Managing municipal solid waste (MSW) costs money. These costs (external costs) are usually not included in the market price.
- A company may choose to be environmentally responsible and cover the external costs of a product they sell.
- The external costs related to climate change and agriculture are in the billions of dollars each year. In both cases, the costs relate to those borne by the environment and the public.

18.3 Developing a Sustainable Economy

Learning Objectives

1. Identify the main economic tools supportive of a sustainable economy.
2. Explain how the marketplace can be used to alleviate pollution and waste.
3. Identify different ways subsidies can promote green business.
4. Provide examples of environmental taxes.
5. Describe the qualities of a green business.
6. Recognize microlending—even with criticism against it—as an innovative model for nurturing economic growth and addressing issues of poverty and pollution.

Is a sustainable economy possible? To follow a pathway to a sustainable economy, we must leave behind classical and neoclassical economic theories and transition to ecological economics and a triple bottom line. Ecological economics takes into account human well-being, the health of ecosystems, and environmental justice. In contrast to classical economic theory, in which companies measure their success only by profit, **triple bottom line theory** (TBL) suggests that companies ought to have three bottom lines: profit, people, and planet. Success is measured in all three areas rather than just profit. In this section, we look into a variety of economic tools that both support the economy and protect the environment.

triple bottom line theory

An economic theory suggesting there ought to be three bottom lines: profit, people, and planet.

The Marketplace Can Be Used to Alleviate Pollution and Waste

marketplace

A place or situation in which companies competitively sell their products.

full-cost pricing

Pricing that accounts for production costs as well as any costs related to use and disposal of product. Also known as true-cost pricing, full-cost accounting, and true-cost accounting.

ecolabeling

Labeling on a product that advertises the sustainable practices used to develop and bring the product to the market.

Fair Trade seal

A certification that a product is environmentally friendly and that those who helped produce the product were treated equitably.

greenwashing

A marketing strategy in which a company provides misleading information about how environmentally friendly their product is.

There are many ways for the **marketplace**—a situation or place where companies competitively sell their products—to encourage further development of a sustainable economy. **Full-cost pricing** and consumer access to information about the sustainability of a product are good examples. Full-cost market pricing inclusive of external costs (i.e., mitigating the effects of pollution associated with a product) translates ecological terminology into clear economic language and thus allows the economic engine to help solve environmental problems. Easy access to information about the sustainability of a product encourages consumers to make informed purchasing decisions, but today's consumers often have difficulty locating this information. However, we are seeing more and more sustainable labeling (**ecolabeling**) such as a Dolphin-Safe symbol or a **Fair Trade seal** on products in the marketplace (see video link: "Ecolabeling"). When given an option, sustainability-minded consumers choose the more environmentally friendly products. If enough consumers follow this trend, the change in purchasing behavior encourages manufacturers to produce more of these products. This economic feedback loop provides incentives for companies with products that are not environmentally friendly to change their production processes and supply chains. Buyers beware, because some product labels have misleading information. Unethical companies hoping for a competitive advantage may use the tactic of **greenwashing**, essentially indicating their product is more environmentally friendly than it really is. Another example of the marketplace encouraging the development of a sustainable economy is Singapore's bidding system to own a car (see "Critical Thinking Activity: A Bidding System to Control the Number of Cars and Lower Air Pollution").

 Ecolabeling

An introduction to ecolabels.

View in the online reader

Critical Thinking Activity: A Bidding System to Control the Number of Cars and Lower Air Pollution

In Singapore (see "Case Study: Singapore's Use of Sustainable Economics"), the number of cars and, indirectly, air pollution from vehicular exhaust, is controlled by a bidding system. The Land Transport Authority agency closely monitors and sets the permissible number of vehicles in the country. They do this by requiring every would-be car owner to first obtain a Certificate of

Entitlement (COE), which can easily exceed the market value of the vehicle the person plans to purchase. There is a limited number of COEs available, and the number of bids always exceeds the set quota. COE quotas are set for each category of car (A, B, C, D, and E). In this exercise, you will explore how the cost of a COE reflects the quota of large cars (Category B). Visit an interactive graph of the Land Transport Authority's data here. Scroll down to the graph titled COE Quotas Since 2002. Click on the category box in the upper left and select category B (Cars above 1600 cc). The graph immediately reflects your selection and displays the quota of COEs every two weeks (in blue), total bids received (in red), and the price of the COEs (green line). The data support a strong trend of high costs with small quotas. This mirrors what is happening with smaller cars (see [Content Removed: #shostell_1-31754-20220613-211006-476424]), except in this case, the COEs are slightly more expensive. Analyze the number of bids compared to the available COEs for sale. On every date, the number of bids exceeds the quota. Select two dates in addition to January 9, 2013, and January 7, 2009, and complete Table 18.2. Record the quota of COEs, total number of bids, price of COE in Singapore dollars, and price in American dollars.

TABLE 18.2 Certificate of Entitlement—Bids, Quotas, and Prices

Date	Quota of COEs	Total Number of Bids	Price of One COE (in Singapore Dollars)	Conversion Factor for Converting Singapore Dollars to U.S. Dollars	Price of One COE (in U.S. Dollars) (Multiply Singapore Dollars by 0.73)
Jan 9, 2013	363	470	96,210.00	0.73	70,233.30
Jan 7, 2009				0.73	
				0.73	
				0.73	

What are the takeaways from these data? Supply and demand of the COEs control the cost of COEs. Singaporean families scrutinize their finances and compare the convenience of owning a car to the expense of a COE. A great number of Singaporeans elect to no longer own a car. Only about one in ten own a car, a much lower percentage relative to the United States.

No national economic system is a full-market economy, in which all prices are determined solely by supply and demand. The United States has a mixed economy that relies on supply and demand but is also influenced by subsidies, regulations such as cap and trade, and various incentives. **Cap and trade** policy is an example of an economic strategy intended to address environmental pollution problems. In this system, the government establishes an overall emissions cap for a particular pollutant. Companies that emit the pollutant are then allotted a fraction of this cap, and can sell any surplus ("unused" emissions) to another company that has exceeded their fraction (see Figure 18.11). Cap and trade has been a successful economic tool for reducing carbon dioxide emissions (Zhang and Xu 2013). Forward-thinking and profit-seeking businesses in this competitive marketplace conduct a carbon footprint analysis to identify ways in which they can improve efficiency and reduce carbon emissions. The analysis might reveal potential savings, for example by adopting energy-efficient technologies that reduce the company's carbon footprint. Some companies choose to leverage their position and optimize their supply chains to curb emissions even further. For example, in a carbon cap and trade system, incentivized retailers reexamine their product sources and, when possible, order from sources that emit less carbon dioxide (Song and Leng 2012).

The Environmental Protection Agency's Acid Rain Program is probably the best-known cap and trade system. Because of this system, the nation's sulfur dioxide and nitrogen oxide emissions from power plants have declined 94 percent and 86 percent, respectively, relative to 1990 emission levels. These changes have significantly reduced acid rain formation in the United States (See "Critical Thinking Activity: The Effects of a Cap and Trade System on Acid Rain Formation".)

cap and trade

A government establishes an overall emissions cap for a particular pollutant and companies are allotted a fraction (an allowance) of this cap. Companies can buy and sell allowances.

FIGURE 18.11

Cap and trade has been used to reduce carbon dioxide emissions from power plants. Each power plant in the system is allotted an emissions cap. Those over the cap (A) purchase unused allowances from companies that are under the cap (B). To increase profits, power plants work on reducing their carbon dioxide emissions.

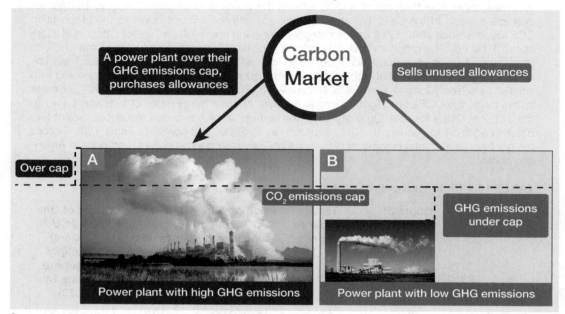

Sources: Joseph Shostell; © Shutterstock, Inc.; Steve Heap/Shutterstock.com

Critical Thinking Activity: The Effects of a Cap and Trade System on Acid Rain Formation

The Acid Rain Program was the first time the United States used a cap and trade system to protect the environment. It was established when Congress passed the 1990 amendments to the Clean Air Act, and was implemented in 1995 as a response to the deterioration of lakes, rivers, and forests. The objective was to reduce emissions of sulfur dioxide and nitrogen oxides from fossil fuel power plants, because both pollutants are precursors to the formation of acid rain. In this critical thinking exercise, you have the opportunity to compare and contrast sulfur dioxide, nitrogen oxides, and acid rain formation pre- and post-implementation of the acid rain cap and trade program. Conclude for yourself whether the program was the resounding success claimed. Go to the EPA's interactive website here. There are three interactive graphs. Hover your cursor over the vertical line on the right side of the "Annual Sulfur Dioxide Emissions" map (the top map). The map displays the annual sulfur dioxide emissions in 1990 by using circles. The larger the circle, the greater the emission. Based on the legend, the largest circles represent emissions of 300,000 tons of sulfur dioxide per year. Move the vertical line from right to left over the graph by moving your mouse. Now, the map shows the annual sulfur dioxide emissions for the most current year. Did you observe the difference in the size of the circles? Go down to the map showing the annual emissions of nitrogen oxides and repeat the process. Both maps show strong decreases in emissions (smaller circles over time). Next, go down to the Annual Wet Sulfate Deposition map. Wet sulfate is a strong indicator of acid rain. This map's legend is different from the previous two. Darker colors of red signify higher concentrations of acid rain. What is immediately noticeable in the 1989–1991 timeframe is the much greater acid rain on the east side of the United States. As before, move the vertical line from right to left to determine the effects of the cap and trade program on acid rain formation. All of the dark red has disappeared, indicating a significant reduction in acid rain formation.

Additionally, consumers and investors are placing increasing demands on the companies they support. They expect environmental and social responsibility and will opt to purchase and invest elsewhere when these expectations are unmet. The largest pension fund in the United States (California Public Employees Retirement System), with holdings of $290 billion, has successfully leveraged its size to require companies holding its investments to include a climate change expert on their board. Expectations from investors and consumers and an increase in the number of socially and environmentally responsible corporations have ushered in an age of annual sustainability reporting. This reporting is now the norm for businesses (see Figure 18.12). In 2011, only 20 percent of S&P companies published annual sustainability reports, compared to over 90 percent today. The transparency of a company's activities, coupled with investors who care about sustainability, favors green practices.

FIGURE 18.12
Sustainability reporting. (A) Sustainability reporting by S&P 500 companies has increased significantly over the years. (B) Image of the Standard & Poor's 500 index.

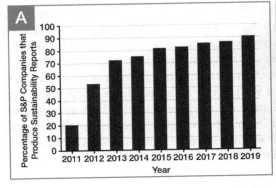

Sources: Joseph Shostell; data from G&A, https://www.ga-institute.com/research-reports/flash-reports.html; Pavel Ignatov/Shutterstock.com

Taxing Pollution and Waste

Environmental taxes are powerful economic tools used to encourage sustainable behavior of corporations and individuals. In essence, governments often choose to tax behavior that is harmful to the environment. These environmental taxes (**green taxes**) have several benefits. First and foremost, they enhance environmental protection, but they also increase economic competitiveness and generate revenue for environmental improvements. France's ecotax on flights departing from France is one example. Beginning in 2020, all departing flights have an added tax of €1.5 ($1.70) to €18 euros ($20.00) per passenger. The new tax is expected to generate more than €200 million annually that will be used to invest in more environmentally friendly transport.

There are many examples of environmental taxes in America. In San Francisco, property owners pay a climate tax to fund habitat restoration and cleanup projects. The tax is expected to raise $500 million in just twenty years. Also in San Francisco, diners in select restaurants pay a 1 percent climate surcharge tax. San Francisco's environmental action plans demonstrate the powerful effects of multiple types of initiatives to tackle an environmental problem. They have effectively reduced carbon dioxide emissions 35 percent below 1990 levels while at the same time increasing population size and growing the economy (SFDE 2018). Their success is attributed to a combination of environmental taxes, an imposed carbon cap and trade system, a cleaner electric system, more efficient energy system, and the construction of green buildings. San Francisco is an environmental leader among large American cities. They banned single-use plastic bags in 2007, and then in 2019 they banned sales of single-use plastic bottles on public property, including the airport.

green taxes

A tax that discourages nonsustainable practices.

Green Business

A **green business** is an environmentally friendly business. There are many examples of green businesses across the economy. While one green business may only rely on natural products and renewable energy, another may have a reduced water footprint and conduct all of its activities in ecofriendly buildings. A third green business may embrace all of these and, furthermore, only use sustainable supplies. Green businesses aim to follow a cradle-to-cradle management strategy (see Chapter 2), which is based on rethinking the way we design, manufacture, use, and reuse products and their components. In essence, waste becomes nonexistent (see Figure 18.13). Swedish clothing company H&M Group, for example, takes in old clothes from consumers and shreds them to create stock material for new garments. In 2019, they recycled over 29,000 tons of textiles. In a completely different market sector, the LED light bulb manufacturer Signify offers a business service model to corporations and cities that enables the manufacturer to maintain ownership of their light products and recycle them at end-of-life. No upfront investments by the consumer are needed. Washington, DC, signed a ten-year service contract with Signify to create a more efficient, reduced-carbon-emissions light system across the city. Signify replaced inefficient high-pressure sodium lights with long-lasting light emitting diodes (LED), thus preventing the release of an estimated 11,000 metric tons of CO_2 (see Figure 18.13). In these examples, green business models help the economy and the environment (see video link: "Fast Fashion").

FIGURE 18.13

Green business: (A) A cradle-to-cradle management approach is beneficial for economics, human health, and the environment. Signify is an example of a green business because it facilitates recycling and replaces inefficient sodium lights with LEDs. (B) A road lit with high-pressure sodium lights. Note their yellow hue. (C) LEDs giving off an umbrella of white light.

Sources: Joseph Shostell; © Shutterstock, Inc.

Green businesses often need financial assistance to get started. Green bonds, which represent about 4.5 percent of the bond market, offer loans with a fixed, long-term interest rate to green businesses. The World Bank issued the first green bond in 2008, and since then, the amount and value of green bonds have risen sharply. Between 2012 and 2020, the total value of all green bonds that have been issued has increased from $3 billion to $300 billion (Bieliński and Mosionek-Schweda 2018). The Massachusetts Clean Water Trust became the first entity in the United States to issue green bonds. Part of the first $100 million dollars went to upgrading a wastewater treatment plant to eliminate pollutants and nutrients from the water (MCWT 2018).

Fast Fashion

Listen to how the fashion industry is going against the traditional throwaway culture.

View in the online reader

Microlending

Microlending offers a means to reduce poverty and environmental degradation while growing the economy. Dr. Muhammad Yunus introduced the idea in one of the poorest areas of Bangladesh (see Figure 18.14). He reasoned that offering mini loans with certain conditions to the poor would help break the cycle of poverty and boost the local economy. In his pilot study, he gave out mini loans to basket weavers living in abject poverty. These women had been taking on other loans to purchase weaving supplies, but the high interest rates prevented the weavers from making a profit. Thus, with few alternatives, the weavers were stuck in a cycle of poverty. Out of his own pocket, Dr. Yunus gave no-interest loans to the basket weavers, who in turn were able to make a profit from their sales. In time, Dr. Yunus broadened the reach of the microlending model to include thousands of mendicants (beggars). He offered each a $12–$15 loan with the promise of no interest and, importantly, when the amount of the loan was repaid, a person could take out a larger loan in the future. To the mendicants who were actively seeking charitable handouts, he said, "As you go from house to house, would you take some merchandise with you, some cookies, some candy, some toys, some sweets?" Then, he instructed the beggar to give the person an option, to either buy merchandise from them, or give charity. Microlending was a huge success. Ten percent of the beggars became door-to-door salespeople. Dr. Muhammad Yunus was awarded the Nobel Peace Prize for his impactful work. More than 100,000 beggars and millions of others are now in the microlending program. In the years following the spread of the microlending model worldwide, critics have detailed weaknesses in the model. Nevertheless, microlending presents an innovative method to help solve issues of poverty and economics. Because poverty can be a cause of environmental degradation, reducing poverty can also lessen environmental degradation. Dr. Yunus's microlending program helped to establish the Grameen Bank, which, in addition to providing small interest-free loans to the poor, partners with companies to address environmental and health issues affecting communities. For example, the Grameen Bank partnered with Veolia to provide safe drinking water to communities in Bangladesh.

microlending

The provision of small, no-interest loans to those in need; helps break the cycle of poverty and boosts the local economy.

FIGURE 18.14
Nobel Laureate Dr. Muhammad Yunus (A) is credited for his innovative microlending model in Bangladesh. Small no-interest loans are provided to the poor—many of them women beggars (B). The program has spread to other countries and supports about seven million people worldwide.

Sources: ISMAT JAHAN/Shutterstock.com; Jahangir Alam Onuchcha/Shutterstock.com

Economic Policies for a Strong Economy and Environmental Protection

policy

A law, regulation, plan, or intent to guide decision-making about appropriate courses of action for a specific situation.

A **policy** is a plan or intent for a specific situation, and it guides decision-making about appropriate courses of action. A broader definition of *policy* includes laws and regulations. In our case, we use the second definition and apply it to sustainable economics. We have already discussed several examples of sustainable economic policies such as cap and trade that further economic growth while protecting the environment. Sustainable economic policy in England, Singapore, Sweden, Italy, and soon New York stresses congestion pricing to reduce traffic along with its associated air pollution and loss of worker productivity (see "Critical Thinking Activity: How Much Would Congestion Pricing Cost Me?"). We also know that cities with higher economic growth tend to pursue sustainability policies and programs more seriously (Portney 2013). If we accept this relationship and remind ourselves about the significance of environmental justice and social responsibility (see Chapter 1), sustainable economic policy relates to education, human health, standard of living, and equitable rights for all people. They are essential parts of economic growth and environmental protection. Sustainable economic policy also stems from collaborations among multiple countries. The United Nations is the largest example of a coordinated effort to foster global economic growth and, in doing so, supports seventeen interlinked sustainable development goals. One example of the UN's actions is through its United Nations Children's Fund (UNICEF). UNICEF helps build the capacity of local governments to offer programs that protect children and give them equitable opportunities.

Critical Thinking Activity: How Much Would Congestion Pricing Cost Me?

After the success of congestion pricing in Singapore, several countries adopted the economic measure to control traffic and pollution in their own cities. The city of London implemented congestion pricing in 2012 (see Figure 18.15). Congestion pricing is an application of an economic supply and demand tactic applied to transportation. Costs increase with road use and can change depending on the time of day and location within a city. The principal idea behind this economic tool is to have drivers pay the full cost—the true cost—of driving, which includes costs for external factors. These external factors include delays of people in other cars behind the driver (think traffic jam), vehicular exhaust and its associated health problems, and collisions with pedestrians. In this exercise, we are interested in understanding the daily cost of congestion pricing to the average London driver. We'll assume that you are planning to move to London and desire to calculate how the cost will affect your budget.

FIGURE 18.15
Londoners are financially discouraged from driving cars in the central part of the city. Two economic tools—congestion pricing and ultralow emission zones—have helped to reduce traffic and smog. (A) A map of London showing the boundary of the congestion pricing zone (see purple dashed line). (B) London has efficient alternatives to driving, including a highly dependable underground public subway for traveling throughout the city. (C) A sign warns drivers of upcoming congestion pricing (labeled as a capital C) and ultralow emission zone.

Sources: Joseph Shostell; © Shutterstock, Inc.; Christian Mueller/Shutterstock.com; Lorna Roberts/Shutterstock.com

If you drive between 7:00 a.m. and 10:00 p.m., the congestion charge is £15 (£ is the English currency symbol for pound, which is equal to $1.3 U.S.) Therefore, in dollars, you would incur an expense of about $19.50 per day. How would this change your weekly and monthly budget? What would this cost you per year? Calculate these costs and record your findings in Table 18.3. Are there any ways to avoid this fee?

TABLE 18.3 Calculating Congestion Pricing in London

Time	Cost of Congestion Pricing (in English Pounds)	Cost of Congestion Pricing (in American Dollars)
One day	15	18.04
One week (five day work week)	75	
One month		
One year		

A penalty is added to a congestion fee if the driver forgets to pay in advance or to pay on the day of travel: £2.50 if payment is one to three days late, and a whopping £160 after three days. Thus, Londoners are incentivized to pay the charge before late fees are assigned. Cameras at the entrances of congestion zones read license plate numbers, and a software program cross-references the plate numbers against a list of vehicles that have already paid the charge. Users of public transportation and motorcyclists are exempt from the charge. You may find it easier, and certainly much cheaper, to rely on London's famous subway and buses. A trip on the subway (the Underground) into one of London's six zones during peak hours costs £ 5.5 to 6 (6.9–7.5 USD), which is far less than the price of a congestion charge. Subway riders, also do not pay expensive parking fees, which average £ 7.5 (9.4 USD) per hour.

Key Takeaways

- Society benefits from economic policies that foster a strong economy and simultaneously support environmental protection.
- There are many economic tools supportive of a sustainable economy, including full-cost pricing, facilitating consumer access to accurate information about product sustainability, and a cap and trade system.
- Government subsidies for sustainable businesses offer green companies a fighting chance in competitive markets. Reducing or eliminating subsidies that support nonsustainable businesses are also helpful for this purpose.
- Environmental taxes that discourage nonsustainable practices can provide money for sustainable activities and development.
- Microlending is an innovative model that supports local economic growth while addressing poverty.

18.4 A Look to the Future: Fully Adopting Sustainable Economics

Learning Objectives

1. Summarize the significance of adopting sustainable economics.
2. Reflect on Singapore's strategy of promoting green growth with economic tools.

Clearly, we have much good work to do to meet our ambitious and needed sustainable goals. Environmental degradation is rampant all around us. It threatens the ability of ecosystems to maintain ecosystem services, and negatively affects human health and the economy. This is our reality. Society's high-throughput economy produces wastes and consumes natural capital faster than nature's ability to effectively assimilate those wastes and replenish itself. Due to a competitive economy, historically weak sustainable economic policies, and a desire by consumers to pay as little as possible for products and services, it has been easy and generally acceptable for corporations and consumers to offload external costs of their production activities and/or consumption activities onto natural ecosystems and the public. That is, until recently. We now understand that these costs, which are not covered in the market price of products and services we enjoy, are a burden to the economy. The burden includes pollution remediation costs, health-care costs, and any costs from lost ecosystem services. These unpaid expenses are forced upon the public and the environment.

Of course, there are real costs associated with the management of municipal solid waste (MSW), but the tally of these pales in comparison to the cost of massive amounts of accumulated waste in the environment. Similarly, fossil-fuel consumers only pay a fraction of the cost of their energy use. What are these hidden costs? Each year, accelerated climate change due to greenhouse gas emissions bleeds the economy of hundreds of billions of dollars and yet untold cost of acid rain on land and water resources. We are, however, beginning to show signs of positive change in the direction of sustainability, mostly because economic growth and human prosperity cannot continue without appropriate environmental protection. In other words, society is learning how to adapt its activities to benefit both economic growth and the environment. Moreover, we have developed a more sophisticated, accurate understanding of how economic growth is interconnected with human welfare and to the health of the environment. This fact and others mentioned earlier in this section explain the appearance and significance of sustainable economics.

Data-informed governments, businesses, and individuals are becoming involved in the new green economy. A variety of economic tools supportive of a sustainable economy have been discussed in this chapter (see Figure 18.16). Using such tools to implement an ecological economy gives us the potential for a bright future.

FIGURE 18.16
A number of economic tools (in blue boxes) incentivize companies to improve their sustainability. The green arrow indicates movement of a population of companies within a market sector (area under bell-shaped curve) to greater sustainability.

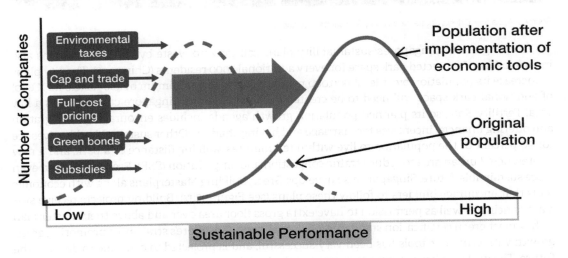

Source: Joseph Shostell

Revisit of Opening Story: Singapore's Future

Singapore has achieved a remarkable feat since the mid-1960s, changing from a developing nation with inadequate infrastructure, large slums, and serious environmental degradation to its high standard of living today. A deft, centralized, single-level government carefully planned for decades how it would grow economically along with its population, and how to do so sustainably. Improvements in basic services and urban infrastructure, along with implementation of smart designs and green building practices, have led to Singapore's being one of the most desirable places to live in the world. Implementation of economic tools such as a bidding system for car ownership (COE) and congestion pricing have helped Singapore to minimize traffic on its roads and curtail pollution. Economic tools have helped its citizens and companies make sustainable, responsible decisions. Today, Singapore is the envy of Southeast Asia, for it has one of the highest GDPs per capita and runs the world's busiest maritime capital. Dedicated green space and a clean environment are tenets of Singapore's plans for economic growth. Its citizens came to understand and appreciate the connection between preserving green space and attracting foreign investors to help drive the economy. These insights came from a history of losing almost all of the nation's primary forest post-colonization in the nineteenth century, and dealing with a heavily polluted Singapore River in the mid-twentieth century.

FIGURE 18.17
Singapore's master plan calls for at least 80 percent of its buildings to be certified as green by 2030, and 90 percent of its citizens living within ten minutes, walking distance from a park. (A) Singapore's jewel, Changi airport, is one example of a green building design. (B) The Gardens by the Bay is one of the most well-known attractions in Singapore. Cropping up amid the natural foliage are eighteen tree-like sculptures rising 82–164 feet (25–50 m) into the air. Visitors can stroll paths at ground level or choose the elevated pathways between these super-trees.

Sources: Alexander Ortega/Shutterstock.com; S-F/Shutterstock.com

Looking ahead, Singapore's sustainability plans call for zero waste by 2030. These plans also include 0.8 ha of protected park space for every additional 1,000 residents (Chin 2008). The city plans to increase its population by at least 600,000 people by 2030, so a minimum of 480 ha (0.8 ha X 600) of additional park space will need to be created in the short term. Singapore currently has a low Total Fertility Rate, so its planned population growth agenda includes encouraging immigration and offering financial incentives for marriage and having children. Other sustainable objectives are for 90 percent of the population to live within ten minutes' walking distance of a park, and a new car-restricted urban area to reduce traffic congestion and air pollution (SSB). Preparing for an even more sustainable future, Singapore also develops Green Building Masterplans along with economic tools that encourage builders to follow these plans (see Figure 18.17). Building projects receive special financing as well as permission to have extra gross floor area over and above their master plan if they meet green certification standards (Qian et al. 2016). Singapore's strategy of promoting green growth with economic tools has been very successful, and is projected to continue to do so in the future. The goal is to have at least 80 percent of the buildings as "green" by 2030 (BCA 2014).

Powerful economic tools that can reduce pollution in a country have no direct impact on pollution that comes from other nations. Singapore's compact nature and proximity to other nations in Southeast Asia make it highly susceptible to such transboundary pollution. In 2013, Singapore experienced its worst air quality as measured on the Pollutant Standard Index (PSI). It creeped up to 401, a level deemed hazardous and life-threatening. This one-week episode was the result of fires in Indonesia (Nurhidayah et al. 2015). Singaporeans were forced to wear masks and stay inside as much as possible. Although Singapore could not directly extinguish the fires on foreign soil, its Parliament had a quick response. Within one week of the episode, the Singapore government introduced the Transboundary Haze Pollution Bill, which was signed into law in 2014. The law allows the suing of companies—domestic or foreign—that cause environmental pollution in Singapore. International onlookers question the strength of the law because Singapore has little if any control of events outside its borders, yet Singapore considers the law complementary rather than antagonistic to regulations and laws of surrounding nations. Looking to the future, and given the scope of environmental problems currently faced by all countries, strong international agreements are essential to simultaneously protect individual nations and the world at large. This is why Singapore and many other forward-thinking countries have signed international agreements such as the Paris Accord to reduce greenhouse gas emissions.

Our health and the environment's health depends on these effective international agreements along with the continued development of sustainable economies and sustainable communities. Our success in living sustainably relies on the behaviors and actions of people like you and me. As Jane Goodall stated, "You cannot get through a single day without having an impact on the world around you. What you do makes a difference, and you have to decide what kind of difference you want to make."

Key Takeaways

- Society's current high-throughput economy continues to generate wastes and consumes natural capital faster than nature's ability to assimilate and replenish. To continue along this route compromises the health of the environment and the prosperity of future generations. Sustainable economics offers a means to protect the environment while growing the economy.
- Singapore is one of the global leaders in implementing economic tools to solve environmental problems. It was the first to introduce a bidding system for car ownership (COE) and congestion pricing. These and other economic tools have helped Singapore to free roads, curtail pollution, and create one of the most livable cities in the world.

FIGURE 18.18 Visual Overview: Sustainable Economics
Summarizing figure: Sustainable economics takes into account the real value of the environment (18.1) and the cost of environmental degradation (18.2). More and more, we are transitioning to ecological economics and using economic tools to support economic growth and environmental protection (18.3) for the benefit of the world today and in the future (18.4).

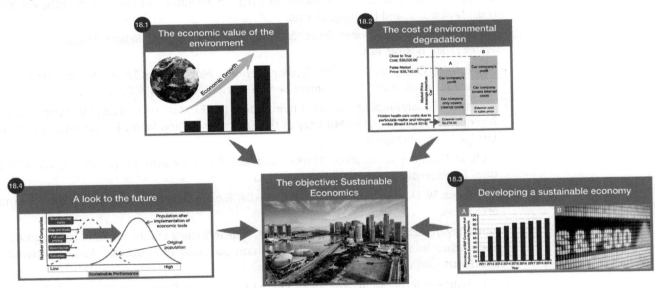

Source: Joseph Shostell; See previous citations for image credits.

18.5 References

- Andor, M., and A. Voss. 2014. "Optimal renewable-energy subsidies." *SSRN*. https://doi.org/10.2139/ssrn.2470546.
- Borucke, M., D. Moore, G. Cranstonm, K. Gracey, K. Iha, J. Larson, E. Lazarus, J. C. Morales, M. Wackernagel, and A. Galli. 2013. "Accounting for demand and supply of the biosphere's regen-

erative capacity: The national footprint accounts' underlying methodology and framework." *Ecological Indicators* 24: 518–533.

- Brand, C., and A. Hunt, 2018. *The health costs of air pollution from cars and vans.* Technical Report. https://doi.org/10.13140/RG.2.2.25409.86886.

- Building and Construction Authority (BCA). 2014. 3rd Green Building Masterplan. Building and Construction Authority. Singapore.

- Burtraw, D., A. E. Farrell, L. H. Goulder, and C. Peterman. 2006. "Lessons for a cap-and-trade program." In *Managing Greenhouse Gas Emissions in California*. The California Climate Change Center at UC Berkeley. Berkeley, CA.

- Chin, S. 2008. "Biodiversity conservation in Singapore." *BGjournal* 5, no. 2: 11–14.

- Chu, J., M. W. Bo, and A. Arulrajah. 2009. "Soil improvement works for an offshore land reclamation." *Geotechnical Engineering* 162: 21–32.

- Fankhauser, S. 1992. *Global warming damage costs: some monetary estimates. CSERGE GEC Working Paper 92-29.* Center for Social Economic Research on the Global Environment. University College London and University of East Anglia.

- Frame, D. J., M. F. Wehner, I. Noy, and S. M. Rosier. 2020. "The economic costs of Hurricane Harvey attributable to climate change." *Climatic Change* 160: 271–281.

- Han, R. B. H., and H. H. Khoo. 2006. "Impact assessment of waste management options in Singapore." *J. Air & Waste Manage Assoc* 56: 244–254.

- House of Representatives (H. R.). 2020. H.R. 5115. *Realizing the Economic Opportunities and Value of Expanding Recycling Act.* 116 Congress, United States.

- Jones, C. I. 2016. "The facts of economic growth." In: *Handbook of Macroeconomics, Volume 2A.* (Eds: Taylor, J. B., and H. Uhlig) Elsevier B. V.

- Massachusetts Clean Water Trust. 2018. *Annual Green Bonds Report.* Massachusetts Clean Water Trust. Boston, MA.

- McKinsey & Company. 2016. *The Circular Economy: Moving from Theory to Practice. McKinsey Center for Business and Environment Special Edition.* McKinsey & Company.

- Ministry of Sustainability and the Environment (MSE). 2016. *Sustainable Singapore Blueprint.* A cooperation between the Ministry of the Environment and Water Resources and Centre for Livable Cities Singapore.

- Moh, W. H., and P. L. Su. 2009. "Marina Barrage—A unique 3-in-1 project in Singapore." *Structural Engineering International* 19, no. 1: 17–21.

- Nordhaus, W. D., and J. Boyer. 1999. *Roll the DICE again: economic models of global warming.* MIT Press.

- Nurhidayah, L., S. Alam, and Z. Lipman. 2015. "The influence of international law upon ASEAN approaches in addressing transboundary haze pollution in Southeast Asia." *Contemporary Southeast Asia* 37, no. 2: 183–210.

- Oil Change International. 2017. *Dirty Energy Dominance: Dependent On Denial How the U.S. Fossil Fuel Industry Depends on Subsidies and Climate Denial.* Oil Change International, Washington, DC.

- O'Neill, D. W. 2015. "The proximity of nations to a socially sustainable steady-state economy." *Journal of Cleaner Production* 108: 1213–1231.

- Parry, I., S. Black, and N. Vernon. 2021. *Still Not Getting Prices Right: A Global and Country Update of Fossil Fuel Subsidies.* International Monetary Fund. Washington, DC.

- Pimentel, D. 2009. "Environmental and economic costs of the application of pesticides primarily in the United States." In: *Integrated Pest Management: Innovation-Development Process.* (Eds.: Pershing, R. and A. K. Dhawan). Springer Science+Business Media B. V.

- Portney, K. E. 2013. "Local sustainability policies and programs as economic development: Is the new economic development sustainable development." *Cityscape* 15, no. 1: 45–62.

- Qian, Q. K., K. Fan, and E. H. W. Chan. 2016. "Regulatory incentives for green buildings: gross floor area concessions." *Building Research and Information* 44, no. 5–6: 675–693.
- San Francisco Department of Environment (SFDE). 2018. *2018 San Francisco Geographic Greenhouse Gas Emissions Inventory at a Glance*. San Francisco Department of Environment Climate Program.
- Simeonova, E., J. Curriem, P. Nilsson, and R. Walker. 2019. "Congestion pricing, air pollution and children's health." *NBER Working Paper Series*. Working Paper 24410. National Bureau of Economic Research, Cambridge, MA.
- Song, J., and M. Leng. 2012. "Analysis of the single-period problem under carbon emission policies." *International Series in Operations Research and Management Science* 176: 297–312.
- United States Department of Agriculture (USDA). 2020. NIFA Impacts: Saving the Ogallala Aquifer, supporting farmers. USDA.
- Zhang, B., and L. Xu. 2013. "Multi-item production planning with carbon cap and trade mechanism." *International Journal of Production Economics* 144, no. 1: 118–127.

Index